NEW
LESSONS
IN
ARC WELDING

Published as an educational service to the
welding industry

This book may be ordered from any dealer or representative
of The Lincoln Electric Company, or through any recognized
book dealer in the world or direct from:

THE LINCOLN ELECTRIC COMPANY
22801 ST. CLAIR AVENUE, CLEVELAND, OHIO 44117
Int'l Telex: 98-5471

LINCOLN ELECTRIC CO. OF CANADA, LTD.
Toronto, M4G 2B9
Telex: 062-2180

LINCOLN ELECTRIC CO. (Europe) S.A.
Rouen, France 76120
Telex: 842-770881

LINCOLN ELECTRIC CO., (Australia) PTY., LTD.
Sydney 2211
Telex: 790-22792

INTRODUCTION

This edition of *NEW LESSONS IN ARC WELDING* is the 5th revision of a text resulting from an enlargement of the lessons used in the Lincoln Arc Welding School. This school has been in operation since 1917. The methods and material presented here are not the ideas of any one person. They are the result of information gathered from the staff of the Lincoln Arc Welding School, weldors in the field, welding teachers, field engineers, and the comprehensive engineering and research facilities of The Lincoln Electric Co.

Arc welding has progressed tremendously in the past 10 years. New electrodes, machines and processes have been developed. This book presents concisely the latest technical information on the practice of arc welding.

The text is divided into several areas. Lessons 1.1 to 1.48 contain the basic information necessary to become familiar with manual electrodes. Some ability to perform each job should be learned before attempting the next. Information lessons are presented as they are needed to adequately understand the process, equipment or materials encountered in the welding jobs.

Lessons 2.1 to 6.3 contain information and operating procedures on specific manual machines and electrodes manufactured by The Lincoln Electric Company. These are representative of machines and materials encountered by the weldor in his work the world over. The name or trade mark of The Lincoln Electric Company is your guarantee of the highest quality in machine, accessory and electrode design, manufacturing and service.

Section 7 has been added to cover the semiautomatic welding processes available today: flux-cored, gas-metal-arc, and submerged arc. To make the most effective use of today's welding technology, one must become familiar with these processes. Indeed, some shops today use virtually no stick electrodes.

Section 8 covers the TIG process and the unique equipment it requires to make high quality welds on virtually any metal.

The Welding Application Supplement in Section 9 contains information and procedure data for minimizing welding costs, supplementary information to help weldors better understand the welding process and its use.

Further and more detailed technical information on the field of arc welding and its application may be obtained from the latest edition of the *"Procedure Handbook of Arc Welding"* or any of the specialized books as described in Lesson 10.3.

NEW LESSONS IN ARC WELDING will be useful to anyone engaged in the welding industry.

The student or beginning weldor will find step-by-step procedures for performing basic welding operations, as well as information on welding equipment, supplies and processes. The lessons may be used as instruction sheets to supplement teacher demonstrations and classwork, or as self-instruction units.

The experienced weldor may refresh his memory on technical phases of the welding field, pipe and alloy welding, or those seldom-encountered jobs and repairs.

The welding foreman or job shop operator will find that new electrodes and machines have been developed that will do special jobs as well as run-of-the-mill jobs better, faster and at reduced cost.

The designer or draftsman will find information on welding symbols, types of joints, welding design and electrode specifications to aid in planning and designing jobs using welded fabrication.

The Lincoln Electric Company is interested in the weldor and in helping him increase his knowledge and skill toward maximum job proficiency. Correspondence is invited with weldors or persons concerned with welding in regard to problems they may have.

The Lincoln Electric Company will appreciate having called to its attention any errors that have escaped the editors and invites correspondence on subjects about which the reader may have questions or comments.

The information contained in this book represents that developed by experience. In its use, however, The Lincoln Electric Company or its subsidiaries can assume no responsibility. The results obtained in joining metals by arc welding depend upon the individual circumstances and individual applications, as well as the recommended procedures. This book is a guide; the user is responsible for how he applies that guide.

Much of the information in this book has been obtained from The Lincoln Electric Company engineering laboratories, field engineers, and areas of experience of other personnel. To all those who made possible the accumulation of information and data, The Lincoln Electric Company acknowledges a debt of gratitude.

A special word of appreciation is in order for Emmett A. Smith, Jerry Hinkel, Randy E. Glassburn, William Sellon, Robert E. Greenlee, Jesse Guardado, and Ted Bullard, Jr. for their technical expertise and professional assistance.

THE LINCOLN ELECTRIC COMPANY

Richard S. Sabo, Manager of Educational Services

– 1 –

SECTION VI — WELDING CAST IRON AND NON-FERROUS METALS

SECTION VII — SEMIAUTOMATIC ARC WELDING

INNERSHIELD

GAS METAL ARC

SUBMERGED ARC

SECTION VIII — TIG (Tungsten Inert Gas) WELDING

SECTION IX — SUPPLEMENTARY DATA

Introduction

SECTION X — APPENDIX

SECTION I

ARC-WELDING
THEORY AND TECHNIQUES

LESSON
1.1

Object:
To study safe work habits while welding.

SAFETY PRACTICES IN WELDING

Introduction

Arc welding is a safe occupation when sufficient measures are taken to protect the welder from potential hazards. When these measures are overlooked or ignored, however, welders can encounter such dangers as electric shock, overexposure to fumes and gases, arc radiation, and fire and explosion; which may result in serious, or even fatal injuries.

This bulletin is written with the arc welding operator in mind, containing both mandatory safety practices and those based on shop experience. Be sure to read ANSI Z49.1, and refer to the other publications listed at the end of the bulletin for more detailed information on specific topics of arc welding safety, as well as the manufacturers' instructions and material safety data sheets (MSDS's).

Important Note:
So that you can protect yourself against these hazards, every welder should be familiar with American National Standard ANSI Z49.1, "Safety in Welding and Cutting," and should follow the safety practices in that document. Z49.1 is now available for download at no charge at:

http://www.lincolnelectric.com/community/safety/ or at the AWS website *http://www.aws.org*.

Download and read it!

Personal Protective Equipment

PROTECTIVE CLOTHING

Welders, like firemen, must wear clothing to protect them from being burned. Of all injuries to welders, burns are the most common due to sparks landing on bare skin. Welding arcs are very intense and can cause burns to skin and eyes with just a few minutes of exposure.

The actual gear varies with the job being performed, but generally **protective clothing** must allow freedom of movement while providing adequate coverage against burns from sparks, weld spatter, and arc radiation. Many types of clothing will protect you from ultra-violet radiation exposure, which appears as a skin burn (much like sunburn). Under the worst conditions, however, severe burns and skin cancer may result from excessive radiation.

Because of its durability and resistance to fire, wool clothing is suggested over synthetics (which should never be worn because it melts when exposed to extreme heat) or cotton, unless it is specially treated for fire protection. If possible, keep your clothes clean of grease and oil, as these substances may ignite and burn uncontrollably in the presence of oxygen.

Avoid rolling up your sleeves and pant-cuffs, because sparks or hot metal could deposit in the folds; also, wear your trousers outside your work boots, not tucked in, to keep particles from falling into your boots. While we're on the subject, we suggest leather high-tops with steel toes (especially when doing heavy work).

Other protective wear for heavy work or especially hazardous situations includes: flame-resistant suits, aprons, leggings, leather sleeves/shoulder capes, and caps worn under your helmet.

Heavy, flame-resistant gloves, such as leather, should **always** be worn to protect your hands from burns, cuts, and scratches. In addition, as long as they are dry and in good condition, they will offer some insulation against electric shock.

As to preventing electric shock, the key word is **dry**! We'll have more on the subject later, but for now keep in mind that moisture can increase the potential for and severity of electric shock. When working in wet conditions, or when perspiring heavily, you must be even more careful to insulate your body from electrically "live" parts and work on grounded metal.

⚠	WARNING

ARC RAYS can burn.
 • **Wear eye, ear and body protection.**

Arc Rays

It is essential that your **eyes are protected** from radiation exposure. Infrared radiation has been known to cause retinal burning and cataracts. And even a brief exposure to ultraviolet (UV) radiation can cause an eye burn known as "welder's flash." While this condition is not always apparent until several hours after exposure, it causes extreme discomfort, and can result in swelling, fluid excretion, and temporary blindness. Normally, welder's flash is temporary, but repeated or prolonged exposure can lead to permanent injury of the eyes.

Other than simply not looking at an arc, the primary preventive measure you can take is to use the proper shade lens in your helmet. Refer to the lens shade selector chart in Supplement 1 for the recommended shade numbers for various arc welding processes. The general rule is to choose a filter too dark to see the arc, then move to lighter shades without dropping below the minimum rating. The filters are marked as to the manufacturer and shade number, the impact-resistant variety are marked with an "H."

Helmets and hand-held face shields (see Figure A) offer the most complete shading against arc radiation. The shade slips into a window at the front of the shield so that it can be removed and replaced easily. The shields are made from a hard plastic or fiberglass to protect your head, face, ears, and neck from electric shock, heat, sparks, and flames. You should also use safety glasses with side shields or goggles to protect your eyes from flying particles.

Visible light can also be harmful, but it is easy to tell if the light is dangerous: if it hurts to look at, then it's too bright. The same is true for infrared radiation: it can usually be felt as heat. However, there's no real way for you to tell if you're being over exposed to UV radiation, so just don't take chances: always wear eye protection (see Supplement 1 for recommended lens shade numbers).

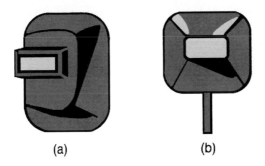

(a)   (b)

Figure A. A helmet (a) required for protecting the welder's eyes and face and (b) a hand-held face shield that is convenient for the use of foremen, inspectors, and other spectators.

Noise

There are two good reasons to **wear ear muffs or plugs:**

a) to keep flying sparks or metal out of your ears; and

b) to prevent hearing loss as a result of working around noisy arc welding equipment, power sources, and processes (like air carbon arc cutting or plasma arc cutting).

As with radiation exposure to the eyes, the length and number of times that you are exposed to high levels of noise determine the extent of the damage to your hearing, so be sure to avoid repeated exposure to noise. If it is not possible to reduce the level of noise at the source (by moving either yourself or the equipment, utilizing sound shields, etc.), then you should wear adequate ear protection.

If the noise in your work area becomes uncomfortable, causing a headache or discomfort of the ears, you could be damaging your hearing and should immediately put on ear muffs or plugs.

In fact, the use of ear protection at all times is a good idea, as hearing loss is both gradual and adds up over time. Damage to your hearing may not be noticed until you have a complete hearing test, and then it could be too late.

Inspection and Maintenance of Equipment and Work

Before starting any arc welding operation, you should make a **complete inspection** of your equipment. All it takes on your part is 5-10 minutes before you turn on your welder; is that too much to spend in preventing injury to yourself or your co-workers?

To begin with:

• Have you read the instruction manual and do you understand the instructions? The instruction manual for your welder is available upon request to your welding distributor or the manufacturer. Manuals for Lincoln Electric welders may be downloaded from lincolnelectric.com at no charge.

• Have you read the warnings and instructions on the equipment nameplates and decals as well as the consumables labels and material safety data sheets? (For older equipment see Supplement 5 to request a FREE Warning Label.)

For the welder:

• Are all the connections tight, including the earth ground?

• OSHA regulations require output terminals to be insulated. Rubber boots are available for that purpose.

• Are the electrode holder and welding cable well insulated and in good condition?

• Are the settings correct for the job you're about to begin?

For an engine-driven welder:

• Is it running OK?

• Are all the hoses on tight?

• Is the fuel cap on tight?

- Is the engine leaking fuel or oil? Some jobsites look for this and may refuse entry if your engine is leaking.
- Is the original enclosure and fan guarding in place? Check with your welding equipment distributor if you are unsure. (See Supplement 6.)

For the work in general: (See also Supplements 4 and 7)
- Are the work area conditions such that normal safety precautions can be observed or must special equipment (i.e., ventilation, exhaust, or respirator, welding equipment, protective equipment, safety equipment) or procedures be used?
- Many jobsites require permits for any welding or cutting. Be sure you have any permits you will need.
- If you will be working in a confined space, many special OSHA regulations and jobsite requirements may apply in addition to the arc welding precautions in this brochure. Understand which of these apply to your jobsite and comply with them.
- Are the cables the right size for your job? Be sure any damaged cable insulation is repaired.
- Are they spread out and run neatly to prevent overheating?
- Is the gas cylinder connected properly?
- Is the cylinder secure?
- Is the work stable and easy to reach from where you're standing?
- Is the Work Lead connected securely?
- Is there enough dry insulation between your body and the work piece?
- Is there adequate ventilation in your work area?

Take some personal responsibility for your own safety. Notify your supervisor if equipment is in need of repair or not working properly or any unsafe condition. You have the most to lose if you get hurt. Don't allow yourself to work in a hazardous situation without taking appropriate safety precautions.

If the hazard is serious and cannot be corrected readily, the machine should be shut down until the needed repairs are made. If the problem is limited to the outside of the welder, such as a loose connection or a damaged cable that needs to be replaced, **disconnect power to the welder** and correct the problem per the manufacturers instructions in the operating/service manual. If the hazard requires repairs to the inside of the welder or to the electrical input supply lines, call a service technician or an electrician. Never attempt to make these repairs if you are untrained.

Important Safety Note:

Consider whether the area in which you will be working creates or increases the level of hazard to you thus requiring special procedures or equipment. Factors such as electrical safety, fume ventilation/exhaust and risk of fire or explosion may be affected. See later sections on those topics and other documents in "Bibliography and Suggested Reading" for further information.

Care and Cleaning of the Work Area

Keeping the area around your work neat is as important as maintaining your equipment. Perhaps even more-so, as the risk of injury is amplified by the larger group of people involved. You may have already inspected your equipment and found it to be OK, but all your caution won't matter when, for example, a co-worker trips over your cable, causing you, and/or the people around you, to be injured by shock, hot metal, or from falling.

Keep all your equipment, cables, hoses, cylinders, etc. out of any traffic routes such as doors, hallways, and ladders. A good practice is to avoid clutter...and **clean up your work area** when you're done! Not only will it help to protect yourself and others, you'll find it much easier for you to work efficiently.

Also, bear in mind that while you're paying attention to your work, other welders may be preoccupied with their own tasks and not watching where they're going. So be sure that there are protective screens in place, just in case somebody happens to be passing into your work area or walks into a shower of sparks or spatter.

Gas Cylinders

Because of the high pressure gas in cylinders, you must pay particularly close attention to their storage and use. Examine the cylinders as you did the rest of your equipment; check the cylinder label to make sure it is the correct shielding gas for the process, and that the regulators, hoses, and fittings are the right ones for that gas and pressure, and are in good condition.

Cylinders must be secured in an upright position, with the valve caps in place, in an area away from combustibles and fuels, and safeguarded from damage, heat, and flames. When in use, keep them out of traffic routes and flying sparks, with all hoses run neatly to the welding area. Never allow the electrode or other "electrically hot" parts of your welder to touch a cylinder. "Crack" the valve open to prevent dirt from entering the regulator; open the cylinder valve only when standing to one side of the cylinder, away from welding or other sources of ignition. Return damaged cylinders to the supplier. Refer to the Compressed Gas Association pamphlet P-1, "Safe Handling of Gas Cylinders," for further information.

⚠ **WARNING**

CYLINDER may explode if damaged.
- **Keep cylinder upright and chained to support.**
- **Never allow welding electrode to touch cylinder.**

- -

Electric and Magnetic Fields

Electric current flowing through any conductor causes localized Electric and Magnetic Fields (EMF). Welding current creates EMF fields around welding cables and welding machines. EMF fields may interfere with some pacemakers, and welders having a pacemaker should consult their physician before welding. Exposure to EMF fields in welding may have other health effects which are now not known. All welders should use the following procedures in order to minimize exposure to EMF fields from the welding circuit:

- Route the electrode and work cables together – Secure them with tape when possible.
- Never coil the electrode lead around your body.
- Do not place your body between the electrode and work cables. If the electrode cable is on your right side, the work cable should also be on your right side.
- Connect the work cable to the workpiece as close as possible to the area being welded.
- Do not work next to welding power source.

Specific Concerns

POSSIBLE SHOCK HAZARDS

The hazard of electric shock is one of the most serious and immediate risks facing you as a welder. Contact with metal parts which are "electrically hot" can cause injury or death because of the effect of the shock upon your body or a fall which may result from your reaction to the shock. The electric shock hazard associated with arc welding may be divided into two categories which are quite different:

– Primary Voltage Shock (i.e., 230, 460 volts); and

– Secondary Voltage Shock (i.e., 20-100 volts).

⚠ **WARNING**

HIGH VOLTAGE can kill.
- **Do not operate with covers removed.**
- **Disconnect input power before servicing.**
- **Do not touch electrically live parts.**

- -

The **primary voltage shock** is very hazardous because it is much greater voltage than the welder secondary voltage. You can receive a shock from the primary (input) voltage if you touch a lead inside the welder with the **power to the welder** "on" while you have your body or hand on the welder case or other grounded metal. Remember that turning the welder power switch "off" does not turn the power off **inside the welder**. To turn the power inside the welder "off", the input power cord must be unplugged or the power disconnect switch turned off. You should never remove fixed panels from your welder; in fact, always have a qualified technician repair your welder if it isn't working properly. Also, your welder should be installed by a qualified electrician so it will be correctly wired for the primary voltage which supplies it power and so the case will be connected to an earth ground. When electrical supply lines are connected to a welder, check the welder capacity nameplate and connection instructions to be sure the input is the correct phase (single phase or three phase) and voltage. Many welders may be set up for single phase or three phase and

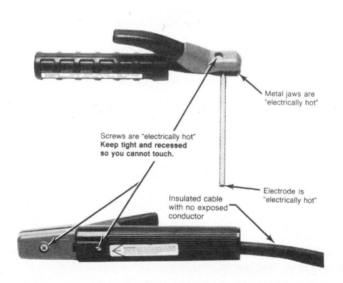

Metal jaws are "electrically hot"

Screws are "electrically hot"
Keep tight and recessed so you cannot touch.

Electrode is "electrically hot"

Insulated cable with no exposed conductor

Figure B. Always inspect your electrode holder before turning the welder on.

for multiple input voltages. Be certain the welder is set up for the electrical supply to which it is connected. **Only a qualified electrician should connect input power.** The case must be grounded so that if a problem develops inside the welder a fuse will blow, disconnecting the power and letting you know that repair is required. Never ignore a blown fuse because it is a warning that something is wrong.

⚠ WARNING

ELECTRIC SHOCK can kill.
- **Do not touch electrically live parts or electrode with skin or wet clothing.**
- **Insulate yourself from work and ground.**

If welding must be performed under electrically hazardous conditions (in damp locations or while wearing wet clothing; on metal structures such as floors, gratings or scaffolds; when in cramped positions such as sitting, kneeling or lying, if there is a high risk of unavoidable or accidental contact with the work piece or ground) use the following equipment:
- **Semiautomatic DC Constant Voltage Welder**
- **DC Manual (Stick) Welder**
- **AC Welder with Reduced Voltage Control**

- -

A **secondary voltage shock** occurs when you touch a part of the **electrode circuit** — perhaps a bare spot on the electrode cable — at the same time another part of your body is touching the metal upon which you're welding (work). To receive a shock your body must touch both sides of the welding circuit — electrode and work (or welding ground) — at the same time. To prevent secondary voltage shock, you must develop and use safe work habits. Remember the voltage at the electrode is highest when you are not welding (open circuit voltage).
- Wear **dry** gloves in good condition when welding.
- Do not touch the electrode or metal parts of the electrode holder with skin or wet clothing.
- Keep **dry** insulation between your body (including arms and legs) and the metal being welded or ground (i.e., metal floor, wet ground).
- Keep your welding cable and electrode holder in good condition. Repair or replace any damaged insulation.

These rules are basic to welding and you should already know them. Check out the warning on your welder or electrode box next time you weld. You will probably not have a shock while welding if you follow these rules.

Though it may be more difficult to follow the rules under some conditions, the rules still apply. Keep your gloves **dry** even if you have to keep an extra pair. Use plywood, rubber mats, or some other **dry** insulation to stand or lie upon. Insulate your body from the metal you are welding. Don't rest your body, arms, or legs on the workpiece, especially if your clothing is wet or bare skin is exposed (and it should not be if you are dressed properly). In addition to the normal safety precautions, if welding must be performed under electrically hazardous conditions (in damp locations or while wearing wet clothing; on metal structures such as floors, gratings or scaffolds; when in cramped positions such as sitting, kneeling or lying, if there is a high risk of unavoidable or accidental contact with the work piece or ground) use the following equipment:

- Semiautomatic DC Constant Voltage Welder
- DC Manual (Stick) Welder
- AC Welder with Reduced Voltage Control

The condition of your electrode holder and electrode cable is also very important. The plastic or fiber insulation on the electrode holder protects you from touching the metal "electrically hot" parts inside. Always inspect your electrode holder before turning the welder on. Replace the holder if it is damaged — don't try to repair it unless you have replacement parts.

The same is true of the electrode cable except that when not replaced it may be repaired using good electrical tape. If your cable has been repaired, be sure to check and see that the tape is secure before you turn the welder on.

Remember, a stick electrode is always "electrically hot" when the welder is on — treat it with respect. If you do experience a shock, think of it as a warning — check your equipment, work habits and work area to see what is wrong before continuing to weld.

⚠ WARNING

WELDING SPARKS can cause fire or explosion.
- **Keep flammable material away.**

- -

Fire Hazards

Because of the extreme temperatures associated with any arc welding process, you should always be aware of fire hazards. The heat of the welding arc can reach temperatures of 10,000°F, but this heat in itself is not generally a fire hazard. The danger of fire actually results from the effects of this intense heat upon your work and in the form of **sparks and molten metals**. Because these can spray up to 35 feet from your work, you must recognize and protect combustible materials from the welding arc, sparks and spatter. It is also important to be sure the work is not in contact with any combustible which it may ignite when heated. These materials fall into three categories: liquid (gasoline, oil, paints, and thinners); solid (wood, cardboard, and paper); and gaseous (acetylene and hydrogen).

Watch where the sparks and metals are falling from your work: if there are flammable materials including fuel or hydraulic lines in your work area and you can't move either your work or the combustible substances, put a fire-resistant shield in place. If you're welding above the ground or off a ladder, make sure that there are no combustibles underneath. Also, don't forget about your co-workers, and everybody else who may be in the work area, as they probably wouldn't appreciate being hit with slag or sparks from your work.

Particular care must be taken when welding or cutting in dusty locations. Fine dust particles may readily oxidize (burn) and without warning result in a flash fire or even an explosion when exposed to the welding arc or even sparks.

If you are not sure of the combustible or volatile nature of residue or dust in the work area, no welding or cutting should take place until a responsible person has inspected the area and given approval for the work.

Before you start welding, inspect the surface of your work, looking for flammable coatings or any unknown substances that would ignite when heated. Because of the extreme fire and explosion hazards inherent to welding on or around containers and piping that may have combustible materials, such work should be handled only by experienced welders who review and follow the safety practices recommended in the American Welding Society document F4.1, "Recommended Safe Practices for the Preparation for Welding and Cutting of Containers and Piping Which Had Held Hazardous Substances."

Know where the fire alarms and fire extinguishers are located, and check the pressure gauges so you don't rely upon one that's empty. If there are none in the area, make sure that you have access to fire hoses, sand buckets, fire-resistant blankets, or other fire fighting equipment. If you're welding within 35 feet or so of flammable materials, you should have a fire watcher to see where your sparks are flying, and to grab an extinguisher or alarm if needed. Both you and the fire watcher should wait for a half hour after all welding is finished to find and put out any smoldering fires that may have resulted from your welding.

As with other emergencies that may result from welding accidents, the first rule is: don't panic. Depending on the size of the fire, sound the fire alarm to warn others and call the fire department; shut off your welder; and get to the fire exits as quickly as possible.

⚠ WARNING

FUMES & GASES can be dangerous to your health
- **Keep fumes and gases from your breathing zone and general area.**
- **Keep your head out of the fumes.**
- **Use enough ventilation or exhaust at the arc, or both, to keep fumes and gases from your breathing zone and general area.**

- -

Fumes and Gases

Because of the variables involved in fume and gas generation from arc welding, cutting and allied processes (such as the welding process and electrode, the base metal, coatings on the base metal, and other possible contaminants in the air), we'll have to treat the subject in a rather general way, lumping all but the more hazardous situations together. The precautions we describe will hold true for all arc welding processes.

The **fume plume** contains solid particles from the consumables, base metal, and base metal coating. For common mild steel arc welding, depending on the amount and length of exposure to these fumes, most immediate or short term effects are temporary, and include symptoms of burning eyes and skin, dizziness, nausea, and fever. For example, zinc fumes can cause metal fume fever, a temporary illness that is similar to the flu.

Long-term exposure to welding fumes can lead to siderosis (iron deposits in the lungs) and may affect pulmonary function. Bronchitis and some lung fibrosis have been reported.

Some consumables contain certain compounds in amounts which may require special ventilation and/or exhaust. These Special Ventilation products can be identified by reading the labels on the package. If Special Ventilation products are used indoors, use local exhaust. If Special Ventilation products are used outdoors, a respirator may be required. Various compounds, some of which may be in welding fume, and reported health effects, in summary, are:

Barium: Soluble barium compounds may cause severe stomach pain, slow pulse rate, irregular heart beat, ringing of the ears, convulsions and muscle spasms. In extreme cases can cause death.

Cadmium also requires extra precautions. This toxic metal can be found on some steel and steel fasteners as a plating, or in silver solder. Cadmium fumes can be fatal even under brief overexposures, with symptoms much like those of metal fume fever. These two conditions should not be confused. Overexposure to cadmium can be enough to cause fatalities, with symptoms appearing quickly, and, in some circumstances, death a few days later.

Chromium: Chromium is on the IARC (International Agency for Research on Cancer) and NTP (National Toxicology Program) lists chromium as posing a carcinogenic risk to humans. Fumes from the use of stainless steel, hardfacing and other types of consumables contain chromium and/or nickel. Some forms of these metals are known or suspected to cause lung cancer in processes other than welding and asthma has been reported. Therefore, it is recommended that precautions be taken to keep exposures as low as possible. OSHA recently adopted a lower PEL (Permissible Exposure Limit) for chromium (see Supplement 3). The use of local exhaust and/or an approved respirator may be required to avoid overexposure.

Coatings on the metal to be welded, such as paint, may also contain toxic substances, such as lead, chromium and zinc. In general, it is always best to remove coatings from the base metal before welding or cutting.

Cobalt: Exposure to cobalt can cause respiratory disease and pulmonary sensitization. Cobalt in metallic form has been reported to cause lung damage.

Copper: Prolonged exposure to copper fume may cause skin irritation or discoloration of the skin and hair.

Manganese: Manganese overexposure may affect the central nervous system, resulting in poor coordination, difficulty in speaking, and tremor of arms or legs. This condition is considered irreversible.

Nickel: Nickel and its compounds are on the IARC (International Agency for Research on Cancer) and NTP (National Toxicology Program) lists as posing a carcinogenic risk to humans.

Silica: Crystalline silica is present in respirable dust form submerged arc flux. Overexposure can cause severe lung damage (silicosis).

Zinc: Overexposure to zinc (from galvanized metals) may cause metal fume fever with symptoms similar to the common flu.

The **gases** that result from an arc welding process also present potential hazard. Most of the shielding gases (argon, helium, and carbon dioxide) are non-toxic, but, as they are released, they **displace oxygen** in your breathing air, causing dizziness, unconsciousness, and death, the longer your brain is denied the oxygen it needs. Carbon monoxide can also be developed and may pose a hazard if excessive levels are present.

The **heat and UV radiation** can cause irritation to the eyes and lungs. Some degreasing compounds such as trichlorethylene and perchlorethylene can decompose from the heat and ultraviolet radiation of an arc. Because of the chemical breakdown of vapor-degreasing materials under ultraviolet radiation, arc welding should not be done in the vicinity of a vapor-degreasing operation. Carbon-arc welding, gas tungsten-arc welding and gas metal arc welding should be especially avoided in such areas, because they emit more ultraviolet radiation than other processes. Also, keep in mind that ozone and nitrogen oxides are formed when UV radiation passes through the air. These gases cause headaches, chest pains, irritation of the eyes, and an itchiness in the nose and throat.

There is one easy way to **reduce the risk** of exposure to hazardous fumes and gases: **keep your head out of the fume plume!** As obvious as this sounds, the failure to follow this advice is a common cause of fume and gas overexposure because the concentration of fume and gases is greatest in the plume. Keep fumes and gases from your breathing zone and general area using natural ventilation, mechanical ventilation, fixed or moveable exhaust hoods or local exhaust at the arc. Finally, it may be necessary to wear an approved respirator if adequate ventilation cannot be provided (see Ventilation section).

As a rule of thumb, for many mild steel electrode, if the air is visibly clear and you are comfortable, then the ventilation is generally adequate for your work.The most accurate way to determine if the worker exposure does not exceed the applicable exposure limit for compounds in the fumes and gases is to have an industrial hygienist take and analyze a sample of the air you are breathing. This is particularly important if you are welding with stainless, hardfacing or Special Ventilation products. All Lincoln MSDS have a maximum fume guideline number. If exposure to total fume is kept below that number, exposure to all fume from the electrode (not coatings or plating on the work) will be below the TLV.

There are also steps that you can take to identify hazardous substances in your welding environment. First, read the product label and material safety data sheet for the electrode posted in the work place or in the electrode or flux container to see what fumes can be reasonably expected from use of the product and to determine if special ventilation is needed. Secondly, know what the base metal is, and determine if there is any paint, plating, or coating that could expose you to toxic fumes and/or gases. Remove it from the metal being welded, if possible. If you start to feel uncomfortable, dizzy or nauseous, there is a possibility that you are being overexposed to fumes and gases, or suffering from oxygen deficiency. Stop welding and get some **fresh air** immediately. Notify your supervisor and co-workers so the situation can be corrected and other workers can avoid the hazard. Be sure you are following these safe practices, the consumable labeling and MSDS and improve the ventilation in your area. Do not continue welding until the situation has been corrected.

NOTE: The MSDS for all Lincoln consumables is available on Lincoln's website: *www.lincolnelectric.com*

Before we turn to the methods available to control welding fume exposure, you should understand a few basic terms:

Natural Ventilation is the movement of air through the workplace caused by natural forces. Outside, this is usually the wind. Inside, this may be the flow of air through open windows and doors.

Mechanical Ventilation is the movement of air through the workplace caused by an electrical device such as a portable fan or permanently mounted fan in the ceiling or wall.

Source Extraction (Local Exhaust) is a mechanical device used to capture welding fume at or near the arc and filter contaminants out of the air.

The ventilation or exhaust needed for your application depends upon many factors such as:
- workspace volume
- workspace configuration
- number of welders
- welding process and current
- consumables used (mild steel, hardfacing, stainless, etc.)
- allowable levels (TLV, PEL, etc.)
- material welded (including paint or plating)
- natural airflow

Your work area has **adequate ventilation** when there is enough ventilation and/or exhaust to control worker exposure to hazardous materials in the welding fumes and gases so the applicable limits for those materials is not exceeded. See Supplement 2 for the legal limits, the OSHA PEL (Permissible Exposure Limit), and the recommended guideline, the ACGIH TLV (Threshold Limit Value), for many compounds found in welding fume.

Ventilation

There are many methods which can be selected by the user to provide adequate ventilation for the specific application. The following section provides general information which may be helpful in evaluating what type of ventilation equipment may be suitable for your application. When ventilation equipment is installed, you should confirm worker exposure is controlled within applicable OSHA PEL and/or ACGIH TLV. According to OSHA regulations, when welding and cutting (mild steels), natural ventilation is usually considered sufficient to meet requirements, provided that:

1. The room or welding area contains at least 10,000 cubic feet (about 22' x 22' x 22') for each welder.
2. The ceiling height is not less than 16 feet.
3. Cross ventilation is not blocked by partitions, equipment, or other structural barriers.
4. Welding is not done in a confined space.

Spaces that do not meet these requirements should be equipped with mechanical ventilating equipment that exhausts at least 2000 cfm of air for each welder, except where local exhaust hoods or booths, or air-line respirators are used.

Important Safety Note:
When welding with electrodes which require special ventilation such as stainless or hardfacing (see instructions on container or MSDS) or on lead or cadmium plated steel and other metals or coatings which produce hazardous fumes, keep exposure as low as possible and below exposure limit values (PEL and TLV) for materials in the fume using local exhaust or mechanical ventilation. In confined spaces or in some circumstances, for example outdoors, a respirator may be required if exposure cannot be controlled to the PEL or TLV. (See MSDS and Supplement 3 of this brochure.) Additional precautions are also required when welding on galvanized steel.

Source Extraction Equipment

Mechanical ventilation is an effective method of fume control for many welding processes. Because it captures fume near the arc or source of the fume, which is more efficient in most cases, local exhaust, also called "source extraction," is a very effective means to control welding fume.

Source extraction of welding fumes can be provided by mobile or stationary, single or multi-station, exhaust and/or filtration equipment designed with adjustable fume extraction arms nozzles or guns, by fixed enclosures, booths or tables with extraction canopies also known as down-draft, or by back-draft or cross-draft tables/booths. Source extraction of weld fume falls into two categories: low vacuum/high volume, or high vacuum/low volume.

Low Vacuum/High Volume

Mobile or stationary, single or multi-station, large centralized exhaust and/or filtration equipment designed with adjustable fume extraction arms are usually low vacuum/high volume systems. When correctly positioned, the capture rate of adjustable fume extraction arms is suitable for all position welding and cutting. For more difficult to reach work areas, flexible hose may be used in place of adjustable fume extraction arms.

These arms generally move between 560 and 860 cubic feet per minute (CFM) (900 – 1400 m^3/hr) of air, but use low vacuum levels (3 to 5 inches water gauge [750 – 1250 Pa]) to minimize power requirements. Water gauge (WG) is a measure of negative pressure: higher numbers mean more negative pressure (more "suction"). With this volume of airflow, the end of the arm can be placed 6 to 15 inches (160 – 375 mm) away from the arc and still effectively capture weld fume.

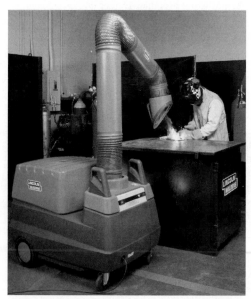

Mobiflex™ 200-M low vacuum mobile fume extraction unit.

Fume extraction arms generally use a 6 or 8 inch diameter hose, or hose and tubing combinations. Arm lengths are typically 7, 10, or 13 feet (2, 3, or 4 m), with boom extensions available. The arms may be wall mounted, attached to mobile units, or incorporated into a centralized system.

In general, the farther the extraction hose is from the arc, the more volume of air movement is required to effectively capture welding fume. Overhead hoods (canopies), for example, capture most of the fume, but care must be taken to be sure fume is not pulled through the breathing zone of the operator.

Fixed enclosures, booths or tables with extraction canopies also known as **down-draft, back-draft or cross-draft booths/tables** are a variation of overhead hood technology and can be used as source extraction equipment. A booth is a fixed enclosure that consists of a top and at least two sides that surround the welding operation. These systems use a plenum with openings to the side, back or bottom of the work space rather than above it to capture the weld fume. The weld fume is extracted through the plenum and away from the breathing zone of the operator that is welding or cutting. Down-draft or back-draft booths/tables can be mobile or stationary, single or multi-station, exhaust and/or filtration systems. They are particularly suitable for in-position bench welding or cutting jobs and can be effective when small parts are being welded. The airflow required for effectiveness varies depending upon the installation design, but may be 1,000 CFM or higher.

There are advantages and limitations associated with low vacuum/high volume source extraction systems.

Advantages	*Limitations*
Source extraction with large volume of air being extracted from welder breathing zone.	If not using filtration unit, exhausting air to outside requires make-up air systems and make-up heaters (ie. large volumes of displaced air need to be replaced, resulting in increased utility costs).
Auto-stop delay assists with removal of residual fumes.	Welder must stop to reposition arm over weld area(s).
Low noise level.	Filtration systems larger due to volume of air flow.
Flexible arm for repositioning.	Depending on design, ductwork can be large.
Low installation costs (ductwork).	
Low energy consumption (small fan unit with low rpm).	
Adjustable arms suitable for all-position welding.	

High Vacuum/Low Volume

High vacuum/low volume fume extraction systems are designed for close proximity (2 to 4 inches) positioning. High vacuum/low volume weld fume extraction is achieved with lower airflow rates than those encountered when utilizing low vacuum/high volume systems. There are two methods of high vacuum extraction: welding guns with built-in extraction (fume extraction guns), or separate suction nozzles of various designs.

Fume extraction guns use fume capture nozzles built into the gun tube and handle. The extraction airflow is approximately 35 to 60 CFM (60 – 100 m³/hr) for integrated fume extraction guns. Therefore, no repositioning is required, since the suction automatically follows the arc. The vacuum level is high (40 to 70 inches WG [9.96 X 103 to 1.74 X 104 Pascal]) permitting the use of hose featuring longer lengths (10 to 25 feet) and smaller diameters (1.25 to 1.75 inches). Fume extraction gun designs have been improved to be more ergonomic and user friendly. Depending upon the type of welding, particularly "in position" welding, extraction guns may be a good solution.

Suction nozzles are positioned near the weld, and commonly use capture distances of less than four inches. Depending upon the design, airflow of suction nozzles is typically between 80 to 100 CFM (135 – 170 m3/hr). Suction nozzles must be kept near the arc to be used effectively.

The capture rate for fume extraction guns or nozzles is highest when used in flat and horizontal welding positions. High vacuum equipment ranges from small, portable, mobile units to stationary, single or multi-station, large centralized filtration systems.

There are advantages and limitations associated with high vacuum/low volume source extraction systems.

Advantages	*Limitations*
When using a fume extraction gun, welder does not need to stop and reposition extraction device.	Required when using a suction nozzle. Welder may need to stop to reposition extraction device.
Low volume of air is displaced - results in energy efficiency and conservation.	High noise level due to increased air velocity and high motor rpm of the fan unit.
Ductwork smaller in diameter (3 to 10 inches) vs. low vacuum systems.	Possible removal of shielding gases affecting weld integrity if nozzle or gun placed too close to source.
Low obstruction of welder vision.	Greater energy consumption (large fan unit with high rpm).
Suitable for heavier particulate (ie. grinding dust).	Residual fumes not extracted.
Suitable option for confined, difficult to reach work spaces.	Less effective in out-of-position welding.
Smaller filter systems due to less volume of airflow.	

Fume extraction is only one component in reducing welding fume. Users should also consider the selection of the welding process, welding procedure, or consumable. Many times a combination of fume extraction, training, process change, and/or consumable change is needed to reduce the amount of fume to acceptable levels. Solutions to a particular application may involve one or all of these factors and the user must determine which solution best fits their application.

OSHA regulations include specific requirements for exhaust systems which should be reviewed when selecting fume extraction systems (see Supplement 2).

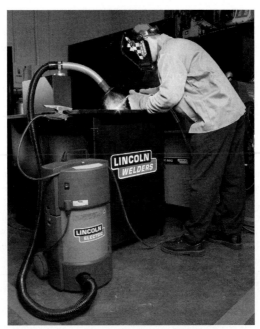

Miniflex™ high vacuum portable fume extraction unit.

Exhaust vs. Filtration

<u>Source extraction exhaust equipment</u> captures and extracts weld fumes from the source and exhausts the fumes to the outside atmosphere. This technique removes welding fume from the breathing zone of the welder but can also displace large volumes of conditioned air which may lead to increased utility and heating costs.

<u>Source extraction filtration equipment</u> captures and extracts weld fumes from the source and filters the fumes by passing them through a cellulose and/or polyester filter cartridge or electrostatic filter. Depending on the weld application, environment, federal or local regulations, and filtration efficiency levels, filtered air may be re-circulated back into the facility or exhausted to the outside atmosphere. By re-circulating filtered air back into the work environment compared to exhausting to the outside, source extraction filtration equipment can be more economical to operate. Particularly in winter months, substantially lower heating costs may be recognized, as less replacement air is required with filtration versus exhaust systems.

Using a cellulose or polyester filter cartridge or electrostatic filter will depend upon the weld application. Electrostatic filters may also be used however, they lose efficiency if they are not frequently washed.

Regardless of the type of mechanical ventilation (exhaust or filtration) source extraction system used, the important factor is that it is a tool designed to control exposure to welding fume and its constituents. All forms of mechanical ventilation or source extraction equipment require routine maintenance. In addition, when using weld fume source extraction equipment, sparks from welding, cutting or grinding processes can cause fire within the equipment. To control this potential fire hazard, operation, service and maintenance instructions for source extraction equipment should be followed.

Note:

It is the equipment owner and operator's responsibility to comply with Occupational Safety, Health Administration (OSHA) Permissible Exposure Limits (PELs) or American Conference of Governments Industrial Hygienists (ACGIH) TLVs for welding fume. It is the responsibility of the equipment owner to research, test and comply with regulations which may apply to filtered air recirculated inside the facility or unfiltered air is exhausted outside of the facility.

Working in Confined Spaces

When arc welding in a confined area, such as a boiler, tank, or the hold of a ship, bear in mind that all the hazards associated with normal arc welding are amplified, so the precautions mentioned here are even more important. This subject is very complicated and only basic precautions related to arc welding will be discussed in this brochure. Per OSHA document 29 CFR 1910.146, a particular area is considered a confined space if it:

1) Is large enough and so configured that an employee can bodily enter and perform assigned work; and
2) Has limited or restricted means for entry or exit (for example, tanks, vessels, silos, storage bins, hoppers, vaults, and pits are spaces that may have limited means of entry.); and
3) Is not designed for continuous employee occupancy.

There is a greater danger that enough **flammable gases** may be present in the confined space to cause an explosion. The metal of the enclosure can become part of the welding circuit, so any metal you touch (the walls, floor, ceiling) is **electrically "hot."** Welding fumes can accumulate more rapidly, with a higher concentration; gases can force out the **breathable air**, suffocating you in the process.

Per OSHA document 29 CFR 1910.146(d)(5)(iii); after an area has been deemed a confined space, the existence of the following atmospheric hazards are to be determined:

1) Test for oxygen
2) Test for combustible gases and vapors
3) Test for toxic gases and vapors

The workplace and OSHA rules regarding confined spaces must be followed. Make sure that your body is insulated from the work-piece using dry insulation. Wear dry gloves and only use a well-insulated electrode holder. Semiautomatic constant voltage welders with cold electrode or stick welders equipped with a device to lower the no-load voltage are recommended, especially when the work area is wet. Make sure that there is adequate ventilation and exhaust (a respirator or an air-supplied respirator may be necessary depending on the application), and that there are no flammable coatings, liquids or gases nearby.

Lastly, you must have someone outside the enclosure trained to handle emergencies, with rescue procedures and a means to disconnect power to your equipment and pull you out if danger arises. We cannot stress this strongly enough: however experienced you are, do not attempt work of this nature without constant communication with the person outside the confined area. When welding within a confined area, problems which arise can immediately become very serious and, in some cases, life-threatening. It is for that reason that OSHA regulations and workplace procedures for confined space work must be followed.

Review Questions

1. Why is moisture or water dangerous to both the welder and the operator?

2. How do you determine what shade of filter plate is worn for arc welding?

3. Must a filter plate be worn when observing as well as when welding?

4. When must safety glasses be worn?

5. Why is it necessary to know what an empty container held before welding?

6. Why is it important to disconnect a welder before working on it?

7. Why is it important to keep ones head out of welding fumes?

SUPPLEMENT 1
Guide for Shade Numbers

OPERATION	ELECTRODE SIZE 1/32 in. (mm)	ARC CURRENT (A)	MINIMUM PROTECTIVE SHADE	SUGGESTED[1] SHADE NO. (COMFORT)
Shielded metal arc welding	Less than 3 (2.5) 3-5 (2.5–4) 5-8 (4–6.4) More than 8 (6.4)	Less than 60 60-160 160-250 250-550	7 8 10 11	– 10 12 14
Gas metal arc welding and flux cored arc welding		Less than 60 60-160 160-250 250-500	7 10 10 10	– 11 12 14
Gas tungsten arc welding		Less than 50 50-150 150-500	8 8 10	10 12 14
Air carbon Arc cutting	(Light) (Heavy)	Less than 500 500-1000	10 11	12 14
Plasma arc welding		Less than 20 20-100 100-400 400-800	6 8 10 11	6 to 8 10 12 14
Plasma arc cutting	(Light)[2] (Medium)[2] (Heavy)[2]	Less than 300 300-400 400-800	8 9 10	9 12 14
Torch brazing		–	–	3 or 4
Torch soldering		–	–	2
Carbon arc welding		–	–	14
PLATE THICKNESS				
	in.	**mm**		
Gas welding Light Medium Heavy	Under 1/8 1/8 to 1/2 Over 1/2	Under 3.2 3.2 to 12.7 Over 12.7		4 or 5 5 or 6 6 or 8
Oxygen cutting Light Medium Heavy	Under 1 1 to 6 Over 6	Under 25 25 to 150 Over 150		3 or 4 4 or 5 5 or 6

[1] As a rule of thumb, start with a shade that is too dark, then go to a lighter shade which gives sufficient view of the weld zone without going below the minimum. In oxyfuel gas welding or cutting where the torch produces a high yellow light, it is desirable to use a filter lens that absorbs the yellow or sodium line the visible light of the (spectrum) operation

[2] These values apply where the actual arc is clearly seen. Experience has shown that lighter filters may be used when the arc is hidden by the workpiece.

Data from ANSI Z49.1-2005

SUPPLEMENT 2
Bibliography and Suggested Reading

ANSI Z87.1, *Practice for Occupational and Educational Eye and Face Protection*, American National Standards Institute, 11 West 42nd Street, New York, NY 10036.

Arc Welding and Your Health: A Handbook of Health Information for Welding. Published by The American Industrial Hygiene Association, 2700 Prosperity Avenue, Suite 250, Fairfax, VA 22031-4319.

NFPA Standard 51B, *Cutting and Welding Processes*, National Fire Protection Association, 1 Batterymarch Park, P.O. Box 9146, Quincy, MA 02269-9959.

OSHA General Industry Standard 29 CFR 1910 Subpart Q. OSHA Hazard Communication Standard 29 CFR 1910.1200. Available from the Occupational Safety and Health Administration at http://www.osha.org or contact your local OSHA office.

The following publications are published by The American Welding Society, P.O. Box 351040, Miami, Florida 33135. AWS publications may be purchased from the American Welding society at http://www.aws.org or by contacting the AWS at 800-443-9353.

ANSI, Standard Z49.1, *Safety in Welding, Cutting and Allied Processes*. Z49.1 is now available for download at no charge at http://www.lincolnelectric.com/community/safety/ or at the AWS website http://www.aws.org.
AWS F1.1, *Method for Sampling Airborne Particulates Generated by Welding and Allied Processes.*

AWS F1.2, *Laboratory Method for Measuring Fume Generation Rates and Total Fume Emission of Welding and Allied Processes.*

AWS F1.3, *Evaluating Contaminants in the Welding Environment: A Strategic Sampling Guide.*

AWS F1.5, *Methods for Sampling and Analyzing Gases from Welding and Allied Processes.*

AWS F3.2, Ventilation Guide for Welding Fume Control

AWS F4.1, *Recommended Safe Practices for the Preparation for Welding and Cutting of Containers and Piping That Have Held Hazardous Substances.*

AWS SHF, *Safety and Health Facts Sheets*. Available free of charge from the AWS website at http://www.aws.org.

SUPPLEMENT 3
Listed below are some typical ingredients in welding electrodes and their TLV (ACGIH) guidelines and PEL (OSHA) exposure limits

INGREDIENTS	CAS No.	TLV mg/m³	PEL mg/m³
Aluminum and/or aluminum alloys (as Al)*****	7429-90-5	10	15
Aluminum oxide and/or Bauxite*****	1344-28-1	10	5**
Barium compounds (as Ba)*****	513-77-9	****	****
Chromium and chromium alloys or compounds (as Cr)*****	7440-47-3	0.5(b)	.005(b)
Fluorides (as F)	7789-75-5	2.5	2.5
Iron	7439-89-6	10*	10*
Limestone and/or calcium carbonate	1317-65-3	10	15
Lithium compounds (as Li)	554-13-2	10*	10*
Magnesite	1309-48-4	10	15
Magnesium and/or magnesium alloys and compounds (as Mg)	7439-95-4	10*	10*
Manganese and/or manganese alloys and compounds (as Mn)*****	7439-96-5	0.2	5.0(c)
Mineral silicates	1332-58-7	5**	5**
Molybdenum alloys (as Mo)	7439-98-7	10	10
Nickel*****	7440-02-0	1.5	1
Silicates and other binders	1344-09-8	10*	10*
Silicon and/or silicon alloys and compounds (as Si)	7440-21-3	10*	10*
Strontium compounds (as Sr)	1633-05-2	10*	10*
Zirconium alloys and compounds (as Zr)	12004-83-0	5	5

Supplemental Information:
(*) Not listed. Nuisance value maximum is 10 milligrams per cubic meter. PEL value for iron oxide is 10 milligrams per cubic meter. TLV value for iron oxide is 5 milligrams per cubic meter.

(**) As respirable dust.

(*****) Subject to the reporting requirements of Sections 311, 312, and 313 of the Emergency Planning and Community Right-to-Know Act of 1986 and of 40CFR 370 and 372.

(b) The PEL for chromium (VI) is .005 milligrams per cubic meter as an 8 hour time weighted average. The TLV for water-soluble chromium (VI) is 0.05 milligrams per cubic meter. The TLV for insoluble chromium (VI) is 0.01 milligrams per cubic meter.

(c) Values are for manganese fume. STEL (Short Term Exposure Limit) is 3.0 milligrams per cubic meter. OSHA PEL is a ceiling value.

(****) There is no listed value for insoluble barium compounds. The TLV for soluble barium compounds is 0.5 mg/m³.

TLV and PEL values are as of April 2006. Always check Material Safety Data Sheet (MSDS) with product or on the Lincoln Electric website at http://www.lincolnelectric.com

SUPPLEMENT 4

⚠ WARNING

⚠ CALIFORNIA PROPOSITION 65 WARNINGS ⚠

Diesel engine exhaust and some of its constituents are known to the State of California to cause cancer, birth defects, and other reproductive harm.	The engine exhaust from this product contains chemicals known to the State of California to cause cancer, birth defects, or other reproductive harm.
<u>The Above For Diesel Engines</u>	<u>The Above For Gasoline Engines</u>

ARC WELDING CAN BE HAZARDOUS. PROTECT YOURSELF AND OTHERS FROM POSSIBLE SERIOUS INJURY OR DEATH. KEEP CHILDREN AWAY. PACEMAKER WEARERS SHOULD CONSULT WITH THEIR DOCTOR BEFORE OPERATING.

Read and understand the following safety highlights. For additional safety information, it is strongly recommended that you purchase a copy of "Safety in Welding & Cutting - ANSI Standard Z49.1" from the American Welding Society, P.O. Box 351040, Miami, Florida 33135 or CSA Standard W117.2-1974. A Free copy of "Arc Welding Safety" booklet E205 is available from the Lincoln Electric Company, 22801 St. Clair Avenue, Cleveland, Ohio 44117-1199.

BE SURE THAT ALL INSTALLATION, OPERATION, MAINTENANCE AND REPAIR PROCEDURES ARE PERFORMED ONLY BY QUALIFIED INDIVIDUALS.

FOR ENGINE powered equipment.

1.a. Turn the engine off before troubleshooting and maintenance work unless the maintenance work requires it to be running.

1.b. Operate engines in open, well-ventilated areas or vent the engine exhaust fumes outdoors.

1.c. Do not add the fuel near an open flame welding arc or when the engine is running. Stop the engine and allow it to cool before refueling to prevent spilled fuel from vaporizing on contact with hot engine parts and igniting. Do not spill fuel when filling tank. If fuel is spilled, wipe it up and do not start engine until fumes have been eliminated.

1.d. Keep all equipment safety guards, covers and devices in position and in good repair. Keep hands, hair, clothing and tools away from V-belts, gears, fans and all other moving parts when starting, operating or repairing equipment.

1.e. In some cases it may be necessary to remove safety guards to perform required maintenance. Remove guards only when necessary and replace them when the maintenance requiring their removal is complete. Always use the greatest care when working near moving parts.

1.f. Do not put your hands near the engine fan. Do not attempt to override the governor or idler by pushing on the throttle control rods while the engine is running.

1.g. To prevent accidentally starting gasoline engines while turning the engine or welding generator during maintenance work, disconnect the spark plug wires, distributor cap or magneto wire as appropriate.

1.h. To avoid scalding, do not remove the radiator pressure cap when the engine is hot.

ELECTRIC AND MAGNETIC FIELDS may be dangerous

2.a. Electric current flowing through any conductor causes localized Electric and Magnetic Fields (EMF). Welding current creates EMF fields around welding cables and welding machines

2.b. EMF fields may interfere with some pacemakers, and welders having a pacemaker should consult their physician before welding.

2.c. Exposure to EMF fields in welding may have other health effects which are now not known.

2.d. All welders should use the following procedures in order to minimize exposure to EMF fields from the welding circuit:

2.d.1. Route the electrode and work cables together - Secure them with tape when possible.

2.d.2. Never coil the electrode lead around your body.

2.d.3. Do not place your body between the electrode and work cables. If the electrode cable is on your right side, the work cable should also be on your right side.

2.d.4. Connect the work cable to the workpiece as close as possible to the area being welded.

2.d.5. Do not work next to welding power source.

ELECTRIC SHOCK can kill.

3.a. The electrode and work (or ground) circuits are electrically "hot" when the welder is on. Do not touch these "hot" parts with your bare skin or wet clothing. Wear dry, hole-free gloves to insulate hands.

3.b. Insulate yourself from work and ground using dry insulation. Make certain the insulation is large enough to cover your full area of physical contact with work and ground.

In addition to the normal safety precautions, if welding must be performed under electrically hazardous conditions (in damp locations or while wearing wet clothing; on metal structures such as floors, gratings or scaffolds; when in cramped positions such as sitting, kneeling or lying, if there is a high risk of unavoidable or accidental contact with the workpiece or ground) use the following equipment:
- **Semiautomatic DC Constant Voltage (Wire) Welder.**
- **DC Manual (Stick) Welder.**
- **AC Welder with Reduced Voltage Control.**

3.c. In semiautomatic or automatic wire welding, the electrode, electrode reel, welding head, nozzle or semiautomatic welding gun are also electrically "hot".

3.d. Always be sure the work cable makes a good electrical connection with the metal being welded. The connection should be as close as possible to the area being welded.

3.e. Ground the work or metal to be welded to a good electrical (earth) ground.

3.f. Maintain the electrode holder, work clamp, welding cable and welding machine in good, safe operating condition. Replace damaged insulation.

3.g. Never dip the electrode in water for cooling.

3.h. Never simultaneously touch electrically "hot" parts of electrode holders connected to two welders because voltage between the two can be the total of the open circuit voltage of both welders.

3.i. When working above floor level, use a safety belt to protect yourself from a fall should you get a shock.

3.j. Also see Items 6.c. and 8.

ARC RAYS can burn.

4.a. Use a shield with the proper filter and cover plates to protect your eyes from sparks and the rays of the arc when welding or observing open arc welding. Headshield and filter lens should conform to ANSI Z87. I standards.

4.b. Use suitable clothing made from durable flame-resistant material to protect your skin and that of your helpers from the arc rays.

4.c. Protect other nearby personnel with suitable, non-flammable screening and/or warn them not to watch the arc nor expose themselves to the arc rays or to hot spatter or metal.

FUMES AND GASES can be dangerous.

5.a. Welding may produce fumes and gases hazardous to health. Avoid breathing these fumes and gases. When welding, keep your head out of the fume. Use enough ventilation and/or exhaust at the arc to keep fumes and gases away from the breathing zone. **When welding with electrodes which require special ventilation such as stainless or hard facing (see instructions on container or MSDS) or on lead or cadmium plated steel and other metals or coatings which produce highly toxic fumes, keep exposure as low as possible and below Threshold Limit Values (TLV) using local exhaust or mechanical ventilation. In confined spaces or in some circumstances, outdoors, a respirator may be required. Additional precautions are also required when welding on galvanized steel.**

5.b. The operation of welding fume control equipment is affected by various factors including proper use and positioning of the equipment, maintenance of the equipment and the specific welding procedure and application involved. Worker exposure level should be checked upon installation and periodically thereafter to be certain it is within applicable OSHA PEL and ACGIH TLV limits.

5.c. Do not weld in locations near chlorinated hydrocarbon vapors coming from degreasing, cleaning or spraying operations. The heat and rays of the arc can react with solvent vapors to form phosgene, a highly toxic gas, and other irritating products.

5.d. Shielding gases used for arc welding can displace air and cause injury or death. Always use enough ventilation, especially in confined areas, to insure breathing air is safe.

5.e. Read and understand the manufacturer's instructions for this equipment and the consumables to be used, including the material safety data sheet (MSDS) and follow your employer's safety practices. MSDS forms are available from your welding distributor or from the manufacturer.

5.f. Also see item 1.b.

WELDING and CUTTING SPARKS can cause fire or explosion.

6.a. Remove fire hazards from the welding area. If this is not possible, cover them to prevent the welding sparks from starting a fire. Remember that welding sparks and hot materials from welding can easily go through small cracks and openings to adjacent areas. Avoid welding near hydraulic lines. Have a fire extinguisher readily available.

6.b. Where compressed gases are to be used at the job site, special precautions should be used to prevent hazardous situations. Refer to "Safety in Welding and Cutting" (ANSI Standard Z49.1) and the operating information for the equipment being used.

6.c. When not welding, make certain no part of the electrode circuit is touching the work or ground. Accidental contact can cause overheating and create a fire hazard.

6.d. Do not heat, cut or weld tanks, drums or containers until the proper steps have been taken to insure that such procedures will not cause flammable or toxic vapors from substances inside. They can cause an explosion even though they have been "cleaned". For information, purchase "Recommended Safe Practices for the Preparation for Welding and Cutting of Containers and Piping That Have Held Hazardous Substances", AWS F4.1 from the American Welding Society (see address above).

6.e. Vent hollow castings or containers before heating, cutting or welding. They may explode.

6.f. Sparks and spatter are thrown from the welding arc. Wear oil free protective garments such as leather gloves, heavy shirt, cuffless trousers, high shoes and a cap over your hair. Wear ear plugs when welding out of position or in confined places. Always wear safety glasses with side shields when in a welding area.

6.g. Connect the work cable to the work as close to the welding area as practical. Work cables connected to the building framework or other locations away from the welding area increase the possibility of the welding current passing through lifting chains, crane cables or other alternate circuits. This can create fire hazards or overheat lifting chains or cables until they fail.

6.h. Also see item 1.c.

6.I. Read and folllow NFPA 51B " Standard for Fire Prevention During Welding, Cutting and Other Hot Work", available from NFPA, 1 Batterymarch Park,PO box 9101, Quincy, Ma 022690-9101.

6.j. Do not use a welding power source for pipe thawing.

CYLINDER may explode if damaged.

7.a. Use only compressed gas cylinders containing the correct shielding gas for the process used and properly operating regulators designed for the gas and pressure used. All hoses, fittings, etc. should be suitable for the application and maintained in good condition.

7.b. Always keep cylinders in an upright position securely chained to an undercarriage or fixed support.

7.c. Cylinders should be located:
• Away from areas where they may be struck or subjected to physical damage.

• A safe distance from arc welding or cutting operations and any other source of heat, sparks, or flame.

7.d. Never allow the electrode, electrode holder or any other electrically "hot" parts to touch a cylinder.

7.e. Keep your head and face away from the cylinder valve outlet when opening the cylinder valve.

7.f. Valve protection caps should always be in place and hand tight except when the cylinder is in use or connected for use.

7.g. Read and follow the instructions on compressed gas cylinders, associated equipment, and CGA publication P-I, "Precautions for Safe Handling of Compressed Gases in Cylinders," available from the Compressed Gas Association 1235 Jefferson Davis Highway, Arlington, VA 22202.

FOR ELECTRICALLY powered equipment.

8.a. Turn off input power using the disconnect switch at the fuse box before working on the equipment.

8.b. Install equipment in accordance with the U.S. National Electrical Code, all local codes and the manufacturer's recommendations.

8.c. Ground the equipment in accordance with the U.S. National Electrical Code and the manufacturer's recommendations.

PRÉCAUTIONS DE SÛRETÉ

Pour votre propre protection lire et observer toutes les instructions et les précautions de sûreté specifiques qui parraissent dans ce manuel aussi bien que les précautions de sûreté générales suivantes:

Sûreté Pour Soudage A L'Arc

1. Protegez-vous contre la secousse électrique:

   a. Les circuits à l'électrode et à la piéce sont sous tension quand la machine à souder est en marche. Eviter toujours tout contact entre les parties sous tension et la peau nue ou les vétements mouillés. Porter des gants secs et sans trous pour isoler les mains.

   b. Faire trés attention de bien s'isoler de la masse quand on soude dans des endroits humides, ou sur un plancher metallique ou des grilles metalliques, principalement dans les positions assis ou couché pour lesquelles une grande partie du corps peut être en contact avec la masse.

   c. Maintenir le porte-électrode, la pince de masse, le câble de soudage et la machine à souder en bon et sûr état defonctionnement.

   d. Ne jamais plonger le porte-électrode dans l'eau pour le refroidir.

   e. Ne jamais toucher simultanément les parties sous tension des porte-électrodes connectés à deux machines à souder parce que la tension entre les deux pinces peut être le total de la tension à vide des deux machines.

   f. Si on utilise la machine à souder comme une source de courant pour soudage semi-automatique, ces precautions pour le porte-électrode s'appliquent aussi au pistolet de soudage.

2. Dans le cas de travail au dessus du niveau du sol, se protéger contre les chutes dans le cas ou on recoit un choc. Ne jamais enrouler le câble-électrode autour de n'importe quelle partie du corps.

3. Un coup d'arc peut être plus sévère qu'un coup de soleil, donc:

   a. Utiliser un bon masque avec un verre filtrant approprié ainsi qu'un verre blanc afin de se protéger les yeux du rayonnement de l'arc et des projections quand on soude ou quand on regarde l'arc.

   b. Porter des vêtements convenables afin de protéger la peau de soudeur et des aides contre le rayonnement de l'arc.

   c. Protéger l'autre personnel travaillant à proximité au soudage à l'aide d'écrans appropriés et non-inflammables.

4. Des gouttes de laitier en fusion sont émises de l'arc de soudage. Se protéger avec des vêtements de protection libres de l'huile, tels que les gants en cuir, chemise épaisse, pantalons sans revers, et chaussures montantes.

5. Toujours porter des lunettes de sécurité dans la zone de soudage. Utiliser des lunettes avec écrans lateraux dans les zones où l'on pique le laitier.

6. Eloigner les matériaux inflammables ou les recouvrir afin de prévenir tout risque d'incendie dû aux étincelles.

7. Quand on ne soude pas, poser la pince a une endroit isolé de la masse. Un court-circuit accidentel peut provoquer un échauffement et un risque d'incendie.

8. S'assurer que la masse est connectée le plus prés possible de la zone de travail qu'il est pratique de le faire. Si on place la masse sur la charpente de la construction ou d'autres endroits éloignés de la zone de travail, on augmente le risque de voir passer le courant de soudage par les chaines de levage, câbles de grue, ou autres circuits. Cela peut provoquer des risques d'incendie ou d'echauffement des chaines et des câbles jusqu'à ce qu'ils se rompent.

9. Assurer une ventilation suffisante dans la zone de soudage. Ceci est particuliérement important pour le soudage de tôles galvanisées plombées, ou cadmiées ou tout autre métal qui produit des fumées toxiques.

10. Ne pas souder en présence de vapeurs de chlore provenant d'opérations de dégraissage, nettoyage ou pistolage. La chaleur ou les rayons de l'arc peuvent réagir avec les vapeurs du solvant pour produire du phosgène (gas fortement toxique) ou autres produits irritants.

11. Pour obtenir de plus amples renseignements sur la sûreté, voir le code "Code for safety in welding and cutting" CSA Standard W 117.2-1974.

PRÉCAUTIONS DE SÛRETÉ POUR LES MACHINES À SOUDER À TRANSFORMATEUR ET À REDRESSEUR

1. Relier à la terre le chassis du poste conformement au code de l'électricité et aux recommendations du fabricant. Le dispositif de montage de la piece à souder doit être branché à une bonne mise à la terre.

2. Autant que possible, l'installation et l'entretien du poste seront effectués par un électricien qualifié.

3. Avant de faires des travaux à l'interieur de poste, la debrancher à l'interrupteur à la boite de fusibles.

4. Garder tous les couvercles et dispositifs de sûreté à leur place.

SUPPLEMENT 5
Warning Label/Operating Manual Request Form

NOTE: S18494 WARNING LABELS, SUCH AS THE ONE BELOW FOR LINCOLN ELECTRIC WELDERS, ARE AVAILABLE FREE OF CHARGE to update your welding equipment. Operating manuals are also available upon request. PLEASE write to The Lincoln Electric Company, 22801 St. Clair Ave., Cleveland, Ohio 44117-1199 or visit www.lincolnelectric.com and make the request online.

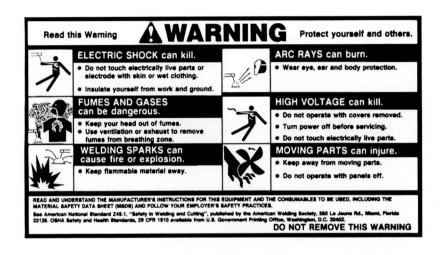

Read this Warning ⚠ **WARNING** Protect yourself and others.

ELECTRIC SHOCK can kill.
- Do not touch electrically live parts or electrode with skin or wet clothing.
- Insulate yourself from work and ground.

ARC RAYS can burn.
- Wear eye, ear and body protection.

FUMES AND GASES can be dangerous.
- Keep your head out of fumes.
- Use ventilation or exhaust to remove fumes from breathing zone.

HIGH VOLTAGE can kill.
- Do not operate with covers removed.
- Turn power off before servicing.
- Do not touch electrically live parts.

WELDING SPARKS can cause fire or explosion.
- Keep flammable material away.

MOVING PARTS can injure.
- Keep away from moving parts.
- Do not operate with panels off.

READ AND UNDERSTAND THE MANUFACTURER'S INSTRUCTIONS FOR THIS EQUIPMENT AND THE CONSUMABLES TO BE USED, INCLUDING THE MATERIAL SAFETY DATA SHEET (MSDS) AND FOLLOW YOUR EMPLOYER'S SAFETY PRACTICES.
See American National Standard Z49.1, "Safety in Welding and Cutting", published by the American Welding Society, 550 Le Jeune Rd., Miami, Florida 33126. OSHA Safety and Health Standards, 29 CFR 1910 available from U.S. Government Printing Office, Washington, D.C. 20402.

DO NOT REMOVE THIS WARNING

SUPPLEMENT 6
Engine Welder Fan Guards

ENGINE WELDER FAN GUARDS

In order to determine whether your engine welder has the proper fan guards, compare your welder with the photo below. If your welder lacks the guards shown, contact your nearest Lincoln Field Service Shop or Distributor for assistance.

NOTE: On some engine welders, including the SA-200, the original fan guard design shown below has been modified to provide added protection and/or to make it more likely to be replaced after maintenance. Check with a Lincoln Field Service Shop or Distributor to determine if updated guarding is available for your welder.

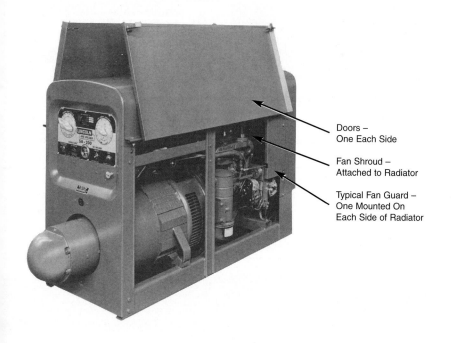

Doors –
One Each Side

Fan Shroud –
Attached to Radiator

Typical Fan Guard –
One Mounted On
Each Side of Radiator

SUPPLEMENT 7
Welding Safety Checklist

HAZARD	FACTORS TO CONSIDER	PRECAUTION SUMMARY
Electric shock can kill	• Wetness • Welder in or on workpiece • Confined space • Electrode holder and cable insulation	• Insulate welder from workpiece and ground using *dry* insulation. Rubber mat or dry wood. • Wear *dry, hole-free* gloves. (Change as necessary to keep dry.) • Do not touch electrically "hot" parts or electrode with bare skin or wet clothing. • If wet area and welder cannot be insulated from workpiece with dry insulation, use a semiautomatic, constant-voltage welder or stick welder with voltage reducing device. • Keep electrode holder and cable insulation in good condition. Do not use if insulation damaged or missing.
Fumes and gases can be dangerous	• Confined area • Positioning of welder's head • Lack of general ventilation • Electrode types, i.e., manganese, chromium, etc. See MSDS • Base metal coatings, galvanize, paint	• Use ventilation or exhaust to keep air breathing zone clear, comfortable. • Use helmet and positioning of head to minimize fume in breathing zone. • Read warnings on electrode container and material safety data sheet (MSDS) for electrode, • Provide additional ventilation/exhaust where special ventilation requirements exist. • Use special care when welding in a confined area. • Do not weld unless ventilation is adequate.
Welding sparks can cause fire or explosion	• Containers which have held combustibles • Flammable materials	• Do not weld on containers which have held combustible materials (unless strict AWS F4.1 procedures are followed). Check before welding. • Remove flammable materials from welding area or shield from sparks, heat. • Keep a fire watch in area during and after welding. • Keep a fire extinguisher in the welding area. • Wear fire retardant clothing and hat. Use earplugs when welding overhead.
Arc rays can burn eyes and skin	• Process: gas-shielded arc most severe	• Select a filter lens which is comfortable for you while welding. • Always use helmet when welding. • Provide non-flammable shielding to protect others. • Wear clothing which protects skin while welding.
Confined space	• Metal enclosure • Wetness • Restricted entry • Heavier than air gas • Welder inside or on workpiece	• Carefully evaluate adequacy of ventilation especially where electrode requires special ventilation or where gas may displace breathing air. • If basic electric shock precautions cannot be followed to insulate welder from work and electrode, use semiautomatic, constant-voltage equipment with cold electrode or stick welder with voltage reducing device. • Provide welder helper and method of welder retrieval from outside enclosure.
General work area hazards	• Cluttered area	• Keep cables, materials, tools neatly organized.
	• Indirect work (welding ground) connection	• Connect work cable as close as possible to area where welding is being performed. Do *not* allow alternate circuits through scaffold cables, hoist chains, ground leads.
	• Electrical equipment	• Use only double insulated or properly grounded equipment. • Always disconnect power to equipment before servicing.
	• Engine-driven equipment	• Use in only open, well ventilated areas. • Keep enclosure complete and guards in place. • See Lincoln service shop if guards are missing. • Refuel with engine off. • If using auxiliary power, OSHA may require GFI protection or assured grounding program (or isolated windings if less than 5KW).
	• Gas cylinders	• Never touch cylinder with the electrode. • Never lift a machine with cylinder attached. • Keep cylinder upright and chained to support.

LESSON
1.2

Object:
To study the shielded metal arc-welding process.

General Information

This lesson provides a general explanation of the arc-welding process, so that future lessons, each covering only one small part of the process, may be understood in relation to each other. This lesson should be understood clearly and be referred to frequently.

What Is Arc Welding?

Arc welding is a method of joining two pieces of metal into one solid piece. To do this, the heat of an electric arc is concentrated on the edges of two pieces of metal to be joined. The metal melts and, while these edges are still molten, additional melted metal is added. This molten mass cools and solidifies into one solid piece.

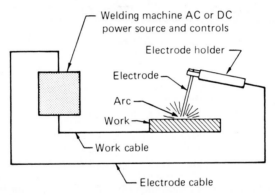

Figure 1. The welding circuit for shielded metal arc welding.

The electric arc is made between the work and the tip end of a small metal wire, the electrode, which is clamped in a holder and held in the hand. A gap is made in the welding circuit (see Figure 1) by holding the tip of the electrode 1/16"-1/8" away from the work or base metal being welded. The electric current jumps this gap and makes an arc, which is held and moved along the joint to be welded, melting the metal as it is moved.

Arc welding is a manual skill requiring a steady hand, good general physical conditions, and good eyesight. The operator controls the welding arc and, therefore, the quality of the weld made.

What Happens in the Arc?

Figure 2 illustrates the action that takes place in the electric arc. It closely resembles what is actually seen during welding.

The "arc stream" is seen in the middle of the picture. This is the electric arc created by the electric current flowing through the space between the end of the electrode and the work. The temperature of this arc is about 6000°F., which is more than enough to melt metal. The arc is very bright, as well as hot, and cannot be looked at with the naked eye without risking painful, though usually temporary, injury.

The arc melts the plate, or base, metal and actually digs into it, much as the water through a nozzle on a garden hose digs into the earth. The molten metal forms a molten pool or crater and tends to flow away from the arc. As it moves away from the arc, it cools and solidifies. A slag forms on top of the weld to protect it during cooling.

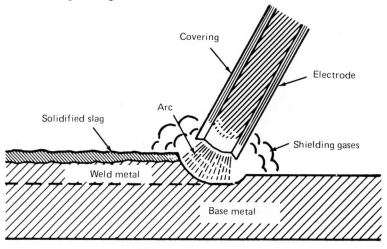

Figure 2. The welding arc.

The function of the covered electrode is much more than simply to carry current to the arc. The electrode is composed of a core of metal wire around which has been extruded and baked a chemical covering. The core wire melts in the arc and tiny droplets of molten metal shoot across the arc into the molten pool. The electrode provides additional filler metal for the joint to fill the groove or gap between the two pieces of the base metal. The covering also melts or burns in the arc. It has several functions. It makes the arc steadier, provides a shield of smoke-like gas around the arc to keep oxygen and nitrogen in the air away from the molten metal, and provides a flux for the molten pool. The flux picks up impurities and forms the protective slag. The principal differences between various types of electrodes are in their coatings. By varying the coating, it is possible to greatly alter the operating characteristics of electrodes.

The Arc-Welding Circuit

The operator's knowledge of arc welding must go beyond the arc itself. He must know how to control the arc, and this requires a knowledge of the welding circuit and the equipment that provides the electric current used in the arc. Figure 1 is a diagram of the welding circuit. The circuit begins where the electrode cable is attached to the welding machine and ends where the work cable is attached to the welding machine. Current flows through the electrode cable to the electrode holder, through the holder to the electrode and across the arc. From the work side of the arc, the current flows through base metal to the ground cable and back to the welding machine. The circuit must be complete for the current to flow, which means that it is impossible to weld if the cables are not connected to the machine or to either the electrode or work.

The several types of welding machines include motor-generators, engine-driven generators, transformers, rectifiers, and combination transformer and rectifiers. Each type has its place and purpose, as will be shown in later lessons, but the basic function of each is the same—providing a source of controlled electric power for welding. This controlled electric power has the characteristic of high amperage at low voltage. The high amperage is required to provide sufficient heat at the arc. The voltage must be low enough to be safe for handling and yet high enough to maintain the arc. The welder (machine) permits the weldor (operator) to control the amount of current he uses. This, in turn, controls the amount of heat at the arc. Some welders also permit the operator to select either a forceful or soft arc and to control its characteristics to suit the job.

The Weldor's Job

A good weldor does more than simply hold the arc. He must, first of all, be able to select the correct size and type of electrode for each job. He must know which machine to use for each job and be able to set the current and voltage controls properly. He must be able to manipulate the electrode and arc so as to make a satisfactory weld under varying conditions. In addition, the weldor must have a knowledge of joint preparation, positioning the work, distortion, and many other factors that enter into the final result—a good weldment. He must be a mechanic and a craftsman. Nearly anyone can "stick two pieces of metal together", but becoming a *good* weldor requires study, training and practice.

The Possibilities of Welding

Though welding is not new, the arc-welding industry is still rapidly expanding. There is room in the industry for every qualified weldor who desires to do a good job for his employer.

The expansion of the welding industry results from the cost reduction welding makes possible in all types of metalworking plants. In most applications, arc welding is less expensive than riveting or bolting. Welding, when applied to proper designs, can also produce substantial savings over iron castings. The possibilities of expansion in the welding industry are immense, but to recognize these possibilities to the fullest requires the best efforts of everyone in the industry. You can add to the expansion and help to secure your own future by consistently doing the best possible welding in the least possible time.

This will mean learning how to use the latest automatic and semiautomatic arc welding processes such as flux-cored Innershield, gas metal arc welding and submerged arc welding. Subsequent units of *"New Lessons"* will prepare the weldor for meaningful employment in many facets of the welding industry.

THE WELL DRESSED WELDOR

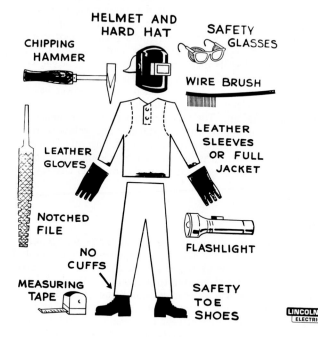

Object:
To study the arc-welding machines and accessories.

General Information

The success of welding as a metal-joining process rests on the fact that a good weld with common steels is as strong or stronger than the plate in which it is made. This success has been established through the years by the gradual development of welding machines, accessories and electrodes that satisfy the complex requirements of the arc process.

Arc welding requires a continuous supply of electric current, sufficient in amount (amperes) and of proper voltage to maintain an arc. This current may be either alternating (AC) or direct (DC), but it must be provided through a source that can be adjusted.

Several different types of welding machines are available for producing satisfactory welding current. Alternating current is produced in special welding transformers (Figure 1). Direct current is produced in either electric motor-generator sets (Figure 2), rectifier sets, or engine-driven generator sets. Combination welders, producing both AC and DC, are basically transformer-rectifier sets.

Figure 1. AC transformer welder.   **Figure 2.** DC motor generator welder.

Welding machines are rated according to their current output, voltage, and duty cycle and are available in a wide range of sizes. The National Electrical Manufacturers Association establishes minimum standards for rating welding machines and most manufacturers follow these standards. The standards are established on a conservative basis, requiring a rating well below the maximum overload capacity of the machine so that it will provide safe operation efficiently over a long period of time. Ratings are given with a percentage duty cycle. The duty cycle of a welder is the percentage of a ten-minute period that a welder can operate at a given output current setting. If a welder is rated 300 amperes at a 60% duty cycle, it means that the machine can be operated safely at 300 amperes welding current for 6 out of every 10 minutes. If this duty cycle is reduced in actual operation, the maximum permissible current is increased. At 35% duty cycle, a 300-ampere machine could be operated at 375 amperes.

Transformer welders are available for operation on single-phase power lines. They transform high-voltage—low-amperage input current to a low-voltage—high-amperage welding current. Current controls must be provided on the transformer to permit its use for welding. There are three basically different types of current-control systems. One type of current control is the movable iron core operated by a crank. This is a continuous current control. A second type is the solid-state electrical circuitry, which is also continuous control. The other is a tap-type control, in which the electrode leads are plugged into different jacks, or taps, to obtain different settings. All accurately regulate the welding current. With either, the operator can select just the welding heat he wants.

Rectifier sets are basically three-phase or single-phase transformers to which have been added silicon or other rectifiers to change the output current from alternating to direct current. These machines have the basic control and output characteristics that are inherent in transformers.

Direct-current generators use an armature rotating in an electrical field. Current is generated in the armature and is taken off for the use through a commutator. The armature is rotated either by an electric motor or an internal combustion engine. When generators are engine-operated, they are independent of electric power and may be operated in the field where power is not available.

Combination welders, producing both AC and DC current, are the most versatile of all types of welders (Figure 3). They are basically a single-phase transformer and a rectifier from which, by turning a switch, either alternating or direct welding current is available. With DC, polarity can be switched to either electrode positive or electrode negative.

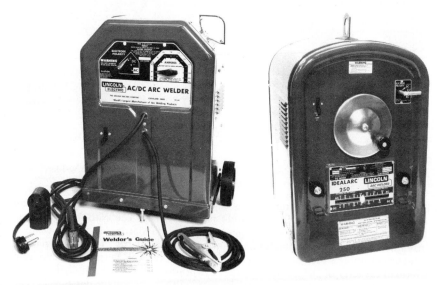

Figure 3. AC & DC welders.

Several factors must be evaluated when selecting a welding power source. The size or rated output of a machine required for a given job depends on the thickness of the metal to be welded and the amount of welding to be done.

There is no need to buy more capacity than will be required by the job. Be sure, however, to check the duty cycle. Machines with a low duty cycle should be used only for maintenance or intermittent welding. 60% duty cycle is normal for industrial welders. Continued operation of a machine beyond its rated capacity will shorten its service life.

In selecting the welder, another consideration is the utility power available. Fortunately, welders are made to be used with all types of power, but certain types are available for only given conditions. Motor-generator sets are generally available for only three-phase AC power, but can be ordered to different cycles and voltages. They are also available for DC power. AC machines are generally available for only single-phase AC power in various cycles, with or without power-factor correction in the machine. Fortunately, in most manufacturing situations, the source of power does not present a limiting factor on the selection of a welder. The decision can be made on the basis of what is the most efficient and economical machine for a given job.

Also, consider what type machine will make the job easiest to do and enable better welding to be done at lower costs. There is one best way to do every welding job.

Input power to the welder should be planned and installed only by qualified electricians. Lines should be of the proper size and properly fused, according to local requirements and correct standards.

Further information concerning specific types of welding machines is covered in Lessons 2.1 to 2.7.

Current-carrying cables, cable lugs, electrode holder, work clamp, weld-cleaning devices, and protective equipment are essential for each welding machine and operator. These are called accessories (Figure 4). For maximum safety and efficiency, good quality accessories must be used.

The welding current is conducted from the source of power to the electrode holder by an insulated copper, extra-flexible cable. This cable is designed expressly for welding and derives its flexibility from the thousands of very fine, almost hairlike wires enclosed in a durable paper wrapping that allows the conductor to slip readily within its insulation when the cable is bent. The high-grade insulation also contributes to flexibility. Wear resistance is provided this cable by an extra tough, braided cotton reinforcing and by the special composition of the covering, which provides a smooth finish, highly resistant to abrasion. For completing the welding circuit, a somewhat less flexible, but equally wear-resistant, cable is used.

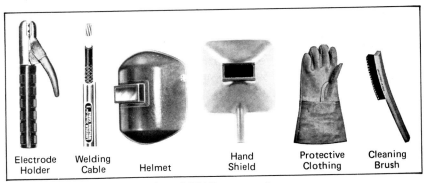

| Electrode Holder | Welding Cable | Helmet | Hand Shield | Protective Clothing | Cleaning Brush |

Figure 4. Welding accessories.

The size (diameter) of the cables used in welding varies, depending upon the capacity of the machine and the length of cable required. Cable size is selected carefully because of its current carrying capacity.

The cable is generally connected to the welder by means of a copper terminal lug. This lug is soldered or clamped to the end of the cable and fits on the welder terminal post.

The electrode holder grips the electrode during the welding process. This holder should be reasonably light, well-insulated, and sturdy enough to withstand the wear of continual handling. The holder should be the correct size for maximum machine output. A spring-grip holder for quick insertion or release of the electrode is best.

A work clamp fastened to the work or the table on which the work is mounted completes the welding circuit. A spring-pressure work clamp is the quickest and easiest to use. Magnetic clamps are available, and may be necessary for a secure connection on broad surfaces where it is difficult to use spring-pressure work clamps

A shield for the face and eyes is necessary for protection from arc rays and heat, and the spatter of molten metal. This shield may have a head band for wearing on the head or a handle attached for holding in the hand. The head shield is most commonly used for welding, as both hands are usually needed for the welding process. The shield should have a number 10 or 12 filter glass for general purpose welding.* The more expensive filter glass should be protected by a clear cover-glass, which may be replaced when covered with arc spatter.

Gloves and apron should be of chrome-tanned leather to protect the hands, body, and clothes from heat and spatter. If welding is done in positions other than flat, leather shoulders and sleeves must be worn.

Safety glasses should be worn under the shield to protect the weldor's eyes when chipping hot slag, grinding metal for joint preparation, and cleaning metal with the wire brush.

A chipping hammer and wire scratch brush should be used to thoroughly clean the beads. A grinder with a wire wheel is handy for cleaning welds and removing rust and scale from the base metal.

A special welding table should be used in the shop for welding practice and for work on small jobs. A workbench soon becomes spattered and burned. This table should be steel for fire-proofness and ease of grounding work. It may be easily made in the shop.

Protection for other persons working in the shop may be provided around the welding area by a booth or shield of fireproof canvas, sheet metal, or transite. This might be a permanent or portable unit, depending upon the work being done.

Review Questions

1. What is the strength of a weld as compared to the base metal?

2. What type of current supply is required for welding?

3. What two types of welders produce DC welding current?

4. What type of welding machine produces AC welding current?

5. What organization sets standards for rating welders?

---

*See Lesson 1-2.

6. What is the duty cycle of a welder?

7. Can a welder be used above rating for short periods?

8. What are the electrical characteristics of welding power, as contrasted with input power?

9. What is the best all-around welder for doing light and heavy jobs in all positions?

10. What type of welder must be used when no electrical power is available?

11. Is it necessary to use a special cable to carry the welding current?

LESSON
1.4

Object:
To study the uses and characteristics of the metal electrode.

General Information

The electrode might be called the weldor's most important tool. It is through the electrode that the weldor is able to handle, concentrate, and vary the characteristics of the intense heat of the electric arc to make it usable for purposes of welding. The success of a weldor depends upon his ability to understand the action of the electrode, and to select and use the correct one for the job.

The electrode universally used for manual welding has a core of wire or rod covered with a baked chemical covering. The core provides filler metal for the joint being welded, and the chemical covering provides a shield for the weld as it is made. The process of "Shielded Metal-Arc Welding" gets it name from the action of this type of electrode. These electrodes are made with a variety of different core wires, coverings, and diameters.

A good weldor should be familiar with the common types of electrodes available. When selecting an electrode, it is necessary to use one that is made for welding with the type of current (AC or DC) being used, for the particular base metal being welded, and for the purpose to which the finished job is intended. Lessons 3.1−6.3 describe in detail the operation and application of types of Lincoln electrodes used in shielded metal-arc welding.

The covering on electrodes has several functions and the chemicals are varied, depending upon the desired weld. These coverings consist of shielding agents such as cellulose, slag formers such as rutile, deoxidizing agents, and fluxing agents which can act as binders. They are evenly applied to the core wire by the process of extrusion, similar to the way toothpaste is squeezed out of a tube. The covering largely determines the operating characteristics of the electrode.

The same core wire is used for most low-carbon steel electrodes. It is the addition of alloy in the covering that makes the difference in the physical properties of the deposited metal.

The chemical covering is called a flux, because it has a mixing and cleansing effect on the weld. This flux has three distinct purposes in metal-arc welding.

Parts of the flux covering are melted and vaporized in the heat of the arc (Lesson 1.1, Figure 2). This forms a smoke or blanket of gas that protects both the droplets of metal projected across the arc and the pool of molten metal from the surrounding air. The air contains oxygen and nitrogen, which combine readily with molten steel, and even more readily with the small droplets as they are projected across the arc gap, to form oxides and nitrides. If these are allowed to form, the finished weld is weakened by being porous and brittle. Its tensile strength and impact resistance are substantially reduced.

Other parts of the flux melt and mix with the weld metal, gather impurities, and float them to the top of the molten pool in the form of slag. This slag protects the hot metal from the air, keeps it from solidifying too rapidly, so that gases may escape, and partly influences the shape of the bead. After the bead solidifies and cools down, the brittle slag may be chipped off, leaving a clean, bright weld.

During the welding process, the flux covering projects over the end of the core wire and influences the action of the arc. It stabilizes and directs the force of the arc and the droplets of molten filler metal. Hence, the covering makes the arc steadier and welding easier.

It is through the covering, also, that electrodes have been made for satisfactory operation with alternating welding current. An AC arc tries to go out 120 times a second on 60-hertz current. This makes arc stability a problem. The problem can be overcome by adding certain chemicals to the covering. These chemicals, when burned in the arc, produce special "ionized" gases that keep the arc going. It follows, then, that any AC electrode will work on DC, but that not all DC electrodes will work on AC.

Electrodes should be stored where it is dry. Excessive moisture can destroy the correct action of the covering. Storing open boxes of electrode in a closed cabinet heated by a heater coil or light bulb is good practice. Wet electrode may be dried out before using, if dried at proper temperatures following procedures recommended by manufacturer. *Caution:* Low hydrogen electrode should not be stored with E6010 or other electrode that requires a higher degree of moisture in the covering for proper operation.

Welding has not always been as easy as you find it today using the shielded electrode. Before covered eletrodes were produced commercially, welding was done with a bare or lightly coated wire. Bare electrodes are still used on some applications and you may run into them. They are used where maximum weld strength is not essential, when filling large grooves, filling cavities in castings, and where complete slag removal is difficult. Because they have no flux and cannot produce a shielded arc, the arc is less forceful and will short out easily as droplets of electrode bridge the gap. This makes them more difficult to use than a shielded electrode. The weldor must carry a consistently short arc. Without the shielding power of the flux, the resultant welds tend to be about one-third weaker in tensile strength and lower in impact resistance, due to porosity and impurities. They can be satisfactorily run only on a DC welder using electrode negative polarity.

Review Questions

1. Why is the electrode considered a tool?

2. Why is the term "Shielded-Arc" used for a type of metal electrode?

3. Why is it necessary to have the correct electrode when making a weld?

4. Are the same chemicals used in all electrode coverings?

5. What are three purposes for putting flux on an electrode?

6. What elements in the air are harmful when mixed with the molten metal?

7. What important characteristic does an AC electrode flux have?

8. Why should the flux be left on the weld deposit during cooling?

9. What is the disadvantage of weld deposits made with bare electrodes?

Object:
To strike and establish an arc.

Equipment:
Lincoln "Idealarc" or DC or AC welder and accessories.

Material:
Mild-steel plate 1/8" or thicker; 5/32" "Fleetweld 5P" (E6010) for DC or "Fleetweld 35" (E6011) for AC.
(See Lessons 3.2A and 3.2C for properties and application of these electrodes.)

General Information

The basis of arc welding is the continuous electric arc. This arc is maintained when the welding current is forced across a gap between the electrode tip and the base metal. A weldor must be able to strike and establish the correct arc easily and quickly. There are two general methods of striking the arc, scratching and tapping.

The scratching method is easier for beginners and when using an AC machine. The electrode is moved across the plate inclined at an angle, as you would strike a match. As the electrode scratches the plate an arc is struck. When the arc has formed, withdraw the electrode momentarily to form an excessively long arc (Figure 1), then return to normal arc length.

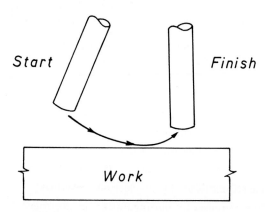

Figure 1. "Scratch" method of arc starting.

In the tapping method the electrode is moved downward to the base metal in a vertical direction. As soon as it touches the metal it is withdrawn momentarily to form an excessively long arc (Figure 2), then returned to normal arc length.

The principal difficulty encountered in striking the arc is "freezing", that is, the electrode sticks or fuses to the work. This is caused by the current melting the electrode tip and sticking it to the cold base metal before it is withdrawn from contact. The extra high current drawn by this "short circuit" will soon overheat an electrode and melt it or the flux, unless the circuit is broken. Giving the electrode holder a quick snap backward from the direction of travel will

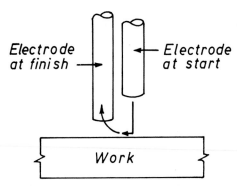

Figure 2. "Tapping" method of arc starting.

generally free the electrode. If it does not, it will be necessary to open the circuit by releasing the electrode from the holder.

Warning: Never remove the shield from the face if the electrode is frozen. Free the electrode with the shield in front of the eyes, as it will "flash" when it comes loose.

Job Instructions

Job A: Strike the arc by the scratching method.

1. Brush the base metal free of dirt and scale.

2. Position metal flat on metal table top or plate.

3. Attach the work clamp securely to work or table.

4. Set the amperage at 130 to 145 for 5/32" electrode.

5. Place the bare end of the electrode in the holder so that it is gripped securely at a 90-degree angle to the jaws.

6. Turn the welder "ON".

7. Assume a natural position and grasp the holder firmly but comfortably by using either one or both hands. Using both hands helps to steady the electrode and reduce fatigue. To use both hands rest the left elbow on the work table and, with the left hand, steady the right hand by holding the right wrist.

8. Hold the electrode above the plate and move it down until it is about an inch above the plate. Hold it upright to the plate, inclined at an angle of 65 to 70 degrees in the direction of travel (Figure 3, Position 1).

9. Place the shield in front of your eyes.

10. Strike the arc like a large match by gently and quickly scratching the electrode on the metal with a wrist motion as shown in Position 2. A sudden burst of light will be produced on contact with the plate.

11. Withdraw the electrode to form an excessively long arc, about 3/16", as in Position 3. This long arc is held only a second or two after which a normal arc length of 1/16" to 1/8", shown in Position 4, is assumed. The long arc prevents the large drops of metal that pass across the arc from shorting out the arc and causing it to "freeze". It also establishes the crater, eliminates

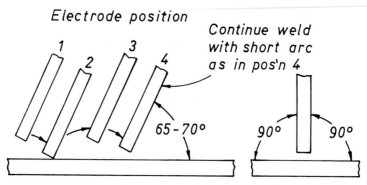

Figure 3. Striking sequence.

excessive build-up of filler metal, and helps to tie in more smoothly with the previously deposited bead.

12. Practice starting the arc, holding it, and breaking it, until you are able to easily strike the arc on first try. From the standpoint of time, the complete motion represented by Positions 1 to 4 takes place in two or three seconds.

Job B: Strike the arc by the tapping method.

1. Follow steps 1 to 7 in Job A, using the same amperage setting.

2. Hold the electrode above the plate in a vertical position, and lower it until it is about an inch above the point you wish to strike the arc (Figure 2).

3. Place the shield in front of your eyes.

4. Touch the electrode gently to the plate by a downward motion of the wrist. With the first burst of light, quickly withdraw it to form a long arc, about 3/16". Hold the long arc for a second or two, then assume a normal arc length, 1/16" to 1/8".

5. Incline the electrode 65 to 70 degrees in the direction of travel as in Job A.

6. Practice striking the arc, holding it, and breaking it.

Review Questions

1. What happens when electric current is forced across an open gap?

2. What two methods are used to strike an arc?

3. Which method is easier for a beginner?

4. Which method works better on an AC welder?

5. When an electrode "freezes" what should be done?

6. Should you remove your shield to see better when freeing a "frozen" electrode?

7. Should base metal be cleaned before welding?

8. Is it correct to use either one or both hands on an electrode holder when welding?

9. What should be done as soon as the arc appears at the tip of the electrode?

10. What is normal arc length?

11 What electrode angle is used?

LESSON 1.6

Object:
To run a straight bead in the flat position.

Equipment:
Lincoln "Idealarc" or DC or AC welder and accessories.

Material:
Mild-steel plate 3/16" or thicker; 5/32" "Fleetweld 5P" (E6010) for DC or "Fleetweld 35" (E6011) for AC.

General Information

The bead is a continuous deposit of weld metal formed by the metallic arc on the surface of the base metal. It is this bead, composed of a fused mixture of base metal and filler metal, that forms the weld.

Spend sufficient time on these jobs to become proficient in holding the proper arc length and electrode angle. Move the electrode along the plate at the correct speed, so as to secure smooth, uniform beads with adequate penetration, as indicated in Figure 1 and 6A. During welding, observe the appearance of the bead and the characteristics of the arc. See how the arc digs into the metal for penetration, how it fills the crater and builds up the bead. Learn to recognize a good bead while you are making it. Keep your eye on the back of the crater as the arc force deposits and builds up the bead, so that you can quickly vary the arc length, electrode angle, or speed of travel to correct a poor bead.

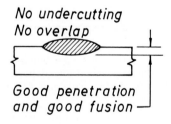

Figure 1.

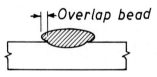

Figure 2.

Normal arc length should be slightly less than the diameter of the electrode, and is usually considered to be 1/16" to 1/8". Judging arc length by fractions of an inch is difficult. Correct arc length will be developed by proper judgment of the weld deposit. With too long an arc, there will be a noticeable increase of spatter; penetration will be poor; overlap will be noticeable; sound of the arc will be more of a hiss than a crackle; the metal will melt off the electrode in large wobbly drops and the slag will be difficult to remove from the completed bead.

When the rate of travel is too fast, the bead will be thin and stringy with poor penetration. If the rate of travel is too slow, weld metal will pile up and roll over with excessive overlap (Figure 2).

Correct amperage setting for any given electrode is important to secure proper shape of bead, proper penetration, and a minimum of spatter. When amperage is set too high the bead will be flat, with excessive spatter and some porosity, and the electrode becomes overheated. If amperage setting is too low, difficulty is experienced in striking the arc and maintaining correct arc length. The weld metal piles up with excessive overlap and poor penetration.

Job Instructions

Job A: Run short beads.

1. Clean base metal and position flat on the table.

2. Check work connection to table or work piece.

3. Set amperage at 130 to 145 for 5/32" electrode.

4. Hold the electrode upright to the base metal, inclined at a 65 to 70 degree angle in the direction of travel.

5. Strike and establish the arc as in Lesson 1.5.

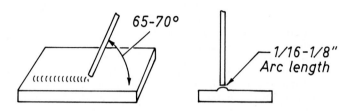

65-70°

1/16-1/8"
Arc length

Figure 3.

6. Maintain a normal arc length, 1/16" to 1/8" (Figure 3), and move the electrode across the plate at a uniform rate. A right-handed weldor normally works from left to right.

7. Observe the back of the molten puddle, or crater, as the arc builds up the bead. Allow the arc force to penetrate the base metal and deposit filler metal. Correct speed will be indicated by the proper shape and size of the bead (Figure 6).

8. Make beads one to two inches long and extinguish the arc by withdrawing the electrode.

9. Restrike the arc and run another bead.

10. Move over the plate, increasing the length of the beads until you are able to stop and start as desired. Practice until you can make uniform beads 3 or 4 inches long.

11. Clean the slag off each bead by chipping with the chipping hammer and brush clean with the wire brush. Slag is removed more easily if the weld is allowed to cool a short time. Always chip slag away from you.

12. Examine the bead for shape, penetration, and uniformity. Compare with Figure 6.

Job B: Run long beads with correct rate of deposition.

1. Follow steps 1 to 7 in Job A.

2. Run parallel beads about 12" in length (Figure 4).

3. Run beads toward you, away from you, and from the right and left.

4. Chip off the slag and inspect the bead for shape, penetration, and uniformity.

5. Check the length of the weld with the length of the electrode used. Correct speed will produce approximately 1 inch of bead for each inch of electrode consumed (for non-iron powder electrodes). An electrode should be used so that about 1-1/2" remains. Longer stubs cause excessive waste, and shorter stubs may damage the electrode holder.

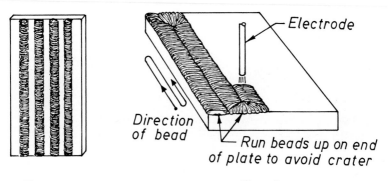

Figure 4.   Figure 5.

6. After you are able to run straight beads, weld in one direction to the end of the plate, move slowly to one side and reverse the direction of travel (Figure 5). Keep the correct electrode angle when changing direction of travel. Try the same job, welding toward and away from you.

7. Study the plate shown in Figure 6 and the accompanying table. Compare with your beads.

Review Questions

1. Why is it important to be able to run a sound bead?

2. What electrode angle is used when running a bead?

3. Will moving the electrode too fast cause poor penetration?

4. Can a good weldor strike beads in any position and run in any direction?

5. How is a weld cleaned?

6. A 14" electrode should produce approximately what length of bead?

7. How long should the stub of an electrode be when it is thrown away?

8. What is penetration?

9. What are four important points to check when running a bead?

STUDY THIS PICTURE AND TABLE

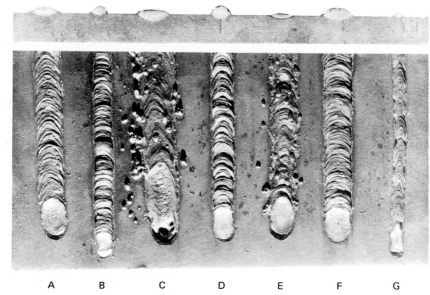

	A	B	C	D	E	F	G

Figure 6. Plan and elevation views of welds made with an E6010 electrode under various conditions. (A) Current, voltage and speed normal. (B) Current too low. (C) Current too high. (D) Voltage too low. (E) Voltage too high. (F) Speed too low. (G) Speed too high.

RESULTING WELD CHARACTERISTICS

Operating Variables	Arc Sound	Penetration — Fusion	Melt-Off Electrode	Appearance of Bead
A. Normal Amps, Normal Volts, Normal Speed	Sputtering hiss plus irregular energetic crackling sounds	Fairly deep and well defined	Normal appearance	Excellent fusion — no overlap
B. Low Amps, Normal Volts, Normal Speed	Very irregular Sputtering Few crackling sounds	Not very deep nor defined	Not greatly different from above	Low penetration
C. High Amps, Normal Volts, Normal Speed	Rather regular explosive sounds	Deep-long crater	Electrode covering is consumed at irregular high rate.	Broad, rather thin bead — Good fusion.
D. Low Volts, Normal Speed, Normal Amps	Hiss plus steady sputter.	Small	Covering too close to crater. Touches molten metal and results in porosity. Electrode freezes.	Sits upon plate, but not so pronounced as for low amps. Somewhat broader.
E. High Volts, Normal Speed, Normal Amps	Very soft sound plus hiss and few crackles.	Wide and Crater deep	Note drops at end of electrode. Flutter and then drop into crater.	Wide — spattered.
F. Low Speed, Normal Amps, Normal Volts	Normal	Crater normal	Normal	Wide bead — overlap large. Base metal and bead heated to considerable area.
G. High Speed, Normal Amps, Normal Volts	Normal	Small, rather well-defined crater	Normal	Small bead — undercut. The reduction in bead size and amount of undercutting depend on ratio of high speed and amps.

LESSON
1.7

Object:
Determining the amount of current required for the job.

General Information

The actual procedure for setting a particular welding machine to the desired current is described for each machine in Section II. However, before you can set the machine, you must first know how much welding current you need.

First, select an electrode. A general rule of electrode selection is that the electrode diameter should not exceed the thickness of the base metal. This rule is only the starting point. Here are some other considerations:

1. Welding speed is the largest factor in welding costs. Use the largest electrode and greatest amperage possible.
2. Position of welding—for vertical, overhead, and horizontal butts, the maximum electrode size is 3/16" for Fleetweld 5P and Fleetweld 35. For low-hydrogen electrode, the maximum size is 5/32".
3. Joint preparation—reaching the bottom of a narrow vee may prevent the use of larger electrodes on first pass.
4. Fitup—burnthrough may occur with large electrodes on first pass. Backup strips permit larger electrodes to be used.
5. Machine capacity—amperage rating on machine may not be sufficient to use largest electrode possible for a given job.

For any given size of electrode, there is an amperage range specified by the manufacturer. This range takes into account the use of this electrode under all types of welding conditions. Somewhere within that range there is an optimum setting for each job with its combination of conditions. For example: a vee joint may require less amperage than a square butt joint; a thin or small article will require less amperage than a thick or heavy article; welding vertically up will require lower amperage for puddle control than vertically down; and better weldors can use higher amperages than the beginner.

During welding practice, or when encountering a new job, it is advisable to set the amperage about the middle of the range recommended for a given electrode. Run a few beads, then observe the arc and examine the completed bead (Lesson 1.6, Figure 6). You will be able to see whether or not the amperage setting is correct, too high, or too low. At first, selecting the correct amperage for a new job will be quite slow and may involve several adjustments. Experience will develop the judgment to select the correct amperage quickly for each job and will also develop the ability to work successfully with maximum amperage settings for each type of electrode, thus obtaining faster welding speeds and reducing welding costs.

Review Questions

1. What factor is most important in the cost of welding?
2. What are the disadvantages of using small electrodes?
3. What general rule governs electrode selection for flat-position welding?
4. What is maximum size electrode for overhead welding?
5. Why can't the manufacturer designate a specific amperage for each electrode?
6. What amperage should be selected when starting on a new job?
7. What two factors give maximum welding speed?

Object
To restart a continuous bead and fill the crater.

Equipment:
Lincoln "Idealarc" or DC or AC welder and accessories.

Material:
Mild-steel plate 3/16" or thicker; 5/32" "Fleetweld 5P" (E6010) for DC or "Fleetweld 35" (E6011) for AC.

General Information

During welding it is often necessary to interrupt a continuous bead, as when finishing one electrode and starting another. Restarting a bead must be done without a depression or a lump to spoil the bead uniformity. After a little practice you will soon know how long to hold and direct the arc into the crater before continuing on with the bead. Holding the arc too long, or directing it too far back on the bead will cause a lump. Not holding it long enough or not directing it back far enough into the crater will cause a depression in the bead.

When craters occur at the end of the joint, there are no further beads to cover them. Unfilled craters cause stress points and are the weakest spot in the completed weld. They must be filled by one of two methods to bring them up to the height of the weld bead.

Job Instructions

Job A: Restart a continuous bead.

1. Clean the base metal and position flat.

2. Check work connection.

3. Set amperage at 130 to 145 for 5/32" electrode.

4. Hold electrode upright, inclined 65–70 degrees in the direction of travel.

5. Strike an arc and run a straight bead for 2 to 3 inches. Extinguish the arc by drawing the electrode tip away. This leaves a bead that tapers off into a crater.

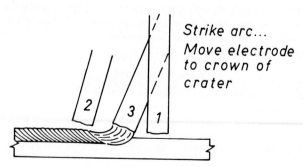

Strike arc...
Move electrode
to crown of
crater

Figure 1. Strike the arc (1). Move the electrode to the crown of the crater (2). Resume forward travel (3).

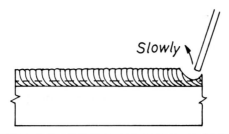

Figure 2.

6. Chip the slag out of the crater and for at least 1/2" back on the bead.

7. Restrike the arc about 1/4" ahead of the crater, move the arc back into the crater, and continue ahead with the bead (Figure 1). By striking the arc ahead of the crater any marks of the arc are covered by the bead.

8. Repeat, welding in the other directions, until a uniform bead is obtained.

Job B: Fill the crater at the end of a weld.

1. To fill the crater as a bead is brought to the end of the plate, draw the electrode up slowly and backward over the completed weld. Slowly drawing up the electrode permits the crater to be filled with metal. Moving back over the weld will minimize the crater by placing it on top of the bead 1/4" to 1/2" from the end (Figure 2).

2. If the crater starts to burn through or spill over the end of the plate, extinguish the arc, chip out the crater, and restrike the arc. Remove the crater by building up in this manner.

3. The other method to overcome the crater depression is to break the arc about 1" to 2" from the end of the plate, jump the electrode tip to the end, restrike the arc, and weld back toward the finished bead. Remember to incline the electrode in the direction of travel when reversing the direction. Continue welding over the crater and extinguish the arc as the top of the two beads run together. This also puts the crater on the top of the bead (Figure 3).

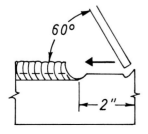
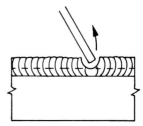

Figure 3.

Review Questions

1. What causes a crater?

2. What are two defects in the bead caused by incorrectly restarting a bead?

3. Why is the arc restruck ahead of the crater?

4. What defects may be caused by unfilled craters?

5. What should be done if the crater starts to burn through the end of the base metal?

6. What two methods may be used to fill a crater?

Object:
To run a bead with a weaving motion.

Equipment:
Lincoln "Idealarc" or DC or AC welder and accessories.

Material:
Mild-steel plate 3/16" or thicker; 5/32" "Fleetweld 5P" (E6010) for DC or "Fleetweld 35" (E6011) for AC.

General Information

Weaving is an oscillating motion, back and forth, crosswise to the direction of travel. These motions are used to float out slag, deposit a wider bead, secure good penetration at the edges of the weld, allow gas to escape, and avoid porosity. The weave pass will be used later on welding and hardsurfacing in all positions.

To make a wide bead, it is necessary to move the electrode from side to side, at the same time moving forward to advance the bead; such a weave is shown in A, Figure 1. The weave should not be wider than 3 times the diameter of the electrode.

Some may find it easier to weave in a crescent motion, as shown in B. The purposes accomplished by both these motions are substantially the same and their use is largely a matter of preference. Weave B is probably the most popular. The "figure 8" motion shown in C or the circular motion shown in D are preferred by some weldors.

Weave E makes a hesitation at each side of the weave to allow a slight buildup or working of the metal into the edges of the joint.

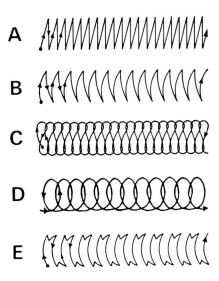

Figure 1. Weaving motions.

Job Instructions

1. Clean the base metal and position flat.

2. Set amperage at 130 to 145 for 5/32" electrode.

3. Hold electrode upright, inclined 65 to 70 degrees in the direction of travel.

4. Strike the arc and carry the bead using the same arc length as when running straight beads. Practice the motions shown in A and B, Figure 1, to form a bead. Make beads 1/2" to 3/4" wide. Bead width should not exceed 3 times the diameter of the electrode.

5. Run weave passes in all four directions.

6. Movements C, D, and E may be practiced if desired until you can obtain the same smooth type of bead deposited by A and B motions.

7. You may find that you will develop a weave slightly different from those shown that works easily for you. Practice these weave motions so they become free and natural and can be done automatically when required.

Review Questions

1. What is a weave pass?

2. Why are weave passes used?

3. Is there more than one type of correct weaving motion?

4. What is the maximum width of a weave pass?

5. Can a weave pass be used only in the downhand position?

LESSON 1.10

Object:
To run a bead with a whipping motion.

Equipment:
Lincoln "Idealarc" or DC or AC welder and accessories.

Material:
Mild-steel plate 1/4" or thicker; 5/32" "Fleetweld 5P" (E6010) for DC or "Fleetweld 35" (E6011) for AC.

General Information

Whipping is an oscillating motion lengthwise with the direction of the bead (Figure 1). A similar motion may be used to obtain two opposite results, keeping the puddle "hot" or keeping it "cool".

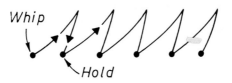

Figure 1.

Whipping may be used on downhand work to keep the puddle "hot" or in a fluid state to obtain good penetration with even ripples and uniform buildup.

For vertical and overhead work or in joints where burnthrough is a problem, the whipping motion is used to keep the puddle "cool" and prevent it from sagging or running down. In the case of thin metal, it keeps the puddle from penetrating too deep.

Job Instructions

Job A: Run a bead with a whipping motion to keep a puddle "hot".

1. Clean the base metal and position flat.

2. Set amperage at 130 to 145 for 5/32" electrode.

3. Hold electrode upright, inclined 65 to 70 degrees in the direction of travel.

4. Assume a position that permits you to see behind and ahead of the arc so that when a faulty action occurs it can be corrected immediately.

5. Strike the arc and carry the bead with a normal arc length during the entire whipping motion.

6. The whipping motion to keep the puddle "hot" or fluid should be about 5/16" forward and 1/8" to 1/4" back toward the crater, depending upon the size of the bead desired. When the backward motion is completed, hesitate in the electrode motion. Penetration is obtained on the forward motion and buildup of the bead is obtained on the "hesitation" of the backward motion. The longer the hesitation, the larger the weld deposit. The length of the

backward motion controls the ripple appearance of the weld. Except for the hesitation, the motion is rapid.

7. Practice the motion using different lengths of return strokes, until you can build up a heavy or light bead.

Job B: Run a bead with the whipping motion used to keep a puddle "cool".

1. Follow steps 1 to 4 in Job A.

2. Strike the arc and carry the bead with a normal arc length on the backward stroke, and a long arc, 3/8" to 1/2", at the hesitation point of the forward stroke.

3. Move the arc ahead with a forward stroke of approximately 3/8", hesitate, holding the long arc, then move backward approximately 1/4", assuming a normal arc length (Figure 2). The long arc on the forward stroke reduces penetration, as well as the amount of metal deposited, and allows the weldor to see how the puddle is solidifying. Shortening the arc on the backward stroke allows a normal deposition of metal. A longer hesitation will allow the crater to solidify more. Returning the arc to the partially solidified crater will not cause slag to be trapped in the weld, because it has not had time to completely solidify.

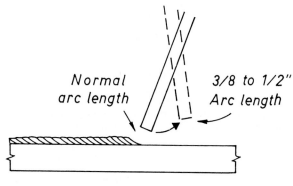

Normal arc length   *3/8 to 1/2" Arc length*

Figure 2.

Review Questions

1. What is the difference between whipping and weaving?

2. What are the two reasons for using a whipping motion?

3. When keeping the metal fluid, what motion provides penetration?

4. Why is a long arc used on the forward stroke to keep the puddle "cool"?

5. Is the hesitation movement in the same place on each type of whipping motion?

Object:
To build a pad.

Equipment:
Lincoln "Idealarc" or DC or AC welder and accessories.

Material:
Mild-steel plate 4x2-1/2x1/4 and bar stock 1-1/2 to 3 inches in diameter; 5/32" "Fleetweld 5P" (E6010) for DC or "Fleetweld 35" (E6011) for AC.

General Information

Padding is a common welding application. It is often necessary to build up metal surfaces with one or more layers of weld deposit. Rebuilding a worn surface or repairing a machining error are two such applications. This work may be done on either flat or curved surfaces by depositing overlapping straight beads or weave passes.

Job Instructions

Job A: Padding on a flat surface.

1. Clean the base metal and position flat.

2. Set amperage at 130 to 145 for 5/32" electrode.

3. Hold electrode inclined 65 to 70 degrees in the direction of travel.

4. Run a straight bead along the edges of the plate. A weave pass may be used, but on the edge more heat control is necessary to keep from melting off the corner of the plate.

5. Chip the bead free of slag before running succeeding passes. This must be done for each pass, so that excess slag will not be trapped in the deposit.

6. Run a second bead parallel to the first, and overlapping it about one third. Use the weaving motion (Lesson 1.9). Make certain that complete fusion is obtained with the plate as well as with the previous bead. Beads should be the same height with no excessive depression or "valley" between them.

7. As succeeding beads are run, a comparatively smooth surface of weld metal should be obtained (Figure 1).

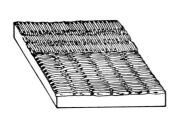

Figure 1.

Figure 2.

8. After the first layer has been deposited, the oxide and scale should be completely removed from the surface by using a chipping hammer and brush. Inspect completed layer for smoothness and penetration.

9. Run the second layer of passes at right angles to the first layer. This is called lacing (Figure 1).

10. Straight overlapping beads without weaving may be laid when padding. Sound passes by either method produce a sound pad. If the pad is being made for practice, alternate layers of weaving and straight passes might be used.

11. Build up the pad to a height of 3/4" to 1" (Figure 2). As the plate is built up, larger size electrode may be used. Control the electrode deposits so that the pad is not only dense, but the edges are built up square and straight. The last layer of passes should be the same length and width as the first layer.

12. To check a pad for dense buildup, it may be sawed through. Check visually for pinholes, pores, and slag inclusions. Do not quench in water, but allow it to cool normally, so that it will saw easier. If a hacksaw is not available, cut through with the arc (Lesson 1.40) and grind the surface.

13. To provide a more thorough method of visual inspection, etching may be used. Grind off the cut surface and etch with a dilute solution of nitric acid. You can then get a comparison of the weld deposit with the base metal. Observe the lines of fusion between the beads, layers, and plate. Check for porosity. *Caution:* Nitric acid causes stains and severe burns. Extreme care must be taken when storing and using acid. Use one part acid to three parts water. Always pour the acid into the water when diluting. Apply the solution with a glass stirring rod. After a few seconds, wash off in warm running water.

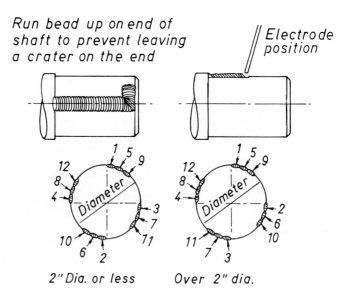

Run bead up on end of shaft to prevent leaving a crater on the end

Electrode position

2" Dia. or less   Over 2" dia.

Figure 3.

Job B: Build up a shaft by padding.

1. Turn the shaft diameter 1/16" to 1/8" under the finished size.

2. Place the shaft in a flat position on vee blocks or a roll positioner, so that it will be steady and may be turned when desired. When doing an actual padding job on a shaft, the type of metal should be known, so that the correct electrode and procedure may be used.

3. Set amperage at 135 to 165 for 5/32" electrode (base metal is thick).

4. Weld parallel to the axis of the shaft if the weld area is close to the end. Place one bead and turn the shaft either 90 or 180 degrees (depending upon the diameter) to place the next bead. The two types of sequence shown in Figure 3 may be used. This is done to minimize warping the shaft.

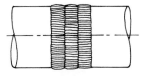

Figure 4.

5. If the place to be welded is some distance from the end, it is advisable to weld around the shaft (Figure 4). This will minimize distortion. Turn the shaft while welding so that the weld metal is always on a slight upward incline for best penetration.

6. Before starting a second pass using either sequence and method of welding, remove all slag and oxide from previous pass. Be certain beads are properly fused together, as well as to the shaft.

Review Questions

1. What is padding?

2. What are some typical applications of padding?

3. Is it necessary to clean each pass before running the next?

4. What is lacing?

5. Is it necessary to use only a weave pass when padding?

6. How may a practice pad be tested?

7. How should nitric acid be mixed with water?

8. Is there a definite pass sequence to be followed when building up a shaft?

9. Why is this sequence necessary?

10. Should the pads be quenched in water after welding?

LESSON 1.12

Object:
To show the types and positions of welded joints.

General Information

There are numerous types of welded joints and various positions in which they are welded. Figure 1 shows a variety of these joints as they may appear on welding jobs.

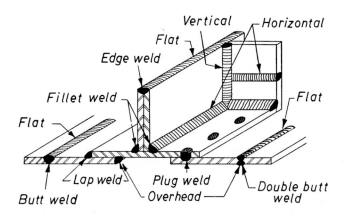

Figure 1.

Figure 2 is a diagram showing the four basic welding positions. It is possible to weld any type of joint in any of the four positions, but whenever possible joints are placed in the flat position. Welding in the flat position is much faster and easier than any of the other positions.

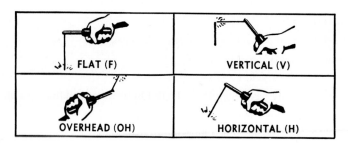

Figure 2.

A summary of the basic types of joints and basic types of welds is shown in Figure 3.

TYPES of JOINTS

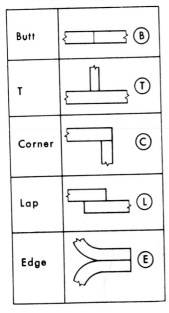

TYPES of WELDS

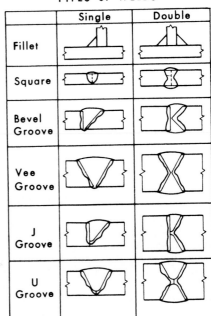

Figure 3.

In a joint, the adjoining members may contact each other in several ways, as illustrated by the butt, T, corner, lap, and edge joints. These general descriptions of the joint geometry, however, do not define the weld joint configuration, since it can be made in various ways. Thus, a welded butt joint can be made square, double-square, single-bevel, double-bevel, single-V, double-V, or by four other joint configurations. A T connection can be made with a double fillet, as shown: or it may be made with a single or double-bevel or single or double J. V and U weld joints are feasible only for butt and corner welds because of the need for the preparation of both surfaces.

Additional information on the edge preparation and setup procedure for most of these joints will be given in succeeding lessons.

Object:
To study and demonstrate the effects of correct and incorrect polarity.

Equipment:
Lincoln "Idealarc" or DC welder and accessories.

Material:
Scrap plate 3/16" or thicker; 5/32" "Fleetweld 5P" (E6010) and two 1/4" DC carbon electrodes.

General Information

The terms "straight" and "reverse" polarity are used around the shop. They may also be expressed as "electrode-negative" and "electrode-positive" polarity. The latter terms are more descriptive and will be used throughout the book.

Polarity results from the fact that an electrical circuit has a negative and a positive pole. Direct current (DC) flows in one direction, resulting in a constant polarity. Alternating current (AC) flows half the time in one direction and half the time in the other, changing its polarity 120 times per second with 60-hertz current.

A weldor should know the meaning of polarity, and recognize what effect it has on the welding process. It is the ability to adjust polarity that lends DC welding its versatility. With few exceptions, electrode-positive (reversed polarity) results in deeper penetration. Electrode-negative (straight polarity) results in faster melt-off of the electrode and, therefore, faster deposition rate. The effect of different chemicals in the covering may change this condition. The high-cellulose covered mild-steel rod, such as "Fleetweld 5", is recommended for use on positive polarity for general welding. Some types of shielded electrodes function on either polarity, though some operate on only one polarity.

The use of the AC transformer-type welder necessitated the development of an electrode that would work on either polarity, due to the constant-changing of polarity in the AC circuit. Though AC itself has no polarity, when AC electrodes are used on DC they usually operate best on one specific polarity. The covering on the electrode designates which polarity is best and all manufacturers specify on the electrode container what polarity is recommended.

For proper penetration, uniform bead appearance, and good welding results, the correct polarity must be used when welding with any given metallic electrode. Incorrect polarity will cause poor penetration, irregular bead shape, excessive spatter, difficulty in controlling the arc, overheating, and rapid burning of the electrode.

Most machines are clearly marked as to what the terminals are, or how they can be set for either polarity. Some machines have a switch to change polarity, whereas on others it is necessary to change the cable terminals. If there is any question as to whether or not the correct polarity is being used, or what polarity is set on a DC machine, there are two easily performed experiments that will tell you. The first is to use a DC carbon electrode, which will work correctly only on negative polarity. The second is to use "Fleetweld 5" electrode, which works outstandingly better on positive polarity than on negative polarity.

Job Instructions

Job A: Determine polarity by using the carbon electrode.

1. Clean the base metal and position flat.

2. Shape the points of the two carbon electrodes on a grinding wheel, so they are identical with a gradual taper running back 2 or 3 inches from the arc tip.

3. Grip one electrode in the electrode holder close to the taper.

4. Set amperage at 135 to 150.

5. Adjust to either polarity.

6. Strike an arc (use shield) and hold for a short time. Change arc length from short to long, affording an observation of the arc action.

7. Observe the arc action. If the polarity is negative (straight) the arc will be stable, easy to maintain, uniform, and conical in shape. If the polarity is positive (reverse), the arc will be difficult to maintain and will leave a black carbon deposit on the surface of the base metal.

8. Change the polarity. Strike an arc with the other electrode and hold for a similar length of time. Observe the arc action as before.

9. Examine the ends of the two electrodes and compare. The one used on negative polarity will burn off evenly, keeping its shape. The electrode used on positive polarity will quickly burn off blunt.

Job B: Determine polarity by the metallic electrode (E6010).

1. Clean base metal and position flat.

2. Set amperage at 130 to 145 for 5/32" electrode.

3. Adjust to either polarity.

4. Strike an arc. Hold normal arc length and standard electrode angle and run a bead.

5. Listen to the sound of the arc. Correct polarity, with normal arc length and amperage, will produce a regular "crackling" sound. Incorrect polarity, with normal arc length and amperage setting will produce irregular "crackling" and "popping" with an unstable arc.

6. See above for characteristics of arc and bead when using metallic electrode on correct and incorrect polarity.

7. Adjust to the other polarity and run another bead.

8. Clean beads and examine. With the wrong polarity, the electrode negative, you will get many of the bad bead characteristics shown in Lesson 1.6.

9. Repeat several times, until you can quickly recognize correct polarity.

Review Questions

1. What is the polarity of the electrode on "straight" polarity?

2. What is the polarity of the work on "reversed" polarity?

3. Can you control polarity on AC current?

4. At which polarity setting is the highest rate of electrode melt-off exhibited?

5. What type of covering is on "Fleetweld 5P" electrode?

LESSON 1.14

Object:
To study arc blow and welding with AC and DC current.

General Information

Weldors who have both AC and DC welding current available must learn which current to use on each job. Also, the question of which type is best frequently comes up during consideration of buying a new welding machine, and it is to the weldor's credit when he can assist in the decision.

As will be shown later, much of the decision rests on the presence or absence of "arc blow". So let's understand arc blow before considering the AC-DC question further.

What Is Arc Blow?

Arc blow occurs when the arc refuses to go where it's supposed to, blows wildly forward or back, and spatters badly. (See Figure 1.) Those weldors who have already encountered arc blow need no description, for trying to weld with severe arc blow makes it difficult to control the molten pool and slag.

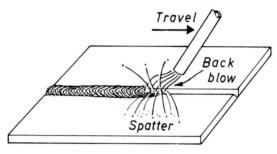

Figure 1.

Arc blow is most frequently encountered at the start and finish of joints, and in corners and deep grooves, particularly when high amperages are being used in welding thick plates. It makes welding very difficult, reduces speed, and lowers weld quality. When the arc blows opposite to the direction of travel, as in Figure 1, it is called "back blow"; when it blows with the direction of travel, it is called "forward blow".

What Causes Arc Blow?

Arc blow is caused by a magnetic force acting on the arc, making the arc "blow" from its normal path. Every wire or conductor that carries current is surrounded by lines of magnetic "flux", or "force", as seen in Figure 2. These lines prefer to travel through steel than air, never touch each other, and exert a force when bunched together. This force is proportional to the amount of current in the conductor. Their normal pattern is a series of concentric rings around the conductor as seen in the center portion of Figure 3.

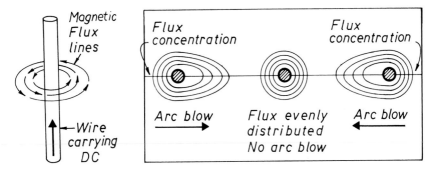

Figure 2.

Figure 3.

The normal pattern of the magnetic flux is distrubed on the ends of the joint where the flux bunches up in the steel, instead of going into the air beyond the end of the joint. A new pattern, such as that seen on either side of Figure 3, results in concentrations on the ends of the joint. In these areas of concentration, the lines are bunched together and exert a force on the arc that pushes, or blows, it.

A similar situation occurs when the conductor is bent as in Figure 4. Again the lines are forced into a bunch and push the arc. This is called "ground effect," because the direction of this blow can be changed by moving the work clamp.

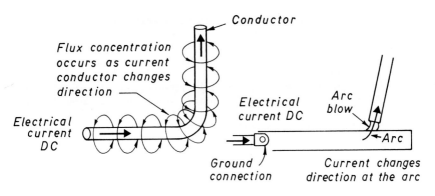

Figure 4.

In welding, both of these situations occur simultaneously, though it should be noted that "ground effect" is less forceful than end concentrations and becomes even less noticeable as the size of the base metal increases. Figure 5 illustrates the effect on arc blow of various combinations of the two types of arc blow.

Similarly, though somewhat more complicated, arc blow is encountered in corners and deep vee joints. In each of these cases, the lines of flux bunch together and exert a force on the arc, causing it to blow and be erratic.

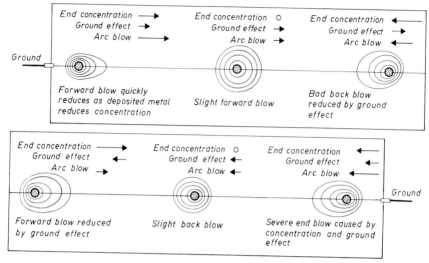

Figure 5.

How to Reduce Arc Blow

To reduce arc blow, one must reduce the causes of arc blow; that is, reduce or counteract the strength of the force, or minimize flux concentrations. Here are several corrective steps which may help:

1. Reduce current.
2. Weld toward a heavy tack or toward a weld already made.
3. Use back-stepping on long welds.
4. Place ground connection as far from joint to be welded as is possible.
5. If back blow is the problem, place ground connection at start of weld and weld towards a heavy tack.
6. If forward blow causes trouble, place ground connection at end of weld.
7. Wrap ground cable around the work piece and pass ground current through it in such a direction that a magnetic field will be set up to neutralize the magnetic field causing the blow.
8. Hold as short an arc as possible to help the arc force counteract the arc blow.
9. If the machine being used is of the type producing both AC and DC, switch to alternating current.

The last step requires some explanation. AC markedly reduces the effect of arc blow by practically eliminating the strength of the flux. With AC, the current goes through zero 120 times a second. This means that the flux lines buildup and collapse 120 times a second. The result of this action is that arc blow is greatly reduced—to the point of elimination on many jobs.

AC or DC?

Now that we have an understanding of arc blow and realize that AC greatly reduces arc blow, let's continue the discussion of AC and DC.

The decision to use either AC or DC is based on which one will permit the operator to produce the best welds in the least time. Generally speaking, AC is best when using iron-powder electrodes or where arc blow is a problem; DC is best for low current or on any application where arc blow is not likely a problem.

The electrode used may determine the type of current required. Jetweld iron-powder-type electrodes operate best on AC, even in the smaller sizes. With AC, they produce a smooth, evenly-shaped bead, while, with DC, they tend to produce a narrower and stringier bead. Most other electrodes operate better on DC. Some electrodes, such as most stainless, nonferrous, low-hydrogen in small sizes, and hardsurfacing electrodes, operate very poorly or not at all on AC.

When electrodes are used that operate on both AC and DC, arc blow is usually the deciding factor. Even when arc blow is not severe, it may be bad enough to reduce welding speeds substantially. Weldors tend to select a welding current that will produce the best weld and make welding easy. Invariably, when arc blow, even slight, is present, operators select a lower current with DC than with AC. Lower current means slower welding. Currents in the neighborhood of 250-300 amperes are sufficient to cause arc blow on most jobs. Therefore, AC should be used on most applications requiring currents this large or larger.

Below 250-300 amperes with electrodes other than iron-powder, DC will usually be preferable. The electrodes operate better and make welding easier on critical jobs, such as sheet metal, vertical, overhead, etc.

In summary, when deciding between AC and DC, one must consider the job, the position of welding, the electrode to be used, and the currents involved. The chart below is a summary of preferred types of current for all sizes of the various steel electrodes. If, as is frequently the case, both types of welding are involved and only one machine is available, it is advantageous to have a combination AC and DC welder, which will provide both alternating and direct currents.

PREFERRED TYPE OF CURRENT

Electrode Type	Electrode Size				
	1/8	5/32	3/16	7/32	1/4
EXX10	DC(+)	DC(+)	DC(+)	DC(+)	DC(+)
EXX11	AC	AC	AC	AC	AC
EXX12	DC(−)	DC(−)	DC(−)	AC	AC
EXX13	DC(−)	DC(−)	DC(−)	AC	AC
EXX14	AC	AC	AC	AC	AC
EXX15	DC(+)	DC(+)	DC(+)	DC(+)	DC(+)
EXX16	DC(+)	DC(+)	AC	AC	AC
EXX18	DC(+)	DC(+)	AC	AC	AC
EXX24	AC	AC	AC	AC	AC
EXX27		DC(−)	AC	AC	AC
EXX28		AC	AC	AC	AC

Review Questions

1. Where is arc blow most frequently encountered?

2. Is arc blow dependent on the amount of current?

3. Is "ground effect" stronger than end concentrations of magnetic flux?

4. On a production job, what is the least desirable method of reducing arc blow? The most desirable?

5. Does AC reduce arc blow? How?

6. What are some electrodes that generally do not operate well on AC?

7. Do Jetweld iron-powder-type electrodes operate best on AC or DC?

8. How much current is required to cause arc blow?

9. How does arc blow affect welding speeds?

10. Will moving the work clamp have any effect on arc blow?

LESSON 1.15

Object:
To study the effects of welding heat on metals.

General Information

Metals become larger when heated, and become smaller upon cooling. During the arc-welding process, the arc heats the metal being welded, causing it to become larger, or expand. As the heat is removed, the surrounding metal and air cause a cooling effect upon the heated area, which results in the metal becoming smaller, or contracting. When this expansion and contraction is not controlled, distortion (warping) is likely to result. On the other extreme, if expansion and contraction is restrained or controlled too rigidly, severe stress and strain may result and impair the weld.

For every degree of temperature rise or fall there is a corresponding change in the size of the metal. Nothing we can do will change the laws of expansion and contraction. We can, however, recognize that changes will take place, figure out how they will affect the work upon which we are welding, and prepare for them.

Three rules can be followed to aid materially in the prevention and control of distortion:

1. REDUCE THE FORCES THAT CAUSE SHRINKAGE.
2. MAKE SHRINKAGE FORCES WORK TO REDUCE DISTORTION.
3. BALANCE SHRINKAGE FORCES WITH OTHER FORCES.

The following discussion gives examples of these rules. In many cases, the application of a single rule will be sufficient. Sometimes a combination of rules may be required.

1. REDUCE THE FORCES THAT CAUSE SHRINKAGE.

(a) **Avoid overwelding.** The addition of excess weld metal not needed to meet the service requirements of a joint is known as "overwelding".

Overwelding causes distortion (Figure 1) and contributes nothing to the performance of the joint. It is a waste of time and money. In certain cases it may even weaken the joint.

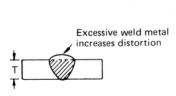

Excessive weld metal increases distortion

Figure 1.

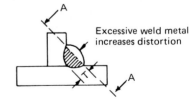

Excessive weld metal increases distortion

Figure 2.

Deposit as little weld metal as possible and make intelligent use of the weld metal that is needed. The strength of a fillet weld for a T joint is determined by the throat size (Figure 2). In this illustration there is an excess of weld metal above line A-A, which does not increase the strength, but obviously increases the shrinkage force, due to the contraction of the large molten puddle.

(b) **Use proper edge preparation and fitup.** It is also possible to reduce shrinkage forces through proper edge preparation. The bevel should not exceed

30 degrees to obtain proper fusion at the root of a weld with a minimum of deposit. Proper fitup is important. Plates should be spaced 1/32" to 1/16" apart (root spacing) to minimize the amount of deposit.

(c) **Use few passes.** Distortion in the lateral direction (across the weld) is a major problem. The use of one or two passes with large electrodes reduces distortion in this direction (Figure 3). As a general rule, lateral distortion is approximately 1 degree per pass.

In some cases, however, distortion is in the longitudinal direction (lengthwise). Due to the greater ability of a small bead to stretch longitudinally, compared to a large bead, the number of passes should be increased rather than decreased.

There is inherent rigidity against the longitudinal bending of a plate, providing the plate is thick enough. Light-gauge sheets have little rigidity in this direction and will buckle easily. Lateral distortion is more common because, unless the two plates are restrained, they will be pulled toward each other as the molten metal cools.

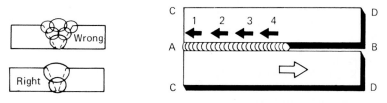

Figure 3.   **Figure 4.**

(d) **Use intermittent welds.** To further reduce shrinkage force by minimizing the amount of weld metal, intermittent welds may sometimes be used instead of continuous welds. It is often possible to use up to two-thirds less weld metal and still obtain the strength required. An example of this is with welding stiffeners for bulkheads and plates of all kinds. The use of intermittent welds also distributes the heat more widely throughout the structure.

(e) **Use "back-step" welding method.** If the job requires a continuous weld, it is possible to reduce shrinkage forces by the "back-step" technique. With this technique, the general direction of welding progression may be from left to right, but each bead is deposited from right to left (Figure 4). Expansion will be less and less with each bead because of the locking effect of each weld. The tendency of plates to spread is locked in by each step.

Where a continuous bead is laid in one direction, in many cases there is a tendency for the plates to spread and become locked in the spread position as the welding progresses. Welding speed is the determining factor here. As a general rule, the greater the speed, the less distortion. In some cases a speed can be found at which the plates will not separate at all.

2. MAKE SHRINKAGE FORCES WORK TO MINIMIZE DISTORTION.

(a) **Locate parts out of position.** A simple way to use the shrinkage force of weld metal to advantage is to obtain proper location of parts before welding. Figure 5a shows spacing of several parts before the weld is deposited. When the weld deposit shrinks it will pull the plates into proper position as in Figure 5b.

(b) **Space parts to allow for shrinkage.** Another method is to space parts before welding. Experience indicates how much space should be allowed for a

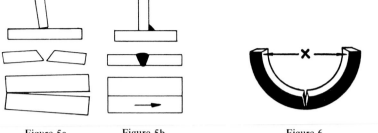

Figure 5a.   Figure 5b.   Figure 6.

given job, so the parts will be in correct alignment after welding. An example is the trunnion arms of a large searchlight as shown in Figure 6. The distance between the two arms had to be accurately controlled. Correct spacing of the parts prior to welding allowed the arms to be pulled into correct position by the shrinkage forces.

(c) Prebend. Shrinkage force may be put to work by prebending or pre-springing the parts to be welded. When the plates in Figure 7 are sprung away from the weld side, the counter force exerted by the clamps overcomes most of the shrinkage tendency of the weld metal, causing it to yield. When the clamps are removed, there is still a slight tendency for the weld to contract. The contraction force pulls the plates into alignment.

3. BALANCE SHRINKAGE FORCES WITH OTHER FORCES.

Often the structural nature of parts to be welded is such as to provide sufficient rigid balancing forces to offset welding shrinkage forces. This is particularly true in heavy sections where there is inherent rigidity because of the arrangement of the parts. If these natural balancing forces are not present, it is necessary to balance the shrinkage forces to prevent distortion.

(a) Balance one shrinkage force with another. Proper welding sequence will place weld metal at different points about the structure. As one section of metal shrinks, it will counteract the shrinkage forces of previous welds. An example is the welding alternately on both sides of a butt weld (Figure 8), or the pass sequence used when building up a shaft (Lesson 1.11).

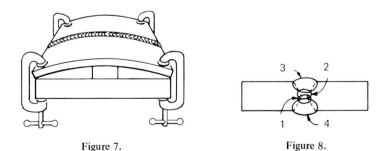

Figure 7.   Figure 8.

Another application of this principle is the staggering of intermittent welds applied in a sequence such as shown in Figures 9a and 9b. Here the shrinkage force of weld No. 1 is balanced by that of weld No. 2; the shrinkage force of weld No. 2 is balanced by that of weld No. 3 and so on.

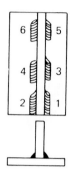

Figure 9a.

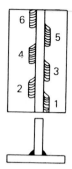

Figure 9b.

(b) **Peening.** This is a mechanical working of the metal by means of hammer blows. Peening stretches the bead, counteracting its tendency to contract as it cools. Peening should be used with great care. Too much peening may damage the weld metal, work-harden it excessively, or damage the base metal.

(c) **Use jigs and fixtures.** The most important method of avoiding distortion, and one in which Rule 3 is applied to the fullest extent, is the use of clamps, jigs, or fixtures to hold the work in a rigid position during welding. In this way, the shrinkage forces of the weld are balanced with sufficient counterforces to prevent distortion.

The balancing forces of the jig or fixture cause the weld metal itself to stretch, thus preventing the distortion.

For a more detailed discussion of this subject, see "Procedure Handbook of Arc Welding".

Review Questions

1. What happens when steel is heated?

2. What happens when steel is cooled?

3. Should shrinkage force be decreased or increased?

4. Does an excess of weld metal increase the shrinkage force?

5. What determines the strength of a fillet weld?

6. What bevel should be used to obtain proper fusion at the root of a weld with a minimum of weld deposit?

7. What is proper root spacing of plates for minimum use of weld metal?

8. Will use of larger electrodes and fewer passes reduce distortion in the lateral direction?

9. Can work be spaced or located out of position and the shrinkage forces be made to pull them into position?

10. Can shrinkage forces be nullified by placing welds in such positions and sequence that they counteract each other?

11. What does peening do to the metal?

12. What is the most important method of avoiding distortion?

LESSON 1.16

Object:
To study electrode identification and operating characteristics.

General Information

The first specification for mild-steel covered electrodes, AWS A5.1, was written in 1940. As the welding industry expanded and the number of types of electrodes for welding steel increased, it became necessary to devise a system of electrode classification to avoid confusion. The system used applies to both the mild-steel A5.1 and the low-alloy steel A5.5 specifications.

TABLE 1 — AWS NUMBERING SYSTEM

a. The prefix "E" designates arc-welding electrode.

b. The first two digits of 4-digit numbers and the first three digits of 5-digit numbers indicate minimum tensile strength:

E60XX	60,000-psi Tensile Strength
E70XX	70,000-psi Tensile Strength
E110XX	110,000-psi Tensile Strength

c. The next-to-last digit indicates position:

EXX1X	All Positions
EXX2X	Flat position and horizontal fillets

d. The last two digits together indicate the type of covering and the current to be used.

e. The suffix (Example: EXXXX-A1) indicates the approximate alloy in the deposit.

-A1	1/2% Mo
-B1	1/2% Cr, 1/2% Mo
-B2	1-1/4% Cr, 1/2% Mo
-B3	2-1/4% Cr, 1% Mo
-C1	2-1/2% Ni
-C2	3-1/4% Ni
-C3	1% Ni, .35% Mo, .15% Cr
-D1 & -D2	.25-.45% Mo, 1.25-2.00% Mn
-G	.50 min Ni, .30 min Cr, .20 min Mo, .10 min V
	(Only one of the listed elements is required.)

Classifications of mild and low-alloy steel electrodes are based on an "E" prefix and a four or five-digit number. The first two digits (or three, in a five-digit number) indicate the minimum required tensile strength in thousands of pounds per square inch. For example, 60 = 60,000 psi, 70 = 70,000 psi, and 100 = 100,000 psi. The next to the last digit indicates the welding position in which the electrode is capable of making satisfactory welds: 1 = all positions— flat, horizontal, vertical, and overhead; 2 = flat and horizontal fillet welding (see Table 1). The last two digits indicate the type of current to be used and the type of covering on the electrode (see Table 2).

Originally a color identification system was developed by the National Electrical Manufacturers Association (NEMA) in conjunction with the American Welding Society to identify the electrode's classification. This was a system of color markings applied in a specific relationship on the electrode, as in Figure

TABLE 2 — AWS A5.1-69 ELECTRODE DESIGNATIONS FOR COVERED ARC-WELDING ELECTRODES

Designation	Current	Covering Type
EXX10	DC(+) only	Organic
EXX11	AC or DC(+)	Organic
EXX12	AC or DC(−)	Rutile
EXX13	AC or DC(±)	Rutile
EXX14	AC or DC(±)	Rutile, iron-powder (approx. 30%)
EXX15	DC(+) only	Low-hydrogen
EXX16	AC or DC(+)	Low-hydrogen
EXX18	AC or DC(+)	Low-hydrogen, iron-powder (approx. 25%)
EXX20	AC or DC(±)	High iron-oxide
EXX24	AC or DC(±)	Rutile, iron-powder (approx. 50%)
EXX27	AC or DC(±)	Mineral, iron-powder (approx. 50%)
EXX28	AC or DC(+)	Low-hydrogen, iron-powder (approx. 50%)

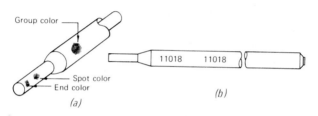

Figure 1. (a) National Electrical Manufacturers Association color-code method to identify an electrode's classification; (b) American Welding Society imprint method.

TABLE 3 — NEMA COLOR CODE FOR MILD-STEEL ELECTRODES

Group Color	No Color		Green	
Spot Color \ End Color	No Color	Black	Blue	Black
No Color	E6010			
White	E6012			
Brown	E6013	E7014		
Green	E6020			
Blue	E6011			
Yellow		E7024		
Black		E7028		
Silver	E6027			
Red			E7015	
Orange			E7016	E7018

1(a). The colors and their significance are listed in Table 3. The NEMA specification also included the choice of imprinting the classification number on the electrode, as in Figure 1(b).

Starting in 1964, AWS new and revised specifications for covered electrodes required the classification number be imprinted on the covering, as in Figure 1(b). However, some electrodes can be manufactured faster than the imprinting equipment can mark them, and some sizes are too small to be legibly marked with an imprint. Although AWS specifies an imprint, the color code is accepted on electrodes if imprinting is not practical.

In addition to the classifications specified by the American Welding Society, electrodes can be classified by the characteristics of the molten metal and molten flux during the welding operation. These broad classifications are fast-freeze, fast-fill, and fill-freeze, the terms being descriptive of the operation of the electrode.

Fast-Freeze Electrodes

Fast-freeze electrodes are compounded to deposit weld metal that solidifies rapidly after being melted by the arc, and are thus intended specifically for welding in the vertical and overhead positions. Although deposition rates are not as high as with other types of electrodes, the fast-freeze type can also be used for flat welding and is, thus, considered an "all-purpose" electrode that can be used for any weld in mild steel. However, welds made with fast-freeze electrodes are slow and require a high degree of operator skill. Therefore, wherever possible, work should be positioned for downhand welding, which permits the use of fast-fill electrodes.

Fast-freeze electrodes provide deep penetration and maximum admixture. The weld bead is flat with distinct ripples. Slag formation is light, and the arc is easy to control.

Applications for fast-freeze electrodes are:

- General-purpose fabrication and maintenance welding.
- Vertical-up and overhead plate welds requiring X-ray quality.
- Pipe welding, including cross-country, in-plant, and noncritical small-diameter piping.
- Welds to be made on galvanized, plated, painted, or unclean surfaces.
- Joints requiring deep penetration, such as square-edge butt welds.
- Sheet-metal welds, including edge, corner, and butt welds.

In this classification are Fleetweld 5 and 5P (E6010) and Fleetweld 35, 35LS, and 180 (E6011).

Fast-Fill Electrodes

Fast-fill electrodes are compounded to deposit metal rapidly in the heat of the arc and are, thus, well suited to high-speed welding on horizontal surfaces. The weld metal solidifies somewhat slowly; therefore this type of electrode is not well suited for out-of-position welds. However, a slight downhill positioning is permissible. Joints normally considered fast-fill include butt, fillet, lap, and corner welds in plate 3/16" or thicker. These joints are capable of holding a large molten pool of weld metal as it freezes.

Arc penetration is shallow with minimum admixture. The bead is smooth, free of ripples, and flat or slightly convex. Spatter is negligible. Slag formation is heavy, and the slag peels off readily.

Applications for fast-fill electrodes are:

● Production welds on plate having a thickness of 3/16" or more.

● Flat and horizontal fillets, laps, and deep-groove butt welds.

● Welds on medium-carbon crack-sensitive steel when low-hydrogen electrodes are not available. (Preheat may be required.)

The coverings of fast-fill electrodes contain approximately 50% iron powder. This powder increases deposition rate by helping to contain the arc heat at the electrode, by melting to add to deposited weld metal, and by permitting currents higher than those permitted by other types of coverings. The thick, iron-bearing covering also facilitates use of the drag technique in welding.

In this classification are Jetweld 1 and 3(E7024), Jetweld LH-3800(E7028), and Jetweld 2(E6027).

Fill-Freeze Electrodes

Fill-freeze electrodes are compounded to provide a compromise between fast-freeze and fast-fill characteristics, and thus provide medium deposition rates and medium penetration. Since they permit welding at relatively high speed with minimal skip, misses, and undercut, and with minimum slag entrapment, fill-freeze electrodes are also referred to as fast-follow electrodes. The electrode's characteristics are particularly suited to the welding of sheet metal, and fill-freeze electrodes are, thus, often called "sheet-metal" electrodes. Bead appearance with this group of electrodes varies from smooth and ripple-free to wavy with distinct ripples. The fill-freeze electrodes can be used in all welding position, but are most widely used in the level or downhill positions.

Applications for fill-freeze electrodes include:

● Downhill fillet and lap welds.

● Irregular or short welds that change direction or position.

● Sheet-metal lap and fillet welds.

● Fast-fill joints having poor fitup.

● General-purpose welding in all positions.

Fast-freeze electrodes, particularly E6010 and E6011, are sometimes used for sheet-metal welding when fill-freeze electrodes are not available, or when the operator prefers faster solidification.

Electrodes in this classification are Fleetweld 7 (E6012), Fleetweld 37 and 57 (E6013), and Fleetweld 47 (E7014).

LESSON 1.17

Object:
To study the characteristics and uses of iron-powder electrodes.

General Information

Iron-powder electrodes as a class are those that have a relatively thick covering containing an appreciable amount of iron powder. The extra metal in the covering is available for deposition, in addition to that of the core wire.

The theory of iron-powder electrodes is not new. They were used in limited production in Europe before being used in the United States. Initially, the high cost and slow speed of manufacturing these electrodes kept them from general use. About 1953, the manufacturing problems were solved when the Lincoln Electric Company introduced "Jetweld", the first iron-powder electrode manufactured and sold in the United States. Since that time, development of iron-powder electrodes has been rapid, because these electrodes appeal both to management and the weldor.

The fast-fill type of iron-powder electrodes all have a thicker covering than other types of electrodes, and the covering is composed of about 50% iron powder. In addition, the thicker covering allows the electrode to weld with higher current without overheating. These characteristics produce higher deposition rates and hence higher welding speeds and lower welding costs. This appeals to management.

The thicker covering permits the electrodes to be used with the drag technique (Lesson 1.19), which makes the welding easier and less tiring. There is little or no spatter, and the slag cleans easily. These things make the electrode appealing to the weldor.

In the fast-fill classification are E7024, E7028, and E6027.

In the fill-freeze classification are E7014 and E7018. The E7018, in addition to being an all-position electrode, is also low-hydrogen.

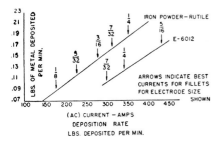

Figure 1. Iron powder electrodes are capable of depositing weld metal approximately 50% faster than E-6012 electrodes.

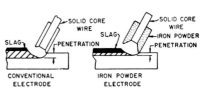

Figure 2. The heavy coating of iron powder electrodes produces a crucible effect so that the electrical energy of the arc is more efficiently used in melting the core wire and coating.

Object:
To make a lap weld in the horizontal and flat positions.

Equipment:
Lincoln "Idealarc" or AC or DC welder and accessories.

Material:
Mild-steel plates, 1/4"; 5/32" "Jetweld 1" (E7024); and "Fleet-weld 7" (E6012). (See Section III for properties and application of electrodes.)

General Information

The lap joint is welded with the bead made on the surface of one plate and the edge of the other. Fit work so there is no appreciable gap. Speed of welding, amperage, and quality of weld vary directly with fitup. "Fleetweld 7" is recommended for poor fitup welds.

On practical applications, most lap welds will be made in the horizontal position, with both the base-metal pieces horizontal. However, when the work can be tilted so that the joint is a trough for the molten pool of weld metal (see Figure 2), much higher welding speeds can be obtained. Tilting the plates at least 10 degrees will usually be sufficient to speed up the welding appreciably.

The electrodes specified are the types recommended for lap welds to obtain maximum speed and minimum cost, although other types may be used. Consult appropriate Lessons for further information on properties and application of these electrodes.

Job Instructions

Job A: Make a horizontal lap weld.

1. Clean base metal, and position the two pieces of 1/4" plate on the table with a 2-inch overlap.

2. Set amperage at 130 to 145 for 5/32" "Fleetweld 7", or 215 to 235 for 5/32" "Jetweld 1".

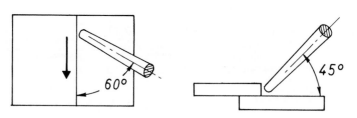

Figure 1.

3. Hold electrode about 45 degrees from horizontal, inclined 60 degrees in the direction of travel. (Figure 1)

4. Tack-weld the joint at each end, so it will not move during welding.

5. Hold electrode lightly against both plates with the arc directed into the corner. Move ahead in a straight line.

6. Observe carefully the bead as it builds up. Change electrode angle or speed if bead sags or there is a tendency to undercut. Faster travel rate must be used with "Jetweld 1".

7. Clean the bead and examine it. It should be uniform and smooth without overlap or undercuts, penetrating evenly into each plate.

8. Break the plates apart if the weld is under 5 inches long, by placing one plate in a sturdy vise and hammering on the back of the other plate. The bead should have even penetration into each plate and completely into the corner.

Job B: Make a flat lap weld.

Follow the same steps as Job A. Position the work as shown in Figure 2. Avoid undercutting the bottom plate.

If a welder of sufficient size is available, larger size electrode and higher amperages can be used, resulting in an increased welding speed. A slight weaving motion can be used to carry a larger bead on heavy plate.

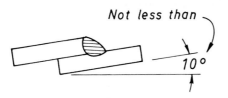

Figure 2.

Review Questions

1. What other weld is similar to the lap weld?

2. Why is it advisable to have a good fitup?

3. What electrode should be used for poor fitup joints?

4. What electrode movement is used when welding a horizontal lap weld?

5. What are the advantages of positioning a lap weld?

6. What electrode movement is used on a positioned lap weld?

7. What does the bead on a broken lap weld look like?

Object:
To make a fillet weld in the horizontal or flat position.

Equipment:
Lincoln "Idealarc" or DC or AC welder and accessories.

Material:
Mild-steel plates 1/4" or thicker; 5/32" "Jetweld 1" (E7024) and "Fleetweld 7" (E6012).

General Information

Joining members or plates coming in at a 90-degree angle to each other with a fillet weld is the most commonly used joint in welded fabrication. The lap joint also uses the fillet-type bead.

Most fillet welds are made in the horizontal position (Figure 1). It is some-times possible, however, to position the fillet flat so the surface of the molten pool is horizontal. Higher amperages and larger electrodes may be used on the positioned welds, resulting in substantially higher welding speeds. Welding may be done more easily on the positioned fillet without too much practice, because there is less tendency to undercut the vertical member of the horizontal fillet.

The arc is directed into the corner if the plates are of the same thickness. If the plates are of unequal thickness, the arc is directed more onto the thicker plate, to heat both plates equally.

The electrodes specified are the types recommended for fillet welds to obtain maximum speed and minimum cost, although other types may be used.

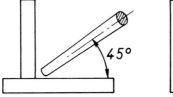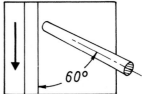

Figure 1.

Job Instructions

Job A: Make a horizontal fillet weld.

1. Clean base metal and place plates as shown in Figure 1.

2. Set amperage at 130 to 145 for "Fleetweld 7" or 215 to 235 for "Jetweld 1".

3. Hold electrode angle as shown in Figure 1.

4. Tack-weld each end of the joint in position with a good fitup.

5. Hold electrode lightly against both plates, with the arc directed into the corner. Move the electrode ahead in a straight line.

6. Observe the bead carefully as it forms under the arc. There may be some tendency to undercut the vertical plate. Vary the electrode angle specified above slightly to get the correct bead shape. If travel speed and electrode angle are correct, the bead will not undercut. Travel faster with "Jetweld 1".

7. Clean the bead, and examine it for signs of overlap or undercut.

8. Break the weld to see if penetration is equal into both plates and complete into the corner.

9. Heavier horizontal fillet welds require more than one bead. Proper procedure is to use the bead sequence shown in Figure 2.

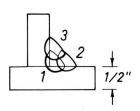

Figure 2.

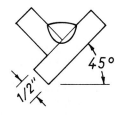

Figure 3.

Job B: Make a flat-positioned fillet weld.

Use same steps as in Job A, except to position the weld (Figure 3). Amperage may be set higher. If the top of the molten pool approaches a horizontal position, a slight weaving motion can be used to carry a larger bead. If subsequent passes are needed to bring the weld up to size, use the weaving technique with the bead sequence shown in Figure 4. A larger electrode may be used with higher amperage settings for maximum speed.

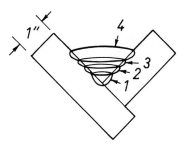

Figure 4.

Review Questions

1. What other weld form is similar to a fillet weld?

2. What arc length is used on fillet welds?

3. How are plates of unequal thickness welded?

4. What are the advantages of positioning a fillet flat?

5. Is it necessary to vary the specified electrode angle during welding?

6. What does a good fillet weld look like when broken?

LESSON

1.20

Object:
To make a butt weld in the flat position.

Equipment:
Lincoln "Idealarc" or DC or AC welder and accessories.

Material:
Mild-steel plates of various thickness; 5/32" and 3/16" "Fleet-weld 5P" (E6010) for DC(+); "Fleetweld 35" (E6011) for AC; and "Jetweld 2" (E6027). (See Section III for properties and application of "Jetweld 2".)

General Information

The joint made by placing the edges of two plates together and fusing them with the arc is called a butt weld.

Preparation for the butt weld depends upon the thickness of the metal, whether it will be welded from one or both sides, and the equipment available for preparing the edge.

A butt weld is most easily made by running beads on both sides of the joint, taking care that the penetrations of the beads on each side meet for maximum strength (Figure 2). Butt welds may also be run from one side only.

This is often the only way a weld can be made, as when doing pipe and tank welding. When welding from one side, be sure that the first pass achieves 100% penetration. Each bead must be cleaned well before subsequent passes are run. When welding from one side, better penetration is insured if metal 1/4" thick and over is beveled equally to form a 60-degree vee along the joint (Figure 3). Make enough passes on either type of joint to bring the weld bead slightly above the surface of the base metal.

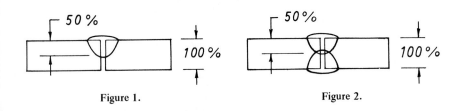

Figure 1.   Figure 2.

Job Instructions

Job A: Make a square butt joint.

1. Clean base metal and place two 1/4" plates flat on the table.

2. Set amperage 130 to 145 for 5/32" "Fleetweld 5 or 35" electrode.

3. Hold electrode perpendicular to the plate and the angle to the seam 65 to 70 degrees in the direction of travel.

4. Tack-weld the plates together with 1/32" to 1/16" root spacing (Figure 1).

5. Run a straight bead to produce the weld in Figure 1.

6. Break the weld apart; check for 50% minimum penetration.

7. For full penetration, turn the plate over and run a similar weld on the reverse side (Figure 2).

Job B: Make a vee butt weld on heavier plate.

1. Prepare 3/8" plate with a 60-degree V groove (Figure 3). If beveled plate is unavailable, use square-edged plates placed at an angle (Figure 4).

2. Clean base metal and position flat on the table.

3. Tack-weld joint at each end with approximately 1/8" root spacing.

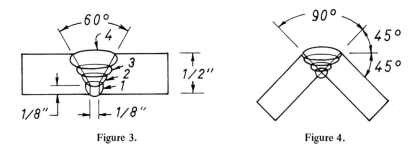

Figure 3.   Figure 4.

4. Lay root pass bead at the bottom of the vee with a 5/32" Fleetweld 5P electrode.

5. Set amperage at 230 to 250 DC(−), or 250-270 AC, for 3/16" "Jetweld 2" electrode.

6. Hold electrode perpendicular to the plate inclined 60 degrees in the direction of travel.

7. Chip off slag if it does not remove itself. Examine the weld for complete penetration and even fusion into each plate.

8. Run second, third, and fourth beads, or enough to fill the vee with a slight reinforcement bead on the last pass. Larger electrode may be used with increased amperages for filler passes on heavier metal. Use a slight weaving motion for filler passes. Wash the deposit up on each plate, so that a slightly concave bead is formed. It is easier to chip, assures a good penetration into each plate, and minimizes slag inclusions along the edge of the bead. When vee becomes wider than 3 times the electrode diameter, lay two beads, rather than weaving a wide one.

9. Practice making U-joint welds on 1/2" or heavier plate, using procedure similar to that for vee joints. Use 3/16" or 7/32" "Jetweld 2" electrode.

10. A backup strip may be used in making butt joints of the vee or U type. Larger electrodes and higher speeds can be used without danger of burn-through. Steel backup strips become a part of the weld and can be removed only by machining. Copper strips 1/4" thick or more may be used for backup. They will not fuse with the weld and may be removed after welding. Root spacing when using "Jetweld 2" with a backup strip should be the diameter of the core wire.

Review Questions

1. What are three edge preparations used for butt welds?
2. What is the easiest way of obtaining full penetration?
3. Why is full penetration important?
4. What precaution must be taken when making a weld from one side?
5. When welding from one side, how many passes are used?
6. Is it necessary to thoroughly clean each pass before running the next?
7. What are the advantages of using backup strips?
8. What type of backup strip may be used?

Object:
To run a bead in the horizontal position.

Equipment:
Lincoln "Idealarc" or DC or AC welder and accessories.

Material:
Steel plates 3/16" or thicker; 5/32" "Fleetweld 5P" (E6010) for DC(+) or "Fleetweld 35" (E6011) for AC.

General Information

When welding out-of-position, the electric arc counteracts gravity with the arc force created by the covering. The arc will deposit droplets of electrode metal into the crater in any position. However, gravity will influence the action of the molten metal once it is deposited in the crater. It is necessary, therefore, that the size of this molten pool be kept small and the force of the arc be used to help keep it in place. Electrode movement and arc length become very important. Electrodes should have fast-freeze characteristics. The importance and effect of practice also become apparent when welding in these positions.

It is necessary at times to make horizontal welds, particularly in the field. These are welds on plate that is in the vertical position, but the joint runs parallel to the ground. Examples of this are girth seams in large vertical storage tanks and butt welds on vertical pipelines.

Job Instructions

1. Clean base metal and position vertically on a scrap plate on the welding table.
2. Set amperage at 130 to 140 amps for 5/32" electrode.
3. Tack-weld metal to the scrap plate (Figure 1) or clamp it in position.

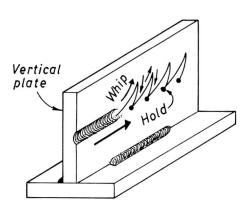

Figure 1.

4. Hold the electrode angle about 5 degrees below perpendicular and inclined approximately 70 to 75 degrees in the direction of travel.

5. Strike an arc on the vertical plate and draw the bead along in a horizontal line, holding a short arc. Make the arc deposit molten metal on the vertical plate. While it is comparatively easy to maintain the arc, it is rather difficult

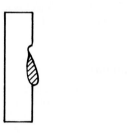

Figure 2.

Figure 3.

to get a uniform, well-shaped bead. The molten metal has a tendency to sag or run down the plate, giving an appearance similar to Figure 2. Reducing the current may assist in obtaining a bead of good shape.

6. If an irregular bead persists, a slight whipping motion such as shown in Figure 1 may be used to assist in overcoming it and obtaining the bead shown in Figure 3. Shortening or "crowding the arc" at the top of the weave will be helpful in controlling the molten metal.

7. For wider beads, such as used on butt welds, a somewhat more extensive weaving motion is necessary, as shown in Figure 4. The upward motion is rapid, and the metal is deposited on the downward motion.

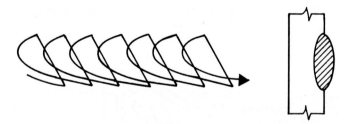

Figure 4.

Review Questions

1. How are the droplets of electrode metal deposited in the crater?

2. What are two important factors influencing welds made in positions other than flat?

3. What are two corrections that may be made for an irregular bead?

4. Can a weaving motion be used in horizontal welding?

LESSON 1.22

Object:
To make a butt weld in the horizontal position.

Equipment:
Lincoln "Idealarc" or DC or AC welder and accessories.

Material:
Mild-steel plates 3/16" and thicker; 5/32" and 3/16" "Fleetweld 5P" (E6010) for DC(+) or "Fleetweld 35" (E6011) for AC.

General Information

There are various horizontal joints that may be encountered in field work, such as butt, lap, fillet, edge, and corner. The lap joint in Figure 1 is similar to the horizontal lap weld (Lesson 1.18) and further discussion is not needed. The lap joint shown in Fig. 2 is made like the overhead lap or fillet weld (Lesson

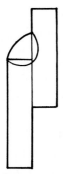

Figure 1.

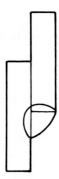

Figure 2.

1.33). The technique used on the edge joint in the horizontal position is similar to running a horizontal bead, and welding a corner joint is similar to the horizontal vee butt weld. Since these types of joints are so similar to other types, the butt weld will be the only one discussed under the horizontal position. The mastery of this weld is very important, because it is encountered frequently in pipe and tank welding.

Horizontal butt joints may be of three types, square, bevel one plate (Figure 3), and bevel both plates (Figure 4).

Job Instructions

Job A: Make a square butt weld in horizontal position.

1. Tack-weld two 3/16" plates together in a square butt joint. Secure in a vertical position.

2. Set amperage at 130-145 for 5/32" electrode.

3. Hold the electrode perpendicular to the plate or 5 degrees under, inclined 80 to 85 degrees in the direction of travel.

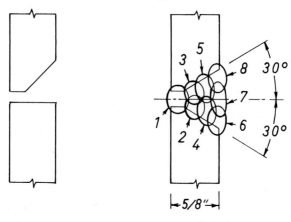

Figure 3.   Figure 4.

4. Hold a short arc length. Run a bead on one side using a slight whipping motion. If spatter is excessive or puddle is difficult to control, reduce heat.

5. Examine the completed bead. Break apart for better inspection if desired. Bead should fuse equally into each plate slightly over halfway through.

6. Repeat the job, welding from both sides for complete penetration.

Job B: Make a vee butt weld as shown in Figures 3 or 4.

1. Set up as for Job A, using plate with 30-degree bevel.

2. Set amperage 130-145 for 5/32" electrode; 160-175 for 3/16" electrode.

3. Use 5/32" electrode for root pass, and 3/16" for filler and cover passes.

4. Hold the electrode angle as shown in Figure 6, inclined 80 to 85 degrees in the direction of travel.

5. Make welds from both sides whenever possible. This allows a larger size electrode (3/16") to be used on the root passes to increase the welding

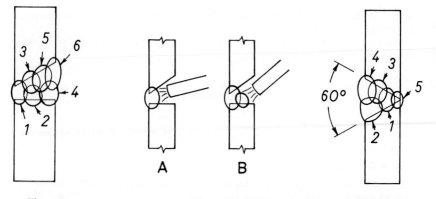

Figure 5.   Figure 6.   Figure 7.

speed. Figure 7 indicates how 1/2" plate should be welded using 3/16" electrode and welding from both sides.

6. In horizontal welding, the beads are usually laid in straight lines without weaving (Figure 5). For the last pass (cover pass), however, a weave may be made, using the motion such as shown in Lesson 1.21, Figure 4. Use a rapid upward motion, and deposit the metal on the downward movement.

Review Questions

1. What other joint is welded similar to the horizontal butt weld?

2. What types of edge preparation may be used on horizontal butt welds?

3. How does the amperage setting for horizontal welding compare with the flat position?

4. What can be done to control excessive spatter?

5. What arc length is used on horizontal butt welds?

Object:
To run a bead in the vertical position welding down.

Equipment:
Lincoln "Idealarc" or DC or AC welder and accessories.

Material:
Mild-steel plate 3/16" thick; 5/32" "Fleetweld 5P" (E6010) for DC(+) or "Fleetweld 35" (E6011) for AC.

General Information

When welding in the field, it is essential that a weldor be able to do vertical welding. There are two ways to make vertical welds; start at the top and weld down or start at the bottom and weld up. Vertical-down welding is recommended on metals 3/16" or less in thickness. Down welding is usually found to be easier than vertical-up welding. The cover pass on heavier metal is sometimes welded down to produce a smooth appearance. Vertical butt welds on horizontal transmission pipelines are generally welded down.

Not as much metal can be carried in a down pass. On heavy metals, therefore, it takes more passes to complete the joint. This can cause excessive distortion and is more time-consuming.

Job Instructions

1. Secure the plate in a vertical position.

2. Set amperage at 130 to 145 for 5/32" electrode.

3. Hold the electrode pointing up at an angle of about 60 degrees with the plate (Figure 1).

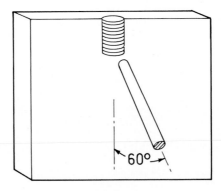

Figure 1.

4. Strike the arc and hold a short, but visible arc. Draw the electrode down in a straight line. Move rapidly enough to keep the slag from running ahead of the molten pool. This will make a thin bead. If the slag runs ahead of the puddle, extinguish the arc, chip the slag from around the crater and ahead of it, and restart the bead.

5. Repeat the operation using a whipping motion as shown in Figure 2A. This will give a narrow bead but one that is well-proportioned.

6. Use a wider weave, such as Figure 2B and C. These weaves will be used later when making joints.

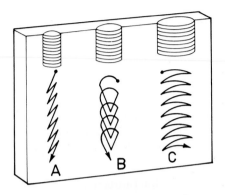

Figure 2.

Review Questions

1. What two methods are used in vertical welding?

2. When is down welding used?

3. What is vertical-up welding used for?

4. Which method is easier?

5. How fast should the electrode travel be on vertical-down welding?

6. Can a weave be used welding down?

Object:
To make a lap and fillet weld in the vertical position welding down.

Equipment:
Lincoln "Idealarc" or DC or AC welder and accessories.

Material:
Mild-steel plate 3/16" thick; 5/32" "Fleetweld 5P" (E6010) for DC(+) or "Fleetweld 35" (E6011) for AC.

General Information

Lap and fillet welding in vertical positions are similar. The bead form is the same, as well as the arc length, electrode angle, and electrode motion. For this reason they will be presented as a single lesson.

Job Instructions

Job A: Make a lap weld in the vertical position welding down.

1. Set amperage at 110-120 amps for 5/32" electrode.
2. Tack-weld two plates together in a lap joint and secure in a vertical position.
3. Hold the electrode pointing upward 60 degrees from the vertical plate and directly into the corner, 45 degrees from the plate surface.

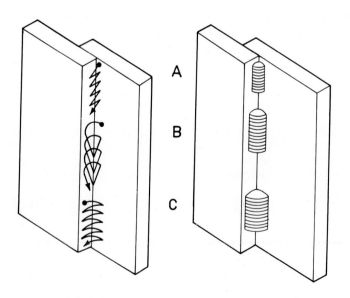

Figure 1.   **Figure 2.**

4. Strike the arc at the top and weld down keeping a short arc length. Use a straight bead or a whipping motion (Figure 1A). Travel downward should be at such a rate that the slag does not run ahead of the crater.

5. Repeat, using weave B. This will result in a slightly heavier bead.

6. Repeat weave A or B, clean the bead well and lay a second bead over it, using weave C. Make certain you are getting penetration into the corner and evenly into each plate.

Job B: Make a fillet weld in the vertical position welding down.

1. Use amperage settings and electrode angle as in Job A.

2. Tack-weld two plates in a tee joint, and secure in a vertical position.

3. Repeat the same passes as in Job A, making a fillet weld (Figure 3). Practice particularly the heavy weave.

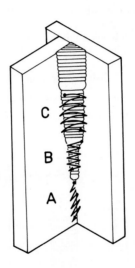

Figure 3.

Review Questions

1. Is vertical welding encountered much in the field?

2. How is a heavier bead run in vertical-down welding?

3. Why are the different weave patterns used?

LESSON

1.25

Object:
To make a butt weld in the vertical position welding down.

Equipment:
Lincoln "Idealarc" or DC or AC welder and accessories.

Material:
Mild-steel plate 3/16" or thinner; 5/32" "Fleetweld 5P" (E6010) for DC(+) or "Fleetweld 35" (E6011) for AC.

General Information

The various edge preparations, spacings, and procedures, for welding butt joints are discussed in Lesson 1.20. As vertical-down welding is generally used on metal up to 3/16" thick, only the square butt will be practiced here. For plate less than 3/16" thick the root should be reduced. It may also be necessary to use a smaller electrode on thinner plate.

In general, the same electrode angle, arc length, and electrode motions are used in making vertical-down butt welds as for fillet and lap welds.

Job Instructions

1. Set amperage at 130 to 145 for 5/32" electrode.

2. Tack-weld two plates together with 1/16" root spacing (Figure 1) and secure in a vertical position.

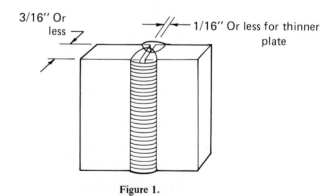

3/16" Or less

1/16" Or less for thinner plate

Figure 1.

3. Hold electrode pointing directly into the joint, upward 60 degrees from the plate.

4. Strike the arc at the top and weld down, keeping a short arc length. Put in the first bead using the whipping motion (Lesson 1.24, Figure 1A).

5. Clean the bead thoroughly and inspect it. Penetration should be adequate as on a downhand bead, and bead should be evenly fused into each plate.

6. Start at the top of the reverse side and put in the second bead, using the same electrode motion.

Review Questions

1. Why is the square butt joint used in vertical-down welding?
2. Why is tack-welding used on joints?
3. Why are the pieces spaced apart?
4. Why are larger electrode sizes not used on vertical-down welding?

Object:
To make a corner weld.

Equipment:
Lincoln "Idealarc" or DC or AC welder and accessories.

Material:
Steel plate 3/16" or 1/4"; 5/32" "Fleetweld 5P" (E6010) for DC(+) or "Fleetweld 35" (E6011) for AC.

General Information

Corner welds are used on a number of jobs, especially in making tanks and containers. They may be used on material of any thickness. No edge preparation is needed. The base metal should be tacked into position with a good fitup. The square plate edges form a vee.

Throat 3/4 of thickness

Figure 1.

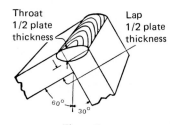

Throat 1/2 plate thickness

Lap 1/2 plate thickness

60° 30°

Figure 2.

A full open joint (Figure 1) may be used for maximum strength, and the half open joint (Figure 2) or closed joint may be used where less strength or only liquid tightness is needed. Corner welds on thin metal tend to warp or spread apart easier than butt welds and will need to be tack-welded at closer intervals. Back-step welding will minimize distortion, as will the use of copper backup strips placed in the corner. The procedure in making a corner weld is similar to a vee butt weld, except that less heat may be required. For maximum strength, a fillet weld is necessary on the inside.

Whenever possible these welds should be made in the flat position, although horizontal and vertical positions may be used. When vertical welding is necessary, down welding is recommended.

Job Instructions

1. Set amperage at 125 to 140 for 5/32" electrode.

2. Tack-weld base metal together. Root spacing of 1/16" (maximum) may be used for penetration if desired.

3. Hold electrode pointing directly into the root of the weld, inclined 75 to 80 degrees in the direction of travel.

4. Strike an arc and carry a short arc laying the bead into the vee with a slight weaving motion. Avoid undercutting along the top of the edges.

5. Clean the bead and examine the weld. Bead should be flush with the top of the vee with no undercutting or overlapping.

Review Questions

1. Where are corner welds commonly used?
2. In what position should corner welds be made?
3. Should vertical-up welding be used?
4. What thickness of material is used for corner welds?
5. What are the three major types of corner joints?
6. Is root spacing used when setting up a corner weld?

LESSON 1.27

Object:
To make edge welds.

Equipment:
Lincoln "Idealarc" or DC or AC welder and accessories.

Material:
Sheet steel, 12 to 16 ga.; 3/32" "Fleetweld 7" (E6012) or "Fleetweld 180" (E6011) for AC.

General Information

Edge welds, sometimes called flange welds, are usually restricted to base metal 1/4" and under, and for joints not subjected to heavy loads. Around the small shop they will probably be used on metal 12 to 16-gauge, due to the difficulty of flanging heavier metal. The stiffening effect of the flanged edge minimizes distortion. Welding procedure is similar to running a bead on a flat plate. The only difficulty encountered will be keeping the bead evenly on the narrow edge. Both types of joints in Figure 1 may also be welded with the arc torch or carbon arc by fusing the flanges together without additional filler metal.

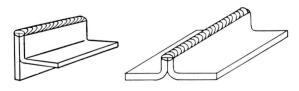

Figure 1.

Whenever possible these welds should be made in the flat position. When vertical welding is necessary, down welding should be used.

Job Instructions

1. Prepare flanges by turning over in a brake or with a hammer. For practice, narrow strips may be cut and put together with the edges up for welding to save the work of bending flanges.

2. Set amperage at 60 to 75 for 3/32" electrode.

3. Tack-weld joint with no root spacing.

4. Hold electrode perpendicular to the joint and inclined 75 to 80 degrees in the direction of travel.

5. Strike the arc and move along rapidly holding a short arc.

6. Clean weld and examine bead. Weld should be fused into both pieces and be uniform in height without depressions melted down into the flange caused by irregular travel or excessive amperage.

7. Edge welds may be run on heavier metal, 1/8" to 3/16", using 1/8" electrode.

Review Questions

1. What size metal is usually used for edge welds?

2. What is another name for edge welds?

3. Are edge welds suitable for joints that receive heavy stresses?

4. What method of welding may be used besides the metal-arc?

5. What position is best for edge welds?

6. How should edge joints be welded vertically?

LESSON
1.28

Object:
To study the welding of thin-gauge metals.

General Information

The use of thin-gauge metal, generally termed sheet metal, around the shop is very common. Technically, sheet metal is any gauge less than 1/8" (approximately 11-ga. U.S.S.). Heavier material is called plate. Much of the work in the shop will be concerned with the thinner gauges of sheet steel, 14-gauge or less. Most sheet metal is mild steel with a coating of oxide (black iron) or zinc (galvanizing). Car and tractor bodies are usually mild steel with a primer and paint coating.

The general procedure for welding sheet metal will be the same as that discussed in the lessons for welding the standard joints. There are some problems, however, that are peculiar to sheet-metal welding and must be taken into consideration before starting a job. Because of its thin gauge, the correct heat must be used when welding sheet metal. There is little room for error. Too little heat will not maintain the arc and too much will burn through the base metal. Distortion due to expansion and contraction is more of a problem in light metal than in heavier, more rigid metal. Lesson 1.15 should be studied before welding sheet metal.

Several precautions may be observed to make it easier to work with thin-gauge metals. Joints should always have a good fitup, and be carefully tack-welded prior to welding. The lap weld is easily set up on sheet metal and provides extra thickness for burnthrough protection. The flange-type welds provide a more rigid joint to minimize warping (Lesson 1.27).

The metal arc is recommended on metal as thin as 16-gauge, and may sometimes be used on 18-gauge (Figure 1). When using the metal arc, a short arc should be held. There are some electrodes made for sheet-metal welding. These have arc characteristics that produce a soft-arc "spray" type of deposit. The E6013 and E6012 electrodes work well. The "deep-penetration" type of electrodes should be avoided. Some welders are equipped with an attachment or adjustment to facilitate the welding of thin metal.

If gaps exist in joints, they should be backed up with 1/4" copper strips to protect against burnthrough (Figure 2). The weld metal will not stick to copper, and its high conductivity assists in carrying away excess heat to reduce distor-

ELECTRODE SIZES FOR SHEET STEEL

Size Gauge	Approximate Thickness in Fractions of an Inch	Approximate Thickness in Decimals of an Inch	Electrode Size	Amperage
11	1/8	.120	1/8"	90 — 100
12	7/64	.106	1/8"	80 — 100
13	3/32	.090	3/32"	45 — 65
14	5/64	.075	3/32"	25 — 45
16	1/16	.060	1/16"	20 — 30
18	3/64	.048	*Carbon-arc	

*Carbon-arc torch or single carbon is preferred for brazing metal of this thickness.

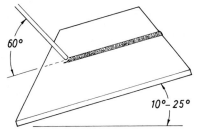

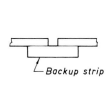

Backup strip

Figure 1.   Figure 2.

tion. Steel backup strips may be used, but they become a part of the joint and must be left on.

Tipping the base metal 10 to 25 degrees (Figure 3) and welding downward is advisable on light metals. Faster forward movement is possible.

The arc torch or carbon arc (Lesson 1.39) provides a method for fusing edge welds and brazing light metals. It is recommended for 18-gauge and thinner. The heat may be controlled more carefully than with the metal arc. The base metal must be clean and free of oxide. Flux must be used when brazing to help clean the metal, retard oxidation during the process, and aid the bronze to flow and adhere to the base metal. The rod is fed into the flame area at an angle of 30 degrees from the joint. The arc flame is played on the joint and the rod, so that the base metal is heated to a dull red, the melting point of the rod. The metal from the rod should flow out as it contacts the base metal. The bronze will follow the heat of the arc along the base metal. If the bare rod and powdered flux is used, the flux is applied to the rod by heating and dipping it into the flux, or a little flux may be spread along the joint. Be careful not to burn the filler rod or overheat the base metal. A minimum of warp will result if the heat is held down and welding speed is rapid.

Warning: Galvanized metal must be welded or brazed outside, or in a well-ventilated area. The zinc fumes are toxic and should not be breathed.

Review Questions

1. What thickness is sheet metal?

2. What base metal is commonly used in sheet metal?

3. What is galvanized iron?

4. What is black iron?

5. What are two major problems confronted by the sheet-metal weldor?

6. What joint works well on sheet metal to provide extra thickness?

7. What is the thinnest gauge generally recommended for welding with the metal arc?

8. What arc characteristics does a sheet-metal electrode have?

9. What should be done with joints with poor fitup?

10. What type of positioning works well when welding sheet metal?

11. Why is the use of the carbon arc recommended on very thin sheet metal?

12. Why is flux used when brazing?

13. What danger is there in welding galvanized metal?

Object:
To run a bead in the vertical position welding up.

Equipment:
Lincoln "Idealarc" or DC or AC welder and accessories.

Material:
Mild-steel plate 1/4" or thicker; 5/32" "Fleetweld 5P" (E6010) for DC(+) or "Fleetweld 35" (E6011) for AC.

General Information

Vertical-up welding is generally used on plate 1/4" or thicker. Greater penetration is possible by vertical-up welding, and more metal can be carried in each pass. This allows welds to be made with fewer passes, thereby reducing distortion and speeding up welding.

Amperage setting is less than for flat welding and vertical-down welding. The puddle must be kept small for easy control.

Some beginners find it easier to run beads on plate inclined 30 to 40 degrees and gradually increasing the angle until it is vertical.

Job Instructions

1. Set amperage 110 to 120 for 5/32" electrode.

2. Position plate inclined or vertical, and tack to a piece of scrap or clamp securely in place.

3. Hold electrode perpendicular with the plate pointing upward about 5 degrees (Figure 1).

4. Strike the arc and establish a puddle holding a short arc.

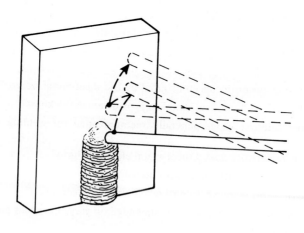

Figure 1.

5. Use the whipping motion to keep the puddle "cool", as practiced in Lesson 1.10. Move the electrode tip ahead of the puddle about 1/2" to 1" holding a long arc, hesitate, and return it to the puddle to deposit more metal with a short arc. Bead uniformity depends upon timing of the whipping motion. If the puddle is difficult to control or excessive spatter is obtained, it may be necessary to reduce the amperage setting. Practice whipping motion until a uniform bead is obtained.

6. Run slightly wider beads using weave motions B, C, and D (Figure 2).

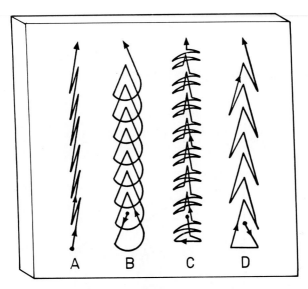

Figure 2.

Review Questions

1. What size plate is generally welded vertically up?

2. Why is heavier plate not welded vertically down?

3. Which method of vertical welding can produce the heavier bead?

4. Why is the whipping motion used in vertical-up welding?

Object:

To make a lap and fillet weld in the vertical position welding up.

Equipment:

Lincoln "Idealarc" or DC or AC welder and accessories.

Material:

Mild-steel plates 1/4" and 3/8"; 5/32" and 3/16" "Fleetweld 5P" (E6010) for DC(+) or "Fleetweld 35" (E6011) for AC.

General Information

The making of lap and fillet joints is similar, using the same weld form, electrode angle, and electrode motion. Maximum penetration on vertical joints in metal 1/4" or thicker is insured by welding up.

Job Instructions

Job A: Make a lap weld in the vertical position welding up.

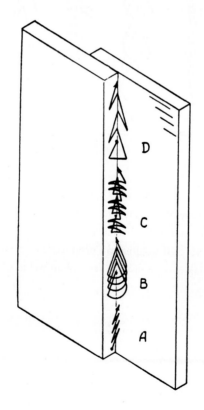

Figure 1.

1. Set amperage 110 to 130 for 5/32" electrode.

2. Tack-weld plates for a lap joint, and secure in a vertical position (Figure 1).

3. Hold electrode pointing upward 5 degrees, directly into the corner.

4. Hold a short arc, and establish a puddle penetrating evenly into each plate.

5. Make first pass using the whipping technique shown in Figure 1A. Whip the electrode tip upward from the crater about 1/2" to 1" holding a long arc, hesitate, and return to the crater with a short arc to deposit more metal. Bead uniformity depends upon proper timing of whipping motions. If puddle is difficult to control, reduce amperage.

6. Practice weaves B, C, and D to obtain a wider bead.

Job B: Make a fillet weld in the vertical position welding up.

1. Use same amperage setting, electrode angle, and electrode motion as for Job A.

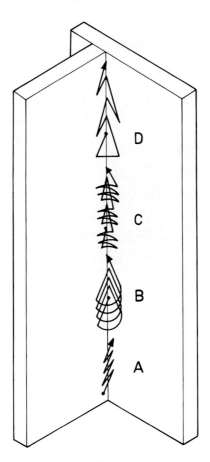

Figure 2.

2. Tack-weld plates for a fillet weld and secure in a vertical position (Figure 2).

3. Use whipping motion A to lay the first bead; cover using weaves B, C, and D.

Job C: Repeat Jobs A and B, welding vertically up using 3/8" plate or thicker.

1. Set amperage 150 to 165 for 3/16" electrode.

2. Tack-weld plates for lap or fillet weld; secure in vertical position.

3. Run the first bead using a whipping motion.

4. The second and third beads should be put in using the weaves shown in Figure 3.

5. Additional beads can be applied, using weaves similar to that shown. A slight pause in the motion should be made at points X. The pause should be somewhat longer for the weave used for the third and fourth beads than for the second bead. These pauses are for the purpose of filling up undercuts in the base metal.

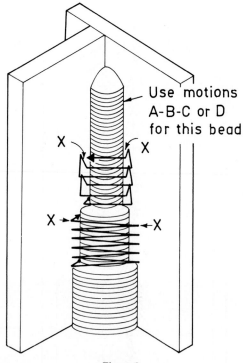

Use motions
A-B-C or D
for this bead

Figure 3.

Review Questions

1. Why are fillet and lap welds 1/4" and over welded vertically up?

2. Why use the whipping motion when welding a fillet vertically up?

3. What is the reason for using the different weave patterns?

Object:
To make a butt weld in the vertical position welding up.

Equipment:
Lincoln "Idealarc" or DC or AC welder and accessories.

Material:
Mild-steel plates 1/4" and 3/8"; 5/32" and 3/16" "Fleetweld 5P" (E6010) for DC(+) or "Fleetweld 35" (E6011) for AC.

General Information

Review the types of butt joints (Lesson 1.20). This lesson will cover only the vee-type butt joint, because it will be used on 1/4" plate or thicker. Similar instructions apply to the groove or double-vee joints. Welding may be done from one side, or both sides when possible.

Job Instructions

Job A: Make a butt weld with 1/4" plate.

1. Set amperage 110 to 120 for 5/32" electrode; 150 to 165 for 3/16" electrode.

2. Prepare edges and set up plate for vee butt weld. Tack-weld with root spacing and secure in the vertical position as shown in Figure 1.

3. Hold electrode pointing upward 5 degrees and directly into the joint.

4. Use a 5/32" electrode for the root pass. Strike the arc and establish a puddle at the bottom on both pieces. Carry the bead up using a whipping motion similar to Figure 3A.

5. Using the same size electrode and current, make the second pass with sufficient weave to fill the groove, motion Figure 3B. This pass should have a slight reinforcement.

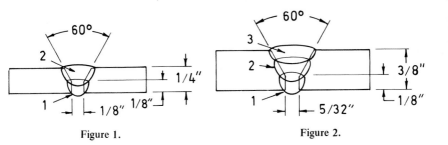

Figure 1.   Figure 2.

Job B: Make a butt weld with 3/8" plate.

1. Set amperage as in Job A.

2. Prepare edges, tack-weld with spacing and secure plates in vertical position (Figure 2).

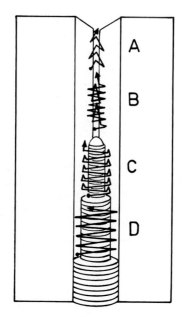

Figure 3.

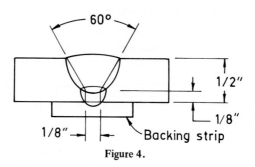

Figure 4.

3. Make the root pass with a 5/32" electrode, using motion A in Figure 3. This will optimize penetration and deposition.

4. Make filler passes with 3/16" electrode, using the motions shown in Figure 3.

5. Figure 4 shows how heavy welds may be made in the vertical position with only two beads, by using a backup strip. Put in the root pass as before, but make the second bead sufficiently heavy to fill out the vee, using a weaving motion like that of Figure 3C.

Review Questions

1. What type of joint preparation may be used on vertical-up butt welds?
2. Can vertical-up butt welding be done from both sides of the joint?

Object:
To run a bead in the overhead position.

Equipment:
Lincoln "Idealarc" or DC or AC welder and accessories.

Material:
Mild-steel plate 1/4" or thicker; 5/32" "Fleetweld 5P" (E6010) for DC(+) or "Fleetweld 35" (E6011) for AC.

General Information

Welding in the overhead position is not difficult after the other positions are mastered. Difficulty may be experienced in keeping the electrode holder steady and the bead from sagging. Using both hands on the electrode holder, and resting one arm or elbow against the body or a solid object, will help to steady the electrode. Holding a short arc and depositing the bead with a whipping motion will keep the puddle small and avoid sagging.

Shoulders, arms, and head should be protected from falling spatter and sparks. Grasp the electrode holder with the back of the hands upward to ward off falling spatter, and stand to one side of the bead.

Job Instructions

1. Set amperage at 125 to 135 for 5/32" electrode.

2. Fasten the plate firmly in a horizontal position by tack-welding or clamping, so that the underside may be easily reached with the electrode by assuming a comfortable position for welding.

3. Hold the electrode perpendicular to the plate, inclined 80 to 85 degrees in the direction of travel (Figure 1).

4. Strike and establish the arc. When striking the arc, hesitate for two or three seconds with a rather long arc until the base metal is molten above the arc.

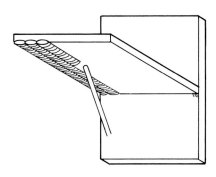

Figure 1.

5. Move ahead in a straight line holding a very short arc to form a short bead. Try this a number of times until you can easily and quickly strike and maintain an arc overhead.

6. Continue to strike the arc and run longer beads. Move the electrode at a steady rate. The whipping motion will be helpful in controlling bead shape. If there is a tendency for the metal to run down and form drops, a very short arc will stop this. You can melt this drop by using a longer arc and, when the drop is molten, quickly shorten the arc.

7. Try a very short arc, a short arc, and a long arc. Observe the performance of each type of arc and the appearance of the resultant bead. Slight changes in amperage setting may be helpful in controlling the puddle. Inspect the beads by chipping and cleaning so that the penetration and fusion may be observed. This lesson will require considerable practice to obtain uniform beads.

8. After making satisfactory straight beads, starting and stopping at will, slight weaving motions such as shown in Figure 2 may be practiced. This will allow you to carry more metal than in the straight bead. The weaving technique has only limited use in the overhead position, and the wide weave is not used.

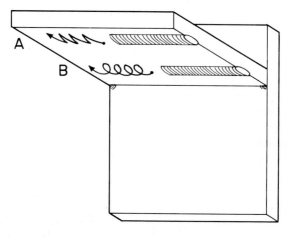

Figure 2.

Review Questions

1. What are two difficulties of overhead welding?

2. How can you help to steady the electrode when welding overhead?

3. Why is it well to turn the backs of the hands upward during overhead welding?

4. What electrode angle is used for overhead welding?

5. How can you keep the puddle from dropping or sagging?

Object:
To make a fillet weld and lap weld in the overhead position.

Equipment:
Lincoln "Idealarc" or DC or AC welder and accessories.

Material:
Mild-steel plates 1/4" and 3/8"; 5/32" and 3/16" "Fleetweld 5P" (E6010) for DC(+) or "Fleetweld 35" (E6011) for AC.

General Information

Fillet and lap welds are made in a similar manner in the overhead position. This lesson, therefore, is on fillet welds in detail.

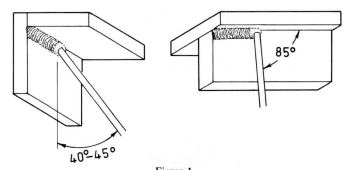

Figure 1.

Job Instructions

1. Set amperage at 125 to 135 for 5/32" electrode.

2. Tack-weld 1/4" plates for a tee joint, and secure in the overhead position so that the underside may be easily reached with the electrode.

3. Hold electrode 40 to 45 degrees out from the vertical plate and inclined 85 degrees in the direction of travel (Figure 1).

4. Strike an arc and establish a puddle evenly on both pieces. Place a single bead in the corner, using the whipping motion.

5. Break the plates apart and inspect for complete penetration into the corner. There should be no undercutting on the horizontal plate, or overlapping on the vertical plate.

6. After making a uniform single-bead fillet weld, make a multiple stringer-bead weld. Follow the general sequence shown in Figure 2. These beads may be made with a slight weaving motion.

7. After mastering the procedure for multiple stringer beads, try a two-pass weld with weaving. Lay first pass with whipping motion.

8. Lay the second bead using weaving motion (Figure 3). Use weaving on a two-pass weld only. Use stringer if more than two passes are required.

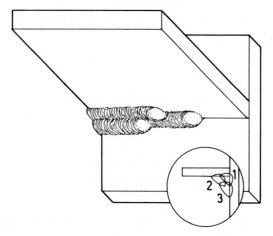

Figure 2.

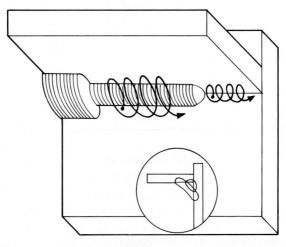

Figure 3.

9. Repeat the job using 3/16" electrode on 3/8" or thicker plate.

Review Questions

1. Are the same procedures used for both fillet and lap welds in each of the four basic positions?

2. What two procedures are used for heavy fillets?

3. What is a straight bead sometimes called?

4. What should be the appearance of an overhead fillet bead?

5. How many passes are recommended for a weave-technique weld?

Object:
To make a butt weld in the overhead position.

Equipment:
Lincoln "Idealarc" or DC or AC welder and accessories.

Material:
Mild-steel plates 3/16" and 3/8"; 5/32" and 3/16" "Fleetweld 5P" (E6010) for DC(+) or "Fleetweld 35" (E6011) for AC.

General Information

Review butt joints in Lesson 1.20 for detailed information on preparation and procedure. All types of butt joints are suitable for overhead welding. depending upon the thickness of the metal.

Job Instructions

Job A: Make a square butt weld in the overhead position.

1. Set amperage at 125 to 135 for 5/32" electrode.

2. Tack-weld two 3/16" plates with 1/16" gap and secure in the overhead position.

3. Hold the electrode pointing directly into the joint inclined 80 to 85 degrees in the direction of travel.

4. Strike an arc and run a straight bead along the joint, fusing the two plates together (Figure 1).

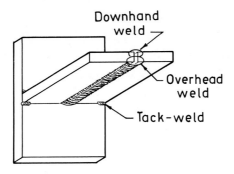

Figure 1.

5. Break the plates apart to examine the quality of the deposit. Penetration should be slightly over half way through, and the bead fused equally into each plate. For plates up to 1/4" thick, a bead can be run on the opposite side for maximum strength. If the joint is not accessible from the reverse side, it must be veed and welded from one side.

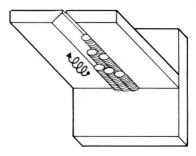

Figure 2.

Job B: Make a vee butt weld in the overhead position.

1. Prepare two 3/8" plates with 30° bevel for a vee butt weld. Tack-weld with 1/16" root spacing and secure in an overhead position.

2. Following the procedure used in Job A and the sequence of passes shown in Figure 2, make the weld with a whipping motion.

3. If difficulty is experienced in making the first bead with proper penetration, a backup strip will be helpful. The backup strip is often not possible or practical to use on construction jobs, so it is important this type of weld be practiced without the use of the strip. A larger root spacing may be used with a backup strip.

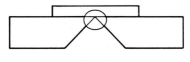

Figure 3.

Review Questions

1. What arc length is held in overhead butt welding?

2. Can a backup strip be used?

3. What type of backup strip can be easily removed after welding?

4. Why is it necessary to practice welding without a backup strip?

Object:
To study the standard welding symbols and their applications.

General Information

Welding has become so important and essential as a process of fabrication that it has become necessary to have some standard means of indicating the pertinent information necessary for each welded joint. The American Welding Society set up a method of symbolizing and specifying welding information. Its general adoption by industry for use on shop drawings has made it a standard for designers, draftsmen, and shop men. Its use fits our modern industrial organization of job specialization and standardization of parts inherent in mass production. To the designer and engineer are assigned the job of figuring loads and strength, specifying where the weld is to be made, what size and form shall be used, and any special information needed for its application. To the shop foreman and weldor are assigned the task of seeing that the proper welds are made and that the correct procedure is used to make the weld specified. It helps to eliminate errors of overwelding, underwelding, or the use of the wrong weld form for the stresses involved.

The AWS welding symbols are relatively easy to understand after a person has studied the basic symbols and their general plan of use. All persons doing or specifying welded fabrication should be familiar with them. From these symbols it is possible to determine the following:
1. Location of each weld.
2. Size of weld (throat, length, spacing)
3. Type of weld (weld form, plate preparation, and spacing)
4. Weld application information relative to individual specifications.

This information is easily and accurately read from a standard symbol placed on the drawing. It is no longer necessary to draw in each weld or letter descriptive notes, such as "weld all joints".

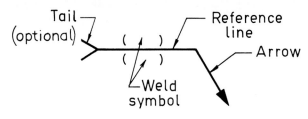

Figure 1.

Welding symbols have four distinct parts. (See Figure 1). The *arrow* points to the joint, the *reference line* is a base for locating the small *weld symbols,* and the *tail* is a place to put special procedures or notes. The tail is now an optional part of the symbol. The weld symbols define the type of weld required. (See Figure 2). The perpendicular leg of the fillet weld symbol is always to the left. All types of welds and joint preparations may be shown. Additional information concerning size, length, finish, etc., is placed around the reference line.

TYPE OF WELD							
Bead	Fillet	Plug or Slot	Groove				
			Square	V	Bevel	U	J
⌓	◺	▽	‖	∨	V	Y	‖

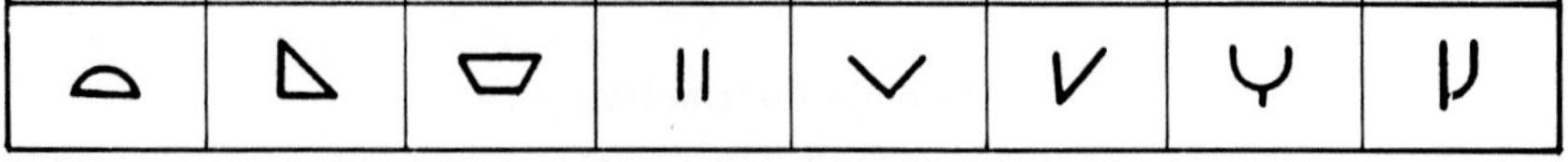

Figure 2.

Each joint has two sides; the "arrow" side to which the tip of the arrow points, and the "other" side. It is possible to designate which side is to be welded. If the small weld symbol is below the reference line the weld is to be made on the "arrow" side; when the symbol is on top of the reference line the weld is to be made on the "other" side.

Sometimes, it is difficult to tell from the drawing just what is the "other" side. Figure 3 illustrates a simple method for properly determining it. If you mentally "look" through the *joint* you can "see" the "other" side. If you try to "look" the wrong way, you will be "looking" at solid metal and cannot "see" through it. Always look through the joint. Remember that the arrow does not

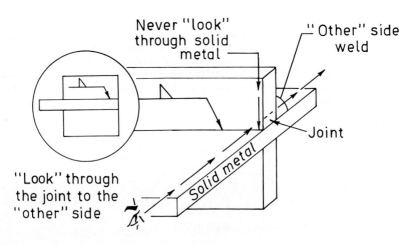

Figure 3. Mental vision method of determining "other" side of a welded joint as indicated by the welding symbol.

necessarily point to the "other" side. This can be clearly seen in Figure 3 where the arrow points through solid metal and does not point to the "other" side. Therefore, don't use the direction of the arrow as a guide to finding the "other" side.

For a detailed discussion of AWS welding symbols and their application see Section 10.1.

Review Questions

1. A complete symbol has how many parts?

2. What information is in the tail of the symbol?

3. How many sides are there to each welded joint?

4. A welding symbol placed below the reference line refers to which side of the joint?

5. To determine the "other" side is it ever necessary to "look" through solid metal?

6. Does the tip of the arrow point to the "other" side?

Object:
To study the preparation and welding of cast iron.

General Information

It is necessary to know what cast iron is and how it acts under heat in order to weld it successfully. Cast iron is a mixture of iron with a high percentage of carbon, between 2 and 4 per cent. This carbon is in two forms; part is in solution with the iron (as it is in steel), and part is in a free form deposited as graphite flakes in little pockets throughout the metal.

The high carbon content in cast iron is responsible for the properties causing the difficulty that is encountered during welding; that is, cast iron has high compression strength, but is low in tensile strength and ductility. It becomes hard and brittle by heating and rapid cooling, such as caused by the welding process. This combination of characteristics causes cast iron to be "crack sensitive". If any stress is placed on this metal that tends to pull it apart rather than squeeze it together, its low tensile strength cannot withstand much pull and its low ductility will not allow it to bend or stretch. All it can do, consequently, is break. This may occur as either a complete break of the entire part, or as a localized crack.

The stresses that cause cast iron to crack during welding usually result from uneven heating and cooling. Welding on a piece of cool cast iron involves two violent thermal processes. The first is a very rapid heating caused by the electric arc. The second is a very rapid cooling of the molten metal caused by the small amount of heat in the puddle being rapidly absorbed by the cold cast iron and air surrounding it. Heating causes the metal to expand and cooling causes the metal to contract. Both of these create stresses.

One other factor involved in the tendency of cast iron welds to crack is the effect of the carbon that is picked up from the base metal and mixed with the weld deposit. Though the electrodes used to weld cast iron have a very low carbon content, the high carbon in the melted base metal mixes with it to give a resultant high-carbon deposit. High-carbon deposits are also crack sensitive. In a good full-thickness bead, this is not much of a problem. In the crater at the end of the bead, however, there is very little thickness and the dilution from the base metal becomes a high percentage of the total deposit. The carbon pickup may make that end of the bead extremely brittle and crack-sensitive. It is at this point that the weld is weakest. A crack will practically always form in the crater if the crater is on the cast iron itself. This crack, once started, may proceed through the entire weld.

There are two ways of avoiding trouble from cracking when welding cast iron, usually termed as the "hot" and "cold" methods. The "hot" method means to preheat the entire part slowly and uniformly to prevent building up stresses during this heating operation. The welding operation takes place on an already hot piece of cast iron. When the welding is completed, the entire piece must be slowly and uniformly cooled.

The "cold" method is used when it is impossible or impractical to evenly preheat the entire casting. It is then necessary to insure that the stresses set up by welding are so small that they cannot cause the part to crack. This must be done by a slow back-step method of welding and peening the deposit. The beads are allowed to cool down enough so that the bare hand may be laid on them before starting the next bead.

The work to be welded must be clean. All dirt, oil, grease, and paint must be removed. This can be done by wire-brushing, grinding, burning, or slowly heating to 400 to 500 degrees.

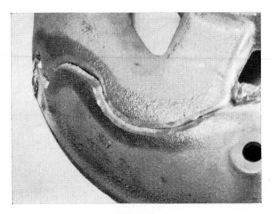

Figure 1.

Joint preparation in cast iron is important to obtain a strong joint. When the casting is broken in two or more pieces, form a vee (Figure 1) by grinding a bevel off the broken edges, leaving 1/16" to 1/8" of the fractured edge to assure proper alignment of the pieces to the original size. This will also insure good fusion throughout the entire thickness of the weld. If the job to be welded is a crack, as is often the case with heavy castings, a hole should be drilled at each end of the crack to prevent its going farther, and to determine the thickness of the casting at that point. The end of the crack can be determined by putting kerosene over the area for a few seconds and wiping it off. Rub some white chalk along the crack. The crack will show up as a dark streak in the white chalk, showing its entire length and any hairline cracks. Vee out all cracks 1/8" to 3/16" deep with a grinder or a diamond point cold chisel. If the casting is under 3/16", vee out half the thickness (Figure 2).

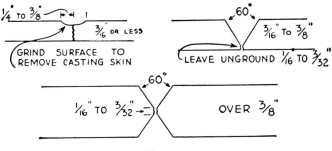

Figure 2.

Welds in cast iron, if of sufficient thickness, may be strengthened by the mechanical method of studding (Figure 3). Steel studs 1/4" to 3/8" in diameter should be used. The cast iron should be veed, and drilled and tapped along the vee so that the studs may be screwed into the casting. The studs should be long enough to be screwed into the casting to a depth of at least the diameter of the studs, and project 3/16" to 1/4" above the surface. If the casting is of sufficient thickness, it may be veed and studded from both sides.

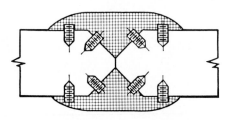

Figure 3.

The cross-sectional area of the studs should be about 25% to 35% of the area of the weld surface. In such cases, the strength of the weld may be safely and conservatively taken as the strength of the studs. It is considered good practice to first weld one or two beads around each stud, making sure that fusion is obtained both with the stud and the base metal. Straight lines of weld deposit should be avoided insofar as possible. Welds should be deposited intermittently, and each bead peened before cooling.

In all cast-iron welding, use the lowest possible current that gives adequate fusion with the base metal. This will keep the carbon pickup to a minimum.

The choice of electrode for welding cast iron is mainly dependent upon cost and machinability. Both steel and nickel electrodes do an excellent job and one is about as easy to use as the other. Nickel electrode (Softweld, Lesson 6.1) is considerably more expensive than the mild-steel electrode (Ferroweld, Lesson 6.1). The nickel electrode is used primarily where a soft, machinable deposit is necessary. If there is no need to drill, tap, or machine a weld, the steel electrode should be used. The weld should be ground to shape, since it is not easily worked with cutting bits. If extensive buildup is necessary, as when filling the groove in a heavy casting, and the top must be machined to shape, the steel electrode may be used for filling. The last two or three layers are then run with the nickel electrode, so a readily machinable surface will be obtained. Either electrode is usable in both the "hot" and "cold" methods of welding.

When welding using the preheating method, very few difficulties are encountered. This is by far the best method, providing adequate means of preheating and slow cooling are available. The welding job can be done as rapidly as desired without taking any particular precautions. It is important that the entire casting be kept at a minimum of 500 degrees (bright metal will turn purple) during the welding operation. Higher temperatures up to cherry red are even better.

If a furnace is not available, it is sometimes possible to make one for small objects. This furnace can be made from firebrick or asbestos sheets. Preheat may be furnished with an arc torch, gas torch, or blow torch. When cooling under these conditions, the entire part should be insulated immediately. This can be done by burying in sand, lime, or some other insulating substance.

If it is impossible to preheat the part uniformly, no attempt should be made to preheat a small section. In this case, welding must be done in such a manner as to keep the part cool at all times. It should be kept cool enough that the bare hand may be put on the weld area immediately after welding. The method of welding in this case is to make short, intermittent beads with a waiting time between. This may seem slow, but don't try to rush it, as that may cause uneven expansion and contraction with resultant cracks. The beads should be 1/2" to 1" long. A back-step technique should be used so that each crater lies on top of the previous bead.

The top of the previous bead has a low-carbon content, so there is little carbon pickup in the crater and thus little tendency to crack. Immediately after each short bead is made, the bead should be peened. Peening, while the bead is cooling, will relieve stress and avoid building up an accumulation of internal stresses in the part as more beads are applied.

It must be remembered that any amount of heat, if uniform, is helpful when welding cast iron. Room temperature is better than freezing, and 200 degrees is better than 100 degrees.

If it is necessary to have the casting liquid-tight after welding, another precaution may be observed. Apply stick sulphur, which may be obtained at any drug store, to the welded joint while it is still warm. The sulphur will melt and seal any cracks or pin holes. Do not apply sulphur until all welding has been completed. Severe porosity will result from welding over sulphur.

Review Questions

1. What happens when cast iron is heated and cooled rapidly?

2. Does cast iron have high compression strength?

3. Does cast iron have high tensile strength?

4. What are the two methods used to weld cast iron?

5. Why does the crater of a cast-iron bead crack after the weld is run?

6. What can be done to avoid cracking through the crater?

7. What is the best method of welding cast iron?

8. When is back-step welding used when welding cast iron?

9. What does peening do the beads?

10. To what temperature must cast iron be preheated for welding?

11. Are vee joints used on cast iron?

12. What does studding do to a cast-iron weld?

13. What amperages should be used for cast-iron welding?

Object:
To become acquainted with the high-strength alloy steels.

General Information

High-Strength Low-Alloy Structural Steels

Higher mechanical properties and, usually, better corrosion resistance than the structural carbon steels are characteristics of the high-strength low-alloy (HSLA) steels. These improved properties are achieved by additions of small amounts of alloying elements. Some of the HSLA types are carbon-manganese steels; others contain different alloy additions, governed by requirements for weldability, formability, toughness, or economy. Strength of these steels is between those of structural carbon steels and the high-strength quenched-and-tempered steels.

High-strength low-alloy steels are usually used in the as-rolled condition, although some are available that require heat treatment after fabrication. These steels are produced to specific mechanical-property requirements rather than to chemical compositions. Minimum mechanical properties available in the as-rolled condition vary among the grades and, within most grades, with thickness. Ranges of properties available in this group of steels are:

1. Minimum yield point from 42,000 to 70,000 psi.
2. Minimum tensile strength from 60,000 to 85,000 psi.
3. Resistance to corrosion, classed as: equal to that of carbon steels, twice that of carbon steels, of four to six times that of carbon steels.

The HSLA steels are available in most commercial wrought forms and are used extensively in products and structures that require higher strength-to-weight ratios than the carbon structural steels offer. Typical applications are supports and panels for truck bodies, railway cars, mobile homes, and other transportation equipment; components for tractors, threshers, fertilizer spreaders, and other agricultural machinery; materials-handling and storage equipment; and buildings, bridge decks, and similar structures.

The high-strength low-alloy steels should not be confused with the high-strength quenched-and-tempered alloy steels. Both groups are sold primarily on a trade-name basis, and they frequently share the same trade name, with different letters or numbers being used to identify each. The quenched-and-tempered steels are full-alloy steels that are heat-treated at the mill to develop optimum properties. They are generally martensitic in structure, whereas the HSLA steels are mainly ferritic steels; this is the clue to the metallurgical and fabricating differences between the two types. In the as-rolled condition, ferritic steels are composed of relatively soft, ductile constituents; martensitic steels have hard, brittle constituents that require heat treatment to produce their high-strength properties.

High-Yield-Strength Quenched-and-Tempered Alloy Steels

The high-yield-strength quenched-and-tempered construction steels are full-alloy steels that are treated at the steel mill to develop optimum properties. Unlike conventional alloy steels, these grades do not require additional heat treatment by the fabricator except, in some cases, for a stress relief.

These steels are generally low-carbon grades (upper carbon limit of about 0.20%) that have minimum yield strengths from 80,000 to 125,000 psi.

Some high-yield-strength grades are also available in abrasion-resistant modifications (AR steels), produced to a high hardness. Although these steels can have yield strengths to 173,000 psi, hardness (up to 400 Bhn) rather than strength is their key characteristic.

The high-yield-strength quenched-and-tempered alloy steels are used in such widely varying applications as hoist and crane components; end, side, and bottom plates for ore and waste-haulage cars, hopper cars, and gondolas; pressure hulls for submarines; and components for dust-collecting equipment. The AR (abrasion-resistant) modifications are used in applications requiring maximum resistance to abrasive materials—in chutes, hoppers, and dump-truck beds, for example. In such uses, strength properties are secondary and are not usually specified.

Good toughness can be combined with abrasion resistance in these steels, for use in buckets, cutter bars, scraper blades, and impact plates. However, the most abrasion-resistant grades sacrifice impact strength to gain maximum wear resistance.

In the ASTM specifications A514 and A517, there are several grades of quenched-and-tempered constructional steels listed. Welding procedures for all of these steels are similar but no one procedure is right for all grades. Welding procedures are available from the steel manufacturers. When in doubt, consult the steel manufacturer. Low-hydrogen electrodes are used—for example, E11018 for A514 and A517 steels.

Review Questions

1. Since HSLA steels are mainly ferritic, what does this imply?

2. What are the main reasons to use a HSLA steel?

3. Since high-yield-strength quenched-and-tempered steels are mainly martensitic, what does this imply?

4. What is an AR steel?

5. What type of electrodes are frequently used on HSLA or high-yield-strength quenched-and-tempered steels?

Object:
To study low-hydrogen electrodes.

General Information

The average weldor owes a great deal to the men who work behind the scenes of any company producing welding materials. It is these research men, metallurgists, chemists, and engineers, who have made the process of arc welding much easier and more dependable for the weldor in the field. Each new machine, electrode, and covering has been developed, tested, and retested as a result of the combined research of these men. They have tried to anticipate many problems encountered by the weldor, and have solved them before they became problems in the field. On the other hand, the weldor can help, and has, by reporting his special problems. In either case, when each problem is solved, another step has been taken in the progress of arc welding.

It was through research and development that the low-hydrogen electrode came into being.

Certain steels of the medium and high-carbon, high-sulphur, and low-alloy groups are crack-sensitive. They can be welded by special methods, using preheating, postheating, or changing welding speed or technique. In most cases, however, the maximum rate of deposition is seriously reduced. Metallurgists found that these steels, while they are in the molten and semi-molten state are affected by the presence of hydrogen. This is contrary to the theory of welding mild steel, as hydrogen is one of the shielding agents for mild steel. In other words, these crack-sensitive metals are allergic to hydrogen. Its presence causes a chemical change resulting in areas of embrittlement that cause stresses and cracks in the weld. Sometimes the crack shows up at the edges of the bead. Other times the crack occurs in the fusion zone under the bead, and is termed as an "underbead crack".

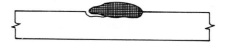

Figure 1. Underbead Cracking.

Through experimentation it was found that a certain type of austenitic electrode would eliminate this trouble. The flux used on this electrode, carbonate of soda and lime, was tried on high-tensile and mild-steel electrodes. The results were the same, except cracking was eliminated or reduced. So was produced the low-hydrogen electrode, as it was called, because the flux is very low in hydrogen content. The electrode, classified as E6015, became very popular for DC welding. The E6016 electrode soon followed as a similar type for use on AC or DC welders. Further design improvements developed the E7018 electrode, a modified E6016 containing powdered iron in its coating.

Applications for low-hydrogen electrodes include:

- X-ray quality welds or welds requiring high mechanical properties.

- Crack-resistant welds in medium-carbon to high-carbon steels; welds that resist hot-short cracking in phosphorus steels; and welds that minimize porosity in sulfur-bearing steels.

- Welds in thick sections or in restrained joints in mild and alloy steels where shrinkage stresses might promote weld carcking.

- Welds in alloy steel requiring a strength of 70,000 psi or more.

- Multiple-pass, vertical, and overhead welds in mild steel.

Electrode Characteristics

E7018: This electrode has fill-freeze characteristics and is suitable for all-position operation. Iron powder in the electrode covering promotes rapid deposition. Moderately heavy slag is easy to remove. (Weld metal freezes rapidly even though slag remains somewhat fluid.) Beads are flat or slightly convex and have distinct ripples, with little spatter.

E7028: The electrode has fast-fill characteristics applicable to high-production welds where low-hydrogen quality is required. It performs best on flat fillets and deep-groove joints, but is also suitable for horizontal fillet and lap welds. Excellent restriking qualities permit efficient skip and tack welding.

The covering on low-hydrogen electrodes is slightly thicker than for the same diameter on other types of electrodes. A short arc must be maintained at all times, making the electrode slightly harder to use. The deposited bead lies flat or slightly convex and is easy to clean. In the as-welded condition, mechanical and impact properties are slightly superior to the E6010 and E6011 electrodes.

Some state highway department codes are specifying low-hydrogen electrode for use on bridges and other structures, due to the possibility of obtaining varying sulphur content in construction steels.

With the importance of low hydrogen in the coatings understood, it is easy to see that the coatings should absorb no moisture (H_2O), as this would allow hydrogen in the coating. Open electrode containers should be kept in a low-temperature oven. Damp electrodes must be thoroughly dried before using.

Review Questions

1. Who develops and tests electrode and equipment before they come out on the market?

2. What can the average weldor do to help welding progress?

3. What is one of the primary causes for cracking in certain crack-sensitive steels?

4. What has proven to be the best way of eliminating cracks?

5. Does hydrogen cause mild steel to crack?

6. What is an "underbead crack"?

7. Why is the electrode called a "low-hydrogen" type?

8. Why are some welding codes specifying low-hydrogen electrodes on construction work?

9. What care must be taken when storing low-hydrogen electrodes?

10. What are the advantages of the iron-powder low-hydrogen electrodes?

LESSON 1.39

Object:
To study the uses of the arc torch and carbon arc.

General Information

Most of your arc welding will be done with the shielded metal arc with which you have been practicing. Some jobs, however, are more easily done with the flame-type heat produced by the arc torch or carbon arc. Both of these methods were important in the early development of arc welding. Shielded metal-arc welding has now all but replaced the manual carbon-electrode arc welding methods.

The arc torch finds many uses in the shop and broadens the range of work possible with an AC transformer type welder (Figure 1). Metal bars, rods, and

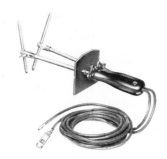

Figure 1.

straps may be heated and bent quickly and inexpensively with the localized flame-type heat of an arc torch. The arc torch will fusion-weld light steels, as well as aluminum, copper, and brass. Loosening rusted nuts and bolts, removing paint and scale, brazing and soldering, hard-surfacing, light forging, preheating, and heat treating may also be done with the heat of this torch.

The heat is produced by the arc between two carbon electrodes. The size of the electrodes, amperage setting, and length of arc govern the amount of heat produced. Three sizes of copper-coated, soft-center carbons are available for the torch, 1/4", 5/16", and 3/8". Table 1 shows the suggested amperage range and electrode size for various thicknesses of base metals. The carbons should be adjusted so that 2 to 3 inches extend below the clamps and the carbons should have a 1/16" gap in the closed position (Figure 2). The torch is easiest to use on

TABLE 1 – SUGGESTED AMPERE RANGE FOR CARBON-ARC CARBONS USED WITH AC WELDERS

Carbon Diameter	Amperage Range	Size Gauge	Approx. Thickness
1/4"	30 – 60	28 – 24	1/64 to 1/40"
5/16"	70 – 80	22 – 20	1/32 to 1/20"
3/8"	90 – 125	16 – 3	1/16 to 1/4"

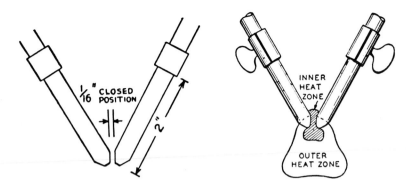

Figure 2.   Figure 3.

an AC transformer welder. It may, however, be used on a DC welder if the carbon on the positive pole is one size larger than the negative carbon. This reduces the burn-off tendency of the positive carbon.

Connect the torch cables to the welder by placing one of the leads from the torch in the electrode holder and the other in the work clamp while the welder is turned "OFF". The work is not grounded. Set the correct amperage on the welder, separate the carbons, turn the welder "ON", lower your shield, and start the arc. The arc is started by bringing the carbons nearly together. A good flame will result from the carbons if the gap is set about 3/16" (Figure 3). To keep from overheating the base metal, the flame may be moved about and the distance between the torch and the base metal varied. The flame is fan-shaped and has no force for penetrating grooves or cavities, but it has good heating qualities. The flame is extinguished by moving the carbons apart, until the voltage will no longer sustain the arc.

The single carbon arc generally utilizes a baked carbon electrode, or in some cases a graphite electrode. The electrode is gripped in the same holder used for metal electrodes, or in a special holder designed for use with carbon electrodes. It must be used with the DC welder on negative polarity. A heating-type flame is produced when it is touched and withdrawn from the grounded base metal. The flame is not as versatile as the arc torch and will extinguish when the electrode is

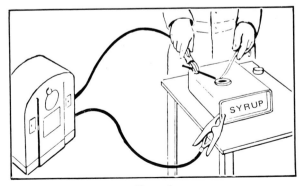

Figure 4.

Warning: Read page 1-9 before welding, cutting or soldering a tank.

moved too far from the base metal. It has the advantage that it can be pin-pointed and concentrated for work on small or thin material.

The carbon arc may be used for soft soldering with either the AC or DC welder, as shown in Figure 4. The amperage is set between 20 and 25 amps. The ground is clamped to the work and the carbon electrode is touched to the work and held there. The electrical resistance between carbon and base metal causes heat at that point and melts the solder. No arc should be drawn when soft soldering. The electrode should be removed from thin metal while it is still in the solder, so that an arc will not be formed and burn through the thin base metal. Use a flux to help the solder flow and adhere to the base metal. No shield need be worn during the soldering operation, but safety glasses are advisable.

When fusion welding with the arc torch and carbon arc, a flange-type joint may be set up (Lesson 1.27) and the weld made by fusing the flanges with the arc flame. Other welds will need the addition of filler rod.

Review Questions

1. What are some of the jobs that can be done with the arc torch?

2. How is the heat produced in an arc torch?

3. What type of carbons are used on the arc torch?

4. What type of welder should an arc torch be used with?

5. What must be done if the torch is used with a DC welder?

6. Is the work grounded when using the arc torch?

7. What gap is needed to produce a good arc flame?

8. Is the arc-torch flame a blowing-type flame?

9. What types of carbons are used in carbon-arc welding?

10. What is one advantage of the carbon-arc flame?

11. Must the work be grounded when welding with the single carbon arc?

12. What is a common use of the carbon arc around the repair shop?

Object:
To cut with the electric arc.

Equipment:
Lincoln "Idealarc" or DC or AC welder and accessories.

Material:
Scrap steel plate 1/4" to 3/4"; 1/4" carbon electrode and 3/16" "Fleetweld 5P" (E6010) for DC(+) or "Fleetweld 35" (E6011) for AC.

General Information

Cutting with the arc consists of melting and removing with the force of the arc a cut or kerf in the metal. Most types of metals can be cut with the arc, such as steel, cast iron, alloys, and nonferrous metals. Rivets or bolts may be removed and holes pierced with the cutting action of the electric arc.

Carbons may be the most economical electrode for certain jobs, but can be used only on DC machines. The shielded electrode may be used on either a DC or AC welder, but cuts more efficiently on DC current.

Avoid cutting in confined areas, as the higher amperages used when cutting cause fumes. *Warning:* Galvanized iron and the nonferrous metals give off toxic fumes that should not be breathed. Read page 1-9 for more information.

Warning: Arc cutting creates a considerable fire hazard, and all combustible materials should be removed or protected in the immediate area. Do not arc-cut used containers until they have been cleaned so thoroughly that there can be no flammable materials present. Read page 1-9 for more information. The weldor should wear the proper protective clothing, especially on the legs and feet where the danger of burns is greatest.

Job Instructions

Job A: Cut mild steel using the carbon arc.

1. Taper the carbon point on an abrasive wheel or belt to approximately half its diameter. The taper should be gradual about 5 to 7 times the diameter back from the point.

2. Grip the carbon close to the taper. If a long length of carbon is exposed, excessive heating due to resistance causes the carbon to vaporize and burn, resulting in waste.

3. Set the machine on negative polarity for a carbon electrode.

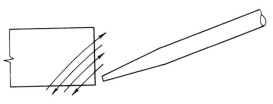

Figure 1.

4. Set amperage at 180 to 200 for 1/4" carbon electrode. Proper amperage depends upon the work to be done. The table (Figure 3) will serve as a guide. Amperages given are the maximum that should be used. Lower amperages may be used, depending upon the weight or thickness of the base metal.

5. Position the plate to be cut so that it projects over the edge of the work table.

6. Position a container beneath to catch the molten metal as it drops from the cut. See that the cables are clear of the hot metal.

7. Strike the arc at some point from which the molten metal may readily flow (Figure 1). Start at a lower corner, then go up the side to the top. Repeat this action as many times as necessary to cut through and across the plate. This allows the molten metal to flow out of the cut.

Job B: Cut and pierce mild steel with the shielded electrode.

1. Put a 3/16" shielded electrode in the electrode holder.

2. Set amperage at 300 to 350 amps for 3/16" electrode.

3. Position the plate so that it projects over the edge of the table, as in cutting with the carbon arc. Place a container underneath to catch the molten metal. See that cables are clear of hot metal.

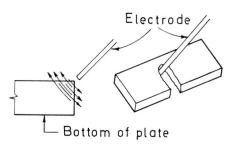

Figure 2.

**MAXIMUM CURRENTS
FOR HAND CARBON ARC**

Size of Carbon Electrode	Maximum Current
5/32"	50
3/16"	100
1/4"	200
5/16"	350
3/8"	450
1/2"	700

Figure 3.

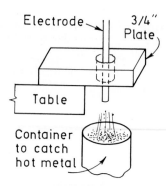

Figure 4.

4. Strike the arc at the edge of the plate. Hold a long arc until a large puddle is melted on the edge. Move the electrode downward to shorten the arc and force the molten metal from the plate. Move upward carrying a long arc and move downward with a shorter arc (Figure 2).

5. Clear the bottom of the plate with each pass to keep "icicles" from forming on the bottom edge of the cut.

6. A 3/16" electrode will put approximately a 1/2" hole through a 3/4" plate.

7. Strike an arc at the point where the hole is to be put. Hold a long arc until a large puddle is formed. Bring the electrode downward and force it through the plate until a hole is pierced. Withdraw the electrode (Figure 4).

Review Questions

1. What type of metal can be cut with the arc?

2. Can holes be pierced with the arc?

Object:
To weld copper with the carbon arc.

Equipment:
Lincoln "Idealarc" or DC welder and accessories.

Material:
Copper plates 1/8" x 3" x 5"; carbon electrode, copper filler rod, phosphor bronze ECuSn-A filler rod or equal.

General Information

The joint to be welded must be clean. If oxides exist they may be removed by using a warm 10% solution of sulphuric acid. Base metal thickness up to 1/4" need not be beveled for welding. Above 1/4" beveling is recommended, using the same edge preparation as for steel joints. Welding is facilitated when the joint is backed up with carbon or graphite blocks. If this is not practical, elevate the two sheets to be welded about 1/16" so that the bottom of the joint and the work table have a space between them. This permits the penetration of a small amount of excess metal on the underside of the root. When the weld is completed, the underside can be machined flush with the base metal.

The manual carbon arc produces the best results. A high capacity, high efficiency DC welder capable of delivering uniform welding current is recommended. This type of arc welder is necessary to maintain the required 40-volt arc. The carbon arc operates with the electrode negative and work positive.

Composition of the filler rod will vary according to the physical characteristics required of the welded structure. If the weld must have low electrical resistance, the filler metal may be pure copper. Where electrical or thermal conductivity are not essential, but where only ductility and physical strength are required, the filler metal may be of "Everdur", silicon copper, or a suitable grade of phosphor bronze.

Generally there should be a space of about 1/8" between the plate edges. The rod is melted into the plate and fed in by hand as the weld progresses. Best results are obtained at high speed.

Preheating is necessary when light currents are used, due to the high heat conductivity of copper. This can be done with the carbon electrode. Hold a long arc, 1 inch or more in length, and move it rapidly over the surface.

Cold-rolled copper may have a tensile strength of 55,000 psi. The strength of welded copper cannot be higher than about 30,000 psi, because the welding heat has annealed the weld deposit and the adjacent area. Further mechanical treatment is necessary to raise this strength.

A long arc should be held. This long arc distance between the carbon electrode and the work allows the carbon monoxide produced by the carbon arc to combine with oxygen in the atmosphere to form an oxide, instead of combining with the weld deposit.

The weld should be made all the way through in one pass. This is where the carbon or graphite blocks are helpful in preventing burnthrough, or excessive weld deposit on the reverse side.

The results will vary with the quality of copper, probably varying with the oxygen content. Best results will be obtained with deoxidized copper.

Steam or moisture-producing fluxes must be kept away from the arc because of the readiness with which molten copper absorbs hydrogen.

There are two characteristics that must be observed. First, welding at high speed produces the best results. Better welds are produced at 20" per minute on 1/4" plate using 600 amperes than will be obtained at 7" per minute using 200 amperes. Second, the voltage of the carbon arc must be high, that is, a long arc must be used to allow the carbon monoxide produced by the carbon arc to combine with the oxygen in the atmosphere instead of going into combination with the copper. Oxides in the weld deposit cause excessive porosity.

Job Instructions

1. Tack-weld two plates together in a square butt joint and position flat. Weld as outlined above.

2. Try the same job on heavier plates. Prepare a vee butt joint and weld by the same procedure.

Review Questions

1. What type of electrode is used to weld copper?

2. What type of edge preparation is used on copper over 1/4" thick?

3. What type of backup strips are used on copper joints?

4. What arc length is used?

5. What travel speed should be used?

6. What polarity is used?

7. How many passes should be used?

8. What type of copper is best for welding?

9. What type of rod should be used for maximum electrical efficiency?

10. What will oxides cause in the weld deposit?

LESSON
1.42

Object:
To study the principles of hardsurfacing with the electric arc.

General Information

Certain surfaces—points or edges on tools, machines, and equipment—wear away at a faster rate than the rest of the part. Hardsurfacing is the process of building up a layer of metal, usually harder or more durable than the base metal. The process has almost unlimited scope and possibilities ranging from building up a worn truck tire chain link to lining a carbon-steel tank with a corrosion-resistant deposit.

The success of a given hardsurfacing application depends largely on the proper choice of materials. Points to take into consideration when choosing a hardsurfacing material are outlined in the lesson.

1. Service Required

A. Cutting Edge to Be Maintained

On earth-cutting tools, such as plow shares, blades of rotary drilling bits, scrapers, ensilage knives, and shredder blades, the edge must stay sharp but the tool may wear back. These tools are intentionally surfaced with a layer of wear-resistant material on the leading edge. The backing metal wears away and exposes a sharp edge of hardsurfacing material for fast cutting. Hardsurfacing materials most resistant to abrasion are used for these applications. The "Facewelds" are used on tools when the abrasive conditions are severe. "Abrasoweld" is unsurpassed when the impact is high and a medium sharp edge is satisfactory.

B. Two Surfaces in Contact—Both to Be Protected

This group presents problems of metal-to-metal wear under various combinations of abrasion, impact, and corrosion. Machine parts that are operated with lubrication, inadequate lubrication, or at elevated temperatures are in this group. Hardsurfacing materials that will wear smooth, have low friction, and a minimum tendency to seize or gall are desirable.

Where wear is not complicated by the entrance of abrasive particles between the wearing surfaces, "Wearweld" is used. Overhead crane wheels are a typical application of this type.

If loads are not excessive and abrasive action is mild, such as on journals, "Aerisweld" may be used to deposit a bronze surface.

As abrasive or corrosive material becomes involved, it is necessary to go to different materials. "Stainweld", "Mangjet", "Jet LH-BU90", "Abrasoweld", and even "Faceweld" may be used, depending on the service conditions.

C. One Surface to Be Protected

This group covers cases where one of the two contacting materials or surfaces is protected while the wear of the other surface is of little or no importance. In some cases it is desirable to have a low-friction surface that will polish, such as a plow or scraper moldboard. In other cases a rough, high-friction surface is desirable.

Application:	Recommended Material:
Railends	"Wearweld"
Mine car wheels	"Jet LH-BU90"
Crusher jaws	"Mangjet" "Abrasoweld"
Sand pump impellers	"Abrasoweld"
Small bucket lips	"Abrasoweld"
Screw conveyers	"Faceweld 12"
Scarifier teeth	"Faceweld 1"
Water turbine blades	"Stainweld 308-15 or 308-16"

2. Service Conditions

The various service conditions to which a hardsurfacing deposit may be subjected are classified under several headings.

A. Abrasion—Grinding action due to rubbing, under low or high pressure, against a rough material such as rock, sand, or clay.

B. Friction—Sliding, rolling, or rubbing action of one metal part against another at low or high pressures.

C. Impact—Forcible contact with hard or heavy materials in various degrees from light to heavy. It tends to deform the surface, cause cracking or chipping.

D. Corrosion—The action of various chemicals, ordinary water (rusting), and oxidation or scaling at elevated temperatures.

E. Heat stability—The ability of a metal to resist warping or distortion at elevated temperatures or variations from low to high temperatures. Carbide and austenitic-type materials are high in this property.

Before the proper choice of hardsurfacing material can be made for a given application, the service conditions must be known. In most applications more than one of the above factors are at work. It becomes necessary to evaluate the relative importance of each.

3. Composition and Condition of Part to be Hardsurfaced

There are thousands of alloy compositions. It is obvious that only a few of these can be considered in this discussion. They can be divided into two general groups, regarding their suitability as a metal for hardsurfacing.

Group A includes those metals or alloys whose physical characteristics are not greatly changed as a result of heating and cooling, and which will withstand sudden localized temperature changes without cracking. This includes plain-carbon steel with a maximum of .30 percent of carbon (mild steel), low-carbon low-alloy steels, austenitic steels such as the stainless chrome-nickel, and the high-manganese steels. Copper and most of its alloys could also be included.

Group B includes those metals or alloys whose physical characteristics are changed considerably (particularly as to hardness) as a result of the application of heat and subsequent cooling, or which will crack with a sudden localized application of heat. This group includes medium to high-carbon steels, tool steels, medium to high-carbon low-alloy ferritic steels, cast irons (gray, white, malleable), and semi-steel. In general, most hard metals and alloys are in this group.

Special precautions must be taken when hardsurfacing metals in Group B. In general, if an arc is struck on a metal that is very hard, it will crack due to thermal shock. To avoid or minimize this thermal cracking, we must either reduce the hardness by annealing or reduce the thermal shock by gradual and uniform preheating. Both methods may be used, depending upon the nature of the alloy. Thermal cracking can thus be prevented in most steels. For gray cast iron that is already in its soft condition but is still brittle, and white cast iron that is hard and very brittle but cannot be annealed easily, there is little that can be done beyond moderate uniform preheating. This will decrease the tendency for thermal cracking. This does not necessarily mean that cast iron should never be hardsurfaced.

In general, preheating to 400 to 600 degrees F will prevent weld-hardening in medium to high-carbon steels. With medium-carbon alloy steels, preheating as above plus slow cooling in lime or sand is advisable. With high-carbon alloy steels such as tool steels and other special wear-resisting alloys, preheating followed by reheating after welding to a temperature in the 800 to 1300 degree range and uniform cooling may be necessary.

Controlled, uniformly slow cooling is always desirable for cast irons to prevent cracking. Their tendency to weld-harden is so great, however, that little can be done to overcome it. When cast iron is hardsurfaced, it is usually a case of building up a hard wear-resistant surface. The part is usually made of white cast iron. The success of this application depends largely upon the choice of hardsurfacing material. The most successful work is done with a deposit that tends to cross-crack upon cooling, such as "Faceweld 12". These cross-cracks tend to relieve the cooling strains and prevent the surface from peeling off in spite of the brittle base metal.

In most cases where the original chilled iron part was not too brittle for the service conditions involved, the hardsurfaced part will also stand up with the added advantage of being a superior abrasion-resistant surface. In most cases the cross-cracks will not be detrimental. If a strong, tough deposit such as "Abrasoweld" is applied to white cast iron, the shrinkage strains will be relieved by cracking under the deposit, with the result that the hardsurfacing will break away.

4. Dimensions

A. Size and Shape of the Part

The heat capacity of the part to be hardsurfaced is largely a function of its size and shape. A part of heavy cross section will heat up slowly during the hardsurfacing operation. It reaches a relatively low maximum temperature, and draws the heat away from the weld area very rapidly. A small part or a thin cross section will heat up rapidly (at least locally). It reaches a higher maximum temperature and draws the heat away from the weld area very slowly. The mass of the metal being surfaced, therefore, determines to some extent the thermal cycle to which it and the deposit are subjected. For this reason, if local welding heat is applied to a large mass of cold metal that is capable of being quench-hardened, the hardening will be drastic. Cracking is likely to occur due to a sharp rise and fall in temperature. If the mass is small the degree of hardening will be less because of its low heat capacity. Cooling will be more uniform throughout, resulting in less severe thermal stresses. If the hardsurfacing material applied in the above examples happens to be one of the types whose hardness is affected by the thermal cycle ("Jet LH-BU90", for example), the hardness of the deposit will be much greater in the case of the large mass because of its quench effect.

B. Size and Location of the Area Surfaced

This will determine the heat input and, therefore, the thermal cycle as above. Location or position of hardsurfacing will influence the choice of material to some extent. Very small areas require the use of small electrodes. Small electrodes are not available in all hardsurfacing material, and a second choice must sometimes be made. Hardsurfacing materials are not well adapted for use in vertical and overhead positions. The cost of doing a job will be much lower if the work can be positioned so that welding can be done in approximately a flat position.

C. Thickness of Weld Deposit

The best general rule in terms of service and economy is to avoid thick deposits of the hard alloys. If a large amount of buildup is necessary, it should be done with "Jetweld LH70" or "Jet LH-BU90". Thick deposits may also be applied with "Stainweld" or "Mangjet".

5. Finish Required

If the hardsurfacing deposit must be machined, the following can be used in the as-deposited condition: "Jetweld LH70", "Shield-Arc 85", "Aerisweld", and "Stainweld".

The following deposits are not machinable in their as-deposited condition. They may be machined, however, when softened by annealing: "Jet LH-BU90", "Wearweld", and "Abrasoweld".

Grinding must be used to shape "Faceweld" deposits.

6. Types of Hardsurfacing Electrodes

As a matter of convenience in this discussion, the Lincoln line of hardsurfacing materials can be divided into three groups, according to the type of deposit they produce. The mild-steel and high-tensile low-allow steel deposits will not be discussed, as their properties are well known. The specific electrodes, their properties, and application are discussed in later lessons.

Ferritic Type

"Jetweld LH-70"

Martensitic Type (listed in their order of increasing hardness)

"Jet LH-BU90", "Wearweld"

These are heat-treatable plain-carbon or alloy steels. Deposits of this group show practically their full hardness in the as-deposited state. They show a relatively small increase in hardness upon cold working. Annealing will reduce their hardness, and quenching from above their critical temperatures will harden them. For this reason, the deposit hardness may also vary somewhat because of variable thermal cycles caused by welding.

Austenitic Type

"Stainweld", "Mangjet", "Abrasoweld" (semi-austenitic)

Austenitic deposits differ from the martensitic principally in that they possess the property of surface-hardening when deformation takes place as in peening, cold working, or through the impact of normal work. The rest of the deposit remains relatively soft and tough.

LINCOLN HARDSURFACING GUIDE

Type of Wear	Hardsurfacing Materials	Impact-Resistance Rating (1 is low — 12 is high .30C Steel is 10)	Abrasion-Resistance Rating (.30C Steel rating is 1)
METAL-TO-METAL FRICTION		Wear from steel parts rolling or sliding against each	
Typical Applications Crawler rollers, idlers, and drive sprockets; power shovel house tumblers; shafts; trunnions; cams; mine car and crane wheels; rail ends (Wearweld).	**Jet-LH BU-90** Low-hydrogen stick electrode	10	1.0 — 1.5
SEVERE IMPACT		Wear from severe pounding which tends to squash,	
Typical Applications Dipper teeth and lips; buckets; crawler track pads and drive sprockets; railroad frogs and crossovers; mill wobblers; dragline pins and links; crusher rolls and heads; dredge pump casings.	**Mangjet** Low-hydrogen stick electrode	12	6 — 7
ABRASION PLUS IMPACT		Wear from gritty material accompanied by heavy	
Typical Applications Bulldozer blades; pump housings; dredge cutter teeth; tractor grouser; conveyor buckets; crusher mantels; shovel tracks; dipper teeth and lips.	**Abrasoweld** Stick electrode	77	8 — 10
SEVERE ABRASION		Wear from gritty materials like sand that grinds or	
Typical Applications Scarifier teeth; grader blades; pug mill paddles; wire-feed rolls; bucket lips; pulverizer jaws; screw conveyors; dredge pump casings.	**Faceweld 1 and Faceweld 12** Tube-type stick electrodes	Faceweld 1 — 4 Faceweld 12 — 3	60 — 70 80 — 100

LINCOLN HARD SURFACING GUIDE (continued)

Special Deposit Characteristics (Deposit thickness, machinability, and special properties)	Deposit Hardness Rockwell C			
other with little or no lubrication.				

a. Recommended for buildup of mild and low-alloy steel parts. b. Deposit thickness unlimited. Use low-alloy procedures. c. Lowest deposits costs of all these hard-surfacing materials. d. Machinability-forgeability. As-welded deposits can be machined with carbide tools if low-alloy procedures and slow cooling rates are used. Harder deposits are finished by grinding or can be annealed, machined, and heat-treated. Deposits are hot-forgeable.	Deposits are partly ferritic and partly martensitic. The harder deposits have higher abrasion resistance.			

On 1/2" Mild Steel As-Welded	Single Layer	Double Layer	Multiple Layer
Jet-LH BU-90	15 — 20	18 — 23	23 — 28

gouge and crack the surface.	

a. The Manganese steel deposits provide best resistance to impact wear. b. Recommended for buildup of manganese steel parts. c. Deposit thickness unlimited. d. Used for joining manganese steel to manganese steel or to carbon steel. e. Machinability-forgeability. Usually used without finishing. Although machining the tough deposits is not recommended, it can be done with rigid equipment and carbide tools. Not hot-forgeable.	The austenitic deposits work-harden when pounded in service to develop maximum hardness and abrasion resistance. Therefore, as-welded hardness is not a measure of abrasion resistance.

Multilayer and on Manganese Steel	Mangjet
As-Welded Work-Hardened	17 — 20 43 — 48

pounding that tends to chip or crack as well as grind away the surface.	

a. Often deposited over buildup layers of "metal-to-metal" or "severe impact" materials. b. Deposit thickness usually limited to 2 layers (5/16" total). c. Machinability-forgeability. Usually used without finishing. If required, finish by grinding or anneal, machine with carbide tools, and heat-treat. Deposits can be hot-forged.	The semi-austenitic deposits work-harden when pounded in service. Hardness of the as-welded deposit is not a measure of abrasion resistance.

On Mild Steel, As-Welded	Abrasoweld
Single Layer Double Layer	24 — 53 28 — 53

erodes the surface. Often accompanied by heavy compression or medium impact.	

a. Often deposited over buildup layers of "metal-to-metal" or "severe impact" materials. b. Good corrosion resistance. c. Good high-temperature (up to 1000°F) abrasion resistance. d. Deposit thickness usually limited to 2 layers (5/16" total). e. Machinability-forgeability. Usually used without finishing. If required, finish by grinding. Not machinable or forgeable.	The deposit consists of hard chromium-carbide crystals in a tough matrix. The harder deposits have better abrasion resistance.

On Mild Steel, As-Welded	Faceweld 1	Faceweld 12
Single Layer	40 — 52	45 — 55
Multilayer	50 — 58	55 — 64
Multilayer @ 1000°F	Ave. 38	Ave. 49
Multilayer @ 1500°F	Ave. 30	Ave. 38

Carbide Type

"Faceweld 1", "Faceweld 12"

These are primarily abrasion-resisting materials, high in carbides of such metals as tungsten, chromium, vanadium, and molybdenum. They are inherently hard and respond little or not at all to heat treatment.

7. Hardsurfacing Guide

The "Lincoln Hardsurfacing Guide" is presented on pages 1-114 and 1-115. This chart is intended to give a comparison between types of hardsurfacing materials, to help the user choose the material best suited to his particular job.

The chart lists the relative characteristics of the complete line of manual hardsurfacing materials. It shows the ability of each of the materials to resist various service conditions. It also gives the relative hardness and ductility of the material as well as the physical limitations of weld size in applying each. This may serve as a guide to help select the hardsurfacing electrode best suited for a job not previously hardsurfaced, as well as to select a more suitable hardsurfacing electrode for a job where present materials have not produced the desired results.

Where failures occur due to cracking or spalling, it usually indicates that a material higher in impact or ductility rating should be used; where normal wear alone seems too rapid, a material higher in the abrasion rating is indicated.

Many times hardsurfacing failures due to cracking or spalling may be caused by improper welding procedures rather than improper choice of hardsurfacing material. Before changing to a different hardsurfacing material, serious consideration should be given to the question of whether or not the material has been properly applied. For almost any hardsurfacing application, good results can be obtained if the following precautions are observed:

1. Do not apply hardsurfacing material over cracks or porous areas. Remove any defective areas down to sound base metal.
2. Preheat. Preheating to 400 to 600 degrees F improves the resistance to cracking and spalling. This minimum temperature should be maintained until welding is completed. The exception to this rule is 11-14% manganese steel, which should be kept cool.
3. Cool slowly. If possible, allow the finished part with its hardsurfacing to cool under an insulating material such as lime or sand.
4. Do not apply more than the recommended number of layers. When more than normal buildup is required, apply intermediate layers of "Stainweld". This will provide a good bond to the base metal and will eliminate excessively thick layers of hardsurfacing material that might spall off.

LESSON
1.43

Object:
To study the importance and fundamentals of pipe welding.

General Information

Piping of all shapes and sizes is used in a variety of applications. Probably most publicized are the gas and oil transmission pipelines, although these are only examples of many equally important applications. Refineries, power plants, and chemical plants use miles of pipe each year. Pipe is also used for water lines, industrial heating and ventilating, and structural jobs. Pipes carry liquids, gases, and even solids mixed with liquids. The use of pipe is growing each year.

Welding has greatly aided the growth of pipe usage. It gives a smooth, pressure-tight joint, which essentially joins any number of separate sections of pipe into one continuous piece. Welding is economical because it is fast and also because it makes a high-quality joint that permits lighter pipe to be used. Welded joints are easier to handle and insulate and require less maintenance than other methods of joining pipe.

Because of the widespread use of pipe, it is important that every welding operator at least be familiar with pipe welding. Sometime in his welding career, he will be required to weld some type of pipe. Pipe welding is usually divided into two categories: the first is transmission-line pipe welding; the second is industrial pipe welding and includes all other types of pipe welding. Regardless of the type of pipe welding involved, it is *all* difficult by comparison to other types of welding. Pipe welding requires a maximum of physical dexterity and ability, as well as a lot of patience. Most pipe welding is code work; that is, work that requires the operators and procedures to be tested and proven satisfactory before starting on the job. They are also periodically retested. Pipe weldors can expect to be required to periodically pass an operator qualification test, regardless of how long they have been welding. As long as they are welding pipe, they can also expect continual inspection of their work, either by X-ray or other means. This is because great damage to people and property could result from a weld failure.

The way in which pipe is welded is a big factor in determining the degree of difficulty to produce a quality weld. For this reason, operator tests are given in different positions to reflect the different levels of skill which are required. Figure 1 shows the positions for welding pipe as established by the American Welding Society. Notice that qualification in the 6G position qualifies for welding in all positions, however, it would be necessary to take several such tests to qualify for a wide range of pipe diameters and wall thicknesses. On cross-country pipelines it is common to require testing on the specific pipe which will be used for that job.

Transmission-Line Pipe Welding

Transmission-line pipe welding dates from the early 1920's and has since made tremendous progress. Welded joints have progressed from the old bell-and-spigot joint, through vee butts with a backup, to the present vee butt without backup. This progression has improved both welding speed and quality. Improvements both in electrodes and operator skill have made these advances possible.

Welding procedures are based on codes that are generally accepted by the industry. The codes specify the requirements of the completed weld and make certain specific procedural recommendations. Based on these codes, pipeline owners and contractors establish procedures that are used on the lines. Operators take qualification tests using these procedures and *must* pass them before they are permitted to

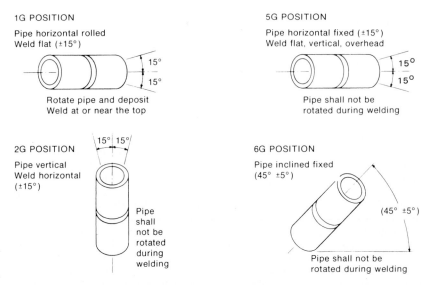

1G POSITION

Pipe horizontal rolled
Weld flat (±15°)

15°
15°

Rotate pipe and deposit
Weld at or near the top

5G POSITION

Pipe horizontal fixed (±15°)
Weld flat, vertical, overhead

15°
15°

Pipe shall not be
rotated during welding

2G POSITION

Pipe vertical
Weld horizontal
(±15°)

15° 15°

Pipe
shall
not be
rotated
during
welding

6G POSITION

Pipe inclined fixed
(45° ±5°)

(45° ±5°)

Pipe shall not be
rotated during welding

The limits of qualification in a given position are shown below:
1. Qualification in the 1G position qualifies only for this position.
2. Qualification in the 2G position qualifies for welding in the 1G and 2G positions only.
3. Qualification in the 5G position qualifies for welding in the 1G and 5G positions only.
4. Qualification in both the 2G and 5G positions qualifies for welding in all positions.
5. Qualification in the 6G position qualifies for welding in all positions, because it includes elements of those positions.
6. Qualification in a position other than the four standard positions described above is valid only for that position (plus or minus 15 degrees).

Figure 1. Test positions used in qualifying procedures for welding pipe and tubing under AWS D10.9.

weld on the job. There are no exceptions to this rule. The extent of detail involved in the procedures may vary from one concern to another, but generally are quite specific, even including the current range to be used for each pass. Once the operator has qualified with a particular procedure, he is expected to continue using it on the job. Inspectors are on most jobs to insure that this is done.

Most transmission-line pipe welding is welded vertical-down, because it is fastest on pipe thickness of less than 1/2″. The joint is a vee butt, approximately 70 degrees, with 1/16″ face and 1/16″ root opening. The first pass is the "stringer" bead and is usually put in with a drag technique. The second pass is called the "hot" pass. Succeeding passes are called "filler" passes, except for the last, which is the "cover" pass.

Figure 2 is an illustration of a typical welding spread on a transmission-line pipe job. This arrangement is called "stovepipe" welding. In this method, all joints are welded to the pipeline one section at a time. Each joint is position-welded. Using this method, it is possible to reduce the size of the crew and the amount of equipment and, thus, keep the operations bunched together under one supervisor. During alignment and tacking, the joint is usually held in place by a line-up clamp "grasshopper". With internal line-up clamps tacking is seldom, if ever, needed. External clamps required tack welds. After tacking, two weldors work simultaneously on both sides of the joint making the complete first, or stringer, bead. A hot-pass crew then moves in to make the second weld. The welds are finished by the filler and cover-pass crews.

The pipe used for cross-country work is usually designated 5L for line pipe or 5LX

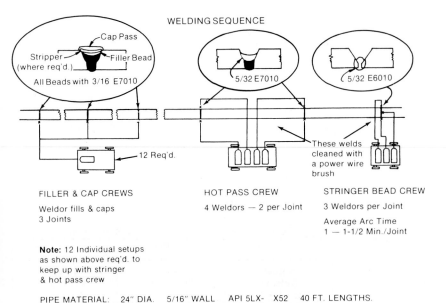

Figure 2. Typical transmission-line pipe-welding crew.

for high test line pipe. The two numbers following the "X" are the first two digits of the minimum yield strength. For example: X60 has a minimum yield strength of 60,000 psi. The table in figure three describes the common API 5LX series of line pipe.

Grade	Yield Min., psi	Tensile Min., psi
X42	42,000	60,000
X46	46,000	63,000
X52	52,000	66,000
X56	56,000	71,000†
X60	60,000	75,000†
X65	65,000	77,000†
X70	70,000	

† Pipe 20" OD and larger with wall thickness 0.375" and less requirement is 3 — 4,000 psi higher.

Figure 3. API 5LX series of line pipe.

For more details refer to API-1104-Standard for Welding Pipe Lines and Related Facilities. Copies can be purchased from: American Petroleum Institute, 2101 L Street N.W., Washington D.C. 20037.

Industrial Pipe Welding

Industrial pipe welding is even tougher than transmission-line work. Like transmission-line weldors, most industrial pipe weldors work under codes and must be qualified and tested regularly. However, because of the greater risk of damage involved, the codes are stricter, and tests are more rigid. In addition to this, a greater variety of alloy steels may be encountered, and both vertical and horizontal pipe joints must be welded. The final complication, common to the industrial pipe weldor, is having to work in cramped quarters and even using mirrors to see what he is welding.

Contrary to the vertical-down welding of the transmission-line pipe joints, most industrial pipe is welded vertical-up. This calls for an increase in the gap to 1/8" to permit full penetration. Otherwise the joint is prepared the same. Welding vertical-up requires smaller electrodes and lower currents. Welding speeds are slower. Industrial pipe weldors do an entire joint, instead of splitting into teams as is done on the field work. Industrial pipe weldors encounter a considerable amount of shop work. When it is possible, they use a roll-welding technique that permits welding the entire joint in the downhand position.

Industrial pipe is usually referred to in terms of a schedule and a nominal diameter. The most common schedules are Schedule 40 (Standard Weight), Schedule 80 (Extra Strong) and Schedule 120 which has an even heavier wall. These pipes are normally arc welded with a nominal diameter of 3" or more. Tables I, II and III describe the differences between these commonly used grades of pipe.

TABLE I — DIMENSIONS OF SCHEDULE 40 (Standard Weight)

Steel and Wrought Iron Pipe			
Nominal Diameter, Inches	Actual Outside Diameter (In.)	Wall Thickness, Inches	Weight Per foot, Pounds
3	3.500	.216	7.58
3½	4.000	.226	9.11
4	4.500	.237	10.80
5	5.563	.258	14.70
6	6.625	.280	19.00
8	8.625	.322	28.60
10	10.750	.365	40.50
12	12.750	.406	53.60
14	14.000	.437	63.30
16	16.000	.500	82.80
18	18.000	.562	105.00
20	20.000	.593	123.00
24	24.000	.687	171.00

TABLE II — DIMENSIONS OF SCHEDULE 80 (Extra Strong)

Steel and Wrought Iron Pipe			
Nominal Diameter, Inches	Actual Outside Diameter (In.)	Wall Thickness, Inches	Weight Per foot, Pounds
3	3.500	.300	10.252
3½	4.000	.318	12.505
4	4.500	.337	14.983
5	5.563	.375	20.778
6	6.625	.432	28.573
8	8.625	.500	43.388
10	10.750	.593	64.400
12	12.750	.687	88.600
14	14.000	.750	107.00
16	16.000	.843	137.00
18	18.000	.937	171.00
20	20.000	1.031	209.00
24	24.000	1.218	297.00

TABLE III — DIMENSIONS OF SCHEDULE 120

Steel and Wrought Iron Pipe			
Nominal Diameter, Inches	Actual Outside Diameter (In.)	Wall Thickness, Inches	Weight Per foot, Pounds
4	4.500	.437	19.0
5	5.563	.500	27.1
6	6.625	.562	36.4
8	8.625	.718	60.7
10	10.750	.843	89.2
12	12.750	1.000	126.0
14	14.00	1.062	147.0
16	16.00	1.218	193.0
18	18.00	1.343	239.0
20	20.00	1.500	297.0
24	24.00	1.750	416.0

TABLE IV — WEIGHT OF PIPE WELD METAL

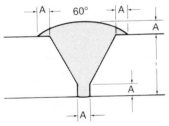

A = 1/16 in. (1.6mm)

These values represent weight of weld metal required in pounds per joint. They do not include stub loss or deposition efficiency of the process.

Nominal 4″ 4.50″ OD				Nominal 5″ 5.5625″ OD				Nominal 6″ 6.625″ OD		
Wall Thickness (in)	Sch.	Weld Metal Weight (lb)		Wall Thickness (in)	Sch.	Weld Metal Weight (lb)		Wall Thickness (in)	Sch.	Weld Metal Weight (lb)
0.156		0.11		0.156		0.13		0.156		0.16
0.172		0.12		0.188		0.17		0.172		0.18
0.188		0.14		0.219		0.21		0.188		0.20
0.203		0.15		0.258	40	0.27		0.203		0.22
0.219		0.17		0.281		0.30		0.219		0.25
0.237	40	0.19		0.312		0.36		0.250		0.30
0.250		0.20		0.344		0.42		0.280	40	0.36
0.281		0.24		0.375	80	0.48		0.312		0.43
0.312		0.29		0.500	120	0.79		0.344		0.50
0.337	80	0.33		0.625	160	1.17		0.375		0.58
0.438	100	0.50		0.750		1.61		0.432	80	0.74
0.531	160	0.70		0.875		2.12		0.500		0.95
0.674		1.06		0.938		2.40		0.562	120	1.17
								0.625		1.41
								0.719	160	1.81
								0.864		2.52
								1.000		3.28
								1.125		4.05

Nominal 8" 8.625" OD		
Wall Thickness (in)	Sch.	Weld Metal Weight (lb)
0.188		0.26
0.203		0.29
0.219		0.33
0.250	20	0.40
0.277	30	0.47
0.312		0.56
0.322	40	0.59
0.344		0.66
0.375		0.76
0.406	60	0.87
0.438		1.00
0.500	80	1.25
0.562		1.54
0.594	100	1.70
0.625		1.87
0.719	120	2.40
0.812	140	3.00
0.875		3.44
0.906	160	3.66
1.000		4.38
1.125		5.44
1.250		6.59

Nominal 10" 10.75" OD		
Wall Thickness (in)	Sch.	Weld Metal Weight (lb)
0.188		0.33
0.203		0.37
0.219		0.41
0.250	20	0.50
0.279		0.59
0.307	30	0.69
0.344		0.83
0.365	40	0.91
0.438		1.25
0.500	60	1.58
0.562		1.94
0.594	80	2.15
0.625		2.35
0.719	100	3.03
0.812		3.79
0.844	120	4.07
1.000	140	5.56
1.125	160	6.91
1.438		10.88

Nominal 12" 12.75" OD		
Wall Thickness (in)	Sch.	Weld Metal Weight (lb)
0.188		0.39
0.203		0.43
0.219		0.48
0.250	20	0.59
0.281		0.71
0.312		0.84
0.330	30	0.92
0.344		0.99
0.375		1.14
0.406	40	1.31
0.438		1.49
0.500		1.88
0.562	60	2.32
0.625		2.81
0.688	80	3.34
0.750		3.92
0.844	100	4.87
1.000	120	6.67
1.125	140	8.30
1.312	160	11.06
1.500		14.19
1.594		15.89
1.625		16.47

Nominal 14" 14" OD		
Wall Thickness (in)	Sch.	Weld Metal Weight (lb)
0.188		0.43
0.203		0.48
0.210		0.50
0.219		0.53
0.250		0.65
0.281		0.78
0.312	20	0.92
0.344		1.08
0.375	30	1.25
0.406		1.44
0.438	40	1.64
0.459		1.78
0.500		2.07
0.562		2.55
0.594	60	2.82
0.625		3.09
0.688		3.69
0.750	80	4.32
0.812		5.00
0.938	100	6.53
1.094	120	8.70
1.250	140	11.17
1.406	160	13.91

Nominal 16" 16" OD		
Wall Thickness (in)	Sch.	Weld Metal Weight (lb)
0.188		0.49
0.203		0.55
0.219		0.61
0.250		0.74
0.281		0.89
0.312	20	1.06
0.344		1.24
0.375	30	1.44
0.406		1.65
0.438		1.88
0.469		2.12
0.500	40	2.37
0.562		2.93
0.625		3.55
0.656	60	3.88
0.688		4.23
0.750		4.96
0.812		5.74
0.844	80	6.17
1.031	100	8.97
1.219	120	12.28
1.438	140	16.75
1.594	160	20.32

Nominal 18" 18" OD		
Wall Thickness (in)	Sch.	Weld Metal Weight (lb)
0.219		0.69
0.250		0.84
0.281		1.01
0.312	20	1.19
0.344		1.40
0.375		1.62
0.406		1.86
0.438	30	2.12
0.469		2.39
0.500		2.68
0.562	40	3.30
0.625		4.01
0.688		4.78
0.750	60	5.60
0.812		6.49
0.938	80	8.49
1.156	100	12.58
1.375	120	17.44

Nominal 20″ 20″ OD		
Wall Thickness (in)	Sch.	Weld Metal Weight (lb)
0.219		0.76
0.250		0.93
0.281		1.12
0.312		1.32
0.344		1.56
0.375	20	1.80
0.406		2.07
0.438		2.36
0.469		2.66
0.500	30	2.98
0.562		3.68
0.594	40	4.07
0.625		4.46
0.688		5.32
0.750		6.24
0.812	60	7.23
1.031	80	11.32
1.281	100	17.04

Nominal 22″ 22″ OD		
Wall Thickness (in)	Sch.	Weld Metal Weight (lb)
0.375	20	1.98
0.406		2.28
0.438		2.60
0.469		2.93
0.500	30	3.28
0.562		4.05
0.625		4.92
0.688		5.87
0.750		6.88
0.812		7.98
0.875	60	9.18
1.125	80	14.73

Nominal 24″ 24″ OD		
Wall Thickness (in)	Sch.	Weld Metal Weight (lb)
0.250		1.12
0.281		1.34
0.312		1.59
0.344		1.87
0.375	20	2.17
0.406		2.48
0.438		2.84
0.469		3.20
0.500		3.59
0.562	30	4.43
0.625		5.37
0.688	40	6.41
0.750		7.52
0.812		8.72
0.875		10.03
0.938		11.43
0.969	60	12.16
1.219	80	18.76

Nominal 26″ 26″ OD		
Wall Thickness (in)	Sch.	Weld Metal Weight (lb)
0.250		1.21
0.281		1.46
0.312		1.73
0.344		2.03
0.375		2.35
0.406		2.69
0.438		3.08
0.469		3.47
0.500	20	3.89
0.562		4.80
0.625		5.83
0.656		6.37
0.688		6.96
0.750		8.17

Nominal 30″ 30″ OD		
Wall Thickness (in)	Sch.	Weld Metal Weight (lb)
0.250		1.40
0.281		1.68
0.312		1.99
0.344		2.34
0.375		2.71
0.406		3.11
0.438		3.56
0.469		4.01
0.500		4.50
0.562		5.55
0.625		6.74
0.656		7.37
0.688		8.05
0.750		9.45

Nominal 32″ 32″ OD		
Wall Thickness (in)	Sch.	Weld Metal Weight (lb)
0.250		1.49
0.281		1.80
0.312		2.13
0.344		2.50
0.375		2.90
0.406		3.32
0.438		3.79
0.469		4.28
0.500		4.80
0.562		5.93
0.625		7.20
0.656		7.87
0.688		8.60
0.750		10.09

Nominal 34" 34" OD		
Wall Thick-ness (in)	Sch.	Weld Metal Weight (lb)
0.250		1.59
0.281		1.91
0.312		2.26
0.344		2.66
0.375		3.08
0.406		3.53
0.438		4.03
0.469		4.55
0.500		5.10
0.562		6.30
0.625		7.66
0.656		8.37
0.688		9.14
0.750		10.73

Nominal 36" 36" OD		
Wall Thick-ness (in)	Sch.	Weld Metal Weight (lb)
0.250		1.68
0.281		2.02
0.312		2.39
0.344		2.82
0.375		3.26
0.406		3.74
0.438		4.27
0.469		4.82
0.500		5.41
0.562		6.68
0.625		8.11
0.656		8.87
0.688		9.69
0.750		11.37

Nominal 40" 40" OD		
Wall Thick-ness (in)	Sch.	Weld Metal Weight (lb)
0.312		2.66
0.344		3.13
0.375		3.63
0.406		4.16
0.438		4.75
0.469		5.36
0.500		6.01
0.562		7.43
0.625		.902
0.688		10.78
0.750		12.65

Review Questions

1. Name four types of applications that could be considered "industrial pipe welding".

2. What are two reasons why welded pipe joints are economical?

3. What are two categories of pipe welding?

4. Should every operator be familiar with pipe welding?

5. Is pipe welding difficult as compared with other types of welding?

6. Is most pipe welding code work?

7. Why is it important that no failures occur in welded pipe joints?

8. Do experienced operators have to take operator qualification tests?

9. On code work, are operators permitted to select their own procedures?

10. How are most transmission-line pipe joints welded?

11. What is the second pass on a transmission-line pipe joint called?

12. What is the root spacing dimension on transmission-line pipe joints?

13. What are some of the added difficulties involved in industrial pipe welding?

14. How are most industrial pipe joints welded?

15. What is the root spacing dimension on industrial pipe joints? Why?

16. Is much industrial pipe welding done in the shop?

Object:
To run beads by "roll welding"; to run vertical down drag beads (1G).

Equipment:
Lincoln "Idealarc" or other DC or AC welder and accessories.

Material:
Steel pipe 6 to 10 inches in diameter; 5/32" "Fleetweld 5P" (E6010) for DC(+) or "Fleetweld 35" (E6011) for AC.

General Information

Before actually attempting to weld a pipe joint, it is necessary to master certain skills not covered in previous lessons. The exercises in this lesson will introduce you to two of these special skills; welding on the top of a pipe as it rolls under the arc, and running beads vertical-down using the drag technique.

Flat or "roll welding" is the easiest method of pipe welding, when it can be used. The arc is struck on the top of the pipe and held there to deposit the bead as the pipe is steadily revolved under the electrode.

The usual method of welding pipe will be in the fixed position. Welding must be done in whatever position is necessary to reach the joint. When the pipe is in the horizontal position, the usual method for welding transmission pipelines is by vertical-down welding. Thick-walled, high-pressure pipe is welded vertically up.

The fundamental difference between plate welding and pipe welding is the greater amount of travel of the hand compared to the travel of the arc end of the electrode. It is important to maintain a constant electrode angle as the bead is run around the pipe.

The drag technique is used to lay the first pass in the vee of the vertically down welded pipe joint. This is called a stringer bead, as it is laid with no sidewise motion.

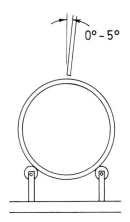

Figure 1. 1G Position – pipe rotates.

Job Instructions

Job A:

1. Clean scale and rust from pipe.

2. Lay pipe in horizontal position on dollies or rolls. Attach work clamp to pipe.

3. Set amperage at 130 to 145 for 5/32" electrode.

4. Hold the electrode perpendicular to the pipe or inclined slightly in the direction of travel (see Figure 1). The curved surface of the pipe makes it necessary to hold this steep angle. If the electrode is inclined too much the arc force will tend to blow the metal over the far side of the pipe.

5. Strike the arc. As the puddle is established and a bead is formed, roll the pipe ahead, so that the downhand position is maintained. Electrode travel is dependent upon a uniform rate of pipe movement.

6. Clean and examine the bead. It should be smooth and uniform, fusing into the pipe on the edges.

Job B:

1. Use the same or a similarly cleaned pipe.

2. Position pipe horizontal, from waist to chest high, where it can be reached on top and underneath.

3. Set the amperage by checking with the drag technique on a flat plate. Set the amperage high enough that the arc does not go out when the electrode is dragged along slowly on the surface of the plate inclined 50 to 60 degrees in the direction of travel.

4. Find the most comfortable position for steady welding to lessen fatigue. Right-handed weldors may rest their left arm on the pipe and steady the right hand at the wrist with the left hand in such a way that there is free wrist motion of the right hand. Left-handed weldors would position themselves in the opposite way.

5. Start at the top of the pipe using the nearly perpendicular electrode angle as in Job A.

6. Strike the arc and drag the electrode along steadily with a slight downward pressure, so that a uniform bead is formed.

7. Weld to the bottom of the pipe and repeat on the opposite side. The start and end of the pass should be chipped out before starting the next pass. The start and end of the two passes should fuse together.

8. Clean and examine beads for uniformity and proper penetration.

Review Questions

1. What is "roll welding"?
2. What electrode angle is used?
3. Why does the electrode angle differ from working on flat plate?
4. What constitutes electrode travel in this weld?
5. Will most pipe welding be done in the fixed position?
6. What is the fundamental difference between pipe welding and plate welding?
7. What pass is the drag technique used for?
8. Should the slag be removed from the crater before starting the next bead?

Object:
To make butt welds on pipe with the axis horizontal, welding down (5G).

Equipment:
Lincoln "Idealarc" or DC or AC welder and accessories.

Material:
Beveled steel pipe pieces 6 to 10 inches in diameter; "Fleetweld 5P" (E6010) 5/32" and 3/16" for DC(+) or "Fleetweld 35" (E6011) for AC.
(See Lesson 3.2 for properties and application of "Fleetweld 5P".)

General Information

The usual method of welding vertical joints on horizontal transmission piping is from the top down.

The pipe bevel specified by API-AGA is 30 (+5, −0) degrees with a 1/16" root face (Figure 1). In practice this results in an approximate 70-degree vee butt joint. It is extremely important that the root face be properly prepared. Thinner face will result in troublesome burn through, while heavier face may result in incomplete penetration.

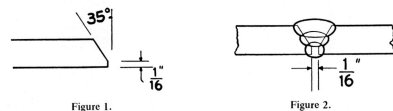

Figure 1.   Figure 2.

In some cases 5/32" electrode may be used for the first pass on .250" wall material although 1/8" is recommended, and much easier for beginners.

DC(+) is normally recommended; however, DC(−) (negative polarity) can be used for the stringer pass to minimize burn through and to reduce internal undercut. This polarity change is especially appropriate for thin wall pipe. Hot pass and subsequent passes should be run DC(+) (positive polarity).

Running DC(−) on the stringer pass will not be harmful to either mechanical or metallurgical properties.

Job Instructions

1. Check the bevel of the pipe. Insure that it is as shown in Figure 1. If necessary the root face may be ground to make it even all the way around.

2. Set amperage for drag pass (Lesson 1.44) with 5/32" electrode.

3. Tack-weld pipe together with 1/16" root spacing (Figure 2) using 4 tacks spaced 90 degrees apart. Use smooth well-fused tacks, so they will fuse in with the stringer bead.

4. Position the pipe about waist high, so it is accessible on top and underneath.

5. Assume a comfortable position for welding.

6. Use "Fleetweld 5P" for stringer bead ("Fleetweld 35" for AC). Strike arc at the top of the pipe and carry the stringer bead down to the bottom of the pipe using the drag technique. Drag welding is used only on the root pass.

7. Clean ends of first pass and run stringer bead on opposite side.

8. Clean and examine the entire bead. It should be fused well into each side of the vee with complete penetration through on the inside of the pipe.

9. The second pass may be put in with either 5/32" or 3/16" electrode. Make necessary amperage adjustment from the drag technique previously used.

10. Do not start or end passes at the same point as the pass underneath.

11. Use a slight weave (A or B, Figure 3), working the weld deposit into each side of the bevel to form a slightly concave bead. Convex beads in a vee are harder to clean, and there is more danger of having slag inclusions when the next pass is run.

12. Use 3/16" electrode for subsequent filler passes. It will be necessary to use a slightly wider weave as the weld is brought up in the vee. Clean each pass carefully.

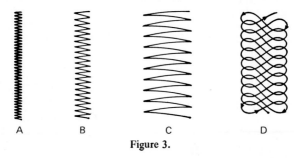

A   B   C   D

Figure 3.

13. Run cover pass with a 3/16" electrode using a wide weave or "figure 8" (Figure 3C or D).

14. This job may be practiced using "Fleetweld 5P" for the stringer bead, and filling with "Shield-Arc 85-P" or "Shield-Arc 70+" (Lesson 3.3). This electrode is used on high-test pipeline.

Review Questions

1. What is the standard bevel for pipe welding?

2. What is the thickness of the root face?

3. What root spacing is used on butt welds?

4. How many tacks are put on a pipe?

5. How many passes are welded with the drag technique?

6. Is a weave used when carrying filler passes?

7. What is the correct shape of a deposited filler bead?

8. Must each bead be chipped if subsequent passes are made immediately?

9. Should the ends of subsequent passes be put directly on top of each other?

10. How much penetration should be obtained on the stringer pass?

Object:
To weld joints in horizontal pipe vertical-up (5G).

Equipment:
Lincoln "Idealarc" or other DC or AC welder and accessories.

Material:
Beveled steel pipe 6 to 10 inches in diameter; 1/8" and 5/32" "Fleetweld 5P" (E6010) for DC(+) or "Fleetweld 35" (E6011) for AC.

General Information

On horizontal pipe used in industrial applications, the joints are welded vertical-up. As in vertical-down transmission-line pipe welding, the edge preparation and fitup of the joint are extremely important. A comparison of a joint tacked for vertical-down with one tacked for vertical-up would show that they are the same, except for the gap. A 3/32 to 1/8" gap is left for vertical-up welding to insure full penetration.

Vertical-up pipe welding is similar to vertical-up plate welding, but considerably more critical. Do not be discouraged if at first these welds seem to be impossible. The guidance of an experienced weldor and plenty of practice and patience are required to make a good pipe weldor.

For those who desire to pass operator qualification tests, the "Pipefitter Welder's Review of Metal-Arc Welding for Qualification Under A.S.M.E. Code Rules" is highly recommended. A 36-page pamphlet, it is available from the National Certified Pipe Welding Bureau, 5530 Wisconsin Avenue, Suite 750, Washington, D.C. 20015, at a nominal charge.

Job Instructions

1. Insure that pipe is properly beveled (Figure 1, Lesson 1.45).

2. Clean the bevel and a small area of pipe next to it.

3. Set welder to 80-100 amperes for 1/8" electrode.

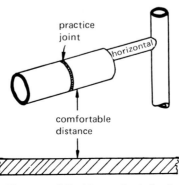

practice joint

horizontal

comfortable distance

Figure 1. 5G Position – pipe is fixed.

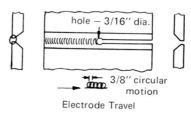

hole — 3/16" dia.

3/8" circular motion

Electrode Travel

Figure 2.

4. Tack-weld the pipe together with a 1/8" gap. Use the bare end of a 1/8" electrode as a spacer. Use four good tack welds equally spaced around the pipe.

5. Clamp or tack-weld the pipe at a convenient height and clear of all obstructions. (Figure 1.)

6. Using 1/8" "Fleetweld 5P", start to weld on the bottom of the pipe. The method of laying in the first pass is shown in Figure 2. A hole slightly larger than the electrode is burned through the joint. The arc is rotated around the hole, so as to burn off the edge in the direction of travel while depositing a bead on the other side. This procedure is continued until the bead is complete to the top of the pipe.

7. Clean the ends of the previous weld and make a similar weld on the other side. Thoroughly clean the entire first pass.

8. Reset the welding machine to 120-150 amperes.

9. Again, starting from the bottom of the pipe (but not at the same spot where the first pass was begun), put in a second pass with 5/32" "Fleetweld 5P" Use a slight side-to-side weave. Be certain to burn well into each side of previous bead to insure complete fusion with each side of the groove and the previous bead.

10. Run a similar bead on the other side. Clean the entire weld. Figure 3 shows the bead contour you should have.

11. Using a wider side-to-side or a Figure 8 weave with 5/32" electrode, put on a third and final pass. This pass should be very neat and should have a contour shown in Figure 4.

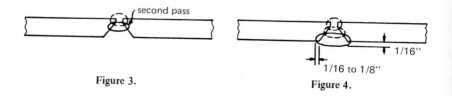

second pass

1/16"

1/16 to 1/8"

Figure 3.

Figure 4.

Review Questions

1. How is most horizontal pipe welded on industrial applications?

2. What is the difference in joint preparation for vertical-up pipe welding, as compared with vertical-down pipe welding?

3. What is the angle of the vee for vertical-up welded pipe?

4. Is it necessary to use backup in order to get full penetration?

5. What size electrode is used on the first pass? The second?

6. How many tack welds should be used? How are they located?

7. What is the gap for vertical-up welding?

8. How large a hole is burned in the pipe for proper welding on the first pass?

9. What electrode motion is used on the second pass?

10. What is the most important consideration in making the second pass?

LESSON
1.47

Object:
To make a horizontal butt weld on pipe with the axis vertical (2G).

Equipment:
Lincoln "Idealarc" or DC or AC welder and accessories.

Material:
Beveled steel pipe pieces 6 to 10 inches in diameter; 5/32" and 3/16" "Fleetweld 5P" (E6010) for DC(+) or "Fleetweld 35" (E6011) for AC.

General Information

Wherever there are pipe installations, there will be vertical pipe requiring horizontal welds for fabrication. The bevel will usually be of the standard type given in Lesson 1.45.

Persons interested in passing operator qualification tests are again referred to the "Pipefitter Welder's Review" (see Lesson 1.46).

Job Instructions

1. Clean rust and scale from bevel and adjacent area.

2. Either a drag technique or a short arc may be held when running the root pass. Set amperage according to the technique used.

3. Tack-weld pipe together with 1/16" root spacing using 4 equally spaced tacks (Figure 1).

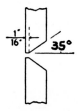   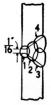

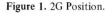

Figure 1. 2G Position.   **Figure 2.** 2G Position.

4. Secure pipe in vertical position with the joint accessible from all sides.

5. Strike the arc at any point on the joint and weld completely around, using either the drag or short-arc technique for root pass. Chip out the crater when restarting the bead with a new electrode.

6. Clean and examine root pass for fusion along the sides of the vee and for complete penetration.

7. Use 5/32" or 3/16" electrode for subsequent filler passes. Run straight passes in the sequence shown in Figure 2.

8. Clean each pass thoroughly before running the next. Do not start and stop beads at the same point as the previous pass. Examine each pass for fusion with the pipe as well as with the previous pass.

Review Questions

1. What type of welding technique is used for root passes?

2. What is root spacing on horizontal butt welds?

3. How many tacks are put on the pipe to hold it while welding?

4. Should craters be chipped out when starting a new electrode?

Object:
To make a weld on pipe with the axis 45° using vertical-up technique (6G).

Equipment:
Lincoln "Idealarc" or DC welder and accessories.

Material:
Beveled steel pipe 6 to 10 inches in diameter; 1/8" "Fleetweld 5P" (E6010) and 3/32" "Jet-LH 78" (E7018).

General Information

For passing tests for certification in pipe welding, the 6G position qualifies for all others. The use of an E6010 electrode for the root pass and low hydrogen E7018 electrodes for fill and cap passes are an excellent combination for strength, ductility, and deposition rates for producing high quality welds at a low cost.

Job Instructions

1. Clean rust and scale from beveled area and approx. 1/4" away from bevel on the inside and outside surface of the pipe.

2. Prepare the pipe with a 3/32" — 1/8" land and gap and tack together using 4 equally spaced tacks as in the two previous lessons.

3. Secure the pipe so it is tilted at a 45° angle (6G position). See Figure 1.

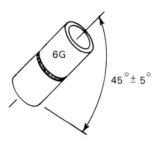

Figure 1. The 6G Position   pipe is fixed.

Making the Weld

Start at the bottom of the pipe (6 o'clock position) with 1/8" E6010 electrode at 75 — 85 amps and push the electrode at an angle of 10 — 15 degrees, see Figure 2. Continue until you are at the top of the pipe. Stop and examine the inside of the pipe. There should be a bead on the inside with a buildup 1/16" — 1/8". Go back to the bottom with a new electrode and repeat on the other half. Always try to eliminate starts and stops with the root pass whenever possible. Clean off all slag thoroughly with a wire brush and chipping hammer. The next pass will start at the bottom of the pipe (6

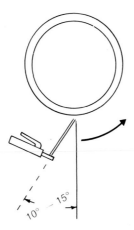

Figure 2. A 10 — 15° push angle.

o'clock position). This is called the "hot" pass. Use 3/32" Lincoln LH-78 (E7018) at 90 — 95 amps. Maintain a very short arc with a pushing angle of 10 — 15°. Travel slow enough to burn out "wagon tracks" and other possible defects from the first pass. The weld should be almost even with the outside diameter of the pipe, provided you are using schedule 40 pipe. Stop when you reach the top of the pipe (12 o'clock position). Clean the starting area of the weld and finish the hot pass on the other side in the same manner. The joint is now secure. The cap pass can be done at any time. Clean the slag thoroughly from the hot pass. Now, you are ready to start the cap pass. Using 3/32" LH-78 at 80 — 85 amps, start at the bottom of the pipe (6 o'clock) and pushing the electrode with a 10° — 15° angle; aiming the electrode at the bottom of the "hot pass", come up around the pipe until you have reached the top. DO NOT weave the electrode; keep it to the lower side of the pipe covering about 50 — 75% of the fill pass.

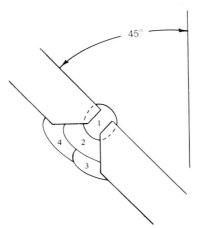

Figure 3. Location of weld passes for 6G welding.

Complete the 4th and final pass by capping the other half of the pipe; pointing the electrode at the top toe of the "hot pass". To make a sound weld, the passes must be made in this order. Passes are always started at the bottom of the pipe and stopped at the top per (ASME). The electrodes should never be weaved. Practice until you are able to make consistent and uniform welds.

If facilities permit you may want to have pipe "coupons" cut and a testing lab can perform the two root and two face bends which are required for certification. After passing you can start looking for a job in the pipe welding field. This just gets you started. To become a "pipeline weldor" takes tremendous skill and often several years of experience.

Review Questions

1. What is the advantage of taking pipe tests in the 6G position?

2. Why are low hydrogen electrodes used for the hot and cap passes?

3. What is the proper technique and angle for guiding the electrode?

4. What organization promotes the vertical-up technique for welding pipe in the 6G position?

5. What are the tests you should expect your samples to pass to become a certified pipe weldor?

SECTION II

ARC-WELDING MACHINES

LESSON

2.1

Object:
To study the Lincoln "Idealarc TM" AC/DC combination welder.

Equipment:
"Idealarc TM" welder and accessories.

Material:
Scrap steel plate; 3/16" "Fleetweld 35" or "Jetweld 1" electrode.

General Information

"Idealarc TM" welders are available in two models—one is a straight AC transformer welder and the other is a transformer-rectifier welder providing a choice of either AC or DC. Both have continuous mechanical current control, as contrasted to the continuous electrical (saturable reactor) control on "Idealarc TIG" welders. (See Lesson 2.8).

Figure 1. AC transformer welder.

Figure 2. Combination AC/DC welder.

The "Idealarc TM" welders have exceptionally fine arc characteristics and are recommended for all manual welding applications except where gas-shielded arc welding is used.

In addition to the choice of straight AC or combination AC/DC models, many optional features may be added to the "Idealarc TM" welders to increase their convenience and usefulness. Remote controls, a low-voltage contactor, and an arc booster are frequently used on these machines.

The remote current control is used on jobs where operators must change electrode sizes frequently and are working some distance from their machines.

The remote current control is a motor inside the case that turns the current control handle. The motor is operated from a toggle switch which the operator carries with him, usually taped to his electrode holder. To change the current, the weldor simply pushes the toggle switch in one direction to increase current or in the other to decrease it. Incidentally, the switch is not intended as a means of reducing current for crater filling or to prevent burnthrough on thin sections.

The low-voltage contactor is frequently used in shipyards and on other jobs where weldors work in confined areas surrounded by steel. It is a safety feature. It reduces the voltage between the electrode holder and the work from a relatively high AC voltage to a very low DC voltage when the arc is broken. Thus it is practically impossible for the weldor to get a shock should he accidentally put himself between the electrode holder and the work. As soon as the arc starts, the DC voltage drops out and the normal AC output of the welder takes over to provide good welding characteristics. This is automatic and requires no action by the operator.

Generally, you will use DC on all 3/16" and smaller electrodes except the iron-powder types and AC on all larger electrodes and iron-powder types. This is because non-iron-powder electrodes generally operate best on DC except when arc blow is present. As discussed in Lesson 1.14, AC is preferred when the arc blow is present.

To change a combination AC/DC "Idealarc TM" from AC to DC, you simply move the selector switch to the polarity you desire. Then set the current to the value you want, using the proper scale on the indicator dial. No other changes are necessary.

Note that the "Idealarc TM" welders have considerable welding capacity beyond their rating. A 300-ampere machine will have a range from 45 to 375 amperes DC and 30 to 450 amperes AC. However, when you use higher currents you must reduce duty cycle in order to give the machine adequate time to cool. Even so, it is good to know that you can get plenty of current out of the "Idealarc TM" welders.

Job Instructions

1. Check the "Idealarc TM" welder to see whether it is a straight AC or an AC/DC model. If it has a selector switch, it is a combination machine; otherwise it is a straight AC welder.

2. Check to see whether there are other optional features.

3. Set current for electrode being used. Run a few beads then adjust the current up and down, each time running a few beads to see how current adjustment affects welding heat.

4. If the machine is an AC/DC model, run Fleetweld 35 on all three positions of the selector switch and note the effect of polarity on arc action. Be sure to set current to same value for each position.

5. If welder is equipped with other optional features, try each to become familiar with its operation.

LESSON

2.2

Object:
To study the "Shield-Arc" SAE DC welder.

Equipment:
Lincoln "Shield-Arc" SAE welder and accessories.

Material:
Scrap steel; 3/16" "Fleetweld 7" electrodes.

General Information

Dual continuous control of the "Shield-Arc" SAE welder gives the operator complete freedom in choice of DC arc characteristics and current. Self-indicating dials of this control make the proper setting practically automatic. This enables the operator to set the machine for the proper volt- ampere combination to do any kind, type, or position of welding.

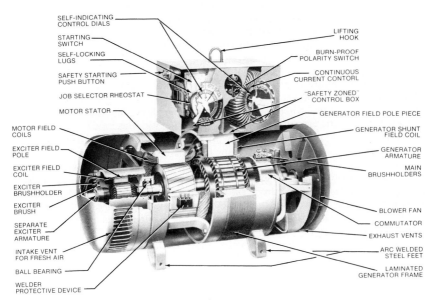

Figure 1. "Shield-Arc" SAE DC motor-generator welder.

Setting the self-indicating dials is as simple as operating the radio. When you tune in a radio station, one dial gives you the station you want while the other varies the volume. In the same manner, weldors can "tune in" the arcs to suit their various welding jobs, (Figure 2). The left-hand dial, the "Job Selector", is for selecting the proper *type* of arc. The other is the current adjustment dial that provides the proper arc *intensity*.

Figure 2. Control on SAE welder.

The "Job Selector" or open-circuit voltage control is divided into three differently colored segments, labeled "Large Electrodes", "Normal Welding", "Vertical and Overhead", and a fourth segment in black for special low-current applications. The setting labeled "Large Electrodes" has the highest voltage, and the others are successively lower in the order named.

The Current Selector has colored arrows corresponding to the segments of the voltage control. In setting the machine, the operator should first choose the voltage-control setting required by the work and desired results. Then set the arrow of corresponding color on the current control to the exact current suitable for the work.

To understand the principle of dual continuous control, it must first be realized that there are two types of welding voltage. These are the *open-circuit* voltage and the *arc* voltage. The open-circuit voltage is the voltage generated by the welding machine when no welding is being done. The arc voltage is the voltage between the electrode and the work during welding.

Open-circuit voltages are between 50 and 100; arc voltages are between 18 and 36. The open- circuit voltage drops to the arc voltage when the arc is struck and the welding load comes on the machine. Value of the arc voltage is determined largely by the length of the arc and, to some degree, by the type of electrode being used. If the arc is *shortened*, the arc voltage *decreases*. If the arc is *lengthened,* the arc voltage *increases*. The value of open-circuit voltage of the welding machine has little effect on the arc voltage, but it does determine the *arc characteristics.*

To understand this, first, recognize that, as the arc length changes the arc voltage, the current also changes. The amount that it changes depends on the volt-ampere curve of the welder. This curve shows what happens to current as voltage changes. Figure 3 shows how this happens. When a short arc is held, the arc voltage is 20 volts and the welding current is 140 amperes. As the arc length is increased, the arc voltage and current move up the curve, until, at 30 volts, the welding current has reduced to 100 amperes.

The volt-ampere curve, shown in Figure 3, is for one particular setting of the Job Selector and Current Control. Changing either of these controls will change the shape of the curve. The Job Selector moves the entire curve up and down the voltage axis, as shown in Figure 4; the Current Control moves the bottom of the curve back and forth across the current axis, as shown in Figure 5. By operating both of the controls, virtually an infinite number of different curves can be obtained.

The shape of the curve determines the type of arc. Figure 6 shows two different curves obtained for two different settings of the welder. The current

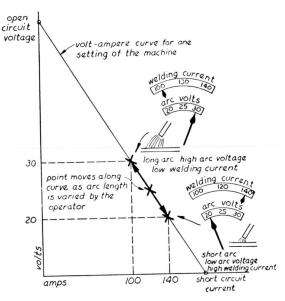

Figure 3.

and arc voltage at point "X" is the same for both curves. However, note what happens when the arc length is varied. On curve "A", there is very little difference in welding current between the long arc and the short arc; on curve "B", there is a sizeable current change for the same change in arc length. The type of arc resulting from curve "A" is a soft steady arc that is excellent for fast production welding; the type of arc resulting from curve "B" is a sensitive arc that is best for out-of-position welding. With dual continuous control, it is possible to select just exactly the type of arc needed for each job.

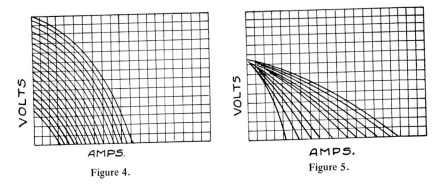

Figure 4.   **Figure 5.**

Simplifying the above, it can be said that the Job Selector controls the type of arc available, or the "arc characteristics". As the dial is moved toward the "Special Applications" range (low open-circuit voltage), a sensitive arc is produced; moving the dial toward the "Large Electrode" range (high open-circuit voltage) produces a smooth, steady arc. Further, it can be said that the

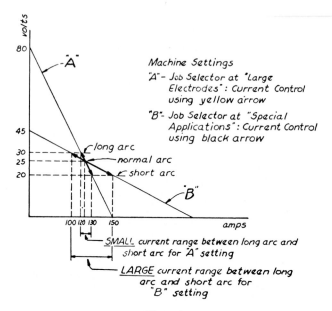

Figure 6.

Current Control controls the current. To set the machine, simply set the Job Selector to give the type arc desired and then, using the correspondingly colored arrow, set the Current Control to the required current.

Job Instructions

1. Connect the welding cables to the output studs on the rear of the welder, being sure that they are connected to the correct studs.

2. Start the welder by pushing the green button on the end of the control box.

3. Set the welder for 200 amperes using the "Large Electrode" setting on the Job Selector. Set the polarity switch to the "Negative" position. Weld with 3/16" Fleetweld 7 electrode. Vary the Job Selector Control either way and note the change in welding heat. Note that this control may be used as a fine current adjustment as well as for control of arc characteristics. Vary the arc length and note that there is little change in welding heat.

4. Set the welder for 200 amperes using the "Overhead and Vertical" range on the Job Selector. Note that, though the current is still the same as for the previous setting, the arc characteristics have changed considerably. Use a short arc length and note the large increase in welding heat; draw the arc out and note that the welding current reduces noticeably.

Note: Although the Motor Generator type welder has excellent arc characteristics it is falling off in popularity. Motor Generators have a higher initial cost as well as a higher operating cost when compared to welders of the transformer-rectifier type design.

Object:
To study the "Lincwelder" DC motor-generator welder.

Equipment:
"Lincwelder" DC welder, 250-ampere size.

Material:
Scrap steel plate; 3/32", 1/8", 3/16" "Fleetweld 37" and "Fleet-weld 5P" or other mild-steel electrodes, both straight and reverse-polarity types.

General Information

The "Lincwelder" DC vertical welders are designed to do all types of welding with every type of electrode and are particularly well suited to maintenance, general repair, and sheet-metal applications. Similar to the large "SAE" Lincoln welders, they are equipped with dual control to permit selection of desired arc characteristics, as well as welding current.

The fact that these machines occupy a minimum floor space and are very portable make them flexible and desirable where it is frequently necessary to move the welder, such as when they are used for plant maintenance or in repair shops.

Operators find this welder very easy to set and use. It has a steady output, regardless of input voltage fluctuations. The rugged construction of the "Linc-

Figure 1.

Figure 2.

welder" insures long, trouble-free life.

The machine is set to the desired current by first setting the voltage control to the desired value (50-60 is used for most applications; 40-50 is used for sheet-metal and out-of-position welding). Then, using the mark on the current control that corresponds to the voltage setting, select the desired current. For example, to set the machine for 150 amperes for flat welding, set the voltage control to 55; then set the line marked "55" on the current control to 150 amperes. If the arc is found to be too hot, either control may be turned clockwise to reduce the current; if it is too cold, either control may be turned counterclockwise.

Facing the welder, the negative terminal is on the right rear of the machine, while the positive terminal is on the left rear. This is indicated on the nameplate. To obtain "straight", or "negative", polarity, connect the electrode cable to the negative stud and the work, or ground, cable to the positive terminal. To use "reversed", or "positive", polarity, simply reverse the cable connections.

Job Instructions

1. Connect the cables for electrode-negative polarity.

2. Set the welder for 100 amperes (50 volts), using the procedure described above.

3. Start the welder.

4. Connect the ground cable to the work and insert a 1/8" Fleetweld 37 or other straight-polarity electrode in the electrode holder.

5. Run a bead.

6. Move the voltage control to 40 volts and run another bead; set to 60 volts and repeat welding. Note how the current varies as the voltage control is changed.

7. Reset the voltage control to 50 and change the current control to 80 amperes. Run a bead. Set to 120 amperes and run another bead. Though both controls will change the current, on most jobs it is best to use a higher voltage setting because this gives a smoother arc.

8. Change the polarity as described above and run several beads with Fleetweld 5 or other reverse-polarity electrode.

9. Weld with 3/32" and 3/16" electrodes to determine the range of welding current available.

Object:
To study the Lincoln AC welders.

Equipment:
Lincoln AC-225-S welder and accessories.

Material:
Scrap steel plate; 1/8" and 5/32" "Fleetweld 180" and "Fleetweld 37" electrodes.

General Information

This AC welder is a transformer welder that has found wide acceptance in a variety of applications. A versatile machine, it is capable of welding, hard-surfacing, soldering, brazing, and metal cutting.

Figure 1.

Current control on the AC-225-S is extremely simple. A selector switch on the front panel has eleven positions, each corresponding to a different output current. Each position is labeled so the operator knows what current is being delivered. The eleven positions are selected to give finer current control on the lower range of the machine. Operators are able to get just the current they need for any job.

Job Instructions

1. Using Fleetweld 180 electrodes, run beads at several different current settings. Note that the difference between steps is greater at higher currents than at lower currents.

2. Connect an arc torch to the electrode and ground cables and start the arc. (See Lesson 1.39.) Note how the heat of the arc torch is varied when the welding current is changed.

3. Weld first at the minimum position on the current switch and then at the maximum position to determine the total range of welding current available.

Object:
To study the Lincoln "Weldanpower" welders and power units.

Equipment:
Lincoln "Weldanpower 150" or "Weldanpower AC/DC" machines.

Material:
Scrap steel plate, 1/8" and 5/32" thick; "Fleetweld 180" and "Fleetweld 37" or other AC electrodes.

General Information

The "Weldanpower" machine is a combination of a welder and an auxiliary power source. The machine is designed for situations where the primary need is an auxiliary or emergency power generator and a portable arc welder is also needed. These units have a wide range of applications on the farm and in steel construction, mining, quarrying, dredging and other operations.

The "Weldanpower 150"

As a power source, these units are 115/230 volt, single-phase, 60-hertz generators with a total maximum output of 4.5 KVA or 40 amps at 115 volts or 20 amps at 230 volts. They have two 115 volt receptacles each of which is rated at a maximum of 20 amps and two 230 volt receptacles each of which is rated at a maximum of 15 amps. A 1-1/2-HP motor is the largest size that can be operated continuously from one receptacle.

Equipment plugged into the Weldanpower receptacles should be double-insulated or else connected to a separate solid earth ground. Do NOT ground to

Figure 1. The "Weldanpower 150" welder and power generator.

Figure 2. "Weldanpower AC/DC" welder and power generator.

the Weldanpower frame or panel and do not replace 2-prong receptacles with 3-prong grounding receptacles. If power tools have a grounding-type plug, use an adaptor in the Weldanpower receptacle and connect the pigtail to a solid earth ground. Newer machines have 3-prong receptacles but should have a separate earth ground for safe operation.

The welding output is rated at 150 amps at 25 arc volts, 60-hertz AC current. It is rated at 100% duty cycle on all settings. Duty cycle is based on a ten-minute period. This means the arc can be drawn for ten minutes out of each ten-minute period without any danger of overheating.

An optional electric start is available. It provides for pushbutton starting and also has a 12 volt battery, ammeter, and a battery-charging rate control.

Job Instructions

Connect the electrode cable to the "Electrode" stud and the work cable to the "To Work" stud. The output amperes are marked at each position of the current selector switch. Turn the switch to the current required for each job.

There is a slight amount of play at each switch position. It is good practice to move the switch back and forth once within this play after switching to a new position. This wiping action keeps the contacts free of dirt and oxides.

DO NOT TURN THE SELECTOR SWITCH WHILE WELDING AS THIS MAY DAMAGE THE CONTACTS.

Start the engine. For detailed engine starting, see the operating instructions supplied with the welder. Allow the engine to run a few minutes before starting to weld.

Do NOT attempt to draw power from the output receptacles until the engine is operating at full speed. If the power load is turned on when starting the engine, the machine may fail to generate full voltage.

Weld with different electrode sizes to check the current control.

Connect some 100-watt lamps to one power receptacle and a power tool to the other receptacle. Check the operation of the power tool.

When stopping the engine, first remove the load and allow the engine to run idle for a few minutes.

The "Weldanpower AC/DC"

The "Weldanpower AC/DC" is similar to the "Weldanpower 150" but with greater welding capacity, greater auxiliary power capacity, and other features that contribute to increased versatility.

As a power source, there are four 115-volt, 60-hertz three-wire receptacles mounted on the panel. Each receptacle has a capacity of 20 amperes continuous duty. In addition, there are two three-wire 230-volt receptacles with a capacity of 15 amperes each. Any combination may be used so long as the total does not exceed 6000 watts.

The generator has separate internal windings for welding and power use, so that welding may be done at the same time the unit is being used as a power source. When used simultaneously, the outputs should not exceed the values in the table below.

RANGE OF SIMULTANEOUS WELDER & POWER OPERATION

Welding Output		Permissible Power
AC	DC	
180 — 225 amps	130 — 210 amps	None
165 amps	120 amps	240 watts
115 amps	90 amps	2500 watts
60 amps	50 amps	5000 watts
None	None	6000 watts

When used as a welder, the "Weldanpower AC/DC" is rated 225 amps at 25 volts AC with a duty cycle of 100%. The usable current range is 40 to 225 amps.

The unit comes standard with electric start and an optional HI-FREQ unit is available for TIG welding.

Job Instructions

Use the same instructions as for the "Weldanpower 150" except notice the smoother arc characteristics when the unit is used as a welder with DC polarity.

LESSON
2.6

Object::
To study the "Lincwelder" DC engine-driven welder.

Equipment:
"Lincwelder" DC-225/3-AS welder and accessories.

Material:
Scrap steel plate; 1/8", 5/32" and 3/16" "Fleetweld 5P," "Fleetweld 37", or other mild-steel electrodes.

General Information

The "Lincwelder" DC engine-driven welder, though designed primarily for farm or general repair welding, is widely used by contractors for light work. The DC-225/3-AS is driven by an air-cooled engine and also supplies auxiliary power to run electric hand tools.

Figure 1. "Lincwelder DC-225/3 AS."

The welder is lightweight and compact and can be easily transported, either on a truck or wagon or on an undercarriage. It provides a wide range of welding current and is easy to use.

To weld with the machine connect the welding cables to the output studs, which are marked "Positive" and "Negative". Set the "Current Range Control" to the number nearest the desired current. Weld. Adjust the "Fine Adjustment" continuous-current control to the exact amperage required. The engine can be equipped with an automatic idling device that reduces engine speed automatically to a low idle speed when not welding. Current output ranges from 40 amperes minimum to 225 amperes maximum. The welding duty cycle is 30% at 225 amperes (if used for more than three minutes at 225 amperes during several successive ten-minute periods, it may over heat), and 50% at 180 amperes.

An AC power output of 3000 watts, 115 volts, 50 hertz continuous-duty is available for lights or power tools. The machine can also be built for 3000 watts, 230 volts.

Job Instructions

1. Start the welder.

2. Set the machine for the size of electrode being used. Weld.

3. Change the settings to become familiar with the controls.

4. Change polarity and use different electrodes.

Object:
To study the "Shield-Arc" SA-200 gasoline-engine-driven welder.

Equipment:
"Shield-Arc" SA-200 welder.

Material:
Scrap steel; 3/16" "Fleetweld 5P" and "Fleetweld 7" electrodes.

General Information

The "Shield-Arc" DC welder is widely used for all types of field welding such as repair work, pipeline welding, and structural steel erection. It is equipped with dual controls to permit selection of the proper amount and type of welding current. This welder is also equipped with a 1000-watt power outlet plug to permit use of 115-volt DC power tools and lights.

The engine of this welder is a water-cooled Continental, model F-163. This engine is capable of supplying more than enough power to operate the welder. This reserve power tends to make the arc steadier and settings more stable. Also, the output of the welder will not drop as the engine becomes older and less efficient. An idling device reduces the speed of the welder to a low idle when the operator is not actually welding. The engine speed picks up to normal speed when the operator strikes the arc. A 12-volt electric starter system is standard.

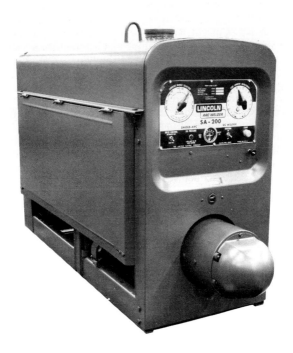

Figure 1.

Figure 2.

Connect the electrode and work cables of the appropriate size to the studs located on the gas-tank mounting rail. For positive (reverse) polarity, connect the electrode cable to the terminal marked "Positive". For negative (straight) polarity connect the electrode cable to the "Negative" stud.

The "Current Range Selector" provides five overlapping current ranges. The "Fine Current Adjustment" adjusts the current from minimum to maximum within each range. Open-circuit voltage is also controlled by the "Fine Current Adjustment", permitting control of the arc characteristics.

DO NOT TURN THE CURRENT RANGE SELECTOR WHILE WELDING, because the current may arc between the contact and damage the switch.

When a forceful "digging" arc is required, usually for vertical and overhead welding, use a higher "Current Range Selector" setting and a lower open-circuit voltage. For example: to obtain 175 amps and a forceful arc, set the "Current Range Selector" to the 240-160 position and the "Fine Current Adjustment" for about 20 on the scale.

A high open-circuit voltage setting provides the soft "buttering" arc with best resistance to pop-outs preferred for most welding. To get this characteristic, set the "Current Range Selector" to the lowest setting that still provides the current you need and set the "Fine Current Adjustment" near maximum. For example: to obtain 175 amps and a soft arc, set the "Current Range Selector" to the 190-120 position and the "Fine Current Adjustment" for 65 on the scale.

DO NOT attempt to set the "Current Range Selector" between the five points designated on the nameplate. These switches have a spring-loaded cam that almost eliminates the possibility of setting this switch between the designated points.

Job Instructions

1. Start the welder (see instructions above).

2. Connect the welding cables for electrode-positive polarity.

3. Tap the electrode to the work, (use a shield) but do not start the arc. Note how the engine speed picks up and then drops back to a low idle after a few seconds.

4. Turn the "Fine Current Adjustment" all the way to the left and set the "Current Range Selector" on the 240-160 position. Weld with 3/16" Fleet-weld 5. Without changing the "Current Range Selector", move the "Fine

Current Adjustment" all the way to the right. Weld with the same size electrode and note the change in welding heat. Repeat for several other settings of each control.

5. Change to electrode-negative polarity by interchanging the welding cable connections at the output studs of the welder. Weld with Fleetweld 7.

6. Connect a DC or universal motor-driven power tool to the auxiliary power output plug on the control panel of the welder. Note that it is possible to use power and weld simultaneously.

Object:
To study the Lincoln "Idealarc SP-200" combination wire feeder/power source.

Equipment:
"Idealarc SP-200" welder with accessories and the proper safety equipment.

Material:
Scrap steel plate, Lincoln .068" diameter Innershield NR-211.

General Information

The "SP-200" offers a compact unit featuring a wire feeder and power source in one economical package. It has been designed to weld with the Innershield process or with the gas-metal-arc process; both of which are described in detail in Section 7. The standard unit operates from either 208 volt or 230 volt, 60 Hz, single phase input power.

The smooth constant voltage DC output from the transformer/rectifier makes semiautomatic welding easy to learn. The five overlapping voltage ranges with continuous control within each and the calibrated wire feed speed control make it easy to set procedures. The solid-state electronically controlled wire feeder automatically compensates for line voltage fluctuations and instantaneously responds to wire drag. This results in consistent positive arc starting and steady wire feeding when welding.

The SP-200 may be set up for Innershield welding as we are about to do here or for GMAW welding in Lesson 7.16. Lesson 7.16 describes welding material as thin as 22 gage which has many sheet metal applications such as auto-body repair.

Figure 1. The SP-200.

Job Instructions

Make sure the SP-200 is equipped with the drive rolls for feeding .068″ Innershield wire. Place the coil of .068″ NR-211 electrode on the wire reel so that the reel turns in a clockwise direction when you pull on the electrode. Straighten the first six inches and push it through the drive rolls while depressing the gun trigger. The K-126 or K-309 gun is recommended. Continue feeding the wire until it protrudes from the gun by about 1/2 inch.

Check to see that the SP-200 has been set up for DC straight polarity. Trying to run NR-211 on DC reverse polarity will cause excessive spatter and an inferior weld. The contact tip should be in good condition and not worn. Connect the work clamp to your workpiece. Set the SP-200 for about 18 arc volts and 75 inches per minute of wire feed speed. This one setting will allow you to weld 12 gage and heavier steels in all positions without changing procedures. Try downhand and vertical welds with material of different thicknesses. Note how easy it is to control the weld puddle. The minimal slag is easily removed with a wire brush.

Figure 2. The SP-200 setup for Innershield.

SECTION III

CARBON-STEEL
ELECTRODES

LESSON 3.1

Object:
To become familiar with the basic groups of Lincoln mild-steel and low-alloy steel electrodes.

General Information

Lincoln mild-steel electrodes can be classified and studied in four basic groups according to their operating characteristics: "FAST-FREEZE", "FAST-FILL", "FILL-FREEZE", which includes "FAST-FOLLOW", and a group for welding hard-to-weld steels.

"FAST-FREEZE" electrodes include Lincoln electrodes in the AWS classes EXX10 and EXX11. These electrodes are basically similar in operation, with an outstanding ability for the molten metal and slag to freeze rapidly. Compared to other electrodes, they do not have fast-fill or fast-follow ability.

The "FAST-FILL" group includes Lincoln electrodes in the AWS classes EXX24 and EXX27. They are similar in operation, but each electrode has been designed for a particular type of joint. The ability of these electrodes to rapidly fill a joint with weld metal is unsurpassed. They have little fast-freeze and limited fast-follow.

The "FILL-FREEZE" group includes electrodes in the EXX12, EXX13, and EXX14 AWS classes. Each electrode has, to some degree, both "filling" and "freezing" abilities. However, the proportion of each ability varies considerably from one electrode to another. The differences in operating characteristics of the various electrodes within the group are quite noticeable. Also, some of these electrodes exhibit a special ability termed "FAST-FOLLOW".

The fourth group of electrodes is for welding steels high enough in sulfur, carbon, or phosphorus to require special consideration in the choice of electrodes to produce crack-free welds. Heavier thicknesses of mild steel also present a problem because of the severe quenching of the welds. This quenching may result in cracks. The first consideration in welding these steels is selecting an electrode that will produce crack-free welds; speed and ease of welding are secondary considerations. Electrodes for these applications are the AWS EXX18 and EXX28 classifications.

Lessons 3.2, 3.3, 3.4, and 3.5 present information on each group in the following manner: information common to the entire group is presented in the "General Information" portion of the lesson; special characteristics that set apart individual electrodes are given in the sub-lessons (3.2A, 3.2B, etc.) along

Fast Freeze   Fast Follow   Fast Fill

(medium Fast Freeze and Fill)

Figure 1. Basic groups of mild-steel electrodes.

with specific instructions for jobs that will bring out both the group and individual characteristics of the electrode.

Electrode Groups

The terms "fast-freeze", "fast-fill", "fill-freeze", and "fast-follow" describe an electrode's basic characteristic and indicate the type of job for which it is *best* suited. These characteristics correspond to job requirements. Any mild-steel production welding job can be described by one or a combination of these terms. Proper electrode selection depends on matching the characteristics of the electrode to the requirements of the job.

It may seem unnecessary to have more than one electrode in each group. It becomes understandable, however, when it is recognized that additional requirements beyond the basic requirements must be considered for maximum efficiency. Operation on AC or DC, bead appearance, penetration, and arc force are some of the other operating characteristics that must be varied and changed to meet different job requirements.

The proper approach to electrode selection, then, is to first study the application and determine what basic characteristics are required. Then, compare the electrodes within the appropriate group to determine which one best meets the special considerations of the job. It's like shopping for household goods. If one needs a chair, he first goes to a furniture store that sells chairs; then, he selects a chair that meets the special considerations of style, color, etc., which are necessary to best complement the room in which it is to be used.

How to Determine Basic Requirements

An understanding of the terms will help determine basic requirements. "FAST-FREEZE" means ability to deposit a weld that solidifies rapidly. This consideration is of importance *only* when there is some danger of the molten metal and slag spilling or running out of the joint. Such conditions are found when welding in a vertical, horizontal, or overhead position or on a circular part. Metal and slag must stay in the joint until it has solidified. This consideration overrides all others, including the natural desire to deposit metal faster so that greater welding speeds are attained.

Figure 2. A fast-freeze application.

The other extreme is where fast-freezing is no concern, but rather the main concern is to melt metal into the joint as fast as possible. Electrodes designed expressly to deposit a large amount of weld metal rapidly are termed "FAST-FILL" electrodes. These electrodes are limited to the flat, or very near flat, position and horizontal fillets, where gravity helps to hold the deposit in the joint, rather than attempting to pull it out. The more the work is moved out-of-position, the more "fast-fill ability must be sacrificed, until, eventually, a point is reached where "fast-freeze" becomes more important than "fast-fill".

Although many jobs clearly fall into either "fast-fill" or "fast-freeze" classifications, even more applications overlap these groups and require electrodes with a combination of characteristics. Electrodes of this type are called "FILL-

Figure 3. Fast-follow application.

Figure 4. A fast-fill application.

FREEZE". Though belonging to the same group, they have distinctive characteristics. For example, Fleetweld 47 has just enough "fast-freeze" ability to weld slightly downhill joints. On the other hand, Fleetweld 7 has considerable "fast-freeze" ability and can weld steep downhill joints.

Some "fill-freeze" electrodes also have a distinct characteristic called "fast-follow" – the ability to move along a joint at high speeds and make a continuous weld without skips or misses. These welds require that the molten pool closely follow the tip of the fast-moving electrode; hence, the name "fast-follow".

The "fast-follow" characteristic of this group is utilized to best advantage on fillet and lap joints in light-gauge metals, 10-gauge down to 20-gauge, for production jobs welded at speeds in excess of 20 inches per minute. For this type of joint, actually little or no deposited metal is required. Any deposited metal is in excess of what is actually required to make the lap joint. This application is the extreme of "fast-follow", as the only practical limit to the speed of electrode travel is the rate at which the molten pool is able to follow the electrode's tip, so that a continuous bead will be made.

Determining the application of electrodes for HARD-TO-WELD STEELS is easy. Whenever it is known that the material to be fabricated contains high carbon or sulfur or other crack-producing alloys, or the joints are highly restrained, these electrodes should be used. If, while welding a steel of unknown analysis, cracks or porosity are encountered, then these electrodes should be used – regardless of the joint or position. They will produce sound welds and reduce or eliminate preheat.

The next four lessons are arranged by the above groups. For the beginning weldor, the best approach would be to carefully study the "General Information" section of each lesson to first learn the basic differences between the groups. Then, return to the sub-lessons (3.2A, 3.2B, etc.) to pick up the differences between individual electrodes within the group. Study these lessons carefully, for they contain the key to proper electrode selection.

JOINT TYPES IN TERMS OF
ELECTRODE FREEZE-FILL-FOLLOW CHARACTERISTICS

'FREEZE' JOINTS	'FILL' JOINTS

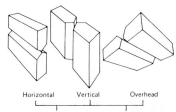

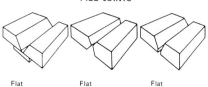

			Flat 3/8 In. and Thicker Fill (E6027, E7028)	Flat 3/8 In. and Thicker Root Pass Fill-Freeze (E7018) All Other Passes Fill (E6027, E7028)	Flat 3/8 In. and Thicker Root Pass Fill-Freeze (E7018) All Other Passes Fill (E6027, E7028)
Horizontal	Vertical	Overhead			
3/16 to 5/8 In. Plate **Freeze** (E6010, E6011)	Plate over 5/8 In. **Fill-Freeze** (E7018)				

'FILL' AND 'FILL-FREEZE' JOINTS

Fillet Welds Over 10 to 12 In. in Length on 3/16 In. or Thicker Plate

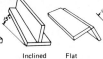

Flat	Horizontal	Inclined	Flat	Inclined	Vertical	
Fill (E7024, E7028)	**Fill** (E7024, E7028)	**Fill-Freeze** (E7014, E7018)	**Fill** (E7024, E7028)	**Fill-Freeze** (E7014, E7018)	3/16 to 5/8 In. Plate **Freeze** (E6010, E6011)	Plate 5/8 In. & Over **Fill-Freeze** (E7018)

'FOLLOW' JOINTS — SHEET METAL

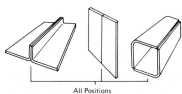

			Preserve Edge	Fuse Edge
All Positions **Follow-Freeze** (E6010, DC; E6011)		All Positions **Follow** (E6012, DC) (E6013, AC)	All Positions **Follow** (E6012, DC) (E6013, AC)	All Positions **Follow-Freeze** (E6010, DC; E6011)

Object:
To study the use and applications of Lincoln "FAST-FREEZE" electrodes.

General Information

These are versatile all-position, all-purpose Lincoln electrodes, and are *best* for most vertical and overhead welding and some sheet-metal applications.

Included in the "FAST-FREEZE" group are the following: Fleetweld 5, Fleetweld 5P, Fleetweld 35, Fleetweld 35LS, Fleetweld 180, and the low-alloy, high-tensile electrodes Shield-Arc 85, Shield-Arc 85P, Shield-Arc HYP and Shield-Arc 70+.

Operating Characteristics

Deposition: FAST-FREEZE — best of all Lincoln electrodes when used on DC, electrode positive; also has good "fast-follow" ability.

Arc: FORCEFUL — deep penetration with maximum admixture.

Slag: LIGHT — little slag interference and incomplete slag coverage.

Bead: FLAT — with distinct ripples.

Current: DC — normally used on DC, electrode positive (AC with Fleetweld 35 and Fleetweld 180), to give the arc characteristics described above. May also be used on DC, electrode negative, to give a spray-type arc.

Positions: ALL — truly "all-position"; exceptionally good for vertical and overhead work.

Application Information

The versatile, all-purpose character of these electrodes has resulted in their use on many different types of applications. They have excellent physical properties and produce X-ray-quality welds. DC, electrode positive (or AC with Fleetweld 35 and Fleetweld 180), is used on all applications except sheet metal (No. "6" below).

1. ALL VERTICAL AND OVERHEAD WELDING is best done with these electrodes, except for high-speed vertical-down lap and fillet welds on sheet metal and light plate. "Fast-freeze" permits fastest out-of-position welding on applications such as structural steel erection and pipe welding.
2. GENERAL-PURPOSE MAINTENANCE WELDING is best done with these electrodes. Frequently welding is out-of-position and work may be dirty, rusty, or greasy and cannot be cleaned. Deep penetration and light slag produce best results possible under these adverse conditions.
3. X-RAY-QUALITY JOBS welded out-of-position require these electrodes. These electrodes produce X-ray-quality welds in all positions for all types of joints.
4. JOINTS REQUIRING DEEP PENETRATION, such as square-edge butt welds on 3/8" plate, are welded in the flat position with the larger sizes. By taking advantage of the deep penetration, welds can be made faster and plate beveling is eliminated.

5. GALVANIZED STEEL is best welded with these electrodes because the forceful arc with light slag bites through the galvanizing with little bubbling or porosity to produce sound quality welds.
6. SHEET-METAL EDGE AND BUTT WELDS on 14 to 22-gauge sheet are welded with DC, electrode negative. The spray-type arc and fast-follow ability obtained with this polarity produce the fastest possible welds.

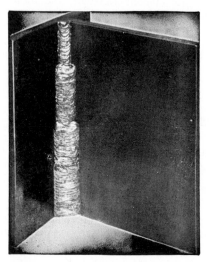 

Figure 1. Vertical welding, repair work, and x-ray-inspected pipe welding are applications of "fast-freeze" electrodes.

Procedures

DC, electrode positive (AC for Fleetweld 35, Fleetweld 35 LS, and Fleetweld 180), is used on all applications except sheet metal.

VERTICAL — For best penetration, welding is usually done vertical-up, though vertical-down is used for most cross-country pipeline welding because it is faster for the particular joint involved. Use a stringer bead for the first pass. This bead is usually applied with a whipping technique for fillet welds and a circular motion for V-butt joints. Succeeding passes are applied with a weave, pausing slightly at the edges to insure penetration and to wash-in without undercut. Use currents in the lower portion of the range.

OVERHEAD — These welds are best made with a series of stringer beads, using a technique similar to that described for vertical welding.

HORIZONTAL BUTT — Use a procedure similar to that employed for overhead welding.

FLAT — Permit the tip of the electrode to lightly touch the work or hold a very short arc. Tip the electrode forward in the direction of travel and move fast enough to stay ahead of the molten pool. Use currents in the middle and higher portion of the range.

SHEET METAL EDGE AND BUTT — Use DC, electrode negative; hold a comparatively long arc. Lean the electrode forward in the direction of travel and move as rapidly as possible while maintaining good fusion. Welding is fastest when done 45 degrees downhill. Use currents in the middle of the range.

Object:
To study the special characteristics of Lincoln Fleetweld 5P electrodes.

Equipment:
Lincoln "Idealarc" or other DC welder and accessories.

Material:
Scrap 3/16" plate, 14-gauge sheet metal, and beveled pipe (see Lesson 1.45); 1/8", 5/32", and 3/16" Fleetweld 5P electrode.

FLEETWELD 5P

An E6010 electrode, Fleetweld 5P is an improved version of one of the first shielded-arc electrodes. The most widely used electrode of this group, it has been industry's standard for electrodes of this type for many years. The easiest way to study electrodes of this group is to first become familiar with Fleetweld 5P and then compare the other Lincoln electrodes of this group with it. The following "Job Instructions" bring out the typical characteristics of this entire group of electrodes; "Job Instructions" for other electrodes of this group bring out characteristics peculiar to the individual electrode.

MECHANICAL PROPERTIES	AS-WELDED	STRESS-RELIEVED (1150°F)
Tensile Strength, psi	62,000 – 69,000	60,000 – 69,000
Yield Point, psi	52,000 – 62,000	46,000 – 56,000
Elongation, % in 2 inches	22 – 32	28 – 38
Impact Resistance (Charpy V-Notch) ft-lbs	20 to 60 @ −20°F	71 @ 70°F

Job Instructions

1. With 1/8" Fleetweld 5P, make fillet welds in the flat, vertical, and overhead positions. Use 3/16" plates. Also, select a particularly dirty plate and weld without prior cleaning. Note the following: (1) the easy operation of Fleetweld 5P in all positions; (2) the forceful arc and deep penetration that is characteristic of this type electrode; (3) the very light slag, which does not

FLEETWELD 5P – ALL POSITIONS		
Electrode Size		Amperage Range
Diameter	Length	DC(+)
3/32"	12"	40 – 75
1/8"	14"	75 – 130
5/32"	14"	90 – 175
3/16"	14"	140 – 225
7/32"	18"	200 – 275
1/4"	18"	220 – 325
5/16"	18"	240 – 400

interfere or tend to spill when welding out-of-position; (4) the ability to weld dirty plate when it is not possible to properly clean it; (5) the ability to maintain a stable arc under even very low currents.

2. Using 1/8" and 5/32" Fleetweld 5P and the techniques presented in earlier lessons on pipe welding, make both vertical-down and vertical-up pipe welds.

3. Make square-edge butt welds on the 3/16" plate in the flat position using the 3/16" Fleetweld 5P. Note that it is possible to make a 100%-penetration joint with a pass from either side without beveling.

4. With DC, electrode-negative polarity, make edge and butt welds on 14-gauge sheet metal. Note the arc characteristics. Weld in several positions and note that welding is fastest when the work is positioned 45 degrees downhill.

Object:
To study the special characteristics of Lincoln Fleetweld 35 electrodes.

Equipment:
Lincoln "Idealarc" or other AC welder and accessories.

Material:
Scrap 1/4" plate, 14-gauge sheet metal, and beveled pipe; 1/8", 5/32", and 1/4" Fleetweld 35 electrodes.

FLEETWELD 35

Fleetweld 35, an E6011 electrode, is an AC version of Fleetweld 5P and is used on applications identical to those described for Fleetweld 5P, except that an industrial AC welder is used instead of a DC welder. It can, of course, also be used on DC. On sheet-metal applications where DC, electrode negative, is used, Fleetweld 35 is actually preferred to Fleetweld 5P because it has a slightly finer spray, which makes welding easier. On other applications, Fleetweld 5P is normally preferred, if DC welders are available.

MECHANICAL PROPERTIES	AS-WELDED	STRESS-RELIEVED (1150°F)
Tensile Strength, psi	62,000 – 68,000	60,000 – 66,000
Yield Point, psi	50,000 – 62,000	46,000 – 56,000
Elongation, % in 2 inches	22 – 30	28 – 36
Impact Resistance (Charpy V-Notch) ft-lbs	20 to 90 @ –20°F	70 @ 70°F

Job Instructions

1. Repeat the jobs done for Fleetweld 5 using an industrial AC welder and Fleetweld 35. In performing these jobs, compare Fleetweld 5 and Fleetweld 35. Note that, with either electrode, DC is preferred over AC for out-of-position welding.

ALL POSITIONS		
Electrode Size		Current Range
Diameter	Length	AC
1/8"	14"	75 – 120
5/32"	14"	90 – 160
3/16"	14"	120 – 200
7/32"	14"	150 – 260
1/4"	18"	190 – 300

LESSON 3.2C

Object:
To study the special characteristics of Lincoln Fleetweld 180 electrodes.

Equipment:
Lincoln AC-225-S or other AC welder and accessories.

Material:
Scrap steel plate and angles; 1/8" and 5/32" Fleetweld 180 electrodes.

FLEETWELD 180

Fleetweld 180, an E6011 mild-steel electrode, is designed for operation with limited input AC welders for all-purpose welding. It will operate on DC, though other electrodes of this group are usually preferred. The deep penetration, light slag, and easy out-of-position welding make Fleetweld 180 the best electrode for maintenance and repair welding when a light-duty welder is being used. It is also used for welding thin sections to heavy members where minimum slag inclusion is desired.

MECHANICAL PROPERTIES	AS-WELDED
Tensile Strength, psi	62,000 − 71,000
Yield Point, psi	50,000 − 64,000
Elongation, % in 2 inches	22 − 31
Impact Resistance (Charpy V-Notch) ft-lbs	20 to 54 @ −20°F

Job Instructions

1. To become familiar with Fleetweld 180, weld vertical and overhead with the electrode; particularly weld on dirty plate.

Figure 1. Repairs cracked rim on farm implement wheel with single-pass weld.

Figure 2. Adds reinforcing strap on rear axle housing of truck to carry heavier loads on rough roads.

ALL POSITIONS		
Electrode Size		Current Range
Diameter	Length	AC
3/32" 1/8" 5/32"	12" 14" 14"	40 — 90 60 — 120 115 — 150

2. Use Fleetweld 180 and the procedure described in Lesson 1.40 to cut steel plate.

**LESSON
3.2D**

Object:
To study the special characteristics of Lincoln Shield-Arc 85 electrodes.

Equipment:
Lincoln "Idealarc" DC welder.

Material:
Scrap 1/4" plate and beveled pipe; 1/8", 5/32", and 1/4" Shield-Arc 85 electrode.

SHIELD-ARC 85

An E7010 electrode, Shield-Arc 85 operates very nearly like Fleetweld 5P. Its principle difference is in physical properties; Shield-Arc 85 has a higher tensile strength. It is used on all applications similar to those of Fleetweld 5P, except for sheet metal where its extra strength is not required. **NOTE**: For downhill pipe welding, many find Shield-Arc 70+ to be the first choice.

MECHANICAL PROPERTIES	AS-WELDED	STRESS-RELIEVED (1150°F)
Tensile Strength, psi	70,000 − 78,000	70,000 − 80,000
Yield Point, psi	60,000 − 71,000	57,000 − 69,000
Elongation, % in 2 inches	22 − 26	22 − 28
Impact Resistance (Charpy V-Notch) ft-lbs	68 @ 70°F	64 @ 70°F

Job Instructions

1. To become familiar with Shield-Arc 85, repeat the "Job Instructions" for Fleetweld 5P, excluding No. "4" (Lesson 3.24). Note that its operation is nearly identical to that of Fleetweld 5P and that it is used on similar applications where the base metal is 70,000-psi tensile-strength steel.

ALL POSITIONS		
Electrode Size		Amperage Range
Diameter	Length	DC
3/32"	12"	50 − 90
1/8"	14"	75 − 130
5/32"	14"	90 − 175
3/16"	14"	140 − 225

Figure 1. Forty miles of 16" gas line welded with "Shield-Arc 85", an excellent electrode for welding high-pressure cross-country pipeline.

Object:
To study the characteristics of Lincoln Shield-Arc 85P, Shield-Arc HYP and Shield-Arc 70+ electrodes.

Equipment:
Lincoln "Idealarc" DC welder.

Material:
Scrap beveled pipe; 3/16" Shield-Arc 85P and 5/32" and 3/16" Shield-Arc HYP and Shield-Arc 70+ electrodes.

SHIELD-ARC 85P, HYP, 70+

All of the above electrodes are of the EXX10 type and are especially designed for welding circumferential joints of pipe.

Shield-Arc 85P is similar to Shield-Arc 85 and is designed to eliminate surface pinholes in fill and cover-pass welds on high-strength pipe. It is made only in 3/16" size.

Shield-Arc HYP is designed specifically for vertical-down welding on 5L or 5LX and X42 through X65 pipe. It features easy operation, minimum wagon tracks and windows, and almost no tendency for fill and cover-pass pinholes. Shield-Arc 65+ is designed for line pipe with low temperature impact requirements and/or pipe steels exceeding .1% silicon or containing aluminum, titanium or other strong reducing agents.

Shield-Arc 70+ is similar to Shield-Arc HYP except it has a higher tensile strength. It is designed for vertical-down welding of low-carbon API 5LX-X70 pipe, but also can be used for welding X42 through X65 pipe.

NOTE: Many find Shield-Arc 70+ to have the greatest operator appeal of any of these electrodes.

MECHANICAL PROPERTIES	AS-WELDED	STRESS-RELIEVED (1150°F)
SHIELD-ARC 85P		
Tensile Strength, psi	70,000 − 78,000	70,000 − 74,000
Yield Point, psi	57,000 − 63,000	57,000 − 65,000
Elongation, % in 2 inches	22 − 27	22 − 27
Impact Resistance (Charpy V-Notch) ft-lbs	68 @ 70°F	68 @ 70°F
SHIELD-ARC HYP		
Tensile Strength, psi	70,000 − 84,000	80,000 − 82,000
Yield Point, psi	65,000 − 77,000	72,000 − 76,000
Elongation, % in 2 inches	22 − 23	24 − 27
Impact Resistance (Charpy V-Notch) ft-lbs	30 @ −20°F	30 @ −20°F

MECHANICAL PROPERTIES	AS-WELDED	STRESS-RELIEVED (1150°F)
SHIELD-ARC 70+		
Tensile Strength, psi	80,000 − 92,000	80,000 − 84,000
Yield Point, psi	70,000 − 83,000	71,000 − 76,000
Elongation, % in 2 inches	19 − 24	22 − 26
Impact Resistance (Charpy V-Notch) ft-lbs	40 @ −50°F	30 @ − 50°F

For Shield-Arc 85P, HYP, 70+, and 65+:

PIPE CIRCUMFERENTIAL WELDS	
Electrode Size	**Current Range**
Diameter	**DC(+)**
1/8″	75 − 130
5/32″	90 − 185
3/16″	140 − 225
7/32″	160 − 250

Job Instructions

Same as for Shield-Arc 5P in Lesson 3.2A, excluding No. "4". Note that these electrodes have similar characteristics to Fleetweld 5P. Also that Shield-Arc 85P is made in the 3/16″ size only and is only to be used for the cap pass. Shield-Arc HYP is the only electrode made in the 7/32″ size in this group.

Object:
To study the characteristics of Lincoln Fleetweld 35LS electrode.

Equipment:
Lincoln "Idealarc" AC and DC welder.

Material:
Scrap plate and sheet metal; 5/32" Fleetweld 35LS electrode.

FLEETWELD 35LS

Fleetweld 35LS is an excellent low-slag electrode for tack welding, particularly when the joint is to be welded with an automatic process. It is also used for vertical-down welding, making stringer beads, bridging gaps, and AC pipe welding.

MECHANICAL PROPERTIES	AS-WELDED	STRESS-RELIEVED (1150°F)
Tensile Strength, psi	62,000 − 67,000	60,000 − 65,000
Yield Point, psi	50,000 − 60,000	46,000 − 51,000
Elongation, % in 2 inches	22 − 31	28 − 33
Impact Resistance (Charpy V-Notch) ft-lbs	20 to 57 @ -20°F	120 @ 70°F

TACK — VERTICAL-DOWN — STRINGER BEADS			
Electrode Size		Current Range	
Diameter	Length	AC	DC
1/8"	14"	80 − 130	70 − 120
5/32"	14"	120 − 160	110 − 150

Job Instructions

Repeat the same jobs and make the same observations as for Fleetweld 35. Note the differences with AC and DC.

Object:
To study the use and applications of Lincoln "FILL-FREEZE" electrodes.

General Information

Lincoln "FILL-FREEZE" electrodes are best for joints with poor fitup and for most applications that are downhill, but not actually vertical. Those electrodes in the group that also have "FAST-FOLLOW" ability are the best electrodes for high-speed, light-gauge fillet and lap welds.

Included in the "FILL-FREEZE" group are Fleetweld 7, Fleetweld 37, Fleetweld 47, and Fleetweld 57.

Operating Characteristics

Deposition: FILL-FREEZE, or a combination of both "fast-fill" and "fast-freeze". Electrodes within the group differ considerably. Some electrodes also have outstanding "FAST-FOLLOW" ability.

Arc: QUIET – medium penetration with slight spatter.

Bead: CONVEX – smooth with even ripples in the downhand positions; more distinct ripples on vertical-up and overhead joints.

Slag: MEDIUM – gives good slag coverage.

Current: DC or AC – all electrodes will operate on either; AC is preferred for Fleetweld 37 and Fleetweld 47; DC, electrode negative, is best for the other electrodes of this group, unless arc blow is a problem.

Positions: ALL – most widely used in the flat or downhill positions, but has some limited application in vertical and overhead positions.

Application Information

Where costs are important, these electrodes are used because of their distinctive operating characteristics. Of the following applications, the first depends on "fast-follow" ability, while the others depend on "fill-freeze" characteristics. They are also sometimes used on other applications because of their ease of operation.

1. HIGH-SPEED LAP AND FILLET WELDS ON 1/4-INCH TO 20-GAUGE MATERIAL, where the welding speed is determined only by fast-follow ability and bead size is unimportant, are the specialty of these electrodes. Fast-follow ability becomes important when welding speeds in excess of 20 inches per minute are employed. The "Fast-Follow" electrodes excel on applications of this type.

2. DOWNHILL LAP AND FILLET WELDS, which are too steep for the "Fast-Fill" electrodes, but not steep enough to require the "Fast-Freeze" electrodes, are best made with electrodes of this group. This application is the major use for this type of electrode. The application varies widely because of the combinations of angle of incline and the size of the weld. Each electrode in the group has individual characteristics that recommend it for particular

applications. For example, Fleetweld 7 will make a 3/16" weld on a 60-degree incline, while Fleetweld 47 is limited to a 20-degree slope for the same size weld. Each job must be considered separately and the various electrodes compared for speed and ability.

3. POOR FITUP JOINTS, where the "Fast-Fill" electrodes would spill through, are welded with this group. The moderate fast-freeze eliminates spilling, yet gives reasonably fast deposition rates. Fleetweld 7 is the best electrode of the group for these applications.

4. GENERAL-PURPOSE WELDING, where most of the work is of the type described in "2" and "3" above, is a common application for electrodes of this group.

Procedures

DOWNHAND — use stringer beads for first pass and either additional stringer beads or a weave for succeeding passes. Where poor fitup is encountered, it may be necessary to use a slight weave on the first pass. Hold a very short arc or lightly touch the electrode on the work. Tip the electrode forward into the direction of travel and travel as fast as possible while maintaining a molten pool. Light material is best welded 45-90 degrees vertical-down. Use currents in the middle to higher portions of the recommended range.

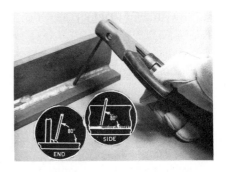

Figure 1. Angle of electrode for beads against vertical plate — multiple-pass fillet.

VERTICAL-DOWN — use stringer beads or a very slight weave. Do not try to deposit too much metal with one pass. Drag the electrode on the joint or hold a very short arc. Tip the electrode well into the direction of travel so that the arc force tends to push the molten metal back up the joint. Move fast enough to stay ahead of the molten pool. Use currents in the higher portion of the range.
VERTICAL-UP — use a wide triangular weave. Build a shelf of weld metal and, with the weave, deposit layer upon layer of metal as the weld progresses up the joint. Do not use a whip technique or take the electrode out of the molten pool. Point the electrode directly into the joint and slightly upward to permit the arc force to assist in controlling the puddle. Travel slow enough to maintain the shelf without causing the metal to spill. Use currents in the lower portion of the range.
OVERHEAD — use a whipping technique with a slight circular motion in the crater to produce stringer beads without undercut. Do not use a weave. Point the electrode directly into the joint and tip slightly forward into the direction of travel. Use a fairly short arc. Travel fast enough to avoid spilling. Use currents in the lower portion of the range.

Object:
To study the special characteristics of Lincoln Fleetweld 7 electrodes.

Equipment:
Lincoln "Idealarc" AC and DC welder.

Material:
Scrap plate and 14-gauge sheet metal; 1/8", 3/16", and 1/4" Fleetweld 7 electrodes.

FLEETWELD 7

Fleetweld 7 is the original and most widely used electrode of the group. It is an E6012 electrode and will operate on either DC or industrial AC welders. It is the best of the group for general-purpose welding because, of those in the group, it operates best in the vertical and overhead positions as well as flat. It is fastest for 90-degree vertical-down welding of sheet-metal lap and fillet welds. On production jobs, it is widely used on jobs with poor fitup. It operates on AC and is faster than Fleetweld 37. For steep downhill work, it is better than Fleetweld 47.

MECHANICAL PROPERTIES	AS-WELDED	STRESS-RELIEVED (1150°F)
Tensile Strength, psi	67,000 − 79,000	67,000 − 84,000
Yield Point, psi	55,000 − 70,000	55,000 − 73,000
Elongation, % in 2 inches	17 − 22	17 − 24
Impact Resistance (Charpy V-Notch) ft-lbs	58 @ 70°F	62 @ 70°F

Job Instructions

1. Make fillet and lap welds on 14-gauge sheet metal, both in the downhand and 60-degree downhill positions, using 1/8" electrodes. Note the speed of welding and the outstanding fast-follow ability of this electrode. Fleetweld 7 is the fastest electrode for fast-follow applications that are welded downhill at an angle of greater than 60 degrees.

ALL POSITIONS		
Electrode Size		Amperage Range
Diameter	Length	DC(−)
1/8"	14"	80 − 135
5/32"	14"	110 − 180
3/16"	14"	155 − 250
7/32"	18"	225 − 295
1/4"	18"	245 − 325

2. Repeat the above on heavier stock with 3/16" electrode. Vary the angle of incline and, for each position, make as large a weld as possible. Note that the steeper the angle, the smaller the bead must be in order to stay ahead of the molten pool.

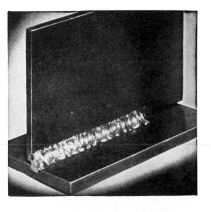

Figure 1. Horizontal fillet weld with poor fitup (gap of 1/8") in 1/4" plates welded with 'Fleetweld 7.'

3. Intentionally prepare a fillet joint with poor fitup. Weld this joint with Fleetweld 7. Note that it is possible to make reasonably fast welds without the metal spilling through the joint. If the fitup is poor enough, it may be necessary to use a slight weave on the first pass. Usually it is preferable to use a stringer bead to be sure that adequate penetration is obtained. The ability to weld poor fitup joints with Fleetweld 7 results from its deposition of a fairly fast-freezing weld.

4. Use 1/4" Fleetweld 7 with high currents on heavier plate, with AC to eliminate arc blow. Become familiar with the operation of Fleetweld 7 on AC, because its operation will be compared with that of other electrodes in the following lessons.

5. Using 1/8" Fleetweld 7, make vertical-down, vertical-up, and overhead welds with the procedures described above. Note that it operates best vertical-down, but that vertical-up and overhead welds may be made with reasonable ease. Fleetweld 7 is the most versatile out-of-position electrode of the "Fill-Freeze" group, but lacks the complete flexibility of the "Fast-Freeze" electrodes on applications of this type.

Figure 2. Fleetweld 7 is widely used for structural fabrication.

Object:
To study the special characteristics of Lincoln Fleetweld 37 electrodes.

Equipment:
Lincoln AC-225-S or a limited-input AC welder.

Material:
Scrap plate and 14-gauge sheet metal; 1/8" and 3/16" Fleetweld 37 electrodes.

FLEETWELD 37

Fleetweld 37 is an E6013 electrode with better operation on AC than E6012 electrodes. It also has a softer arc and smoother bead with slightly more slag and less spatter. Fleetweld 37 is widely used on sheet-metal lap and fillet welds where appearance and ease of operation are more important than welding speed. It can be used on low open-circuit voltage (OCV), limited-input welders where general-purpose welding is its principal application.

MECHANICAL PROPERTIES	AS-WELDED	STRESS-RELIEVED (1150°F)
Tensile Strength, psi	67,000 − 74,000	67,000 − 74,000
Yield Point, psi	55,000 − 68,000	55,000 − 68,000
Elongation, % in 2 inches	17 − 28	17 − 29
Impact Resistance (Charpy V-Notch) ft-lbs	70 @ 70°F	32 @ 70°F

Job Instructions

1. Make sheet-metal lap and fillet welds with 1/8" Fleetweld 37 similar to those made with Fleetweld 7. Note that the bead is smoother and the arc is softer with less spatter, but that it is slower than the other electrodes.

ALL POSITIONS			
Electrode Size		Current Range	
Diameter	Length	AC	DC(±)
3/32"	12"	65 − 100	70 − 95
1/8"	14"	90 − 140	90 − 135
5/32"	14"	120 − 190	135 − 180
3/16"	14"	200 − 260	185 − 235

2. Make welds in all positions with Fleetweld 37. Note that, like the E6012 electrodes, it operates best flat and vertical-down, but can also be used on vertical and overhead joints with reasonable ease. This ability qualifies Fleetweld 37 as a general-purpose electrode, particularly where low OCV, limited-input welders are used.

3. Compare Fleetweld 37 and Fleetweld 7 for stability and ease of operation on low OCV welders. Note that Fleetweld 37 is markedly superior.

Object:
To study the characteristics of Lincoln Fleetweld 57 electrode.

Equipment:
Lincoln AC-225-S or a limited-input AC welder.

Material:
Scrap plate and 14-gauge sheet; 1/8" and 3/16" Fleetweld 57 electrodes.

FLEETWELD 57

Fleetweld 57 is an E6013 electrode for all-position general-purpose welding, designed to make better welds with less effort. Operates with a drag technique in all positions and makes beads that look machine-made. The electrode gives good AC operation on low OCV transformer welders, and is excellent for poor fitup.

MECHANICAL PROPERTIES	AS-WELDED	STRESS-RELIEVED (1150°F)
Tensile Strength, psi	67,000 − 77,000	67,000 − 70,000
Yield Strength, psi	55,000 − 71,000	60,000 − 61,000
Elongation, % in 2 inches	17 − 26	24 − 30
Impact Resistance (Charpy V-Notch) ft-lbs	55 @ 70°F	55 @ 70°F

ALL POSITIONS		
Electrode Size	Current Range, Amps.	
Diameter	AC	DC(−)
5/64"	45 − 80	40 − 75
3/32"	75 − 105	70 − 95
1/8"	100 − 150	90 − 135
5/32"	150 − 200	135 − 180
3/16"	200 − 260	180 − 240
7/32"	250 − 310	225 − 280
1/4"	300 − 360	270 − 330
5/16"	360 − 460	330 − 430

Job Instructions

Make the same test welds and the same observations as with Fleetweld 37.

Object:

To study the special characteristics of Lincoln Fleetweld 47 electrodes.

Equipment:

Lincoln "Idealarc" or other AC or DC welder and accessories.

Material:

Scrap plate; 1/8", 3/16"; and 1/4" Fleetweld 47 electrodes.

FLEETWELD 47

Fleetweld 47 is an E7014 electrode. Iron powder in its coating produces operating characteristics that are very similar to those of the "fast-fill" electrodes. However, it retains sufficient "fast-freeze" ability to operate in all positions, though it is seldom used in the vertical or overhead positions. On those few applications where it is used vertical, the vertical-up procedure is generally preferred. Its principal use is on downhill applications where the "fast-fill" electrodes would be used if the joint were in the flat position. It can be used on joints with moderately poor fitup.

MECHANICAL PROPERTIES	AS-WELDED	STRESS-RELIEVED (1150°F)
Tensile Strength, psi	67,000 − 77,000	67,000 − 70,000
Yield Point, psi	55,000 − 71,000	60,000 − 61,000
Elongation, % in 2 inches	17 − 26	24 − 30
Impact Resistance (Charpy V-Notch) ft-lbs	55 @ 70°F	55 @ 70°F

Job Instructions

1. Make flat fillet and lap welds with Fleetweld 47. Note the outstanding speed as compared with other "fill-freeze" electrodes.

ALL POSITIONS			
Electrode Size		Ampere Range	
Diameter	Length	AC	DC(−)
1/8"	14"	110 − 160	100 − 145
5/32"	14"	150 − 225	135 − 200
3/16"	14"	200 − 280	180 − 250
7/32"	18"	260 − 340	235 − 305
1/4"	18"	280 − 425	260 − 380

2. Make downhill fillet and lap welds with varying degrees of incline. Note that where it can be used it is faster than other electrodes of this group. Note, also, that it cannot be operated on as steep an incline. Many production welding jobs contain some welding that must be done at an angle of 10-20 degrees downhill, and it is on these jobs where speed is important that Fleetweld 47 is widely used.

3. Note on all of the above applications the ease of operation and excellent appearance of the weld. Fleetweld 47 is preferred by many operators for these reasons.

4. Weld vertical-up and overhead with Fleetweld 47.

LESSON 3.4

Object:
To study the use and applications of Lincoln "FAST-FILL" electrodes.

General Information

Lincoln "FAST-FILL" electrodes are best suited for production welding of downhand joints where it is desired to deposit a specified amount of metal in the shortest possible time, and for exceptionally easy downhand welding by inexperienced welders.

Included in this group are Jetweld 1, Jetweld 2, and Jetweld 3. (See Lesson 1.17 for further information on iron-powder-type electrodes.)

Operating Characteristics

Deposition:	FAST-FILL — exceptionally high deposition rates are possible with these electrodes.
Arc:	SOFT — has little force or penetration and negligible spatter.
Slag:	HEAVY — very fluid and covers the weld completely.
Bead:	FLAT — or slightly concave with a smooth, glossy appearance.
Current:	AC — DC may also be used, but is less desirable.
Positions:	FLAT — may also be used slightly downhill.

Application Information

The industrial fast-fill electrodes are used because of their very high deposition rates, excellent appearance, and ease of operation. The group is limited to operation in the flat position and horizontal fillets.

1. FLAT AND HORIZONTAL FILLETS on 1/4" and heavier material are made with Jetweld 1, which produces fast, smooth welds with easy slag removal. Where X-ray requirements must be met, Jetweld 2 is used.
2. DEEP GROOVE WELDS IN THE FLAT POSITION are best made with Jetweld 2, which washes well into the sides of the joint and has an extremely friable slag that is easily removed and will not lock in the joint.
3. MEDIUM-CARBON CRACK-SENSITIVE STEELS are readily welded with Jetweld 1. Its light penetration and high physical properties permit fastest welding without cracks.

Procedures

FLAT — Use a drag technique to deposit stringer beads. Hold the electrode perpendicular to the work and tipped forward into the direction of travel approximately 30 degrees. Travel fast enough to stay 1/4" to 3/8" ahead of the molten pool. Avoid high currents, especially on X-ray-quality work.

HORIZONTAL FILLETS — The procedure is the same as that described for FLAT, except that the electrode is pointed directly into the joint at an angle of 45 degrees, touching both legs of the joint instead of being held perpendicular.

Object:
To study the special characteristics of Lincoln Jetweld 1 and Jetweld 3 electrodes.

Equipment:
Lincoln "Idealarc" AC and DC welder.

Material:
Scrap 1/4" or heavier plate, including some of high-carbon content; 3/16" Jetweld 1 and Jetweld 3.

JETWELD 1 AND JETWELD 3

Jetweld 1 and Jetweld 3 are "Fast-Fill" electrodes. The arc is very soft, the travel speed is fast, and, under some conditions, the heavy slag curls off the weld without chipping. Both electrodes operate best on AC, although DC electrode-positive may be used on the 3/16" and smaller sizes.

Jetweld 1 is recommended when the primary need is for a smooth-running electrode with outstanding operator appeal combined with high travel speeds and deposition rates. Jetweld 3 has similar operating characteristics, but is recommended when the highest travel speeds and deposition rates are required.

Figure 1. Horizontal fillet weld. Plate size is 3/8", fillet size 1/4", "Jetweld 1" electrode size 3/16". Current is 275 amps AC, arc speed 15 inches per minute.

Figure 2. "Jetweld 1" bead made on flat plate was bent to show ductility. Notice the smoothness of the weld and its freedom from face cracks.

MECHANICAL PROPERTIES	AS-WELDED	STRESS-RELIEVED (1150°F)
	JETWELD 1	
Tensile Strength, psi	72,000 – 91,000	72,000 – 89,000
Yield Point, psi	60,000 – 80,000	60,000 – 78,000
Elongation, % in 2 inches	17 – 26	22 – 26
Impact Resistance (Charpy V-Notch) ft-lbs	39 @ 70°F	39 @ 70°F

MECHANICAL PROPERTIES	AS-WELDED	STRESS-RELIEVED (1150°F)
	JETWELD 3	
Tensile Strength, psi	72,000 — 87,000	72,000 — 87,000
Yield Point, psi	60,000 — 77,000	60,000 — 75,000
Elongation, % in 2 inches	17 — 27	20 — 28
Impact Resistance (Charpy V-Notch) ft-lbs	40 @ 70°F	37 @ 70°F

For Jetweld 1 and 3:

ALL POSITIONS			
Electrode Size		**Current Range**	
Diameter	**Length**	**AC**	
3/32''	12''	65 — 120	
1/8''	14''	115 — 175	
5/32''	14''	180 — 240	
3/16''	18''	240 — 300	
7/32''	18''	300 — 380	
1/4''	18''	350 — 440	

Object:
To study the special characteristics of Lincoln Jetweld 2 electrodes.

Equipment:
Lincoln "Idealarc" AC and DC welder.

Material:
Beveled scrap 3/8" or heavier plate; 3/16" Jetweld 2 electrodes.

JETWELD 2

Jetweld 2 is similar to Jetweld 1, but is different in that it washes up better in a deep groove, has a slag that crumbles for easy removal, and produces a weld of X-ray quality. It is an E6027 electrode and operates best on AC, though DC electrode-negative may also be used.

MECHANICAL PROPERTIES	AS-WELDED	STRESS-RELIEVED (1150°F)
Tensile Strength, psi	62,000 − 70,000	62,000 − 70,000
Yield Point, psi	50,000 − 62,000	50,000 − 59,000
Elongation, % in 2 inches	25 − 32	25 − 32
Impact Resistance (Charpy V-Notch) ft-lbs	20 to 59 @ −20°F	79 @ 70°F

Electrode Size		Overall Range Amps (AC)	Max. Amps. for X-Ray	Recommended Amps. for Fillets
Diameter	Length			
5/32"	14"	190 − 240	240	220
3/16"	18"	250 − 300	300	270
7/32"	18"	300 − 380	350	310
1/4"	18"	350 − 450	400	350

Job Instructions

1. Make deep-groove butt welds with Jetweld 2 and note the characteristics described above.

2. Make fillet and lap welds similar to those made with Jetweld 1. Note that, while Jetweld 1 is preferred, Jetweld 2 is readily applied and can be used on joints of this type where X-ray quality is required.

3. Weld with Jetweld 2 using both AC and DC, electrode negative. Note that the same results are obtained as were noted for Jetweld 1.

LESSON
3.5

Object:

To study the use of Lincoln low-hydrogen electrodes for hard-to-weld and alloy steels.

General Information

Certain types of steel are crack-sensitive, in that the heating and cooling of welding tends to create cracks. These are medium and high-carbon steels, high-sulphur and low-alloy steels. Certain types of cracks in these steels are directly traceable to hydrogen. Low-hydrogen electrodes produce hydrogen-free welds, eliminating the cracking. They also prevent the formation of gases, such as hydrogen sulphide, which cause either internal or surface porosity. Consequently, deposits are dense with exceptional ductility. (See Lesson 1.38 for further information.)

Lincoln low-hydrogen electrodes are available in seven different classifications and three tensile strengths. The operating characteristics of all are similar, so that they differ only in physical properties and deposit analysis. Iron powder in their coverings produces higher deposition rates than that of low-hydrogen electrodes without iron powder.

Application Information

The ability to satisfactorily weld hard-to-weld steels is the outstanding feature of these electrodes. They produce porosity-free and micro-crack-free welds and reduce the amount of preheat required on heavier sections.

Low-hydrogen coverings substantially improve ductility by depositing dense, sound welds. This is particularly valuable in the higher-strength steels.

Low-hydrogen electrodes generally reduce the amount of preheat required by 200 to 300 degrees F. Also, they weld on phosphorus or sulphur-bearing steels without "hot-short" difficulties or surface holes.

Applications of these electrodes utilize the above characteristics of the low-hydrogen family. Which particular electrode is used on any job depends principally on the tensile strength of the base metal. Jetweld LH-70 and LH-3800 are used on mild steels and steels with 70,000-psi tensile strength, while the other electrodes are used on higher-tensile steels. Typical applications include:

1. ALL TYPES OF JOINTS ON HARD-TO-WELD STEELS, including high-tensile steels. The low-hydrogen characteristics reduce or eliminate the need for preheat. They produce porosity-free welds on high-sulphur material and prevent "hot-shortness" in phosphorus-bearing steels.

2. LARGE WELDS ON HEAVY PLATE, where shrinkage stresses tend to cause cracks at the root of the weld. Bead shape of the Jetweld LH electrodes, plus good mechanical properties, produce crackless welds and reduce the need for stress relief.

3. PRESSURE PIPING and other applications that require the specific deposit analysis available from Jetweld LH-90 or Jetweld LH-110.

4. WELDS THAT ARE TO BE PORCELAIN-ENAMELED, particularly if the weld is not to be annealed before enameling. Low-hydrogen properties produce the best possible bonding between the porcelain and the weld metal.

Procedures

DOWNHAND — on the first pass, or wherever it is desired to reduce admixture with a base metal of poor weldability, use low currents. On succeeding passes, use currents as high as possible consistent with the plate thickness. Lightly drag the electrode or hold a very short arc. Do *not* use a long arc at any time, since this type of electrode relies principally on molten slag for shielding. Stringer beads or a small weave are preferred to wide weave passes. When starting a new electrode, strike the arc ahead of the crater, move back into the crater, and then proceed in the normal direction. Use lower currents with DC than with AC. Electrode should point directly into the joint and be tipped forward about 45 degrees in the direction of travel. Travel speed should be governed by the desired bead size.

VERTICAL — Weld vertical-up. Use a triangular weave. Build a shelf of weld metal, and, with the weave, deposit layer upon layer of metal as the weld progresses up the joint. Do not use a whip technique or take the electrode out of the molten pool. Point the electrode directly into the joint and slightly upward to permit the arc force to assist in controlling the puddle. Travel slow enough to maintain the shelf without causing the metal to spill. Use currents in the lower portion of the range.

OVERHEAD — Use a slight circular motion in the crater. Maintain a short arc with the whip. Do not use a weave. Point the electrode directly into the joint and tip it slightly forward into the direction of travel. Travel fast to avoid spilling weld metal, but do not be alarmed if the slag spills some. Use currents in the lower portion of the range.

Redrying Low-Hydrogen Electrodes

Low-hydrogen electrodes must be dry if they are to perform properly. Electrodes in unopened, hermetically sealed containers remain dry indefinitely in good storage conditions. Opened cans should be stored in a cabinet at 250 to

DRYING LOW-HYDROGEN ELECTRODES

	Drying Temperatures	
Nature of Moisture Pickup	E7018-28	E8018-X, E9018-X, E11018-X
Electrodes exposed to air for less than one week; no direct contact with water. Welds not subject to X-ray inspection.	300°F	300°F
Electrodes exposed to air for less than one week; no direct contact with water. Welds subject to X-ray inspection.	700°F	750°F
Electrodes have come in direct contact with water, or have been exposed to extremely humid conditions as indicated by core wire rusting at the holder end. Before redrying at 700 – 750°F, predry electrodes in this condition at 180°F for 1 to 2 hours. This minimizes the tendency for coating cracks or oxidation of the alloys in the coating.	700°F	750°F

Note: One hour at the listed temperatures is satisfactory. Do not dry electrodes at higher temperatures or for more than 8 hours. Several hours at lower temperature are not equivalent to using the specified temperatures. Remove the electrodes from the can and spread them out in the furnace. Each electrode must reach the drying temperature. (Cardboard can liners char at about 350°F.)

300°F. Supplying weldors with electrodes twice a shift minimizes the danger of the moisture pickup. Return electrodes to the heated cabinet for overnight storage.

When containers are punctured or opened so that the electrode is exposed to the air for a few days, or when containers are stored under unusually wet conditions, low-hydrogen electrodes pick up moisture. The moisture, depending upon the amount absorbed, impairs weld quality. Redrying completely restores ability to deposit quality welds. The proper redrying temperature depends on the type of electrode and its condition. Drying procedures are listed in the table.

Object:
To study the special characteristics of Lincoln Jetweld LH-70 electrodes.

Equipment:
Lincoln "Idealarc" or other AC or DC welder.

Material:
Scrap high-sulphur and high-carbon steel; 5/32" Jetweld LH-70, Fleetweld 5P and Fleetweld 37.

JETWELD LH-70

Jetweld LH-70 E7018 electrodes are 70,000-psi tensile-strength electrodes of the Lincoln low-hydrogen electrode family. They are also suitable for 60,000-psi-tensile mild steel. The E7018's are the most used of the Lincoln family of low-hydrogen electrodes and can be used on all low-hydrogen applications except those requiring other physical or chemical properties.

MECHANICAL PROPERTIES	AS-WELDED	STRESS-RELIEVED (1150°F)
Tensile Strength, psi	72,000 – 81,000	65,000 – 74,000
Yield Point, psi	60,000 – 69,000	55,000 – 60,000
Elongation, % in 2 inches	22 – 30	24 – 34
Impact Resistance (Charpy V-Notch) ft-lbs	20 to 110 @ −20°F	120 @ −20°F

Job Instructions

1. Weld on high-sulphur scrap steel with both Jetweld LH-70 and Fleetweld 5P. Note that Jetweld LH-70 eliminates the porosity encountered with the conventional electrodes. This is because Jetweld LH-70 does not have hydrogen in its covering and does not form the hydrogen sulphide gas that causes the porosity with conventional electrodes.

ALL POSITIONS			
Electrode Size		Amperage Range	
Diameter	Length	DC(+)	AC
3/32"	12"	70 – 100	80 -- 120
1/8"	14"	90 – 150	110 – 170
5/32"	14"	120 – 190	135 – 225
3/16"	14"	170 – 280	200 – 300
7/32"	18"	210 – 330	260 -- 380
1/4"	18"	290 – 430	325 – 440
5/16"	18"	375 – 500	400 -- 530

2. Weld with both Jetweld LH-70 and Fleetweld 37 on heavy stock, high-carbon steel. Note that the Jetweld LH-70 eliminates cracks encountered with Fleetweld 37. This is, again, due to the low-hydrogen content of the covering.

Object:
To study the special characteristics of Lincoln Jet-LH 72 and Jet-LH 78 low-hydrogen electrodes for plate and pipe.

Equipment:
Lincoln "Idealarc" or other AC or DC welder.

Material:
Scrap heavy plate, preferably beveled or square edge butts with backup, also pipe nipples (beveled) 1/8" Jet-LH 72, 1/8" Jet-LH 78, and 1/8" Fleetweld 5P.

JET-LH 72 AND JET-LH 78

Jet-LH 72 and Jet-LH 78 are E7018 electrodes with weld metal deposit characteristics similar to Jetweld LH-70. Jet-LH 72 has a lighter slag cover and less arc blow than Jetweld LH-70. This leads to more puddle control which is most helpful for overhead and pipe welding. Jet-LH 78 has an even lighter slag to provide the greatest puddle control of the E7018's. Jet-LH 78 is especially recommended for deep V-grooves and difficult pipe joints because of its excellent wash-in and ability to run at higher amperages.

MECHANICAL PROPERTIES	AS-WELDED	STRESS-RELIEVED ($1150°F$ 1 hr.)
	JET-LH 72	
Tensile Strength, psi	$72,000 - 82,000$	$72,000 - 77,000$
Yield Strength, psi	$60,000 - 74,000$	$60,000 - 65,000$
Elongation, % in 2 inches	$22 - 31$	$25 - 31$
Impact Resistance (Charpy V-Notch) ft-lbs	20 to 110 @ $-20°F$	120 @ $-20°F$
	JET-LH 78	
Tensile Strength, psi	$72,000 - 89,000$	$71,000 - 86,000$
Yield Strength, psi	$60,000 - 79,000$	$56,000 - 72,000$
Elongation, % in 2 inches	$22 - 30$	$27 - 33$
Impact Resistance (Charpy V-Notch) ft-lbs	20 to 110 @ $-20°F$	90 @ $-20°F$

Job Instructions

1. Compare the arc action and puddle control of Jet-LH 72 and Jet-LH 78 in the horizontal position with a deep V-groove and in the vertical up position. You should notice the puddle control is better with Jet-LH 78 and it can also handle slightly higher currents than Jet-LH 72. Remember to keep a short arc length.

2. Obtain beveled pipe as in lesson 1.45. Attempt to put in the root pass with either E7018 as was done with Fleetweld 5P. Note the inability to attain adequate penetration and produce a bead on the inside of the pipe. Now put

in the root pass with Fleetweld 5P. Practice the fill and cap passes with Jet LH-72 and Jet-LH-78 to determine a personal preference. This procedure will produce a joint with mostly low-hydrogen properties (especially if the E6010 root pass is ground smooth) which is often used in steam or other high pressure lines. The low-hydrogen fill and cap passes are also sometimes used with the root pass made by the TIG process.

Object:
To study the special characteristics of Lincoln Jetweld LH-90, Jet-LH 8018-C3, and Jet-LH 8018-C1 electrodes.

Equipment:
Lincoln "Idealarc" or other AC or DC welder.

Material:
1-1/4% chromium, 1/2% molybdenum scrap pipe or plate; 5/32" Jetweld LH-90, Jet-LH 8018-C3, and Jet-LH 8018-C1 electrodes.

JETWELD LH-90, JET-LH 8018-C3 AND JET-LH 8018-C1

Jetweld LH-90, an E9018 electrode that also meets the requirements of E8018-B2, is a 90,000 psi tensile-strength electrode of the Lincoln low-hydrogen electrode family. It has a nominal alloy content of 1-1/4% chromium and 1/2% molybdenum, and is intended for pressure piping or general fabrication where the joint requires either the specific alloy or the high-strength deposits of this analysis. Its operating characteristics are similar to those of Jetweld LH-70.

Jet-LH 8018-C3 is an 80,000-psi tensile-strength electrode and meets the requirements of E8018-C3. The weld deposit contains 1% nickel. Operating characteristics are the same as Jetweld LH-70.

Jet-LH 8018-C1 is an 80,000-psi tensile-strength electrode and meets the requirements of E8018-C1. The weld deposit contains 2-1/4% nickel. Operating characteristics are also the same as Jetweld LH-90.

MECHANICAL PROPERTIES	AS-WELDED	STRESS-RELIEVED ($1275°F$ 1 hr.)	($1150°F$ 1 hr.)
	JETWELD LH-90		
Tensile Strength, psi	97,000 − 107,000	80,000 − 94,000	90,000 − 107,000
Yield Strength, psi	84,000 − 97,000	67,000 − 81,000	77,000 − 93,000
Elongation, % in 2 inches	17 − 24	19 − 26	17 − 24
Impact Resistance (Charpy V-Notch) ft-lbs	40 @ $70°F$	60 @ $70°F$	60 @ $70°F$
	JET-LH 8018-C3	($1150°F$ 2 hrs.)	
Tensile Strength, psi	80,000 − 93,000	81,000 − 86,000	
Yield Strength, psi	68,000 − 80,000	65,000 − 76,000	
Elongation, % in 2 inches	24 − 27	24 − 29	
Impact Resistance (Charpy V-Notch) ft-lbs	20 to 50 @ $−40°F$	20 to 117 @ $−20°F$	
	JET-LH 8018-C1	($1150°F$ 1 hr.)	
Tensile Strength, psi	80,000 − 95,000	80,000 − 98,000	
Yield Strength, psi	67,000 − 81,000	67,000 − 83,000	
Elongation, % in 2 inches	19 − 25	19 − 28	
Impact Resistance (Charpy V-Notch) ft-lbs	30 to 60 @ $−75°F$	20 to 40 @ $−75°F$	

Job Instructions

1. Use Jetweld LH-90 on pressure piping to become familiar with the characteristics of this electrode when welding pipe. Generally follow the procedures for vertical-up welding as outlined in Lesson 3.5, with modifications to compensate for the pipe joint.

ALL POSITIONS			
Electrode Size		Current Range	
Diameter	Length	DC(+)	AC
1/8″	14″	90 — 150	110 — 160
5/32″	14″	110 — 200	140 — 230
3/16″	14″	160 — 280	200 — 310

2. Weld flat, vertical, and overhead on 90,000-psi scrap plate to become familiar with the operating characteristics of all the electrodes.

Object:
To study the special characteristics of Lincoln Jetweld LH-110 electrode.

Equipment:
Lincoln "Idealarc" or other AC or DC welder.

Material:
Scrap high-tensile steel; 5/32" Jetweld LH-110 electrode.

JETWELD LH-110

Jetweld LH-110 is the 110,000-psi tensile-strength electrode of the Lincoln low-hydrogen electrode family. It is classified E11018-G. It is particularly intended for welding the quenched-and-tempered steels as well as any other application where high-strength weld metal is necessary. Its operating characteristics are similar to those of Jetweld LH-70.

MECHANICAL PROPERTIES	AS-WELDED	STRESS-RELIEVED (1025°F 1 hr.)
Tensile Strength, psi	110,000 – 126,000	110,000 – 120,000
Yield Strength, psi	98,000 – 109,000	95,000 – 108,000
Elongation, % in 2 inches	20 – 24	20 – 23
Impact Resistance (Charpy V-Notch) ft-lbs	20 to 50 @ −60°F	30 to 45 @ −60°F

Job Instructions

1. Weld with Jetweld LH-110 on all types of joints in scrap HY-80 or T-1 steels to become familiar with its operation. Note that its operating characteristics are very similar to those of Jetweld LH-70 and Jetweld LH-90, but that it is used on applications where its high tensile strength is required.

ALL POSITIONS			
Electrode Size		Current Range	
Diameter	Length	DC(+)	AC
3/32"	12"	70 – 100	80 – 110
1/8"	14"	85 – 155	110 – 170
5/32"	14"	120 – 195	135 – 225
3/16"	14"	160 – 280	200 – 310
7/32"	18"	190 – 310	240 – 350
1/4"	18"	230 – 360	290 – 410

LESSON 3.5E

Object:
To study the special characteristics of Lincoln Jetweld LH-3800.

Equipment:
Lincoln "Idealarc" AC and DC welder.

Material:
Scrap high-sulphur and high-carbon steel plate; 3/16" Jetweld LH-3800 electrodes.

JETWELD LH-3800

Jetweld LH-3800 is an E7028 iron-powder low-hydrogen electrode. It is particularly suited to making flat groove welds and flat or horizontal fillet welds and in other production welding where the high-deposition rate can be effectively used to lower welding costs. AC current is preferred, with DC (+) and 10% lower current the second choice. Jetweld LH-3800 is limited to making welds in the flat and horizontal positions only.

MECHANICAL PROPERTIES	AS-WELDED	STRESS-RELIEVED (1150°F)
Tensile Strength, psi	72,000 — 95,000	84,000 — 89,000
Yield Point, psi	60,000 — 87,000	73,000 — 77,000
Elongation, % in 2 inches	24 — 26	25 — 27
Impact Resistance (Charpy V-Notch) ft-lbs	24 @ 0°F	85 @ 70°F

Job Instructions

1. Weld on high-sulphur and high-carbon scrap stock as with Jetweld LH-70. Note that Jetweld LH-3800 duplicates the performance advantages previously observed when performing the Job Instructions 1 and 2 for Jetweld LH-70.

FLAT OR HORIZONTAL			
Electrode Size		Current Range	
Diameter	Length	AC	DC(+)
5/32"	18"	180 — 270	170 — 240
3/16"	18"	240 — 330	210 — 300
7/32"	18"	275 — 410	
1/4"	18"	360 — 520	

2. Make a flat-position weld with Jetweld LH-3800 and then Jetweld LH-70. Note the difference in deposition rate and welding speed. Also observe that Jetweld LH-3800 develops a larger weld crater and produces more slag. These characteristics limit its use to flat and horizontal welds.

SECTION IV

STAINLESS-STEEL ELECTRODES

Object:
To study the use of Lincoln lime-covered stainless steel electrodes.

Equipment:
Lincoln "Idealarc" or other DC welder and accessories.

Material:
Scrap stainless-steel plate, manganese-steel casting, and mild-steel plate; 1/8" and 3/16" Stainweld 308-15 electrodes and 3/16" Stainweld 310-15 electrodes.

General Information

Lincoln lime-covered electrodes are made in a variety of analyses for all-position use on stainless-steel applications.

Characteristics

The operating characteristics of all Lincoln lime-covered stainless-steel electrodes are quite similar. A fairly forceful arc with deep penetration and light slag produce a FAST-FREEZE ability that permits good operation on out-of-position joints.

Type: E308-15 – Stainweld 308-15 – 19-9 unstabilized
E347-15 – Stainweld 347-15 – 19-9 columbium-stabilized
E310-15 – Stainweld 310-15 – 25-20 unstabilized

Covering: Lime-type

Current: DC – normally used on DC, electrode positive, though DC, electrode negative, is sometimes used on sheet-metal applications.

Positions: Versatile all-position electrodes.

Application Information

Within the group of lime-covered stainless electrodes the selection of a particular electrode for a given application depends entirely on the alloy of the stainless base metal. The stainless steels for which each electrode is suited are

Figure 1. Welding stainless-steel liner in a pulp-mill-smelter blow nozzle is representative of a typical stainless-steel electrode application.

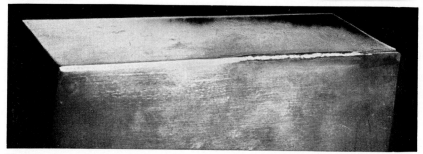

Figure 2. Corner weld in 18-8 stainless-steel welded with "Stainweld 308-15." Left-hand portion is ground. Note smoothness.

given above. The stabilized electrodes may be used on either stabilized or unstabilized base metal, while the unstabilized electrodes are used only on unstabilized base metal.

When welding a stainless steel to a mild steel, it is best to use a stainless electrode with higher alloy than the material being welded. This additional alloy

ELECTRODE SELECTION TABLE FOR
CHROMIUM-NICKEL STAINLESS STEELS

Base Metal AISI Desig.	Popular Designation	Recommended Electrode
201 202 301 302 304 205 308	17-4 MN 18-5 Mn 17-7 18-8 19-9 18-10 20-10	Stainweld 308-15 or -16
304L 308L	19-9 ELC	Stainweld 308L-16 Stainweld 347-15 or -16
309 309S 309Cb	24-12 24-12 LC 24-12 Cb	Stainweld 309-16 Stainweld 309-16 E309 Cb (1)
310 310S	25-20	Stainweld 310-15 or -16
316 316L	18-12 Mo 18-12 Mo ELC	Stainweld 316L-16 (2)
317	19-13 Mo	E317 or E317L (1) (2) Stainweld 316L-16 (2)
317L	19-13 Mo ELC	E317L (1) (2) Stainweld 316L-16 (2)
D319	19-13 Mo	Stainweld 316L-16 (2)
321 347 348	18-8 Ti 18-8 Cb 18-8 Cb	Stainweld 347-15 or -16

(1) Not manufactured by Lincoln.

(2) Heat treatment necessary for service in hot acids.

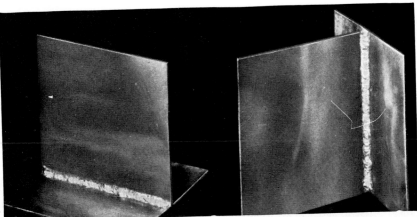

Figure 3. Fillet welds in 16-gauge 25-12 stainless steel. Left: Downhand weld. Right: Vertical weld, welded upward.

will compensate for the loss in alloy caused by admixture with the mild steel.

Out-of-position welding is a specialty of the lime-covered electrodes where their fast-freeze ability is most desirable.

Strength welds in manganese steel are best made with the higher-alloy electrodes. Stainweld 310-15 is most widely used.

Hardsurfacing buildup is usually done with Stainweld 308-15. On such applications, the stainless may be used as the only surfacing material to prevent wear

PROPERTIES AND OPERATING DATA

STAINWELD®		308-15	310-15	347-15
Typical Mechanical Properties				
Tensile Strength, psi		90,000	93,000	97,000
Ductility		40%	34%	35%
Typical Deposit Composition				
Carbon %		.06	.17	.06
Chromium %		20.1	27.0	19.8
Nickel %		9.6	20.5	9.5
Molybdenum %		—	—	—
Columbium %		—	—	.80
Operating Data				
Polarity	Dia.	DC(+)	DC(+)	DC(+)
Current Range	5/64"	—	—	—
for DC(+)	3/32"	30-70	30-70	30-70
	1/8"	50-100	45-95	50-100
	5/32"	75-130	80-135	75-130
(Ranges for AC	3/16"	95-165	100-165	95-165
about 10% higher)	1/4"	150-225	—	—

Recommended Optimum Currents:

For Flat Welding — about 10% below maximum

For Vertical-Up Welding — about 20% below maximum.

For Vertical-Down Welding (Lime-coated electrodes only) — about maximum.

or corrosion, or it may be used as a base between the original base metal and more abrasion-resistant material such as one of the Faceweld electrodes. In the latter case, the ductile stainless acts as a cushion to absorb the shock of impact loads and prevent the harder surfacing material from spalling off.

Procedures

All of these electrodes operate on DC, electrode positive (reverse polarity).

Three characteristics peculiar to stainless steel make welding with stainless-steel electrodes different than welding with mild steel: higher electrical resistance, lower thermal conduction, and higher thermal expansion. This means that the electrode gets hotter, the molten pool cools more slowly, and distortion is a greater problem. To counteract these characteristics, less current is used, greater care must be taken in cleaning and fitting the joint, and provisions must be made to take the heat away on light sheet metal by such means as copper chill bars placed under the joint.

FLAT — Use as short an arc as possible without choking or sticking. Use stringer beads for all passes and avoid weaving. Use currents as low as possible consistent with good arc action and proper fusion.

VERTICAL AND OVERHEAD — Use only stringer beads made with a slight whip and a circular motion in the crater. Use currents as low as possible.

Job Instructions

1. Make welds in the flat position. Note how the electrode has a tendency to overheat and become red. Reduce the current until the arc becomes sticky. The proper setting for the electrode is one that will just maintain the arc smoothly without overheating the electrode.

2. Make welds in the vertical and overhead position to become familiar with the procedure.

3. Weld on sheet metal. Note that the best results are obtained if a copper chill bar is placed behind the joint.

4. Join two pieces of manganese steel with Stainweld 310-15 electrode. When welding on manganese steel it is important to keep the base metal cool; each bead should be allowed to cool enough so that it can be touched with the bare hand before another bead is applied. If the manganese is allowed to stay at a high temperature for very long, it will become very hard and may crack either during welding or in service.

5. Build a pad of surfacing with Stainweld 308-15. Note that this deposit is very tough and will stand severe impact. A layer of hardsurfacing material on top of the stainless pad will increase the abrasion resistance of the surface without materially reducing the impact resistance.

LESSON 4.2

Object:
To study the use and application of Lincoln titania-covered stainless steel electrodes.

Equipment:
Lincoln "Idealarc" AC or DC welder and accessories.

Material:
Light and heavy-gauge scrap stainless steel and mild steel; 3/32" and 5/32" Stainweld 308-16 electrode, 1/8" Stainweld 309-16.

General Information

Lincoln titania-covered stainless steel electrodes are for use with AC.

Characteristics

The titania-covered electrodes have a less forceful arc than the lime-covered stainless electrodes with medium penetration and a smoother bead shape.

Type: E308-16 — Stainweld 308-16 — 19-9 unstabilized.
E309-16 — Stainweld 309-16 — For high temperature or mild steel to stainless welds.
E347-16 — Stainweld 347-16 — 19-9 columbium stabilized.
E308L-16 — Stainweld 308L-16 — 19-9 extra low carbon.
E316L-16 — Stainweld 316L-16 — For extra corrosion resistance.
E310-16 — Stainweld 310-16 — 25-20 unstabilized.

Covering: Titania-type.

Current: AC & DC — Electrode-positive polarity is used with DC. On AC, industrial-type welders are preferred.

Positions: Is capable of operation in all positions, though flat-position welds are preferred.

Application Information

The titania-covered stainless-steel electrodes are principally used where AC is the power source. Because of their softer arc and smoother bead, they are sometimes preferred even when DC is available.

GENERAL-PURPOSE WELDING on stainless steels, particularly where exceptionally smooth appearance is desired.

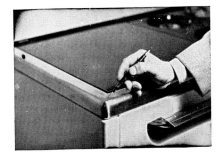

Figure 1. Corner joint in stainless-steel edge band of gas range, welded with "Stainweld 308-16." Grinding and buffing make weld indistinguishable.

SURFACING APPLICATIONS, either where it is desired to obtain a particularly tough and ductile or corrosion-resistant surface, or for intermediate layers between base metal and a hardsurfacing deposit.

PROPERTIES AND OPERATING DATA

		308-16	308L-16	309-16	310-16	316L-16	347-16
		Typical Mechanical Properties					
Tensile Strength psi		90,000	90,000	87 000	89,000	82,000	95,000
Ductility		42%	41%	36%	38%	41%	35%
		Typical Deposit Composition					
Carbon %		.06	.033	.080	.14	.030	.06
Chromium %		20.0	20.5	23.9	27.0	19.2	20.0
Nickel %		9.7	9.8	12.4	21.1	12.4	9.7
Molybdenum %		—	—	—	—	2.2	—
Columbium %		—	—	—	—	—	.80
		Operating Data					
	Dia.	DC(+) or AC	DC(+) or AC	DC(+) or AC	DC(+) or AC	DC(+) or AC	DC(+) or AC
Current Range	5/64"	20-45	—	—	—	—	—
	3/32"	36-60	30-65	30-60	30-65	30-65	30-60
	1/8"	55-95	55-100	55-95	55-100	55-100	55-95
	5/32"	80-135	80-140	80-135	80-140	80-140	80-135
	3/16"	115-185	115-190	115-185	120-185	115-190	115-185
	1/4"	200-275	—	200-275	200-275	—	—

Recommended Optimum Currents:

For Flat Welding — 10% below maximum

For Vertical-Up Welding — 20% below maximum

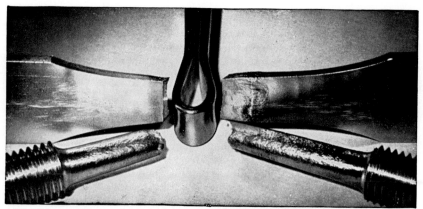

Figure 2. Specimens of 302 stainless steel welded with "Stainweld 308-16." As-welded: weld-metal tensile strength was 88,800 psi, free bend elongation, 53% in outer fibres; tensile pull sample failed in plate at 88,600 psi.

Job Instructions

1. Weld with Stainweld 308-16 using both AC and DC welders, and compare the operating characteristics of the electrode on both types of current. Bend the joint to get a feel for the toughness and ductility of Stainweld electrodes.

2. Repeat job instructions No. 1 through 4 for Lesson 4.1 and compare the operation of Stainweld 308-16 with that of the lime-coated electrodes.

3. Using the Stainweld 309-16, weld a piece of mild steel and stainless together. Note the smooth wash-in on both plates.

SECTION V

HARDSURFACING ELECTRODES

LESSON 5.1

Object:
To study the use of Lincoln hardsurfacing electrodes.

General Information

The principles of hardsurfacing are discussed in Lesson 1.42. This lesson should be studied and thoroughly understood before studying the following lessons in Section V.

As with the mild-steel electrodes discussed in Section III, the important thing in hardsurfacing electrode selection is to properly match the requirements of the application with the properties of the electrode. Also like mild-steel electrodes, the characteristics of applications and electrodes are not clear-cut, but are relative to each other. For any application, there is one electrode that has the best combination of properties, but frequently it is necessary to actually test several electrodes before the best one is found.

A careful study of the application is the starting point for electrode selection. Consider the following: Must two surfaces be protected, or only one? Is a cutting edge required? What is the relative importance of *abrasion, impact,* and *corrosion* on the wear of the part? How large is the part? What finish is required? What is the composition of the part? The cost and available sizes of the electrodes may also have a bearing on the decision.

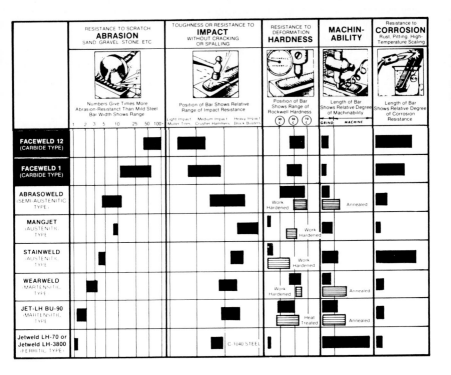

The following lessons are arranged to assist in matching the properties of the electrodes with the requirements of the job. In the "Deposit Properties" portion of each lesson is a chart that compares some of the basic characteristics of the electrodes. Other pertinent characteristics are discussed under "Application Information".

The procedure used to deposit the hardsurfacing electrode also affects the electrode selection. Most of the properties will vary with the procedure used. The amount of admixutre of weld metal and base metal will affect the alloy content of the resulting deposit. Welding current is usually the controlling factor because it controls the amount of penetration. Welding current may also affect the cooling rate, though the use of preheat and slow cooling techniques is usually more important. Cooling rate affects the structure of the deposit, which in turn affects the properties of the deposit. Information on the effect of procedures on each electrode is found in the "Procedures" portion of the lesson.

Study the following examples:

APPLICATION: Dragline bucket tooth working in sandy gravel with some good-sized rocks. The teeth are manganese steel. Only one surface needs protection. No cutting edge is required. Abrasion is the most important source of wear on the part, though impact must also be considered.

The part is large enough to take a heavy bead, and cooling will be rapid. The surface of the bead as-deposited is sufficient; no machining or grinding is required.

As abrasion is most important, the electrodes at the top of the chart receive first consideration. Faceweld 12 has excellent abrasion resistance, but little impact resistance. Faceweld 1 has better impact resistance and with proper procedure may be satisfactory. Abrasoweld has sufficient impact resistance with some sacrifice in abrasion resistance as compared with Faceweld 1. Either of these electrodes may be used on manganese steel, though a layer of Mangjet may be necessary to insure proper bonding to the work-hardened surface of the part.

APPLICATION: Same as above except that the bucket is working in sandy soil. The fact that the bucket is working in sandy soil changes the above study only in that impact is of no concern. Now it is possible to use the most abrasion-resistant material, which is Faceweld 12. Had the soil been changed to one that contained large rocks, it would have been necessary to use a deposit made up entirely of Mangjet.

LESSON 5.2

Object:
To study the use of the Faceweld electrodes.

Equipment:
Lincoln "Idealarc" AC and DC welder and accessories.

Material:
Scrap steel, including a large part; 3/16" Faceweld electrodes.

FACEWELD 1 AND FACEWELD 12

General Information

Lincoln Faceweld 1 and Faceweld 12 electrodes are used for hardsurfacing new and worn parts to resist *severe* abrasion and *moderate* impact.

Deposit Properties

The deposit consists of microscopic chromium carbide crystals held in a tough, hard metal bond. Both the carbides and the bonding metal have high abrasion resistance and moderate toughness.

Electrode	Deposit	Abrasion	Impact	Hardness 30C	50C	70C	Friction Grind	Machin-ability Machine
FACEWELD 12	CHROMIUM CARBIDE	▮	▮		▮		▮	
FACEWELD 1	CHROMIUM CARBIDE	▮	▮		▮		▮	
Abrasoweld	Semi-Austenitic	☐	☐	X ☐			☐	☐ ⊙
Mangjet	Austenitic	☐	☐		☐ X		☐	☐
Stainweld	Austenitic	☐	☐		☐ X			☐
Jet-LH BU-90	Martensitic	☐	☐	☐ ▲			☐	☐ ⊙
Jetweld LH-70	Ferritic	☐	☐	☐				☐

X—Work-Hardened   ▲—Heat-Treated   ⊙—Annealed

Figure 1. Dredge pumps worn by sand abrasion are reclaimed by building up the worn areas with "Fleetweld" and then hardsurfacing with "Faceweld."

Application Information

The Faceweld electrodes produce the *most* abrasion-resistant deposits and are used wherever parts are worn away by the action of a "gritty" or sand-like material but are not subjected to a severe pounding by hard, rock-like particles. The choice between the two Faceweld electrodes depends on the amount of pounding or impact involved on the application. If there is no impact, Faceweld 12 is best; if moderate impact is present, Faceweld 1 should be used. When it is possible to experiment on a job, first try Faceweld 12; if this deposit spalls off in service, then use Faceweld 1.

TYPICAL APPLICATIONS		
Screw conveyors	Bradley and Griffin rings	Pulverizer jaws
Scarifier teeth	Pug mill paddles	Crusher mill plates
Grader blades	Plow shares	Crusher rolls
Cement mill parts	Wire feed rolls	Harrow discs
Coke machinery parts	Conveyor sleeves	Cultivator shovels
Brick plant parts	Gyratory crusher mantles	Bean knives
	Shovel bucket lips	

High temperatures and corrosive atmospheres have little effect on the deposits of these electrodes. Multilayer deposits will maintain hardnesses in the neighborhood of 30 Rockwell C at temperatures of $1500°F$.

Procedures

Faceweld electrodes should be used in the flat position. Either DC, electrode positive (reverse polarity), or AC may be used.

FLAT		
Electrode Size		Amperage Range
Diameter	Length	DC(+) or AC
3/16″	14″	60 − 150
5/16″	14″	145 − 350

Figure 2. Aggregate, falling five feet on to this chute, wears the metal down due to severe abrasion. The plate is hardfaced with "Faceweld 12."

Figure 3. Crusher roll must withstand severe abrasion. Outside diameter is hardsurfaced with multiple layers of "Faceweld 12."

No more than three layers of Faceweld 12 should be used; four layers of Faceweld 1 are permissible. High preheat must be used if a greater number of passes are required. Frequently it is possible to build up with several layers of Jet-LH BU-90 (or Mangjet on manganese steel) and then finish off with one or two passes of Faceweld. Not only is this more economical than applying many layers of Faceweld, but it also reduces the possibility of spalling.

Beads frequently have hairline checks across the bead. These checks are a method of stress relief and normally are not deterimental to the quality of the deposit. If a particular application is such that they *must* be eliminated, preheat the work and cool slowly after welding.

Hold a fairly short arc when using the Facewelds. Weave beads the full width of the deposit if possible.

On single-layer deposits, use lower currents to reduce admixture. When welding on manganese steel, keep the part cool. Let each bead cool down to the point where it can be touched with the bare hand before starting the next bead.

Figure 4. Worn cutting edge of bulldozer blade is built up with impact and abrasion-resisting "Faceweld 1."

Figure 5. Die ring worn by moderate impact and severe abrasion is hardsurfaced with "Faceweld 1."

Job Instructions

1. Weld a pad of Faceweld hardsurfacing on scrap plate to become familiar with the technique required.

2. On a heavy piece of scrap deposit a multilayer pad. Note the cross checks that occur when the pad cools. Preheat the part and repeat the welding. Cool the part slowly. Note that the cross checks have been eliminated.

3. By grinding a sample of each, compare the abrasion resistance of Faceweld deposits with mild steel and other hardsurfacing deposits. Note how difficult it is to grind away the Faceweld deposits.

LESSON

5.3

Object:
To study the use of Abrasoweld electrode.

Equipment:
Lincoln "Idealarc" AC and DC welder and accessories.

Material:
Scrap steel, 3/16" Abrasoweld electrodes.

ABRASOWELD

General Information

Abrasoweld electrodes are used for hardsurfacing new and worn parts to resist wear from both abrasion and impact.

Deposit Properties

The deposit is a high-carbon, chromium alloy that is semi-austenitic in the as-welded condition. It has an unusual combination of good abrasion resistance with moderate toughness and excellent hot-forging properties. Maximum hardness is obtained with single-layer deposits; best abrasion resistance is obtained

Electrode	Deposit	Abrasion	Impact	Hardness 30 C	Hardness 50 C	Hardness 70 C	Friction Grind	Machinability Machine
Faceweld 12	Chromium Carbide							
Faceweld 1	Chromium Carbide							
ABRASOWELD	SEMI-AUSTENITIC			X				⊙
Mangjet	Austenitic				X			
Stainweld	Austenitic				X			
Jet-LH BU-90	Martensitic				▲			⊙
Jetweld LH-70	Ferritic							
		X—Work-Hardened		▲—Heat-Treated		⊙—Annealed		

Figure 1. Dipper tooth for power shovel. Built-up with "Mangjet" and hardfaced (partially) with "Abrasoweld."

with multiple-layer deposits. The deposit work-hardens. This means that as the surface is pounded the thin surface layer becomes harder than the material beneath it.

Application Information

Abrasoweld has the advantage of very good abrasive resistance in combination with toughness and impact resistance. Similar to the Facewelds, it is used wherever parts are worn away by the action of a "gritty" or sand-like material. Unlike the Facewelds, however, the electrode may be used where the part is subjected to severe pounding by hard, rock-like particles. It is for this reason that the bucket lip of a shovel working in sand is best when hardsurfaced with Faceweld, but the same bucket lip working in a rocky soil should be surfaced with Abrasoweld.

TYPICAL APPLICATIONS

Dipper teeth	Scraper blades	Rock crushers
Tractor grousers	Charging rams	Coal mining cutters
Shovel tracks	Screw flights	Conveyor buckets
Shovel drive sprockets	Plow shares	Conveyor rolls
Dipper lips	Scarifier teeth	Gears
Rock crusher hammers	Truck chains	Crusher mantles
Sand pump impellers	Pump housings	Pulverizer plows
Dredge cutter teeth		Mill hammers

Procedures

Abrasoweld is best applied in the flat position. Either DC, electrode positive (reverse polarity), or AC may be used. No more than three layers of Abrasoweld should be applied. If a thicker deposit is required, several layers of Jet-LH BU-90 (or Mangjet on manganese steel) should be used under the Abrasoweld. If thicker deposits of Abrasoweld must be made, apply a layer of Stainweld between every two layers of Abrasoweld and peen each bead while it is hot.

Abrasoweld deposits are not machinable as welded. Grinding is recommended if shaping is necessary. If machining *must* be done, the deposits should be fully annealed at $1650°F$. To restore abrasion-resistance, reheat the part to $1450°F$, quench, and draw at $400°F$.

Electrode Size		Amperage Range
Diameter	Length	
1/8″	14″	40 — 150
5/32″	14″	75 — 200
3/16″	14″	110 — 250
1/4″	14″	150 — 375

When applying Abrasoweld, do not permit the preheat or interbead temperature to remain above $600°F$. Higher temperatures will result in higher hardnesses, but the abrasion resistance is not greatly affected.

Hold a fairly short arc when using Abrasoweld. Weave beads the full width of the deposit if possible. Use at least 3/4″-wide beads.

When welding on manganese steel, keep the part cool. Let each bead cool down to the point where it can be touched with the bare hand before starting the next bead.

Job Instructions

1. Weld a pad of Abrasoweld hardsurfacing on scrap plate to become familiar with the technique required.

2. By grinding a sample of each, compare the abrasion resistance of Abrasoweld with mild steel and other hardsurfacing deposits. Also, note that it is possible to pound on Abrasoweld deposits without causing them to spall off or crack.

Object:
To study the use of Lincoln Mangjet electrode.

Equipment:
Lincoln "Idealarc" AC and DC welder and accessories.

Material:
Scrap manganese steel; 3/16" Mangjet electrode.

MANGJET

General Information

Mangjet is used for building up high (12-14%) manganese steel to resist *moderate* abrasion and extremely *severe* impact. Mangjet is also used for joining manganese steel, either to another piece of manganese steel or to carbon steel, and for building up a manganese steel deposit on carbon steel.

Deposit Properties

The deposit is a 12-14% manganese steel that is fully austenitic and extremely tough. It develops maximum surface hardness by peening or other cold-working.

Electrode	Deposit	Abrasion	Impact	Hardness 30C	50C	70C	Friction Grind	Machin-ability Machine
Faceweld 12	Chromium Carbide							
Faceweld 1	Chromium Carbide							
Abrasoweld	Semi-Austenitic			X				⊙
MANGJET	AUSTENITIC			X	■			
Stainweld	Austenitic				►X			
Jet-LH BU-90	Martensitic				►X			⊙
Jetweld LH-70	Ferritic							

X—Work-Hardened   ▲—Heat-Treated   ⊙—Annealed

Application Information

Build-up — This electrode is used for rebuilding worn manganese steel parts. Mangjet, a covered electrode, deposits a smooth, thin bead. Depending on the

---

TYPICAL APPLICATIONS

Rail cross overs	Crusher pads	Manganese buckets
Rail frogs and switches	Rolling mill parts	Crusher rolls
Dipper teeth	Crusher hammers	Crusher screens
Dipper lips	Chain hooks	Dragline pins and links
Shovel drive sprockets	Strip mill wobblers	Cement grinder rings
Shovel tracks		Dredge parts

service conditions, other hardsurfacing materials may be put over the manganese deposit to improve abrasion resistance. Mangjet is also used to deposit a manganese steel weld on carbon steel parts.

Joining Parts — Mangjet is used to weld manganese steel to manganese steel and manganese steel to carbon steel. These welds are as strong as the manganese base metal.

Procedures

Probably the most important thing to remember in welding manganese steel is to keep the work cool. Other important general considerations are outlined in the "Job Instructions" below and should be followed carefully, if the best results are desired.

Mangjet on manganese steel — Mangjet operates with an exceptionally steady arc for electrodes of this type. To weld on manganese steel, use either DC, electrode positive, or AC and the lowest current possible consistent with good fusion. Travel fast enough to stay ahead of the slag. Use either a drag technique, a short arc, stringer beads, or a weave, depending on which best fits the job. Stay about 1/4" away from work edges and let the molten metal flow to the edge.

Mangjet on carbon steel — DC, electrode positive, is preferred. Also, as compared with the procedures on manganese, it is best to increase the current, lengthen the arc to about 3/16", and tip the electrode into the direction of travel so that the arc force washes metal toward the finished bead.

MANGJET			
Electrode Size		Amperage Range	
Diameter	Length	DC(+)	AC
5/32"	14"	120 – 180	125 – 210
3/16"	14"	160 – 260	175 – 275
1/4"	14"	200 – 350	225 – 375

Job Instructions

1. Deposit a large area of Mangjet weld metal. In so doing, check the following precautions:

   (a) Clean the work and remove any spongy or excessively hard areas of base metal before welding.

   (b) Disperse the beads around the work so that no two beads are laid side-by-side as the area is covered.

   (c) Be sure that the work never gets so hot that you can't touch it with the bare hand.

   (d) Cool the work, not the deposit, if necessary.

   (e) Peen the surface of the hot bead to relieve shrinkage stresses.

Object:
To study the use of Lincoln Wearweld and Jet-LH BU-90 electrodes.

Equipment:
Lincoln "Idealarc" AC and DC welder and accessories.

Material:
Scrap steel; 3/16" Wearweld and Jet-LH BU-90 electrodes.

WEARWELD AND JET-LH BU-90
General Information

Jet-LH BU-90 and Wearweld electrodes are used for hardsurfacing new and worn parts to resist rolling or sliding abrasion, and for fast buildup.

Deposit Properties

Wearweld deposits are a low-carbon chromium-manganese alloy that is partly martensitic and partly ferritic in the as-welded condition. The deposit has uniform hardness and is moderately tough.

Electrode	Deposit	Abrasion	Impact	Hardness 30C	50C	70C	Friction (Grind)	Machinability (Machine)
Faceweld 12	Chromium Carbide							
Faceweld 1	Chromium Carbide							
Abrasoweld	Semi-Austenitic			X				⊙
Mangjet	Austenitic				X			
Stainweld	Austenitic			X				
WEARWELD	MARTENSITIC			X				⊙
JET-LH BU-90	MARTENSITIC			▲				⊙
Jetweld LH-70	Ferritic							
		X—Work-Hardened			▲—Heat-Treated		⊙—Annealed	

Figure 1. Wearweld is used on rail ends.

Jet-LH BU-90 deposits a medium-carbon chromium-manganese alloy, which may be heat-treated to give physical properties comparable to medium-carbon steel. Deposits may be hot-forged. Good machinability can be obtained by annealing. Subsequent heat treatment will restore the deposit to the desired hardness.

Application Information

While similar in nature, the applications for each of these electrodes are fairly distinct.

Wearweld has a spray-type arc, which permits the deposition of a thin and relatively smooth layer of surfacing. This is particularly advantageous when building up parts that are to resist rolling or sliding abrasion, such as rail ends. For applications of this type, Wearweld has an excellent combination of hardness and toughness to resist wear.

Jet-LH BU-90 is a versatile electrode used both for preliminary buildup under higher-alloy hardsurfacing materials and also for hardsurfacing without the addition of other electrodes. It is used both to withstand the abrasion of gritty or sand-like material and also rolling or sliding friction. It will withstand severe impact or pounding. When used on preliminary buildup, Jet-LH BU-90 acts as a cushion under the more abrasion-resistant hardsurfacing deposits.

TYPICAL APPLICATIONS

BU-90 For Both Buildup and Finish Passes	BU-90 As Buildup Prior to Other Hardsurfacing Overlay	Wearweld
Trunnions	Shovel and bucket lips	Rail ends
Shafts	Pump impellers and	Coal mine car wheels
Crane and mine car wheels	housings	Crane wheels
Tractor grousers	Dredge and bucket teeth	Cams
Rolls and idlers	Scraper blades	Craneways
Shovel tracks	Pulverizer plows	Caterpillar treads, sprockets
Drive sprockets	Mill and crusher	& track links
Gears	hammers	
Churn bit points		

Jet-LH BU-90 deposits can normally be machined in the as-welded condition with the use of high-speed or carbide tools. Preheat and slow cooling will aid machinability.

The hardness and abrasion resistance of Jet-LH BU-90 can be increased by water-quenching the deposit from $1600°F$ and drawing at 400 to $800°F$ to achieve the desired toughness.

Procedures

These electrodes are best applied in the flat position. Both electrodes will operate on AC; on DC, use electrode positive with both electrodes.

FLAT			
Electrode Size		Amperage Range	
Diameter	Length	DC	AC
Jet-LH BU-90 (−)			
5/32''	14''	145 − 210	155 − 225
3/16''	14''	180 − 280	200 − 290
1/4''	18''	230 − 360	255 − 375
Wearweld (+)			
3/16''	18''	110 − 275	110 − 275
1/4''	18''	150 − 400	150 − 400

There is no limit to the number of layers of Jet-LH BU-90 that may be applied; no more than three layers of Wearweld should be deposited without using very high preheating and slow cooling.

Use a short arc with both electrodes with a narrow weaving motion.

When welding on manganese steel, keep the work cool. Let each bead cool down to the point where it can be touched with the bare hand before starting the next bead.

Figure 2. Jet-LH BU-90 is used to combat wearing friction on billet manipulators in steel mills.

Job Instructions

1. Weld a pad of hardsurfacing with each electrode to become familiar with the technique required. Note that the Wearweld has a fine spray-type arc and deposits a flat, smooth bead. Jet-LH BU-90, with its iron-powder covering, has a very high deposition rate with a very steady arc and very little spatter. This ease of operation of Jet-LH BU-90 has made it the favorite of welding operators.

2. By grinding a sample of each, compare the abrasion resistance of Wearweld and Jet-LH BU-90 deposits with mild steel and other hardsurfacing deposits. At the same time, note that these deposits are capable of withstanding severe impact.

SECTION VI

ELECTRODES FOR CAST IRON AND NONFERROUS METALS

Object:
To study the use of "Ferroweld" and "Softweld" electrodes.

Equipment:
Lincoln "Idealarc" welder and accessories.

Material:
Some broken pieces of cast iron; 1/8" "Ferroweld" and "Softweld" electrodes.

FERROWELD AND SOFTWELD

General Information

"Ferroweld" is a mild-steel electrode for depositing nonmachinable welds on cast iron; "Softweld" is a nickel electrode for depositing machinable welds on cast iron. See Lesson 1.36 for further information on cast-iron welding.

Ferroweld conforms to AWS Class ESt.

Softweld conforms to AWS Class ENiCI.

Properties

"Ferroweld" deposits are stronger than the cast iron itself. The electrode operates with very low currents to reduce heat input to the base metal and, consequently, to minimize the possibility of weld cracking and hardening along the fusion line. It is excellent for studding.

"Softweld" deposits are soft and easily machined. They are also ductile and have less tendency to crack.

Application Information

Both electrodes are used on similar applications: "Ferroweld" is used on most work except where machining is required; "Softweld" is used on applications requiring machining.

TYPICAL APPLICATIONS

Machine bases	Tractor transmission cases	Fire plugs
Cast boiler sections	Tractor differentials	Pulleys
Headers	Compressor blocks	Wheels
Motor blocks	Steam radiator sections	Frames
Cast-iron wheels	Gear teeth	Blow holes
Motor heads	Cast iron to steel	Printing press rolls
Diesel water jackets	Lamp posts	Gate valves

Procedure

POLARITY — "Ferroweld" — Electrode positive, work negative, or AC. "Softweld" — Electrode negative, work positive, or AC.

ALL POSITIONS		
Electrode Size		
Diameter	Length	Amperage Range
"Ferroweld"		DC(+)
1/8"	14"	80 – 100
"Softweld"		DC(–)
1/8"	14"	60 – 110
5/32"	14"	100 – 135

Job Instructions

1. Set up broken casting, matching edges. Tack together or hold in position. If piece is 3/16" or over in thickness, V out pieces 45° on each side – a total of 90°.

2. Weld with both "Ferroweld" and "Softweld" to become familiar with the operation of each.

Object:
To study the use of "Aerisweld" electrode.

Equipment:
Lincoln Idealarc or DC welder and accessories.

Material:
Copper plates 1/8" x 3" x 5"; 5/32" "Aerisweld."

AERISWELD

General Information

"Aerisweld" is a shielded-arc electrode for welding bronze, brass, and copper in many applications. In repair work, "Aerisweld" builds up and fills in bronze castings. Many types of bronze that are difficult to braze are easily welded with "Aerisweld." Conforms to AWS Class ECuSn-C.

Properties

Dense, high-strength deposit with characteristics of true phosphor bronze.

Characteristics of the base metal are of great importance in determining the characteristics of the joint and fusion zone, due to possible admixture of base metal in welding.

Application Information

TYPICAL APPLICATIONS		
Contact points	Viscose mixers	Bronze check valve discs
Bearing surfaces	Brass pads on steel	"work" connections
Cast iron	Ornamental work	Bronze tubing
Galvanized iron	Bonding rails	Copper vats
Aluminum bronze castings	Repair brass valves	Copper clad fabrication
Copper rivet heater blocks	Impeller blades	Bushings
Fire hose couplings	Bus bars	Pipeline bonds
Copper piping	Malleable iron	Caustic pump blocks
Copper-to-steel	Bronze ship propellers	Copper brew stills

Figure 1. Racks for storage of machined parts. Bronze cushions are welded on steel brackets with "Aerisweld."

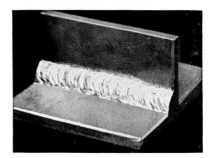

Figure 2. Fillet in 3/16" bronze plate welded with "Aerisweld."

Procedure

POLARITY DC, Electrode positive.

On ferrous metal or thin copper or bronze, it is generally unnecessary to preheat the metal. As the work progresses and the heat builds up, it may be necessary in some cases to reduce the current.

ALL POSITIONS	
Electrode Size	Amperage Range
1/8"	50 — 125
5/32"	70 — 170
3/16"	90 — 220

On heavy copper and bronze, preheating may be necessary due to the high heat conductivity of these metals. This preheating can be accomplished by using a carbon electrode with negative polarity and rapidly moving the arc over the area to be welded.

High current, high temperatures, or considerable penetration will cause a great admixture of the base metal,' and the procedure should take this into account in the case of the first layer. It is therefore advisable to put on as much metal per bead, or layer, as can be conveniently and easily done.

Metals that evolve gases in the molten state, at the point of solidification, result in porosity. In some cases, the use of higher current and keeping the work hot will tend to reduce this porosity.

Holding the electrode at an angle so that the flame of the arc is directed back over the work will aid in permitting the gases to bubble through to the surface.

When the work has to be machined, it is, of course, necessary that the original, or base, metal be cut away so that when the deposit is made the line of machining will come through near the top of the deposit and not at the fusion zone. The work should be laid out to obtain this result.

Warning: Weld brass and bronze in well-ventilated area. Avoid breathing fumes, as they are toxic.

Figure 3. A church bell 116 years old repaired with "Aerisweld." Saved $250 over the cost of recasting a new bell.

Figure 4. Copper condenser of plate and sheet — typical of many copper or brass containers welded with "Aerisweld."

Job Instructions

1. Tack the two copper plates together for a butt weld. Use 5/32" electrode, 100 to 115 amperes, and weld.

2. Try this with copper and then with bronze plates or bronze castings.

3. Note the easy flow of metal and the free-flowing, well-formed type of bead.

4. Repeat, making lap and fillet welds.

Object:
To study the use of "Aluminweld" electrode.

Equipment:
Lincoln Idealarc or DC welder and accessories.

Material:
Aluminum plates 1/8" x 3" x 5" and several pieces of aluminum casting; 5/32" "Aluminweld."

ALUMINWELD

General Information

"Aluminweld" is a 5%-silicon aluminum-alloy shielded-arc electrode for welding aluminum in any form — cast, sheet, shapes, or extrusions. It is designed for either metal or carbon-arc welding.

Properties

"Aluminweld" is provided with a covering that prevents excessive oxidation and will dissolve any aluminum oxide that might be formed. The covering also assists in giving a smooth operating arc, which is so particularly essential in welding aluminum. The resulting weld is dense and possesses high tensile strength. The weld can be polished satisfactorily with little discoloration.

Application Information

TYPICAL APPLICATIONS		
Bottle brackets	Outboard motor gas tanks	Cooking utensils
Racks	Moulding	Portable drill castings
Cylinder heads	White metal die castings	Appliance parts
Ornamental work	Washing machine tubs	Structural aluminum
Laundry chutes	Tanks	Trim
Viscose plant piping	Crank cases	Window frames
Beer barrels	Transport truck tanks	Soap kettle liners

Figure 1. Group of aluminum storage tanks for olive oil. Fabricated with "Aluminweld" electrode.

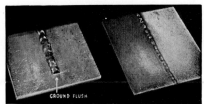

Figure 2. Left: Butt weld in 1/8" aluminum made with "Alumiweld" and ground down at end to show denseness of weld metal. Right: Butt weld in 14-gauge aluminum made with "Aluminweld."

Procedures

POLARITY – DC, Electrode positive.

A short arc should be held, the covering approximately touching the molten pool.

In general, use the highest current possible without melting the edges too far back or burning through. Because aluminum melts off so rapidly, more than the usual amount of heat from the arc is dissipated melting off electrode, and less heat is transferred to the plate. As a result the weld metal is subjected to a severe quench. **Hence, it is recommended that the seam be preheated to 600° to 700°F before welding.**

On striking, the best results are obtained by "scratching" the electrode. To restart an electrode, strike the arc in the crater, then move the electrode quickly back along the completed weld for 1/2"; then proceed as usual, making sure the crater is completely remelted.

Even melting of the flux is facilitated by holding the electrode approximately perpendicular to the work at all times.

Always direct arc so that both edges to be welded are properly and uniformly heated and the electrode advanced along the seam at such a rate that a uniform bead is made.

FLAT	
Electrode Size	Amperage Range
3/32"	20 – 55
1/8"	45 – 125
5/32"	60 – 170
3/16"	85 – 235
VERTICAL AND OVERHEAD	
Not recommended. However, where vertical or overhead welding is required, follow same procedure as for flat work.	

TACKING – Increase recommended currents approximately 50% for tacking. Use a short arc with a rotary motion.

Remove slag from the weld by light hammering and brushing. Last traces may be removed with warm water and a wire brush or by soaking the weld in 5% nitric acid or 10% warm sulphuric acid followed by a warm-water rinse.

Vertical and overhead welding should as far as possible be eliminated. However, where imperative, vertical welding can be done downward or upward with straight beads or by weaving. Overhead welding should be done with a number of straight beads.

"Aluminweld" can be used as a filler rod with the carbon arc or a torch.

Warning: Avoid breathing fumes from electrode. Work in a ventilated area.

Butt Welds – The work should be held in position by jigs and backed up by copper, as illustrated in Fig. 3. When butt-welding plates 1/8" and thicker, the copper backing should be slightly grooved beneath the joint to be welded.

Welding of butt joints in 3/16" plate and heavier should be done with two beads, as indicated in Figures 6 and 7. No backing or clamping is required for welding joints in this manner.

The general procedure as given previously should be followed in making these types of welds.

Fillet Welds – In making fillet welds, the electrode should be held in such a position that the angle between the electrode and the horizontal plate is approxi-

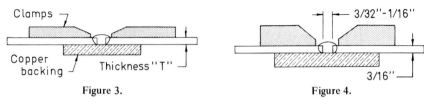

Figure 3.

Figure 4.

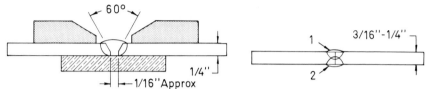

Figure 5.

Figure 6.

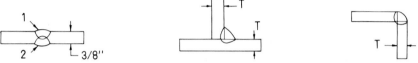

Figure 7.

Figure 8.

Figure 9.

Joint	Beads or Passes	Electrode Size	Current Amps
Figure 3			
18-ga. sheet	1	3/32''	40
16-ga. sheet	1	1/8''	65
1/8'' plate	1	5/32''	120
Figure 4			
3/16'' plate	1	3/16''	170
Figure 5			
1/4'' plate	1	3/16''	170
Figure 6			
3/16'' & 1/4'' plate	1	3/16''	170
	2	3/16''	170
Figure 7			
3/8'' plate	1	3/16''	200
	2	3/16''	200
Figure 8			
1/8'' plate	1	5/32''	120
3/16'' plate	1	3/16''	170
1/4'' plate	1	3/16''	170
Figure 9			
1/16'' plate	1	1/8''	65
1/8'' plate	1	5/32''	120
3/16'' plate	1	3/16''	170
1/4''	1	3/16''	170

mately 45°. The electrode should be manipulated with a small rotary motion, with the arc being played first on the vertical member and then on the horizontal member of the joint. With the above exceptions, the general procedure given previously should be followed in making a fillet weld.

Corner Welds — This type of weld is made by following the general procedure previously given.

Job Instructions

1. Make butt weld on 1/8" plate. If material is available, repeat with thicker plate. Make lap, fillet, and corner welds in light and heavy plate if possible.

2. Prepare butt weld in casting by veeing. Preheat casting before welding.

3. Remove all traces of flux after welding.

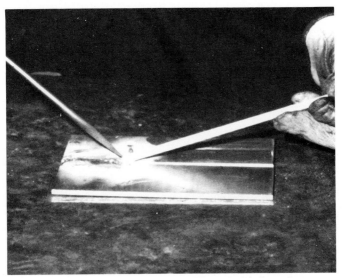

Figure 10. Aluminweld being used as a filler rod with the carbon arc.

SECTION VII

SEMIAUTOMATIC ARC WELDING

LESSON
7.0

Object:
To become acquainted with semiautomatic arc welding.

General Information

In the earlier sections of this book, the information and lessons were concerned with self-shielded metal-arc welding (SMAW) or, as people in the shop call it "stick-electrode" welding. In these sections you learned that the covering on the relatively short electrode under the heat of the arc developed gases, vapors, and flux that shielded the arc and the weld puddle from the atmosphere. Stick electrodes work well, but as you have found in your shop practice, a 14-inch electrode quickly burns down into a 2-inch stub that requires stoppage of welding and the substitution of a new 14-inch "stick" into the electrode holder.

Now, why couldn't an electrode be — not 14 inches — but a hundred or a thousand feet long, so you could keep on welding until you had completed the joint? Why couldn't new electrode material be continuously fed to the arc?

Pondering these questions, technologists came up with several answers. It was obvious that you couldn't coil brittle covered stick electrodes into 100 to 1000-feet lengths, and, even if you could, devise a machine to move them through the electrode holder. But, supposing you forget about the need for an integral arc-shield-generating substance on the electrode, use bare electrode wire, and sprinkle granules of shielding and fluxing materials ahead of the arc. Then, you had submerged-arc welding. Or supposing, you put the shielding, fluxing and metal-conditioning chemicals inside the core of the continuous electrode wire. Then you had Lincoln's Innershield process. Still another alternative was to use a continuous bare-wire electrode in conjunction with a forcible spray of a shielding gas to the arc and weld puddle. So came into being gas metal-arc welding. These have dominated the scene during the last 20 years.

LESSON 7.1

Object:
To become acquainted with the semiautomatic Innershield welding process.

General Information

The Innershield arc-welding process is a development of the Lincoln Electric Company that is widely used in high-production shop work and in the field welding of structural steel. Also called "self-shielded flux-cored arc welding", it amounts to a mechanization of stick-electrode welding. The weldor, instead of working with an electrode holder, uses a gun through which electrode "wire" is fed to the arc when a trigger is pressed. The electrode wire contains within its core the materials needed for shielding the arc, deoxidizing, and fluxing the molten pool, just as the stick electrode contains shielding and conditioning materials in its covering. The semiautomatic gun is light in weight and easy to maneuver. An experienced weldor can become proficient with its use in a day or less of practice.

Figure 1 illustrates the principles of the Innershield process. Full automatic welding with Innershield electrodes is also possible and is employed in high-production applications, such as the automotive industry. In general, semiautomatic use is the type most likely to be encountered by the weldor — and learning to master the semiautomatic Innershield gun is one way to assure a

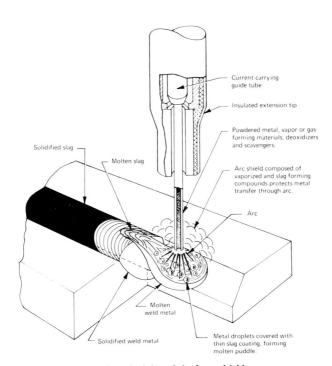

Figure 1. The principles of the Innershield process.

Figure 2. High-production welding is possible in a virtually smoke-free shop with the Inner-shield process utilizing the Lincolnditioner smoke-removal equipment.

progressive welding career. The cost savings that companies have achieved with the process have enabled them to meet competition in an era of inflation.

Figures 2 and 3 show some typical uses of the process.

How Innershield Works

Ever since the introduction of the covered stick electrode, technologists sought for a way "to make it longer" – to eliminate the need for frequent electrode changing and the stub and time losses inherent with it. A stick electrode hundreds of feet long could not be coiled because of the brittle covering, and, if it could, how could electric contact be made at a point in a welding gun close to the arc?

Lincoln solved the problem by the "inside-out" construction of Innershield electrode wire. The "covering" materials were put inside the metal wire. This made possible the coiling of self-shielded electrodes and the making of continuous electric contact close to the arc. Importantly, it also made possible the use of higher amperage – and this increased deposition rates. Were the currents often used with Innershield wire applied to the end of a stick electrode, the resistance heating would be so great that the covering would be damaged.

Advantages of Semiautomatic Innershield Welding

The most obvious advantage of semiautomatic Innershield welding is its fast deposition rate. By drawing electrode continuously from a coil, eliminating lost time in changing electrodes, eliminating electrode stubs, and operating at higher

Figure 3. Making a column weld "high in the air," using semiautomatic Innershield. The self-shielding electrode provides protection for the molten metal in the strong winds encountered at such heights.

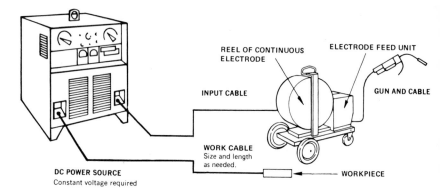

Figure 4. A schematic of the semiautomatic open-arc self-shielded flux-cored electrode (Innershield) process — one of the simplest semiautomatic processes in terms of equipment and the most versatile for steel welding.

amperages, welding costs are reduced substantially. Deposition rates are as much as four times as great as with stick electrodes. Operating factors are increased, and it is not unusual for total welding costs to be decreased by as much as 50 to 75%.

But there are other advantages not so apparent. These include:

* Has exceptional tolerance to poor fitup. With some products, perfect fitup has no great structural value or is extremely difficult or too costly to achieve. In manufacturing where fitup has been a major problem, use of semiautomatic Innershield has reduced rework and repair without affecting product quality. This factor has been of cost-saving value as important to the company as the cost savings resulting from increased deposition rates when changing from covered-electrode welding. The tolerance of the semiautomatic process to poor fitup has expanded the use of tubular steel members in structures by making sound connections where perfect fitup is often economically impractical.

* Eliminates the need for flux-handling and recovery equipment, as in submerged-arc welding, or for gas and gas-storage, piping, and metering equipment, as in gas-shielded mechanized welding. The semiautomatic process is applicable where other mechanized processes would be too unwieldy.

* Has tolerance for elements in steel that normally cause weld cracking when non low hydrogen stick-electrode or one of the other mechanized welding processes are used. Produces crack-free welds in medium-carbon steel, using normal welding procedures.

* Under normal conditions, eliminates the problems of moisture pickup and storage that occur with low-hydrogen electrodes.

* Eliminates the need for wind shelters (see Figure 3) required with gas-shielded welding in field erection; permits fans and fast air-flow ventilation systems to be used for worker comfort in the shop.

- Enables "one-process," and even "one-process, one-electrode," operation in some shop and field applications. This, in turn, simplifies operator training, qualification, and supervision; equipment selection and maintenance; and the logistics of applying men, materials, and equipment to the job efficiently.

- Enables the application of the "long-stickout" principle (see Lesson 7.3) to enhance deposition rates, while allowing easy operator control of penetration.

- Permits more seams to be welded in one pass, saving welding time and the time that otherwise would be consumed in between-pass cleaning.

- Gives the speed of mechanized welding in close quarters. The semiautomatic gun reaches into spots inaccessible by other semiautomatic processes.

Equipment for Innershield Welding

The special equipment for semiautomatic Innershield welding includes the welding gun and wire feeder. Figure 4 shows a schematic of the equipment, and Figures 5 and 6 illustrate the gun types and wire feeders.

The experienced weldor will note from the schematic in Figure 4 that the only difference from the basic stick-electrode welding circuit is that a wire-feeding mechanism with its controls and a reel of electrode wire have been interposed between the power source and the arc, and that the electrode holder has been replaced with the welding gun.

The welding gun (Figure 5) may be of several nozzle designs and amperage ratings. Straight nozzles are favored for fillet welds and when the work flows under the gun. Curved nozzles enhance flexibility and ease in manipulation, but require heavier-duty wire-drive units. Curved nozzles are generally favored and are especially preferred for depositing butt welds in heavy sections. The semi-

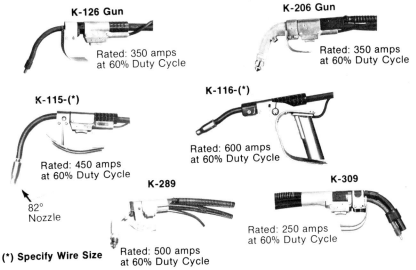

K-126 Gun

Rated: 350 amps at 60% Duty Cycle

K-206 Gun

Rated: 350 amps at 60% Duty Cycle

K-115-(*)

Rated: 450 amps at 60% Duty Cycle

82° Nozzle

K-116-(*)

Rated: 600 amps at 60% Duty Cycle

K-289

Rated: 500 amps at 60% Duty Cycle

K-309

Rated: 250 amps at 60% Duty Cycle

(*) Specify Wire Size

Figure 5. Various types of guns for Innershield welding. The K-206, K-289 and K-309 guns are used with the Linconditioner smoke removal system.

Figure 6. A typical digital solid-state wire-feeding mechanism used for semiautomatic Inner-shield welding. Note the drive-roll and control unit may be separated from the coil of electrode to give greater flexibility to semiautomatic welding. This is available when the NE model is ordered.

automatic welding gun provides internal contacts that initiate wire feed and complete the welding circuit at the press of the trigger switch.

In Figure 6, the drive-roll and control unit can be separated from the reel container. This modification permits working farther from the electrode supply and moving the control mechanism into tighter working quarters. Here, the drive mechanism pulls wire from the reel and then pushes it the remaining distance to the welding gun. Note that the weldor may be working up to 60 feet from his reel of electrode and 15 feet from the wire feeder and control unit.

The K-184 Linconditioner is shown in Figure 7. This unit, when used in conjunction with a Linconditioner gun, enables welding fumes to be removed at a point very close to their source — the welding arc. The system is very effective and can be an excellent answer in applications where welding fumes have become a problem.

Figure 7. The K-184 Linconditioner can be used where welding fumes are a problem.

LESSON 7.2

Object:
To become acquainted with the electrode wires used with semi-automatic Innershield welding.

The electrode wires used with the Innershield process for welding carbon and low-alloy steels are varied in composition — just as stick electrodes — to give fast-fill, fast-freeze, and fill-freeze characteristics (see Lesson 3.1). Here, as in the case of stick electrodes, the type of joint is a factor in the selection.

Flux-cored electrode wires are used with gas-shielded processes as well as with the self-shielded Innershield process, and the American Welding Society's classification system includes both types. Chemical composition and mechanical requirements are used in defining the various classifications. Since flux-cored electrodes are relatively new and in a state of continued development, it is important to consult the manufacturer's literature to make a selection of electrode for a specific type of joint and welding position rather than depending on classification numbers. Performance characteristics within an AWS classification may vary from manufacturer to manufacturer.

In a typical AWS designation, E70T-4, the prefix "E" indicates an electrode for arc welding. The number "7" indicates that the minimum as-welded tensile strength of the weld metal is 72,000 psi. The "0" indicates for welding in the flat or horizontal position. The letter "T" indicates that the electrode is of tubular construction, and the suffix "4" designates a particular grouping based on chemical composition, whether or not carbon dioxide is required as a separate shielding gas, type of current, polarity of operation, and other factors. The users of Innershield will depend upon Lincoln literature for making electrode selec-

Electrode	Sizes	AWS Class per A5.20-79	AWS Class per A5.20-69
NR®-1	.120, 5/32	E70T-3	E70T-3
NR-5	3/32, .120, 5/32	E70T-3	E70T-3
NR-131	3/32	E70T-10	E70T-G
NR-151	.068	E71T-GS	E70T-G
NR-152	.068	E71T-GS	E70T-G
NR-202	.068, 5/64	E71T-7	E70T-G†
NR-211	5/64, 3/32	E71T-11	E70T-G†
NR-203M	5/64, 3/32	E71T-8	E70T-G**
NR-203 Nickel 1%	5/64, 3/32	E71T8-Ni1*	E70T-G**
NR-203 Nickel C	5/64	E61T8-K6*	—
NS-3M	3/32, .120	E70T-4	E70T-4
NR-301	3/32	E70T4-K2	
NR-302	5/64, 3/32	E70T-6	E70T-G**
NR-311	3/32, 7/64	E70T-7	E70T-G†
NR-431	3/32, .120	—	EG70T1***
Lincore M	7/64	—	—
Lincore 40	.120	—	—
Lincore 50	7/64	—	—

*** Per AWS A5.26-78.
** Plus producing 20 ft-lbs at -20°F impact properties.
* Per AWS 5.29-80.
† Also meets requirements of E60T-7.
Note: All 70T-G electrodes are multiple pass except NR-131, NR-151 and NR-152.

tion, but, as background information, the chart on the last page lists the AWS classifications into which Innershield electrodes fall.

Since many still refer to the figures in A5.20-69, they have been included along with the 1979 figures for completeness.

Flux-cored electrode wire is usually packaged in 50-pound or smaller coils. For high-production full-automatic welding, 300 and 600-pound coils are available.

Of more utility than AWS classifications in making a selection of electrode wire for Innershield welding are the Lincoln trade designations of electrode wire types. The trade names are what the man in the shop will encounter, and trade designations, rather than AWS classifications, spell out the practical matter of performance characteristics. The Lincoln Innershield electrodes likely to be used in the shop or in field welding are as follows:

NS-3M

This electrode, conforming to E70T-4, is the extremely fast-fill wire that has revolutionized much of the heavy, manually controlled welding in industry. Used with the semiautomatic gun, it has increased deposition rates by as much as 400% — in some cases enabling the survival of companies hard-pressed by inflated material and labor costs.

NS-3M is recommended for the semiautomatic welding of mild, medium-carbon, and some alloy steels when the joint can be presented in the flat or horizontal positions. It is used for multiple-pass fillet, lap, and deep-groove butt welds and for single-pass 1/4" to 1/2" fillet, lap, corner, and butt welds where a

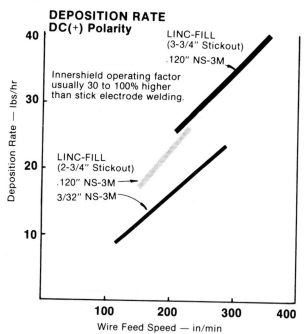

Figure 1. A comparison of the deposition rates (at 100% operating factor) of NS-3M with different sizes and varying stickout. See Lesson 7.3 for explanation of "stickout."

gap and backup plate are practical. The electrode gives welds of exceptional resistance to cracking, even in highly restrained joints and on heavy or medium-carbon plate. Welds are smooth and slag tends to peel off or is easily removed. In laboratory tests, even water-soaked NS-3M wire has been found to give welds as "low-hydrogen" as low-hydrogen stick electrodes. By following standard procedures, NS-3M welds are "low-hydrogen" and of X-ray quality. The resistance of the weld deposit to underbead and micro-cracking has resulted in NS-3M being used for the "problem" welds – those cracking in service – in the manufacture and repair of heavy equipment.

Figure 1 compares the deposition rates of NS-3M electrode wires with a fast-fill E7024 stick electrode. (See Lesson 7.3 for explanation of "stick-out.")

NR-152 and NR-152

These electrodes, conforming to E71T-GS have been designed for single pass welding of 18 gauge to 3/16" (maximum) sheet metal and conform to AWS E70T-G single pass requirements. NR-152 can be used for galvanized sheet metal and NR-151 can be used for Aluminized steel. Both electrodes have excellent fast follow for travel speeds of over 40 inches/minute. NR-152 also has the added advantage of not requiring the end to be clipped for restarts. This is a tremendous boom for productivity. Both electrodes may be used in semi or full automatic applications.

The fast follow, light slag, and smooth bead have made these electrodes increasingly popular with the auto industry in their quest to use galvanized and aluminized steels for increased corrosion protection. They are also finding applications of replacing MIG on mild steel sheet metal because of the increased travel speed. Figure 2 shows typical applications.

Figure 2. Welding sheet metal, galvanized, or aluminized material is fast and easy with NR-151 and NR-152.

DEPOSITION RATE

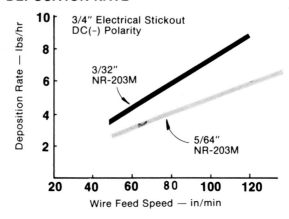

Figure 3. Deposition rates for two sizes of NR-203M electrode.

NR-203M, NR-203 Nickel, NR-203 Nickel C

This self-shielded flux-cored electrode, NR-203M conforming to E71T-8, is an all-position electrode that gives weld metal with Charpy V-notch impact properties exceeding 20 foot-pounds at $-20°$F. It has the fast-freeze out-of-position characteristic, plus the usual advantages of Innershield weld metal. Its elongation (22 to 33% in 2 inches) either meets or exceeds critical specifications, and its Charpy V-notch impact properties run as high as 120 foot-pounds at $-20°$F.

NR-203 Nickel C is recommended when the best physicals are required. It is used for all position work on demanding applications such as off-shore oil rigs.

NR-203M is especially recommended when high impact properties are specified for roundabout groove welds on large, heavy-wall cylindrical weldments, using a vertical-up technique over Fleetweld 35LS root passes. It is also recommended for single and multiple-pass welds in the flat, horizontal, vertical-up, and overhead positions in bridge construction and in hull plate and stiffener welding on ships and barges. Deposition rates of two sizes of NR-203M are shown in Figure 3.

NR-211

This is a general purpose, all position, semiautomatic electrode conforming to E71T-11 for 12 gauge and thicker mild steel, that is especially suited for economic assembly and maintenance welding. It was designed for ease of handling and versatility, and performs well through a range of applications from short assembly welds to situations involving poor fit up.

The "fast-freeze" characteristics are combined with good travel speed, smooth arc, low spatter and excellent appearance making this electrode suitable for the fabrication of many diverse items such as, for example, truck bodies, saddles, tanks, hoppers, duct work and small round-abouts. This electrode also has application in the repair welding of machinery parts.

The weld deposit is comparable to the NS-3M electrode; and is also excellent on crack sensitive steels.

DEPOSITION RATE

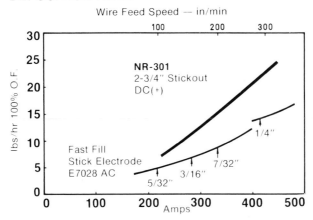

Figure 4. Deposition rate of 3/32" NR-301 compared with E-7028 stick electrode.

NR-301 and NR-302

Conforming to E70T4-K2 and E70T-6 respectively, these fast-fill electrodes also produce weld metal with excellent Charpy V-notch impact properties. They are recommended for single and multiple-pass welds in mild and higher-strength steels in the flat and horizontal positions. Typical applications include bridge, barge, ship, offshore drilling-rig, and machinery construction.

The electrodes are widely used for multiple-pass fillet and lap welds, deep-groove butt welds in the flat position, and single-pass 1/4" to 3/8" fillets. They are also suitable for corner welds and for single-pass butt welds when a gap and backup plate are practical. The welds have good appearance and slag removal is easy. X-ray quality weld metal can be achieved with standard procedures. Figure 4 compares the deposition rate of NR-301 with E-7028 stick electrode.

DEPOSITION RATE: DC(-)

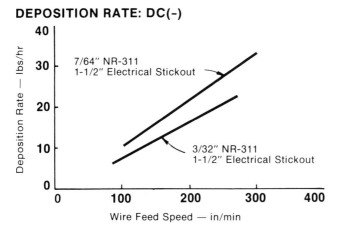

Figure 5. Deposition rates of two sizes of NR-311.

ELECTRODE DATA ON WIDELY USED INNERSHIELD SIZES AND TYPES

Electrode — Polarity Electrical Stickout Weight Electrode/Foot	Normal Setting		Approxi- mate Current (amps)	Weld Metal Deposit Rate (lbs/hr)
	Arc Voltage (volts)	Wire Feed Speed (in/min)		
.068" NR-151	21	185 Max.	360	8.9
DC(−) Polarity	19	125	270	6.2
1/2" Electrical Stickout	17	80 Opt.	185	4.0
	15	60	140	3.0
.068" NR-152	20	110 Max.	310	5.8
DC(−) Polarity	16.5	80	245	4.1
1/2" Electrical Stickout	14.5	50 Opt.	165	2.6
	13.0	30	100	1.5
3/32" NR-131				
DC(−) Polarity	26	250 Max.	470	17.0
1-1/2" Electrical Stickout	24	200 Opt.	400	13.0
.068" NR-202	23	210 Max.	300	8.7
DC(−) Polarity	21.5	155	250	6.2
1" Electrical Stickout	20.5	110 Opt.	200	4.2
	19	70	150	2.4
	18	55	100	1.7
5/64" NR-202	24	230 Max.	400	13.2
DC(−) Polarity	23	185	350	10.5
1" Electrical Stickout	22	145 Opt.	300	8.0
	21	110	250	5.8
	20	75	200	3.7
	19	55	150	2.4
5/64" NR-203M	21	140 Max.	300	6.7
DC(−) Polarity	18	90 Opt.	220	4.4
3/4" Electrical Stickout	17	70	185	3.4
	16	50	145	2.5
3/32" NR-203M	22	120 Max.	350	8.6
DC(−) Polarity	21	110	330	7.8
3/4" Electrical Stickout	20	95 Opt.	300	6.7
	16	50	190	3.5
5/64" NR-203 Nickel (1%)	23	140 Max.	310	7.0
DC(−) Polarity	20	90 Opt.	235	4.3
3/4" Electrical Stickout	18	70	195	3.3
	16	50	145	2.4
3/32" NR-203 Nickel (1%)	24	130 Max.	385	9.5
DC(−) Polarity	22	110	345	8.2
3/4" Electrical Stickout	21	95 Opt.	315	7.2
	18	50	215	3.5
5/64" NR-203 Nickel C	21	110 Max.	275	5.3
DC(−) Polarity	20	90 Opt.	235	4.3
3/4" Electrical Stickout	18	70	195	3.3
	16	50	145	2.4

ELECTRODE DATA ON WIDELY USED INNERSHIELD SIZES AND TYPES
(Continued)

Electrode — Polarity Electrical Stickout Weight Electrode/Foot	Normal Setting		Approximate Current (amps)	Weld Metal Deposit Rate (lbs/hr)
	Arc Voltage (volts)	Wire Feed Speed (in/min)		
.068" NR-211				
DC(−) Polarity	19	110 Max.	230	5.0
3/4" Electrical Stickout	17	75 Opt.	190	3.4
	16	60	165	2.7
5/64" NR-211				
DC(−) Polarity	19	110 Max.	300	6.7
3/4" Electrical Stickout	17	75 Opt.	240	4.5
	16	50	160	3.0
3/32" NR-301	32	330 Max.	440	25.5
DC(+) Polarity	29	220	350	16.7
2-3/4" Electrical Stickout	28	185 Opt.	300	14.0
	27	150	265	11.0
	26	110	220	8.0
5/64" NR-302	26	300 Max.	420	16.3
DC(+) Polarity	24.5	260	395	14.1
7/8" Electrical Stickout	23	220 Opt.	350	11.9
	21	160	265	8.6
3/32" NR-311	30	270 Max.	450	22.0
DC(−) Polarity	27	210	400	16.5
1-1/2" Electrical Stickout	25	150 Opt.	325	11.4
	24	135	300	10.2
	21	75	200	5.4
7/64" NR-311	33	300 Max.	625	33.0
DC(−) Polarity	30.5	240	550	25.5
1-1/2" Electrical Stickout	27	175 Opt.	450	18.0
	25.5	145	400	14.5
	23.5	100	325	10.0
3/32" NS-3M	32	275 Max.	450	22.0
DC(+) Polarity	31	230 Opt.	400	18.0
2-3/4" Electrical Stickout	30	185	350	14.5
	29	150	300	12.0
	28	110	250	8.5
.120" NS-3M	31	225 Max.	550	26.5
DC(+) Polarity	30	200	500	23.0
2-3/4" Electrical Stickout	29	175 Opt.	450	20.0
	28	150	400	17.0
.120" NS-3M	38	355 Max.	600	39.5
DC(+) Polarity	37	300 Opt.	550	34.0
3-3/4" Electrical Stickout	36	250	500	29.0
	35	210	450	25.0

Note: The above electrode data illustrates the approximate relationship between the welding parameters and deposition rate for each electrode. They are not intended to serve as specific procedure recommendations for any application. Contact your Lincoln Representative for specific procedures and techniques.

NR-311

This is the fill-freeze of "fast-follow" electrode wire, conforming to E70T-7, recommended for semiautomatic welding of 10-gauge and thicker mild steels and other higher-strength steels when requirements do not exceed the yield-strength range of the electrode. The good penetration characteristics of the weld often permit the reduction of fillet leg size on 1/4" through 5/8" plate, and the good wetting action allows travel speeds as great as 35 inches per minute on 3/16" horizontal fillets using the 7/64" diameter electrode and the semiautomatic wire feeder. Deposition rates with two sizes of NR-311 are shown in Figure 5.

The electrode is used for single and multiple-pass fillet and lap welds in the flat, horizontal, and downhill position; for horizontal butt welds, such as column-to-column connections in structures; for deep-groove welds with a narrow gap and small bevel angle; and for square-edge butt welds (with gap and backup plate).

NR-311, as other Innershield electrodes, give a weld metal with excellent resistance to cracking. Since this is a deep-penetration electrode, burnthrough can occur with poor fitup, but can be countered by increasing the electrical stickout.

NR-1 and NR-5

These electrodes have excellent fast-follow characteristics for single-pass welding on 18-gauge to 3/16" mild steels, permitting speeds up to 275 inches per minute with full-automatic welding equipment. They are frequently used with the semiautomatic gun (particularly the 3/32" size of NR-5) for making small fillet and lap welds at speeds up to 100 inches per minute in sheet steel. The high-strength sheet-metal welds produced have ample ductility to allow bending and forming welded material. The electrodes produce less porosity than submerged-arc welding on rusty or oily sheet steel.

Lincore M and Lincore 50

These are self-shielded electrodes designed for hardsurfacing. They have the same self-shielding advantages as the other Innershield electrodes and have a deposition rate which is typically 2-4 times faster than manual electrodes producing a similar deposit. Lincore M is the most impact resistant and Lincore 50 has the greatest abrasion resistance.

LESSON 7.3

Object:
To study the techniques used in Innershield welding in general and to become acquainted with the welding characteristics of NS-3M.

Equipment:
A constant-voltage DC power source, either transformer-rectifier or generator; a Lincoln LN-7, LN-8, or LN-9 "Squirt" welder (wire feeder with control box), together with its Operating Manual; a Lincoln K-115 semiautomatic "Squirt" gun or K-289 Lin-conditioner gun.

Material:
Scrap mild steel plate 3/8" or heavier in thickness; a 50-pound coil of 3/32" NS-3M Innershield wire.

General Information

Since the weldor accustomed to stick-electrode work is most likely to be introduced to semiautomatic Innershield welding when his employer has a need for reducing the costs of welds on plate steel, his first experience will probably be with high-deposition NS-3M electrode. Once the flat position techniques with this electrode have been mastered, it will be merely an application of his experience with stick electrodes (with appropriate accommodations) to also master vertical, overhead, and fast-follow sheet-metal welds with fast-freeze and fill-freeze electrode types.

The equipment should be set up according to the Operating Manual that comes with the wire feeder (Manual IM-274, in the case of the LN-8 feeder). Before welding, the control settings should be checked carefully. Control settings should be within the range specified by the procedures; drive rolls and wire-guide tubes should be correct for the wire size, and drive-roll pressure should be adjusted according to the operational instructions. The wire feeder and power source should be set for constant-voltage output. The gun, cable, and nozzle contact tip should be correct for the wire size and the "stickout".

The Meaning of "Stickout"

The weldor will note that the procedures for Innershield welding specify "electrical stickout" along with electrode type and diameter and current and voltage ranges. This is a new variable that comes with the weldor's introduction to semiautomatic work — and, as will be noted by the charts in the figures of Lesson 7.2, different values for electrical stickout influence the deposition rates of Innershield electrodes. The degree of stickout is also a factor by which the weldor can control penetration and burnthrough and handle problems of fitup.

Figure 1 shows the semiautomatic gun nozzle and defines visible and electrical stickout. Note that the electrical stickout is the length of electrode from the contact tip within the nozzle to the work piece. Electrical stickouts prescribed by procedures vary from 1/2" to 3-3/4" for various electrodes. Since the farther the current has to go before it reaches the arc, the greater the resistance heating within the wire, and the closer a point on the wire is to its melting temperature when that point on the moving wire reaches the arc. As a consequence of this resistance heating, the longer the electrical stickout, the faster the melt-off and deposition rates. A "long" stickout can increase the deposition rate by as much as 50%.

The specified electrical stickouts are obtained by using the proper guide tip and visible stickout on the welding gun. Thus, a medium-length guide tip and a 1-3/8" visible stickout provide a 2-3/4" electrical stickout, and a long (3-3/8") guide tip and a 1-3/8" visible stickout produce a 3-3/4" electrical stickout with .120" NS-3M. With the 3/32" NS-3M which we will be using, only the 2-3/4" stickout is used.

An extension guide tip is not used with fill-freeze and fast-freeze electrodes, and electrical stickout is limited. The normal stickout with these electrodes is 3/4" to 1".

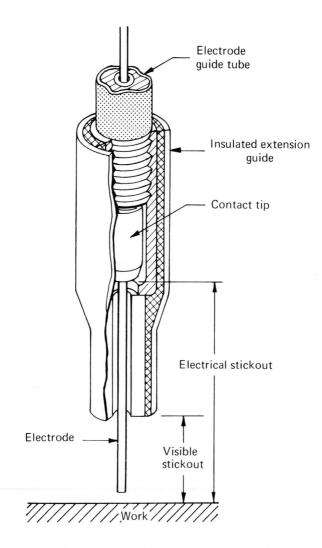

Figure 1.

Semiautomatic Operating Techniques

Starting the Arc: To start the arc, the electrode is "inched" out beyond the nozzle to just short of the visible stickout recommended for the electrode size and guide tip. The tip of the electrode is positioned just off, or lightly touching, the work, and the trigger is pressed to start the arc. The electrode should not be pushed into the joint as it burns away, as in stick-electrode welding, since the mechanical feed will take care of advancing the electrode. When the arc is established, slowly pull the gun back until the recommended stickout is established. Welding is stopped by releasing the trigger or quickly pulling the gun from the work. The instruction manual with the wire feeder usually gives specific recommendations on setting feed speed and open-circuit voltage to facilitate starting.

When a long electrical stickout is to be used, it is best to start with a visible stickout of about 1/2", and increase the visible stickout to the specified amount after the arc has been established.

Accommodating Poor Fitup: As noted in Lesson 7.1, one of the advantages of flux-cored electrode welding is the ability to handle poor fitup. With a fast-fill electrode poor fitup can be accommodated by increasing the visible stickout to as much as 3". Pulling the gun away from the work to increase the visible stickout reduces the current, and thus the penetration, and helps to avoid burnthrough. After a poor fitup area has been traversed, normal stickout should

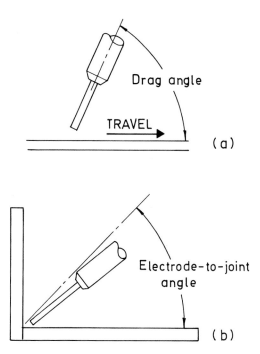

Figure 2. The drag angle (a) and the electrode-to-joint angle (b) are variables that affect performance and weld appearance.

be used for the remainder of the joint. This method of controlling penetration should be used only with the short guide tip.

With the fill-freeze electrodes, poor fitup can be handled by reducing the welding current to the minimum value specified in the procedures. Increasing the stickout to 1-1/2" also helps to reduce penetration and burnthrough.

Removing Slag: Slag removal is easy in Innershield welding. In heavy fast-fill work, the slag often curls up and peels off behind the welding gun. Otherwise, a light scrape with a chipping hammer or wire brush is usually all that is needed to dislodge the slag.

Slag is occasionally trapped on 90° vertical welds or in a downhand convex bead. Entrapment can be avoided by proper bead location and drag angle and by using a smooth, even travel speed to insure good bead shape.

Electrode Position: The drag angle is the angle between the electrode center line and the seam center line in the direction of travel, as illustrated in Figure 2 (a). The desired drag angle is approximately the same as in stick-electrode welding. If slag tends to run ahead of the arc, the drag angle should be decreased.

For best bead shape on most 5/16" and larger horizontal fillets, the electrode should point at the bottom plate, as illustrated in Figure 2 (b), and the angle between the electrode and bottom plate should be less than 45°. With this arrangement, the molten metal washes up onto the vertical plate. Pointing the electrode directly into the joint and using a 45 to 55° angle will decrease root-porosity problems, if they occur, but may produce spatter and a convex bead.

When a follow-freeze electrode is used on sheet or thin plate, arc striking is best accomplished by starting with a 1/2" visible stickout and increasing it slowly to 1". Welding should be done with a stringer-bead technique in all positions, with a steady travel speed. A steady speed is important; hesitation is likely to cause burnthrough, with metal sag developing on the underside of the joint and porosity in the weld. The wire should be pointed directly into the joint with an electrode angle held at about 40°.

Fitup with light material should be tight, although a small gap on 12-gauge to 3/16" steel can be handled by reducing the current and voltage about 10%. A steady whip or weave may help, but these motions should not be overdone.

The light slag on thin-gauge material adheres tightly, but does not have to be removed. A wipe with a weak acid solution before painting will neutralize the weld area and remove smoke deposits.

For out-of-position welding with most of the electrodes, best results are obtained by positioning the work downhill or vertical-down. Stringer beads should be used, with the current settings in the middle to high portion of the range. The gun should be tipped in the direction of travel so that the arc force helps hold the molten metal in the joint.

In vertical-up and overhead welding with fill-freeze electrodes, low-hydrogen techniques, as opposed to E6010 techniques, should be used. Whipping, breaking the arc, moving out of the puddle, or moving too fast in any direction should be avoided. Currents should be in the low portion of the range.

Operating Variables

Four major variables affect welding performance with flux-cored electrodes: arc voltage, current, travel speed, and electrical stickout. These variables are interdependent, and, if one is changed, one or more of the other three usually require adjustment.

Arc voltage variations — with current, travel speed, and electrical stickout held constant — produce these effects:

1. A high arc voltage produces a wider and flatter bead.
2. An excessive arc voltage may produce a porous weld.
3. A low voltage tends to cause a convex, ropey bead.
4. Extremely low voltage may produce a tendency for the wire to stub on the plate. The wire may dive through the molten metal and strike the joint bottom, pushing the gun up.

In most applications, a good bead shape is obtained by using the highest voltage possible without causing porosity. With higher currents, higher voltages can be used without causing porosity.

Current variations — when arc voltage, travel speed, and electrical stickout are held constant — have the following effects:

1. Increasing current increases melt-off and deposition rates.
2. Excessive current produces convex beads, resulting in poor appearance and wasted weld metal.
3. Too low current gives a droplet transfer, with reduced penetration.

As current is increased, arc voltage must also be increased to maintain good bead shape. Increased current also increases the maximum voltage that can be used without porosity occurring.

Travel speed, assuming the other variables are held constant, can have the following effects:

1. Excessive travel speed increases the convexity of the bead and causes uneven edges.
2. Too slow a travel speed results in slag interference and inclusions and a rough, uneven bead.

Travel speed is always faster with self-shielded flux-cored electrodes than with stick electrodes — to accommodate the higher deposition rates. The beginning operator with the semiautomatic process will tend to move too slow because of his experience with stick-electrode welding. As in all other welding processes, travel speed should be that necessary to handle the molten metal and slag and produce the desired weld size.

Uniformity in travel speed is important. It is accomplished by maintaining a uniform distance between the wire and the molten slag behind the wire.

Electrical stickout variations, with the other variables held constant, have the following effects:

1. Increasing the stickout decreases the welding current and vice versa.
2. Increasing the stickout lowers the actual voltage across the arc. Lower arc voltage increases the convexity of the bead and reduces the tendency for porosity.
3. Short stickout gives greater penetration than long stickout.

Job Instructions

The foregoing information has been phrased to be applicable to semiautomatic Innershield generally. The active part of this lesson is to practice with the semiautomatic gun and Innershield NS-3M electrode wire. As stated previously, once you have learned to handle the semiautomatic gun with fast-fill NS-3M wire in the flat position, welding with out-of-position electrode types and with fast-follow wires will come easily.

Before starting welding, recheck your equipment, using the Operating Manual that came with your wire feeder. Be sure that the drive rolls and wire-guide tube are correct for the 3/32" wire size you will be using. Adjust drive-roll pressure for the wire size. Be sure that the wire feeder and power source are set for constant-voltage output characteristics.

Voltage is generally adjusted with controls on the power source. Read the voltage when welding, using the power source or wire-feeder voltmeter. The current is adjusted with the controls on the wire feeder. With Innershield welding, current is increased by increasing the feed speed and reduced by slowing the feed speed. The table at the end of Lesson 7.2 shows the settings that might be used with 3/32" NS-3M. The beginner should probably start with a low wire-feed speed, say 110 inches per minute, at 28 volts — which will give a current of 250 amperes. As competence in handling the gun is achieved, higher currents — and, thus, higher deposition rates — can be achieved by increasing the wire-feed speeds and voltage settings.

CHOOSE THE PROPER GUN AND STICKOUT

Use only the gun and electrical stickout specified for each electrode size and type in the following tables.

For These Electrodes	Use Electrical Stickout	Recommended Gun*
.068" NR-151	1/2"	K-126 or K-206
.068" NR-152	1/2"	K-126 or K-206
3/32" NS-3M	2-3/4"	(to 350 amps) K-126 or K-206 (over 350 amps) K-115, K-116, K-289
.120" NS-3M	2-3/4" or 3-3/4"	K-115, K-116, K-289
3/32" NR-131	1-1/2"	K-115, K-116, K-289
.068" NR-202	1"	K-126, K-206, K-309
5/64" NR-202	1"	K-126, K-206, K-309
5/64" NR-203*	3/4"	K-126, K-206, K-309
3/32" NR-203*	3/4"	K-126, K-206, K-309
5/64" NR-211	3/4"	K-126 or K-206
3/32" NR-211	3/4"	(to 350 amps) K-126 or K-206 (over 350 amps) K-115, K-116, K-289
3/32" NR-301	2-3/4"	K-115, K-116, K-289
5/64" NR-302	7/8"	(to 350 amps) K-126 or K-206 (over 350 amps) K-115, K-289
3/32" NR-311	1-1/2"	(to 350 amps) K-126 or K-206 (over 350 amps) K-115, K-116, K-289
7/64" NR-311	1-1/2"	K-115, K-116, K-289

† Includes all NR-203 types.
* K-126 or K-206 rated 350 amps @ 60% duty cycle.
  K-115 rated 450 amps @ 60% duty cycle.
  K-116 rated 600 amps @ 60% duty cycle.
  K-289 rated 500 amps @ 60% duty cycle.

Make sure that the gun, cable, and nozzle contact tip will handle the wire size. With 3/32" NS-3M, you will want to use a 2-3/4" electrical stickout in the preliminary work. The recommended stickouts with several types and sizes of Innershield electrodes are given in accompanying table. To get the electrical

Welding Position: Flat
Weld Quality Level: Commercial
Steel Weldability: Good or fair

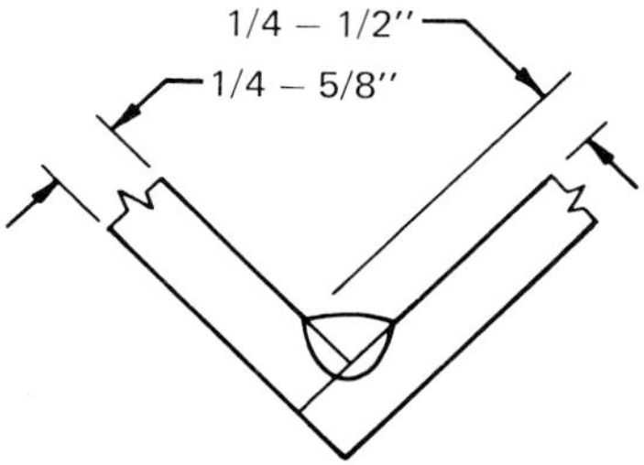

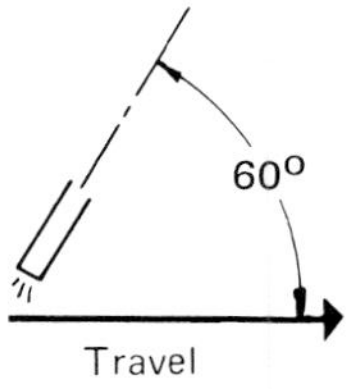

	1/4 (−)	1/4	5/16	3/8	1/2
Weld Size, L (in.)	1/4 (−)	1/4	5/16	3/8	1/2
Plate Thickness (in.)	1/4	5/16	3/8	1/2	5/8
Pass	1	1	1	1	1*
Electrode Type	NS-3M	NS-3M	NS-3M	NS-3M	NS-3M
Size	3/32	3/32	3/32	3/32	3/32
Current (amp) DC(+) (WFS)	360 (206)	375 (220)	375 (220)	375 (220)	375 (220)
Volts	29 – 30	30 – 31	30 – 31	30 – 31	30 – 31
Arc Speed (in./min)	21 – 23	18 – 20	13 – 15	10 – 11	5.2 – 5.8
Electrode Req'd (lb/ft)	0.17	0.21	0.28	0.39	0.67
Total Time (hr/ft of weld)	0.00909	0.0105	0.0143	0.0190	0.0364
Electrical Stickout, 2-3/4 in.					

60°

Travel

1/4 – 1/2"

1/4 – 5/8"

* For better penetration use two passes. Overall speed is the same.

Figure 3. Flux-Cored Arc Welding (Semiautomatic) Self-Shielded.

Welding Position: Horizontal
Weld Quality Level: Commercial
Steel Weldability: Good or fair

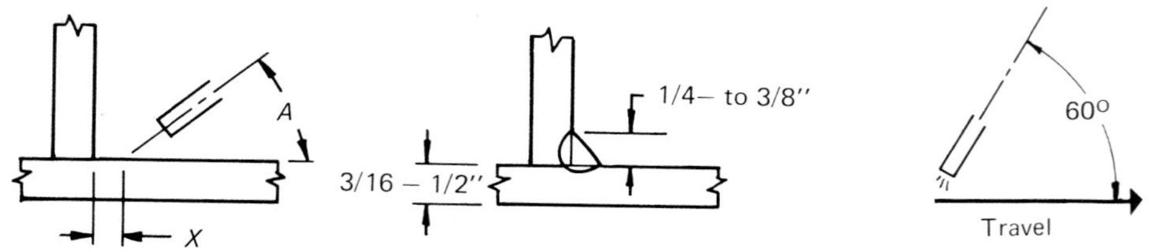

	1/4 (−)	1/4 (−)	1/4		5/16		3/8
Weld Size, L (in.)	1/4 (−)	1/4 (−)	1/4		5/16		3/8
Plate Thickness (in.)	3/16	1/4	5/16		3/8		1/2
Pass	1	1	1	1	1	1	1
Electrode Type	NS-3M	NS-3M	NS-3M	NS-3M	NS-3M	NS-3M	NS-3M
Size	3/32	3/32	3/32	.120	3/32	.120	.120
Current (amp) DC(+) (WFS)	325 (176)	350 (197)	375 (220)	425 (162)	375 (220)	425 (162)	450 (174)
Volts	28 − 29	29 − 30	30 − 31	27 − 30	30 − 31	27 − 30	28 − 31
Arc Speed (in./min)	18 − 20	17 − 19	15 − 17	18 − 20	14 − 16	16 − 18	12 − 13
Electrode Req'd (lb/ft)	0.17	0.20	0.25	0.25	0.27	0.27	0.39
Total Time (hr/ft of weld)	0.0105	0.0111	0.0125	0.0105	0.0133	0.0118	0.016
Electrode location, X (in.)	0	1/16	3/32	1/8	1/8	5/32	5/32
Electrode angle, A (deg)	40	35	35	30	30	25	25
Electrical Stickout, 2-3/4 in.							

Figure 4. Flux-Cored Arc Welding (Semiautomatic) Self-Shielded.

Welding Position: Flat
Weld Quality Level: Commercial
Steel Weldability: Good or fair

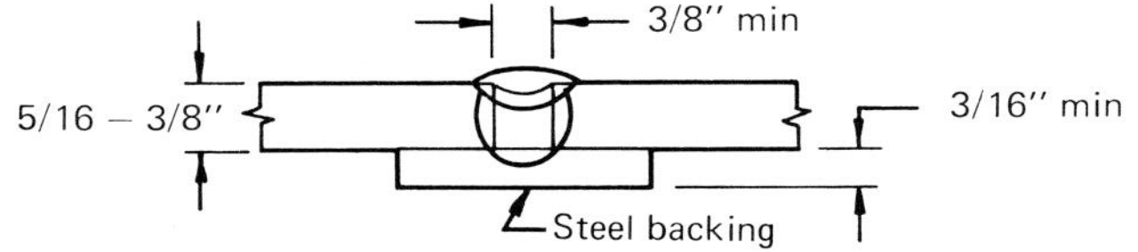

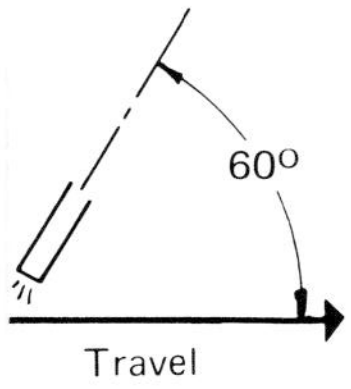

60°
Travel
3/16" min
3/8" min
5/16 – 3/8"
3/8"
Steel backing

Plate Thickness (in.)	5/16				3/8			
Pass	1	2	1	2	1	2	1	2
Electrode Type	NS-3M		NS-3M		NS-3M		NS-3M	
Size	3/32		.120		3/32		.120	
Current (amp) DC(+) (WFS)	400 (244)		475 (187)		400 (244)		500 (200)	
Volts	33 – 34		32 – 33		33 – 34		33 – 34	
Arc Speed (in/min)	12 – 13	19 – 21	14 – 15	23 – 25	10 – 11	18 – 20	12 – 13	20 – 22
Electrode Req'd (lb/ft)	.59		.58		.67		.71	
Total Time (hr/ft of weld)	0.0260		0.0221		0.0295		0.0255	
Electrical Stickout, 2-3/4 in.								

Figure 5. Flux-Cored Arc Welding (Semiautomatic) Self-Shielded.

Welding Position: Horizontal
Weld Quality Level: Commercial
Steel Weldability: Good
Welded from: One side

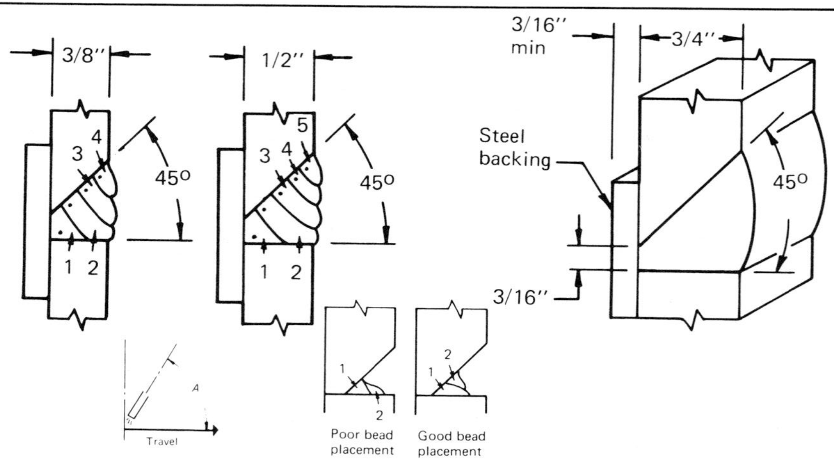

Plate Thickness (in.)	3/8		1/2		3/4			
Pass	1 – 3	4	1 – 4	5	1 – 9	10	1 – 7	8
Electrode Type	NS-3M	NS-3M	NS-3M	NS-3M	NS-3M	NS-3M	NS-3M	NS-3M
Size	3/32	3/32	3/32	3/32	3/32	3/32	.120	3/32
Current (amp) DC(+) (WFS)	300 (135)	250 (100)	300 (135)	250 (100)	350 (176)	300 (135)	400 (150)	300 (135)
Volts	28	25	28	26	30	28	29	28
Arc Speed (in/min)	15 – 17	12 – 13	13.5 – 14.5	10 – 11	14 – 15	10 – 11	14 – 16	10 – 11
Electrode Req'd (lb/ft)	.64		.91		2.29		2.19	
Total Time (hr/ft of weld)	.0535		.0762		.143		.112	
Drag angle, A (deg)	60		60		60		60	
Electrical Stickout, 2-3/4 in.								

Figure 6. Flux-Cored Arc Welding (Semiautomatic) Self-Shielded.

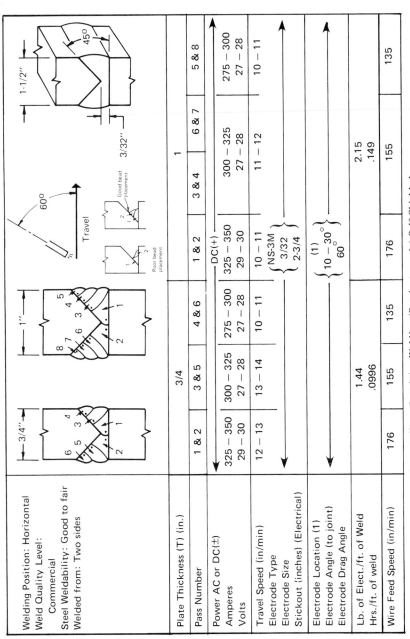

Welding Position: Horizontal
Weld Quality Level: Commercial
Steel Weldability: Good to fair
Welded from: Two sides

Plate Thickness (T) (in.)	3/4			1			
Pass Number	1 & 2	3 & 5	4 & 6	1 & 2	3 & 4	6 & 7	5 & 8
Power AC or DC(±)	DC(+)						
Amperes	325 – 350	300 – 325	275 – 300	325 – 350	300 – 325		275 – 300
Volts	29 – 30	27 – 28	27 – 28	29 – 30	27 – 28		27 – 28
Travel Speed (in/min)	12 – 13	13 – 14	10 – 11	10 – 11	11 – 12		10 – 11
Electrode Type	NS-3M						
Electrode Size	3/32						
Stickout (inches) (Electrical)	2-3/4						
Electrode Location (1)	(1)						
Electrode Angle (to joint)	10 – 30°						
Electrode Drag Angle	60°						
Lb. of Elect./ft. of Weld	1.44			2.15			
Hrs./ft. of weld	.0996			.149			
Wire Feed Speed (in/min)	176	155	135	176	155		135

Figure 7. Flux-Cored Arc Welding (Semiautomatic) Self-Shielded.

stickout specified with the K-115 gun, use a medium guide tip with 1-1/4" visible stickout to obtain a 2-3/4" electrical stickout, and a long guide tip with 1-1/4" visible stickout to get a 3-3/4" electrical stickout. You will start with the medium guide tip.

The instructions with the wire feeder will tell you how to load the wire reel and prepare the feeder and gun for operation. Once you are assured that the feeder, cable, and gun are free from any previously used electrode wire, cut off the bent end of the new electrode, straighten the first six inches, and insert it through the wire guide to the drive rolls. Press the trigger on the gun until the rolls pick up the wire and feed it through the gun cable. Remember, when "inching", the electrode is always hot to ground.

Clean two pieces of 3/8" or heavier plate and tack them to form a T joint. The Innershield gun or stick electrodes such as Fleetweld 35LS, Jetweld LH-70, Jet-LH 8018-C1 or C3, or Jetweld 2 may be used for tacking. Clamp the ground cable to the work so there is a positive contact.

Position the work flat and the wire with a drag angle as shown in Figure 2 for fillet welding. Make sure that the wire has been "inched" beyond the nozzle to approximately 1-1/4". Begin welding by pressing the trigger with the electrode tip just off or lightly touching the work. Note that the main difference in running a semiautomatic weld from the use of stick electrodes is that with the semiautomatic gun you attempt to maintain the nozzle a constant distance from the work, rather than pushing the electrode into the joint. The wire is fed continuously, making such possible and necessary. The travel speed, voltage and amperage being constant, thus determines how much molten metal "piles up" in the pool – or determines the size of the fillet.

With understanding of how to use the gun, you are now ready to run a flat fillet on 3/8" plate, making a "procedure" weld. Figure 3 shows the Lincoln-suggested procedures for such a weld. Note that for 3/8" material, the equipment is set to operate at 375 amperes and 30 to 31 volts to give a 5/16" weld size. Proper handling of the gun will require that you advance the arc at a rate of 13 to 15 inches per minute.

These preliminary experiments will make clear to you that how you traverse the joint with given settings on the wire feeder and power source determines the final results. You can control weld size by travel speed – and, as you will find with practice, you can also control penetration and handle burnthrough problems by allowing the length of the visible stickout to increase or decrease (raising or lowering the nozzle.)

Next, run a horizontal fillet on tacked-up scrap, following the procedures in Figure 4. Note how the electrode is held in relation to the joint – pointing at the bottom plate.

You may next wish to practice running a square-edge butt weld on 3/8" plate. The procedures for 3/32" Innershield electrode are given in Figure 5. Note that a steel backing is used, and the weld is made in two passes. Because the first pass puts down most of the weld metal, the arc speed used is less than that of the second (cover) pass.

Next practice running butt welds in the horizontal position as in Figure 6 and Figure 7. Run stringer beads being careful to place each bead as shown in the diagrams.

LESSON 7.4

Object:
To study the techniques used in vertical and overhead Innershield welding and the operating characteristics of NR-202 electrode.

Equipment:
Same as in Lesson 7.3 except a K-126 gun or K-206 Linconditioner is recommended.

Material:
Mild steel plate 3/8" thick or thicker; a 50-pound coil of .068" NR-202 electrode.

General Information

Downhill and Vertical Down: NR-202

The excellent "fast-follow" characteristics are best utilized for low-cost single-pass welds by positioning the work downhill or vertical down. About a 60° downhill angle and 5/64" electrode usually provide maximum speed. However, the .068 electrode provides more control.

Use stringer beads and currents in the middle to high portion of the range. Tip the gun in the direction of travel so the arc force helps hold the molten metal in the joint. Move as fast as possible consistent with the desired bead shape.

Vertical Up and Overhead: NR-202 and NR-203M

The .068" and 5/64" sizes of NR-202 and the 5/64" size NR-203M can be used in all positions.

When welding out-of-position, use low-hydrogen techniques (as opposed to E6010 techniques). Don't whip, break the arc, move out of the puddle, or move too fast in any direction. Use currents in the low portions of the range. General techniques are illustrated. Experience will show how much hesitation and upward step is required for high quality and smooth appearance.

Where the fitup is poor or if the groove has a feather edge, it may be necessary to weld the first one or two beads with stick electrode. After the root passes have made a sound base, the groove can then be filled with Innershield as shown in Figure 2.

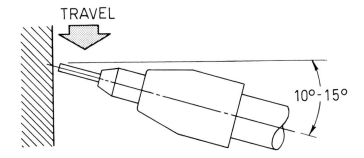

Figure 1. Correct electrode angle for vertical-down Innershield welding.

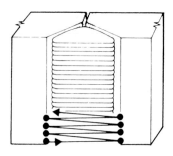

Figure 2. Butt Welds, including pipe, first two passes manual.

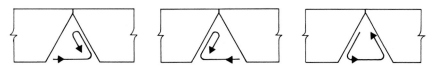

Figure 3. Weave pattern for thick layers, vertical-up.

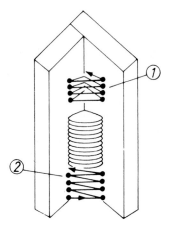

Figure 4. Weave pattern for vertical-up fillet welds.

1. Make a distinct hesitation at the outer edges of bevel.
2. Minimize each upward step. Do not step up at the edges. Come straight out from the hesitation point and move up across the weld.

Single-Pass Technique

Large welds can be made in one pass by well trained operators using the weave pattern, in Figure 3.

This is the simplest weave pattern likely to give uniform large layers. For smaller layers or a cap pass, a simple side-to-side weave may be used with hesitation at the outer edges.

Welding Position: Vertical up
Weld Quality Level: Commercial
Steel Weldability: Good or fair
Welded from: One side

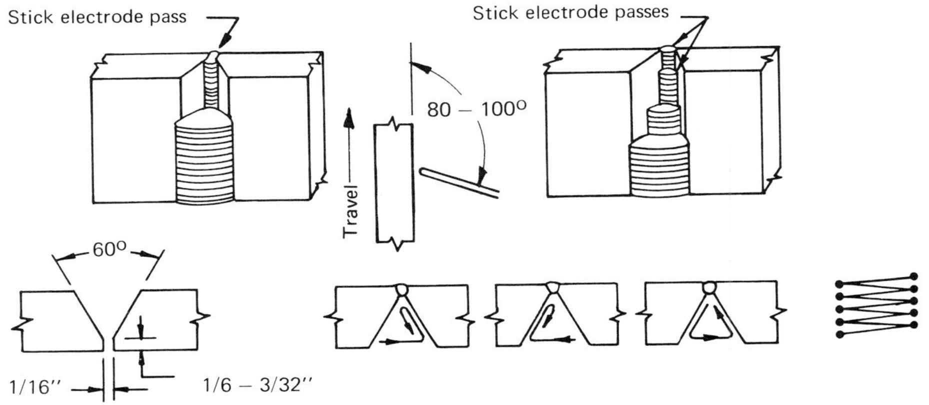

Plate Thickness (in.)	3/8-1/2-5/8	3/8	1/2	5/8	3/4 – 1	3/4		1	
Pass	1	2	2	2	1 & 2	3	4	3	4
Electrode Type	FW35LS	NR-202	NR-202	NR-202	FW35LS	NR-202		NR-202	
Size	1/8	.068	.068	.068	1/8	.068		.068	
Current (amp) DC (WFS)	80 (+)	160(–) (99)	160(–) (99)	160 (–) (99)	80 (+)	180(–) (115)		195(–) (127)	
Volts		19 – 20	19 – 20	19 – 20		20 – 21		20.5 – 21.5	
Arc Speed (in./min)	3.3 – 3.7	2.4 – 2.6	1.3 – 1.4	0.8 – 0.9	3.3 – 3.7	1.5 – 1.7	1.3 – 1.4	1.2 – 1.3	0.7 – 0.8
Electrode Req'd (lb/ft) *	0.227	0.342	0.625	1.02	0.454	1.37		2.49	
Total Time (hr/ft of weld) *	0.0571	0.0800	0.147	0.235	0.114	0.273		0.427	
Electrical Stickout, 3/4 in.									

* Add stick electrode to semiautomatic passes.

Figure 5. Flux-Cored Arc Welding (Semiautomatic) Self-Shielded.

Welding Position: Vertical up
Weld Quality Level: Commercial
Steel Weldability: Good or fair
Welded from: Two sides

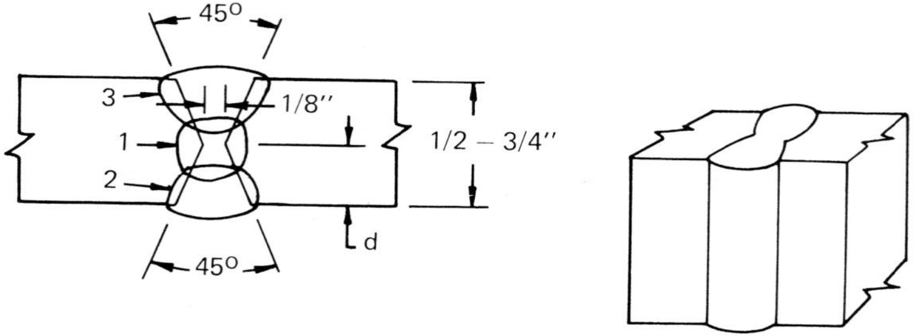

Plate Thickness (in.)	1/2			5/8			3/4		
Pass	1	2	3	1 – 2	3	4	1	2 & 4	3
Electrode Type	NR-202			NR-202			NR-202		
Size	.068			.068			.068		
Current (amp) DC(−) (WFS)	165 (80)			165 (80)			165 (80)		
Volts	19 – 20			19 – 20			19 – 20		
Arc Speec (in/min)	3.5 – 4.0	3.0 – 4.0	3.0 – 4.0	3.5 – 4.0	3.0 – 5.5	3.0 – 5.5	3.0 – 3.5	2.0 – 5.0	2.0 – 5.0
Electrode Req'd (lb/ft)	0.68			0.85			1.2		
Total Time (hr/ft of weld)	0.171			0.213			0.299		
Depth, d (in.)	1/4			5/16			3/8		
Electrical Stickout, 1 in.									

Figure 6. Flux-Cored Arc Welding (Semiautomatic) Self-Shielded.

Welding Position: Overhead
Weld Quality Level: Commercial
Steel Weldability: Good

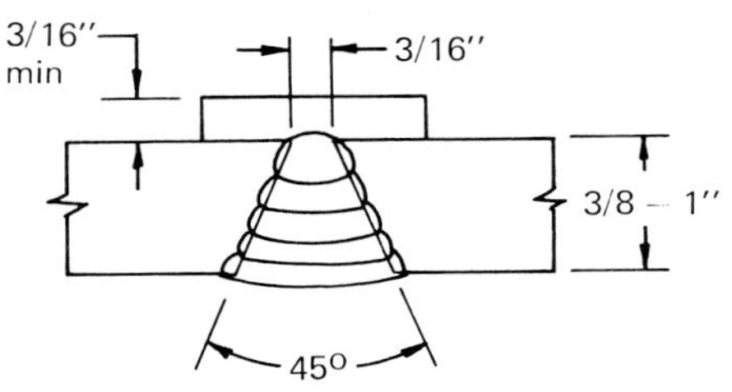

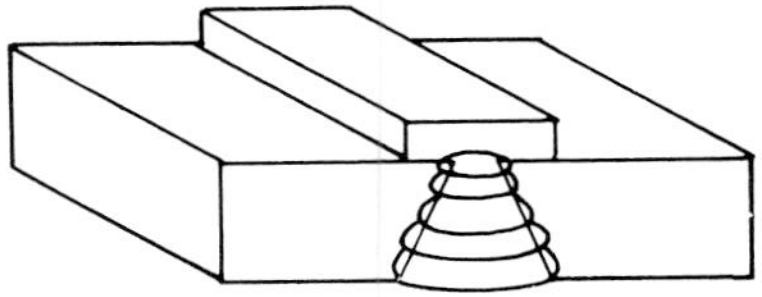

Bead Placement for 5/8" Plate

Plate Thickness (in.)	3/8		1/2		5/8		3/4		1	
Pass	1	2	1	2 – 3	1	2 – 4	1	2 – 5	1	2 – 7
Electrode Type	NR-202		NR-202		NR-202		NR-202		NR-202	
Size	.068		.068		.068		.068		.068	
Current (amp) DC(−) (WFS)	155 (95)		165 (103)		165 (103)		170 (107)		170 (107)	
Volts	18.5 – 19.5		19 – 20		19 – 20		19 – 20		19 – 20	
Arc Speed (in./min)†	3.5 – 3.9	1.6 – 1.8	3.5 – 3.9	2.3 – 2.5	3.5 – 3.9	2.3 – 2.5	3.3 – 3.7	2.3 – 2.5	3.1 – 3.4	2.1 – 2.3
Electrode Req'd (lb/ft)	0.728		1.05		1.45		1.94		3.01	
Total Time (hr/ft of weld)	0.172		0.221		0.354		0.391		0.607	

Electrical Stickout, 3/4 in.

† Arc speeds are average for all passes after the first. Normally speeds decrease on subsequent passes.

Use split layers when bead face width exceeds 3/4 in.

Figure 7. Flux-Cored Arc Welding (Semiautomatic) Self-Shielded.

Vertical Fillet and Lap Welds

1. Make small welds (1/4" welds with NR-202) with vertical-down techniques.
2. Make larger welds with the following techniques:
   a. On 1/4" welds, a short side-to-side motion is usually sufficient.
   b. On larger welds use a triangular weave (see (1) in Figure 4) with a distinct hesitation at the outer edges for the first pass.
   c. Use a side-to-side weave (see (2) in Figure 4) similar to that used for butt welds on the second and latter passes. The first pass should have a face width of 5/16" − 3/8" before starting this weave.

Job Instructions

Prepare a set of plates with a groove design as shown in Figure 5. Make the first two passes with Fleetweld 5P or Fleetweld 35. Finish the weld with Innershield using the procedures and weave patterns shown in Figure 5.

After mastering the techniques for vertical-up welding the Innershield, go to Figure 7 and practice overhead welding.

Figure 8. The portable LN-22 Innershield wire feeder weighs under 50 pounds with a full coil of wire. (14 pound coil.)

Object:
To prepare yourself for job efficiency in semiautomatic Innershield welding.

Material:
The reference matter suggested in this lesson.

General Information

Since there are various Innershield electrode wires intended for specific purposes — and various wire feeders, power sources, guns, cables, nozzles, and nozzle guides are required with different electrodes and welding techniques — it would be impractical for the beginning Innershield weldor to have access to the electrodes and equipment needed for a full practice course in Innershield welding. Personal purchase of the needed items would be beyond reason, and no employer is likely to have on hand at one time all the electrode wires and equipment that the Innershield weldor might use during his career. This means that the weldor must learn his techniques with the equipment and electrode types used by his employer — and broaden his scope by studying or referring to published material on the subject.

In Lesson 7.3, the welding of fillets and a butt joint on 3/8" steel plate with 3/32" electrode wire was discussed and practiced. Three procedures were illustrated by charts. In Lesson 7.4, vertical and overhead techniques with NR-202 electrode were presented. This, of course, hardly constitutes a beginning of the subject. Practically all mild and low-alloy steels that can be welded with stick electrodes can also be welded with Innershield — at greatly increased welding speeds and reduced costs. The 3/32" NS-3M electrode discussed in the prior lesson represents only a moderate example of the speed and efficiency of Innershield welding. Chances are, if your first contact with Innershield should be in heavy industrial or structural welding where fast-fill is required, your employer will be using .120" NS-3M, rather than 3/32", because it is still faster. Possibly, also, he may require the use of long electrical stickout — 3-3/4" instead of 2-3/4" — to get maximum production rates. On the other hand, your first job work might be with NR-203 electrode for overhead — or with NR-202 for vertical-up butt welding. Taking into account the number of variables, the professional Innershield weldor must depend on reference literature for fullness of understanding and "how-to-do" information about this semiautomatic process.

One way to have on hand the information on Innershield welding you might need on your job is to have in possession the various items of literature on Innershield, published by The Lincoln Electric Company. Data sheets on various electrodes are published, which give suggested applications for the specific electrode; the recommended power source, wire feeder, gun, and guide tips; operational characteristics; procedure ranges; and properties of the weld metal. Also available is a booklet entitled "Innershield Production Welding Guide — Using .068" Thru .120" Electrode". This material is free and available on request to The Lincoln Electric Company, 22801 St. Clair Avenue, Cleveland, Ohio 44117.

In Lesson 7.3 and 7.4 procedure charts giving detailed information on the use of NS-3M and NR-202 electrodes were presented. Many more such charts are required to cover the whole range of applications for semiautomatic Innershield welding. Forty-six additional procedure charts, covering various electrode types and sizes, joint types, and metal thicknesses, are included in "The Procedure Handbook of Arc Welding", available from The Lincoln Electric Company. This book, acclaimed as the "Bible" of arc welding, is a massive reference work covering all the common arc-welding processes used with industrial metals. With it and the above-described literature, the weldor will have the background information needed for practical semiautomatic Innershield welding in the shop or in the field.

Object:
Your Introduction to Gas Metal-Arc Welding.

General Information

Gas metal-arc welding (GMAW) is widely used to join all the major commercial metals, including carbon, alloy, and stainless steels; and aluminum, magnesium, copper, iron, titanium, and zirconium. In the shop, gas metal-arc welding is usually called MIG welding, but this is an incorrect term, since it is a letter abbreviation for "metal inert-gas". The gases now used as arc shields with bare-wire electrodes are more often than not actually chemically reactive. Thus, the most popular shielding gas used with gas metal-arc welding is carbon dioxide, which is definitely a reactive substance. It reacts, as an example, with water to form carbonic acid and with sodium hydroxide to form sodium carbonate.

Technically, only the gases helium and argon used with gas metal-arc welding are truly inert. Only when they are used without reactive additions could the GMAW process be correctly called MIG. This little problem in semantics may seem unimportant to the student, but the American Welding Society and others are promoting a lexicon that will be meaningful throughout the world. To call carbon dioxide-shielded welding — or an argon-oxygen mixture — as MIG (metal inert-gas) only creates confusion outside a narrow industrial territory.

In gas metal-arc welding, a bare metal wire fed to the work with a semiautomatic gun or full-automatic welding head constitutes the electrode. It carries the current to the arc a slight distance above or in direct contact with the grounded work. While welding is in process, a gas emitted from the nozzle surrounding the electrode envelopes the arc and the molten pool, forcing away atmospheric air and thus protecting the molten metal from the deleterious effects of unwanted reactions with atmospheric oxygen, nitrogen, and water vapor.

The shielding gas also has other functions. The properly selected gas helps to shape the cross section of the weld deposit, to increase molten metal temperature, to stabilize the arc, and to regulate penetration. The shielding gas used is also a factor in the method of metal transfer from the electrode to the weld joint.

The electrode wire fed from a gun or welding head to the arc may not always be metal corresponding chemically to that of the work. It could, for instance, also have alloying elements to give special properties to the weld. It may contain a deoxidizer to refine the metal in the molten pool. It may also have a light coating to stabilize the arc, a flash copper plate to protect an iron-bearing wire from rusting, or it may have a lubricant film to facilitate travel through the wire-feeding mechanism.

Gas metal-arc welding produces high-quality welds. Most of the irons and steels can be joined by GMAW, including the carbon-free irons, the carbon and low-alloy steels, the high-strength and tempered steels, the chromium irons and steels, the high-nickel steels, and some of the "super-alloy" steels. GMAW is a preferred mechanized process for the welding of aluminum, magnesium, and copper and many of the alloys of these reactive metals. The welding techniques and procedures for the various metals may vary widely. Thus, carbon dioxide or argon-oxygen mixtures are suitable for arc shielding with low-carbon and low-alloy steels, whereas an inert gas (helium or argon) may be essential when welding high-alloy steels. Copper and many of its alloys as well as the stainless steels are successfully welded by the process.

"Hand welding" with the GMAW process means using a semiautomatic welding gun. The wire is fed to the gun from a spool or coil with the press of a trigger closing the welding circuit and initiating gas flow. With fully automatic equipment, the work may travel under the welding head, or the head may travel over the work, the same as with submerged-arc automatic welding.

The GMAW process is versatile in respect to the metals it can weld, and it can produce X-ray-quality welds under appropriate conditions. Why, then, is it not used almost exclusively where semiautomation or full-automation are feasible?

The answer is that it has limitations. Outdoors, in a windy, blustery situation, the arc shield would be blown from the arc and the molten metal. In erection work on a skyscraper, the cost of building a wind shield around every beam-to-column joint would be prohibitive. In a plant fabricating girders and beams from steel plate, or in an outdoor shipyard, there would be no point in using a breeze-vulnerable process when submerged-arc welding or Innershield will give high quality welds without shielding problems. Also, the costs of helium and argon gases, where they must be used are considerable, and even if lower-cost carbon dioxide is the appropriate gas, there is still the cost of a gas-supply and the gas-flow system and regulating mechanisms.

Another limitation of the GMAW process is the fact that the hand operator must manipulate a semiautomatic gun that has not only wire feed but a gas nozzle. On long welds, the bulk of the hand-held equipment can be a tiring problem for the weldor, and there is the additional problem of correctly establishing the flow and pressure of shielding gas. If the temperature of the shop should be too high for comfort, the GMAW operator cannot experience the relief of a cooling fan; it would destroy his arc shield. The process also has limitations in that it is very difficult to use a smoke removal type gun. First and foremost, the smoke removal system would tend to remove the gas shielding; secondly, the gun would be cumbersome and difficult to use because it would have to have one system of hoses to bring gases to the arc and another system of hoses to remove welding fumes. Since the two systems oppose each other, they must be very carefully balanced. There is also a tendency to use much more shielding gas when a smoke removal gun is used.

However, there are numerous applications where gas metal-arc welding is most mandatory — especially with the nonferrous metals. And where GMAW is most applicable, it does an excellent job. Although Lincoln does not manufacture and sell total GMAW units, it is the country's largest manufacturer of electrode wire used in gas metal-arc welding of steel, and Lincoln power sources and wire feeders (adaptations of submerged-arc or Innershield equipment) are widely used in this phase of welding technology.

Review Questions

1. Why are the letters MIG technically incorrect when referring to the gas metal-arc process?

2. What is an inert gas? Name two. Name a widely used GMAW gas that is not inert.

3. What metals can be welded by the GMAW process?

4. If you were hand-welding by GMAW, what equipment would you hold in your hand?

5. What's the purpose of the gas in the GMAW process?

6. How long is an electrode in gas metal-arc welding?

7. Why isn't the GMAW process the most suitable one for building-frame welding?

8. Name some applications where GMAW might be a preferred process.

9. What is the difference between Lincoln Electric Company's Innershield process and semiautomatic gas metal-arc welding?

Object:
Principal Features of the GMAW Process

Figure 0. Gas Metal Arc welding is especially suitable for light gauge metals.

Equipment for Gas Metal-Arc Welding

GMAW welding requires a power source, just as in stick-electrode welding. However, except in rare instances, the power source must be DC, whatever the metal to be welded.

A second requirement is a feeder system for advancing the continuous electrode wire to the welding arc. The speed of feed will depend on the amperage of current and will be limited by the welding characteristics of the work material, the variation of the GMAW process used, the shielding gas, and other factors.

A third is the electrode wire, the chemical composition of which depends upon the metal to be welded, plus any metallurgical changes one might wish to make in the weld puddle, such as deoxidation or alloy addition.

A fourth is the shielding gas, with its supply and flow-control system. The gas selected will depend upon the metal to be welded. It may be an inert gas, such as helium or argon, or it may be a mixture of an inert gas with a reactive gas, such as oxygen. In steel welding, the gas most commonly used for shielding is carbon dioxide.

A gun or torch is the fifth requirement. It will be the terminal of the hose and cable assembly for the electrode wire, gas-emission, and electric welding power.

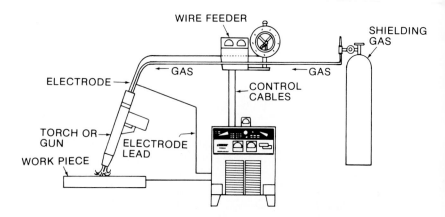

Figure 1. Basic GMAW Equipment.

Figure 1 is a schematic of the basic elements of a GMAW system. Figure 2 shows the general designs of (a) air-cooled and (b) water-cooled guns used with manual GMAW.

At the press of the trigger with the hand-held semiautomatic gun — or the throw of a switch with automatic equipment — that closes the welding circuit, electrode wire advances from the gun or welding head, shielding gas is emitted around the wire, and an arc is generated between the continuously fed wire and the work piece. The heat of the arc melts the wire and a portion of the work, and intermixture of molten metals takes place, forming a weld deposit. As we will see later, in some work the welding current is actually shorted to the work, in a type of GMAW called short-circuit transfer.

The hand-held semiautomatic gun or an automatic torch may also be water-cooled. This, or some provision for air cooling, may be necessary in high-production work. With CO_2 welding, the flow of this gas in hand-held equipment usually provides adequate cooling.

The basic principal of the process — in one of its methods of use — is illustrated in Figure 3. What is shown here is the "globular transfer" open-arc method of GMAW welding. Here, globules of molten electrode wire are moving through the arc into the molten metal within the weld joint. The artist has deliberately shown oxide and mill-

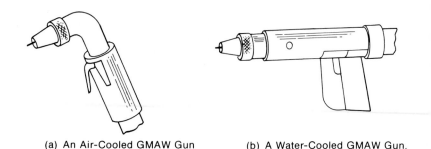

(a) An Air-Cooled GMAW Gun   (b) A Water-Cooled GMAW Gun.

Figure 2.

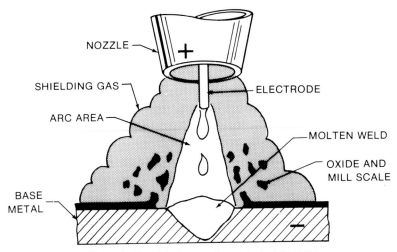

Figure 3. The globular transfer method of GMAW.

scale being blasted away from the weld puddle. This, plus the fact that GMAW does not have a slag, is one of its advantages. The finished weld is clean, bright, and slag-free.

The power sources used with stick-electrode welding are not suitable for gas metal-arc welding. Whatever the metal to be welded, the power must be DC and, preferably, constant voltage. Usually the electrode is positive (DCRP operation); however, DCSP current (electrode negative) may sometimes be used when welding thin-gage metal. AC is not satisfactory with GMAW.

Figure 4 shows a semiautomatic welder with the wire-feeding mechanism. This welder can also be used for Innershield welding and for submerged-arc welding when constant voltage power is satisfactory. Figure 5 shows another constant-voltage DC welder widely used with semiautomatic gas metal-arc welding.

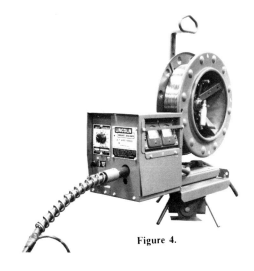

Figure 4.

Figure 5.

For optimum performance GMAW requires a power source with a relatively low maximum open-circuit voltage and a relatively high maximum short-circuit current. The output characteristics of the constant-voltage (potential) power source gives a fairly flat slope to the volt-ampere curve as needed in gas metal-arc welding. See Figure 6.

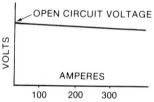

Figure 6. Constant-potential volt-ampere curve — used for GMAW.

Other items of equipment for gas metal-arc welding include the gas-supply tanks and gas-flow regulating meters. Flow rates and pressures are prescribed by the welding procedures and must be carefully controlled for quality welding.

Review Questions

1. Name three methods of welding that are technological responses to the need for lengthening the welding electrode.

2. What are the advantages of semiautomatic welding over stick-electrode welding?

3. What is one advantage of GMAW over semiautomatic submerged-arc? Over flux-cored electrode welding?

4. Why is a constant-voltage power source required in GMAW?

5. If you were welding stainless steel with GMAW, would you have the electrode wire positive or negative?

6. Other than its lower cost, what very practical advantage is derived from using CO_2 as the shielding gas in gas metal-arc welding?

Object:
Gas Metal-Arc Welding Techniques

General Information

Gas metal-arc welding is accomplished by four major techniques, which are defined by the way metal is transferred from the electrode wire to the weld joint. Three of these techniques — spray transfer, globular transfer, and pulsed-circuit transfer — are called "open-arc" methods, which means essentially that there is an opening between the electrode tip and the molten weld puddle. Molten electrode metal leaves the tip, moves through the arc, and is deposited as filler metal in the weld joint. The fourth technique is called the short-circuit method and weld metal is deposited by short-circuit transfer.

Spray Transfer

Spary transfer is aptly named; a mist of tiny drops of molten metal from the electrode wire literally sprays forcibly from the electrode tip, through the length of the arc, and into the weld joint. High currents and voltages are used, resulting in high deposition rates, which tend to limit spray transfer to heavy welds in the flat or horizontal position. The arc length is maintained constant as wire is fed from the tip of the gun, and the arc is smooth and stable. Penetration is often quite shallow, and the puddle is very fluid and usually large in diameter. As shown in Figure 1, the electrode tip is pointed, and the weld metal, under the arc force, is emitted from the point.

Argon, helium, and argon-oxygen and helium-oxygen mixtures are usually used with spray-transfer welding. The technique is most applicable to heavy single-pass or multiple-pass weldments. Aluminum welding can be done by spray-transfer in all welding positions by using very thin aluminum electrode wires, 1/16″ or less in diameter.

Globular Transfer

Globular transfer is illustrated in Figure 3 in the preceding lesson. Globules of molten metal form on the tip of the electrode wire, break loose under the pull of gravity, and fall into the weld joint. The motion through the arc, however, under the influence of forces within the arc, can be erratic, with the shape of the globule being distorted and "bouncing" to the side of the weld joint to produce spatter or back against the electrode to shortout the arc.

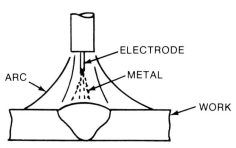

Figure 1. Mechanics of Spray Transfer.

Globular transfer is used primarily with CO_2 or CO_2 with argon addition. Current densities are lower than with spray transfer. Because transfer depends on gravity, the technique can only be used with downhand welding.

Pulsed-Arc Transfer

Pulsed-arc transfer is essentially a "slowed-down" variation of spray transfer. It enables all-position welding by cutting down the vigorous stream of molten metal droplets to a manageable pulsed flow. Figure 2 shows a representation of this method.

Pulsed transfer is accomplished by using one welding current "on top of another". The "background current" is supplied from a three-phase transformer and is adjusted to maintain the welding arc without melting the electrode wire. A pulsed current is then superimposed from a single-phase transformer, switching on and off at either the line frequency or double the line frequency. When "on", discrete droplets of molten metal leave the electrode tip and impinge upon the work. In the fraction of a second that the pulsed current is "off", the main background current maintains the arc and keeps heat flowing into the work piece.

The pulsed current is adjusted to the "spray threshold current" of the type and diameter of electrode wire used. Spray threshold is the amperage at which spray transfer starts with the particular electrode. The pulsed current, of course, must be slightly above this threshold amperage to insure continuous pulsed-spray operation.

With the rate of delivery of metal across the arc under control by the pulsed-arc technique, spray-arc welding becomes more manageable. Out-of-position welding becomes possible and larger electrode wires can be used. Argon is usually the shielding gas of choice. Pulsed-spray welding is normally used only when other GMAW techniques are not applicable or would cause welding problems. Aluminum and high-nickel alloy steels are metals that frequently require the deposition-rate control offered by the pulsed-arc technique.

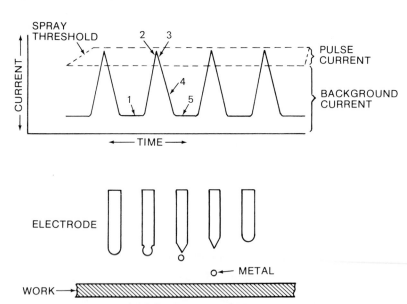

Figure 2. The mechanics of Pulsed-Arc Transfer.

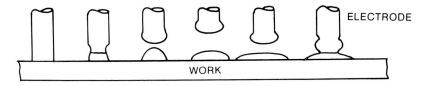

Figure 3. How Short-Circuit Transfer works.

Short-Circuit Transfer

Much of the welding with the gas metal-arc process using CO_2 as the shielding gas is done with the short-circuit transfer technique. In short-circuit transfer, the tip of the electrode wire actually touches the work piece, shorting out the welding circuit. Immediately prior to the moment of contact, the tip of the wire may be molten or near molten. When contact occurs, under the heating effect of the short circuit, the globule at the end of the wire becomes completely fluid and, by surface tension, is drawn to the weld puddle and away from the electrode. A gap occurs and an arc is then re-established. A new cycle of globule-formation at the tip begins while the electrode wire, pushed by the wire feeder, moves toward contact with the work.

Figure 3 is a representation of what happens between the electrode wire and the work with the GMAW short-circuit technique.

The wire-feed speed determines how many short circuits can be made per second with a given type and size of electrode and type of shielding gas. As the wire-feed speed increases, the number of short circuits per second increases. A limit of speed is reached when the wire sticks to the work and the arc is extinguished.

Low voltage and low amperages characterize short-circuit transfer welding. The welding voltage is typically 19 — 20 volts; the amperage, 125 — 150 amperes, and the flow of CO_2 shielding gas, 18 — 20 cubic feet per hour. Every electrode type and diameter have an optimum range of welding conditions. In mild steel welding, the .035″ diameter is most often used with CO_2 or CO_2 mixtures. If the amperage, which controls wire-feed speed, is advanced to much beyond 200 amperes, sticking may become a problem.

Review Questions

1. Both spray and globular transfer are open-arc methods of GMAW. How do they differ in the movement of weld metal through the arc?

2. Why can't globular transfer welding be used in the overhead position?

3. What is meant by "spray threshold current"? Where in GMAW technology is it an applicable consideration?

4. Why is the term "short-circuit transfer" given to this method of gas metal-arc welding?

5. Is the welding current always shorted in short-circuit welding?

6. Which of the four GMAW techniques can be operated at low voltages and low amperages?

7. What could happen if the wire-feed speed is advanced too much in short-circuit welding?

Object:
Consumables for Gas Metal-Arc Welding.

General Information

Metal wire electrodes and shielding gases are the consumables in gas metal-arc welding. Electrode wire is "bare" — except for lubricant films or flashings to prevent oxidation — and is supplied on reels that fit the wire feeder or as coiled wire unwinding helically from a container. Shielding gases may come directly from a gas cylinder equipped with pressure and gas-flow regulating mechanisms or from a bulk supply system. The type of metal to be welded and the technique used dictate composition of electrode wire and its diameter. Usually, the type of metal and the welding technique also determines gas selection.

Shielding Gases

As noted in previous lessons, argon, helium, and mixtures thereof with each other or with reactive gases, such as oxygen and carbon dioxide, are the shielding gases normally used. The correct shielding gas will expedite the welding and give a high-quality weld of desired shape. The wrong shielding gas can lead to difficulties while laying the bead and can cause defects, such as hydrogen embrittlement, underbead cracking, and porosity.

Carbon dioxide (CO_2) is widely used for welding mild steel; almost always with the short-circuit GMAW method. With proper procedures, it helps produce essentially spatter-free X-ray-quality welds. One of its advantages is that it is less costly than the inert gases and another is this shielding gas acts as a coolant for the welding gun assembly.

In the center of the arc, some of the CO_2 gas breaks down into carbon monoxide and oxygen. These dissociated gases recombine on the surface of the weld, thereby releasing to the weld the energy picked up from the arc by the dissociation process. In other words, the arc chemistry favors efficiency in heat transfer from the arc to the weld bead. Most of the CO_2 shielding gas, however, is outside the intense arc-heat area and merely acts as a blanket to push away atmospheric gas and shield the arc and weld puddle.

Carbon dioxide mixed with argon can also be used to weld low-alloy steels. Whether low-carbon or low-alloy steel, the electrode wire used with carbon dioxide must contain adequate deoxidizing agents.

Argon is used as the shielding gas for spray-transfer welding of aluminum, magnesium, copper, and their alloys. This inert gas is supplied in purities better than 99.995% and is nonreactive with all substances. Pure argon can be used as a shielding gas for all metals, but it is not usually used in welding steels, for which argon mixtures are preferable. One of argon's advantages is that it is 38% heavier than air and, thus, holds its shielding well in the flat and horizontal welding positions.

Argon ionizes at a lower potential than helium, thus requiring a lower arc voltage for a given arc length. As a result, less heat is produced with argon than with helium at the same amperage, which makes argon preferable to helium for welding thin sections. Argon costs less than helium, and, since it is about ten times as heavy as helium, less of the gas is required to provide a protective blanket over work in the downhand welding position.

Argon shielding produces a constricted arc column with spray-transfer welding. The energy is concentrated, giving a narrow weld bead, with deep penetration.

Helium, in the pure state, is limited in gas metal-arc welding because of its cost and the need to use a greater volume than with argon to obtain comparable shielding in the flat and horizontal positions. But, as Table 1 shows, mixtures of helium and argon are recommended for welding aluminum, copper, nickel, and their alloys.

TABLE 1 — AWS RECOMMENDATIONS FOR THE GAS-SHIELDED METAL-ARC PROCESS

The recommendations made in this chart are for filler metals and shielding gases.

Base Metal	Shielding Gas	Specific Alloy To Be Welded	Filler Metal	Elect. Diameter	Current Ranges
Aluminum and its alloys	Pure Argon or He-Ar mixture	1100 3003, 3004 5050 5052 5154, 5254 5083, 5084, 5456 6061	1100, 4043 4043 4043, 5554 5554, 5154 5554, 5154 5556, 5356 4043, 5556	0.030 0.045 1/16 3/32 1/8	50-175 90-250 160-350 225-400 350-475
Magnesium and its alloys	Pure Argon or He-Ar mixture	AZ31B, 61A, 81A, ZE10XA ZK20XA AZ31B, 61A, 63A, 80A, 81A, 91C, 92A, 100A, AM80A, ZE10XA XK20XA AZ63A	AZ61A AZ92A AZ63A	0.045 1/16 3/32	220-280 240-390 330-420
Copper	Pure Argon or He-Ar mixtures	Deoxidized Copper	Deox. Cu Si, 0.25% Sn, 0.75% Mn, 0.15%	1/16	300-470
Copper-Nickel alloy	Pure Argon	Cu-Ni alloy 70-30 90-10	Ti dexo. 70-30 90-10	1/16	250-300
Plain low Carbon steel	CO_2 Ar + CO_2 Ar + O_2	Hot or cold rolled sheet ASTM A7, A36 A285, A373 or equivalent	Deox. plain C steel	0.030 0.035 0.045 1/16 5/64	50-150 75-230 100-300 300-450 300-500
Low alloy steel	Ar + O_2 Ar + CO_2	Hot or cold rolled sheet	Deox. low alloy	0.030 0.035 0.045 1/16	50-150 75-230 100-350 300-350
Stainless steel	Argon + O_2	302, 304 321, 347 309, 310 316, etc.	Elect. to match base metal	0.030 0.035 0.045 1/16	75-150 100-160 140-310 280-350
Nickel and Nickel alloys	Argon or He-Ar mixtures	Nickel Monel Inconel	Ti deox. to match base metal	0.035 0.045 1/16	100-150 150-260 200-400
Bronzes	Argon He + Ar mixtures Ar + O_2	Mn Bronze Al Bronze Ni-Al Bronze Sn Bronze	Al Bronze Al Bronze Al Bronze Phos. Bronze	1/16 5/64	225-300 275-350

ADAPTED FROM WELDING HANDBOOK, SIXTH EDITION, SECTION TWO, PUBLISHED BY THE AMERICAN WELDING SOCIETY.

Helium is lighter than air and completely nonreactive with other substances. Its main advantage as a welding shield is the excellent heat conductivity of the ionized gas in the arc column. More heat is produced at a given amperage with helium as the shielding gas than with argon. This leads to a broader weld bead, making helium useful in welding thick sections and highly conductive metals.

Gas Mixtures of the two inert gases, or an inert gas and a reactive gas, offer ways of obtaining some of the best characteristics of each gas for a particular welding job. Note that in Table 1, the American Welding Society recommends gas mixtures for all the listed metals and alloys, with the exception of copper-nickel alloys.

Argon-helium mixtures are favored for the gas metal-arc welding of aluminum, magnesium, copper, nickel, and their alloys.

Argon-oxygen mixtures, containing up to 5% oxygen, are used when welding low-carbon, low-alloy, and stainless steels and some bronzes. Oxygen in the mixture increases the temperature of the metal as it transfers across the arc, thus giving increased flow properties to the molten metal within the weld joint. As a result, the undercut that occurs with argon alone can be eliminated, and the weld bead has a lower crown — necessitating the use of less filler metal and less subsequent grinding to finish the joint.

Argon-carbon dioxide mixtures are used when welding the low-carbon and low-alloy steels by the open-arc transfer methods. Argon in the mixture stabilizes the arc, reduces spatter, and helps achieve the bead shape and penetration desired.

In special applications, especially for the austenitic stainless steels, mixtures of argon, helium, and CO_2 are used with short-circuit transfer. Nitrogen is also used with argon as a gas shield, especially in Europe where helium is not readily available.

GMAW Electrodes

Table 2 shows the American Welding Society specifications for GMAW electrodes (AWS A5.18-69) for low-carbon and low-alloy steels. Specifications for aluminum electrodes are found in AWS A5.10; for copper in AWS A5.6; and for stainless steel in AWS 5.9.

Note that in Table 2, the chemical compositions are closely controlled, except for ER70S-G and ER70S-GB, with silicon (a deoxidizer) making up from 0.3% to more than 1% of the wire composition. ER70S-1B and ER70S-GB are electrodes suitable for low-alloy steel welding.

Much of the bulk of GMAW welding is on low-carbon steel, with the ER70S-3 and ER70S-6 electrode wires being most popular. The most widely used electrode wire of all for gas metal-arc welding of carbon steel is Lincoln's L-50 wire, which was designed as a copper-coated submerged-arc wire and meets the AWS classification of EM-13-K and also meets ER70S-3. The manganese content is between .90 and 1.40%, and the silicon content is in the range of .45 to .70%. It is produced in diameters from .035" to 1/8". The popularity of the L-50 wire in the field results from the favorable experience of weldors and welding machine operators in use of the material and from the fact that having L-50 on hand supplies both the electrode need for submerged-arc and gas metal-arc welding. The copper flash plating on L-50 wire — as on most GMAW wires for carbon steels — protects the wire from oxidation and helps provide good feeding characteristics, without having adverse effect on the weld deposit.

Wire selection is dependent on the metal to be welded, the type of arc transfer, the shielding gas, and welding position. Wire diameter depends upon the above factors and the deposition rate, current density, type of weld joint, thickness of the work material, and penetration characteristics of the GMAW method.

Table 1 shows some of the filler metal requirements for the welding of aluminum, magnesium, copper, nickel, and their alloys, and for stainless steel. Usually the elec-

TABLE 2 — AWS SPECIFICATIONS FOR GMAW ELECTRODES
(AWS A5.18-69)

| Identification | Welding Conditions | | Test Requirements (as welded) | | | Chemical Composition | | | |
AWS Classification	Current Electrode Polarity	External Gas Shield	All Tensile min psi	Weld Yield min psi	Metal El % min 2"	C*	Mn*	Si*	Other
ER70S-1	DC(+)	AO	72,000	60,000	22	0.07 to 0.19		0.30 to 0.50	
ER70S-2	DC(+)	AO & CO$_2$	72,000	60,000	22	0.6		0.40 to 0.70	Ti-0.05 to 0.15 Zi-0.02 to 0.12 Al-0.05 to 0.15
ER70S-3	DC(+)	AO & CO$_2$	72,000	60,000	22	0.06 to 0.15	0.90 to 1.40	0.45 to 0.70	
ER70S-4	DC(+)	CO$_2$	72,000	60,000	22	0.07 to 0.15		0.65 to 0.85	
ER70S-5	DC(+)	CO$_2$	72,000	60,000	22	0.07 to 0.19		0.30 to 0.60	Al-0.50 0.90
ER70S-6	DC(+)	CO$_2$	72,000	60,000	22	0.07 to 0.15	1.40 to 1.85	0.80 to 1.15	
ER70S-G	Not specified	Not specified	72,000	60,000	22	No chemical requirements			
ER70S-1B	DC(+)	CO$_2$	72,000	60,000	17	0.07 to 0.12	1.60 to 2.10	0.50 to 0.80	Ni-0.15 Mo-0.40 to 0.60
ER70S-GB	Not specified	Not specified	72,000	60,000	22	No chemical requirements			

* C — Carbon
* Mo — Manganese
* Si — Silicon

COURTESY THE AMERICAN WELDING SOCIETY

trode wire matches closely the metal or alloy being welded. A deoxidizer of aluminum or silicon is frequently specified as part of the electrode composition.

Review Questions

1. What shielding gas is used most frequently in the gas metal-arc welding of carbon steel? Why?

2. The atmosphere we breathe contains oxygen, nitrogen, carbon dioxide, and argon — all of which are used in shielding gases. Why can't we use bare-electrode wire without any gas shield?

3. What are the advantages of helium gas in GMAW?

4. Oxygen with argon reduces the problem of undercut when gas metal-arc welding. What is the mechanism for this benefit?

5. Why is a copper flash plating often used on steel electrode wires?

6. Lincoln's L-50 electrode wire was designed for submerged-arc welding, yet it is stocked by large fabricators for GMAW purposes for a very practical reason. What is this reason?

7. Where can you find needed specifications for gas metal-arc welding of nonferrous metals?

8. What are the deoxidizers commonly used in GMAW electrode wires?

LESSON

7.10

Object:
To run a straight bead in the downhand position with the Gas Metal-Arc process.

Equipment:
Lincoln "R3S or DC-600" power source and LN-7, 8, or 9 wire feeder.

Material:
Mild Steel Plate 1/4" × 6" × 6"; Lincoln L-50 .035" electrode, CO_2 gas, and the proper safety equipment.

General Information

The basis of GMAW is the continuous electric arc. This arc is maintained when the welding current is shorted across the gap between the electrode and the work piece. The object is to establish a good weld easily and quickly with the right procedure for any given job. It is this bead or series of beads, composed of a fused mixture of base metal and coiled filler metal, that forms the weld.

Spend sufficient time on these jobs to become proficient in:

1. Holding the proper distance away from the base metal and constant travel angle.
2. Move the gun along the plate, so as to secure a smooth, uniform bead.
3. During welding observe the appearance of the molten puddle and learn to recognize a good weld bead while you're making it.
4. Keep your eyes on the sides of the crater as the wire is fed mechanically through the gun assembly to the weld puddle, so that you can quickly vary the speed of travel or gun angle to correct a poor bead.

Correct distance from gun nozzle to work piece will be developed by proper judgement of the weld deposit:

1. If too long an arc, there will be a noticeable increase in spatter and the gun assembly will push the operator's hand away from the work piece.
2. Therefore, penetration will be poor, overlap will be noticeable, sound of the arc will pop and sputter (rather than a steady crackle) or the arc will shut on and off with poor bead appearance as the end result.
3. When the rate of travel is too fast, the bead will be thin and stringy with poor penetration, but if the rate of travel is slow the weld metal will pile up and roll over with excessive overlap.
4. Correct amperage and voltage settings for any given electrode are important to secure the proper procedure for good quality welds.
5. When the voltage is set too high the bead will be flat with excessive amounts of spatter and possibly porosity in the weld.
6. If the amperage setting is too low, burn back of the wire will occur stopping the wire from feeding out of the tip and bird-nesting will result back at the drive rolls.

Removal of the tip at the gun assembly and cutting the tangled wire at the drive rolls would have to be performed before re-establishing an arc.

1. Straighten the first six inches and insert it through the wire guide tubes to the drive rolls.
2. Press the gun trigger until the rolls pick up the wire and feed it through the gun assembly.
3. Replace the old tip with a new one making sure its the same size as the wire.

Job Instructions

Job A: Run stringer beads.

1. Clean the base metal and position flat on table.
2. Check ground connection to table or work.
3. Position the gun with the wire lightly touching the work; visible stickout should be 3/8″ to 1/2″ away from the work piece, too close a stickout will block visibility, yet too long will cause porosity in the weld due to loss of shielding.
   a. Forehand is used for heavy material (push).
   b. Backhand is used for lighter material (drag).

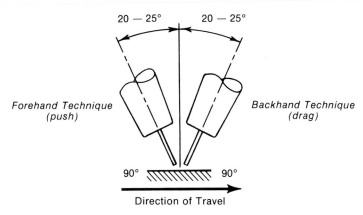

Forehand Technique (push)

Backhand Technique (drag)

Direction of Travel

5. Press the gun trigger to start the weld, and release the trigger and pull the gun away to stop. Some weldors accustomed to manual welding with stick electrodes tend to push the wire into the puddle as it burns away; since the wire is mechanically fed this must be avoided.
6. Adjust voltage and amperage with the controls on the power source or wire feeder (wire feed speed), read the voltage by using the meters and adjust to 19 — 20 volts and 125 amps. The flow of gas (CO_2) should be 18 — 20 cu. feet per hour.
7. Hold the electrode perpendicular to the base metal inclined at a 20 to 25° lead angle in direction of travel.
8. Maintain a normal arc length, 3/8″ to 1/2″, and move the gun across the plate at a uniform rate. A right-handed weldor normally works from left to right and left-handers in the opposite direction.
9. Make stringer beads approximately 1/4″ wide, full length of plate and skip 1/4″ between beads and continue both sides of the work piece.

Step A.

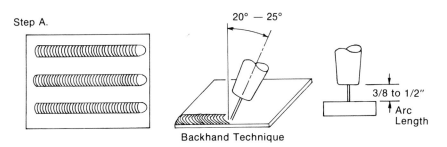

Backhand Technique

Job B: To build a pad.

1. Follow steps 1 to 8 in Job A.
2. Run parallel beads about 6" in length.
3. Run beads toward you, away from you, and from the right and the left.
4. Overlap each new bead on last bead at least 1/4 of an inch.
5. After you are able to run stringer beads completely on one side of plate, turn plate over and use 1/2" weave to build-up pad on opposite side.

Step B.

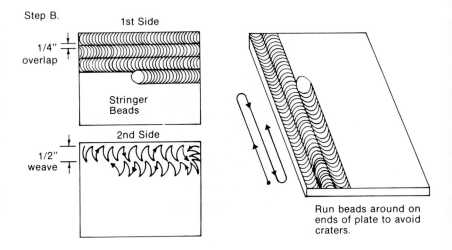

Run beads around on ends of plate to avoid craters.

Review Questions

1. What two techniques are commonly used for GMAW and what determines where they are used?

2. What happens if you have too long an arc with the GMAW process?

3. What will too high a voltage setting do to the weld?

4. What will a low Wire Feed Speed (amperage) setting do to the weld?

5. What to you do if a "bird-nest" occurs?

LESSON

7.11

Object:
To make a butt weld in the downhand position with the gas metal arc process.

Equipment:
Lincoln "R3S" or DC-600 power source and LN-7, 8, or 9 wire feeder.

Material:
Mild Steel Plate 6" × 6" × 3/16" thickness; Lincoln L-50 .035% electrode, CO_2 gas and the proper safety equipment.

General Information

The proper position of the welding gun assembly and the weldment is important for GMAW welding, the flat position (downhand) is preferred for most joints because this position improves the molten metal flow, bead contour, and gives better gas protection. However, on thin gage material, it is sometimes necessary or advantageous to weld with the work slightly inclined 20 to 30 degrees. The welding now can be done in the downhill position with less tendency to burn-through on sheet metal materials. (3/16" and thinner material.)

The butt joint is made by placing the edges of two plates together and fusing them with the arc. A butt weld is most easily made by running beads on both sides of the joint, taking care that the penetration of the beads meet for maximum strength, yet preparation for the butt weld depends upon the thickness of the material.

Job Instructions

Job A: Make a square butt joint.

1. Clean base metal and place two 3/16" plates flat on the table.
2. Adjust voltage and amperage with the controls on the power source, or wire feeder (wire feed speed) read the voltage and amps by using the meters and adjust to 22 volts and 140 amps. Set the flow of gas (CO_2) at 18 — 20 cubic feet per hour.
3. Tack weld the plates together with 1/32" to 1/16" root opening.
4. Run a straight bead to produce the weld in Figure 1, with 3/8" to 1/2" stickout.
5. Break the weld apart; check for 50% minimum penetration.
6. For full penetration weld both sides. (Figure 2.)

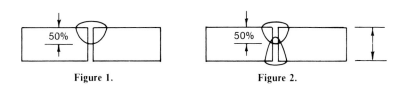

Figure 1.	Figure 2.

Job B: Make a square butt joint in the downhill position.

1. Repeat steps 1 through 3.
2. Secure the plates at a 30° angle to the table in a vertical position.

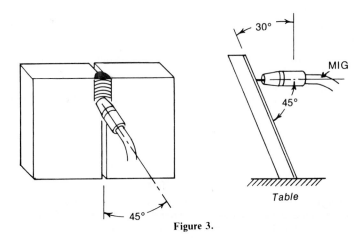

Figure 3.

3. Hold the gun assembly pointing up at an angle of about 45° with the plate.
4. Pull the trigger and start an arc, maintain correct stickout (3/8″ to 1/2″) and draw the gun down the plates at a steady, straight line pace watching the molten puddle area to be sure it is equal on both sides of the seam.
5. Break the weld apart; check for 50% minimum penetration.
6. For full penetration weld both sides.

Review Questions

1. Why is sheet metal often angled downhill for GMAW?

2. Why is the downhand position preferred?

3. What is the proper stickout for GMAW?

LESSON

7.12

Object:
To make a fillet weld in the horizontal position with the gas metal-arc process.

Equipment:
Lincoln "R3S" or DC-600 power source and LN-7, 8, or 9 wire feeder.

Material:
Two pieces mild steel plate $1/4'' \times 6'' \times 6''$; Lincoln L-50 .035" electrode, CO_2 gas and the proper safety equipment.

General Information

Joining members or plates coming in at 90 degree angle to each other with a fillet weld is the most commonly used joint in the welding industry.

Most fillet welds are made in the horizontal position. When placed in this position, the welding speed is increased, the molten metal has less tendency to run, and better penetration is achieved. The strength of this joint depends on the joint fitting close together. For high strength joints make sure both sides of the plate are welded completely.

Job Instructions

Job A: Make a horizontal fillet weld.

1. Clean base metal and tack plates together at 90° angle to each other.
2. Adjust voltage and amperage with the controls on the power source, or wire feeder (wire feed speed); read the voltage by using the meters and adjust to 19 — 20 volts and 125 amps, the flow of gas (CO_2) at 18 — 20 cu. feet per hour.
3. Holding the gun assembly 45° from the horizontal plane, start the weld at the edge of the plate, and maintain $3/8''$ to $1/2''$ arc length away from base metal for entire length of weld.
4. Observe the edges of puddle carefully as it forms under the arc. There may be some tendency to undercut the vertical plate.
5. If travel speed and gun angle are correct, the bead will not undercut.
6. Maintain proper bead shape at beginning, middle, and same size at the end of plate. Bead size should be approximately a $3/16''$ fillet for one pass.

Step A.

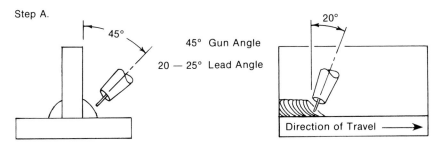

45°

45° Gun Angle

20 — 25° Lead Angle

20°

Direction of Travel ⟶

Figure 1.

Job B: To make a heavier fillet.

1. Follow steps 1 to 6 in Job A.
2. Heavier horizontal fillet welds require more than one bead. Proper procedure is to use the bead sequence shown in Figure 2.
3. The subsequent passes are needed to bring the weld up to correct size.
4. Lay the second bead over the first, placing the third bead on top of first and second welds.

Step B.

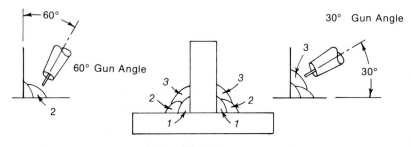

Figure 2.

Review Questions

1. What is the most commonly used joint in the welding industry?
2. What is the proper Gun Angle for making a single pass GMAW fillet?
3. What is the proper Lead Angle for making a single pass GMAW fillet?
4. What is the proper Gun Angle for second and third passes for a GMAW fillet?

LESSON

7.13

Object:
To make a fillet weld in the vertical position welding up with the gas metal arc process.

Equipment:
Lincoln "R3S" or DC-600 power source and LN-7, 8, or 9 wire feeder.

Material:
Mild Steel Plate 3/8" × 3" × 10"; Lincoln L-50 .035" electrode, CO_2 gas and the proper safety equipment.

General Information

When welding in the field it is important that a weldor be able to do vertical-up welding with all different welding applications. Since vertical-up welding is generally used on metal over 1/4" thick, it will be learned here.

Job Instructions

Job A: Make a fillet weld in the vertical-up position.

1. Clean base metal and tack weld plates for a tee joint. Plates are to be at right angles with each other. (Figure 1.)
2. Adjust voltage and amperage with the controls on the power source or wire feeder (wire feed speed). Read the voltage and amps by using the meters and adjust to 22 volts and 140 amps. Set the flow of gas (CO_2) at 25 — 30 cubic feet per hour.
3. Start at the bottom of the plate and hold the gun assembly pointing upward at 20° angle directly into the corner.
4. Hold a distance of 3/8" to 1/2" from nozzle to plate and establish a puddle evenly in each plate 3/8" of an inch wide.
5. Start progression slowly upward with a side-to-side motion hesitating at each side to fuse out any slag pockets and to minimize undercut. Uniformity depends upon proper timing of side-to-side motion. (Figure 1.)

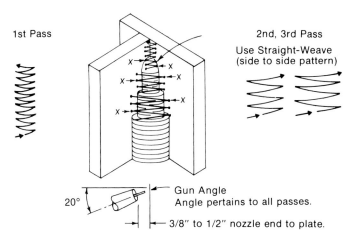

Figure 1.

6. Run the first pass entire length of plate.
7. Using the same amperage and voltage setting, gun angle, and motion as for first pass, widen the weave. The motion should be made at points X and pause somewhat longer for the second and third pass to widen the bead.
8. Try a close arc, a medium, and a long arc. Observe the difference of each type of arc appearance of the bead and spatter accumulation. Slight changes in amperage and voltage settings may be helpful in controlling the puddle. Inspect the beads, so that the penetration and fusion may be observed.
9. This lesson will require considerable practice to obtain uniform beads.

Review Questions

1. What is normally considered the minimum thickness plate for welding vertical-up?

2. Why is timing so important when you are weaving a bead?

3. What is the proper distance from the end of the gun nozzle to the work piece?

4. What is the recommended weaving technique?

Object:
To practice GMAW (Gas-Metal-Arc Welding) 100% open joint on pipe.

Equipment:
Lincoln "R3S" or DC-600 power source and LN-7, 8, or 9 wire feeder.

Material:
Two pieces of 6" mild steel pipe (schedule 40); Lincoln L-50 .035" electrode, CO_2 gas and the proper safety equipment.

General Information

The equipment needed for GMAW of pipe does not differ in any way from that required for other forms of GMAW. Review the process and equipment in Section VII, Lessons 7.6 thru 7.9.

This practice deals with the techniques used for gas-metal-arc welding on standard (schedule 40) pipe and two common welding practices used in the industry today. For the first method the pipe is prepared with a 100% root opening (joint design) to allow for the weld to penetrate completely through the inside of the pipe. The second is to use a back-up ring on the inside of the pipe. These two procedures are explained and discussed for the novice to practice GMAW on pipe.

The skill needed to weld pipe with the GMAW process is very similar to the needed requirements of welding with shielded-metal-arc and the gas-tungsten-arc processes. Special care and concentration are needed by the weldor to make each and every weld a special one. Pipe welding is of growing industrial concern and offers many opportunities for a weldor. Proficient pipe weldors by the hundreds are needed to construct such systems vital to our energy needs. Over 90 percent of all piping installations are welded. For example: the Alaskan Oil Line. More than 800 miles of steel pipe welded together to carry oil to meet our energy crisis. There are many others throughout the U.S. and Canada, Australia and the Middle East where extremes in terrain, weather, and applications call for the dependable process of arc welding.

The GMAW process is limited to noncritical piping where the weld does not have to meet code requirements. There is difficulty when trying to obtain an x-ray quality deposit. The direction of welding may be vertical up or down with all position welding capabilities. The usual method is to weld the first pass down followed by passes that may be welded up or down. The downhill welding techniques are employed in cross-country transmission lines. The uphill welding techniques are employed in pressure and power piping. In general heavy construction either technique produces sound welds when done properly.

When welding on a construction site or inside a shop with the doors open, air movements disturb the gas shielding and porosity in the weld is almost certain. One way to help eliminate this effect is to increase the gas flow rate 5 to 10 cubic feet per hour. This may be the solution. But, sometimes it is necessary to erect draft shields made from canvas or any material to obstruct air movement around the arc. If these welding procedures are followed good results should be attainable.

Some advantages of welding with the GMAW are:
1. The process is fast and in many fabricating jobs faster than other processes.
2. Heavier passes can be made, thus cutting down the number of passes per joint.
3. Since the electrode is continuous wire, stop and start defects are reduced, and there is little electrode stub loss.

4. The elimination of flux and slag reduces cleaning time and chances of trapping foreign materials inside the weld.
5. The process can be used on all pipe sizes and thicknesses where two processes — shielded-metal-arc welding and oxyacetylene were formerly used to handle heavy and thin wall thicknesses.

Job Instructions

Job A: To make a 100% weld with the pipe in the horizontal position (5G). The operator must make a vertical weld on the joint as shown in Figure 3.

1. Clean the scale and rust from pipe.
2. In setting up the weld joint for work according to ASME code, make sure that the root opening is no less that 3/32 of inch and no more than 1/8 inch to insure adequate penetration.

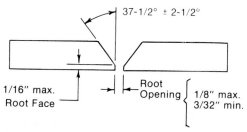

Detail of edge preparation and fitup for ASME code work.

Figure 1.

3. Tack weld pipe together using 3/32 inch bare electrode for spacers. Set up the two nipples in the vertical position and tack weld at four equally spaced places. (12, 6, 3, 9 o'clock position and in that order.) Make sure the pipe remains equally spaced all the way around.

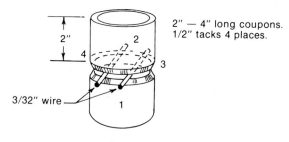

Figure 2.

4. Adjust voltage and amperage with the controls on the power source or wire feeder (wire feed speed). Read the voltage by using the meters set to 18 volts and 120 amps. The flow of gas should be 18 cubic feet per hour of carbon dioxide.
5. Clamp or tack weld the pipe at a convenient height and clear of all obstructions.

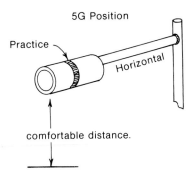

Figure 3.

6. On open butt joint your first pass or "stringer bead" is usually welded vertical down followed by passes that may be welded up or down. Stringer beads can be welded three different ways:
   a. Lightly drag the gun assembly down the bevel of the pipe.
   b. A side-to-side weaving motion.
   c. Rolling it in with small circular movements of the gun.
   Many weldors prefer to move the gun nozzle slightly from side-to-side and walking the molten puddle down the pipe. On 2G (welding horizontally) and 6G (45° angle) roll it in counter-clockwise. This will help overcome the pull of gravity. This procedure is continued until the bead is complete on both sides of the pipe. Be sure to start each stringer at 12 o'clock and finish at 6 o'clock on the stringer bead.
7. Although there will not be a heavy flux deposit to remove, there will be a little dust and black glassy material in spots along the surface of the weld. This substance must be removed with a power wire brush, filed, or hit lightly with a grinder. If not, this material will become entrapped in the weld, causing porosity, and the arc will become unstable making it hard to weld.
8. When starting to weld position the gun nozzle touching the work piece or be very near to it until the arc is established. This technique will avoid excessively long stickout which complicates arc striking.
9. After cleaning the root pass, inspect the weld for evidence of:
   a. Lack of penetration on the inside of the pipe.
   b. Lack of fusion.
   c. Undercut.
   d. Uniformity of the weld.
   e. Stringer bead app. 1/8″ thick.
   f. Build-up on inside of pipe 1/16″ to 1/8″ high, 3/16″ to 1/4″ wide.
10. Starting at the bottom of the pipe (but not the same spot where the first pass was ended) put in a second pass using a slight side-to-side weave. Be certain to burn well into each side of the previous bead to insure complete fusion with the root pass and walls of the pipe.
11. Run a similar bead on the other side. Clean the entire weld. Weld passes should not be more than 1/8 inch thick. All filler passes should have a flat face and be flush with the surface of the pipe.
12. Using a wider side-to-side weave, put on the third and final pass. This pass should be very neat and have a contour as shown in Figure 4. The bead should be about 1/16 inch at the crown and should taper out to the edges of the bead.

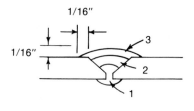

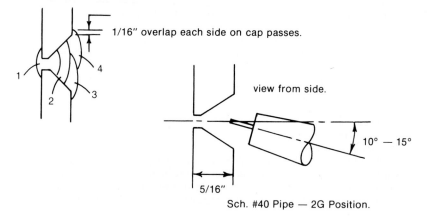

circular motion

side-to-side weave

Figure 4.

Job B: To make a horizontal weld on the pipe with the axis vertical.

1. Whenever there are pipe installations, there will be vertical pipe requiring horizontal welds for fabrication. This position is referred to as 2G. The bevel and root opening will usually be of the standard type given in early practices.
2. Repeat steps 1 thru 8 of previous lesson.
3. Use L-50 .035" or .045" electrode for subsequent passes. Run straight passes in the sequences shown in Figure 5.

1/16" overlap each side on cap passes.

view from side.

10° — 15°

5/16"

Sch. #40 Pipe — 2G Position.

Figure 5.

4. Start your root pass on 2G joints at the tightest area. If a wide fitup is unavoidable use no spacer tacks on one side of pipe and weld the tightest fitup first. This will draw and improve the bad opening.

5. Clean the entire stringer bead.
6. The second pass is usually made with a slight weave or rolling it in with small circles, a uniform travel speed is important. If the travel speed is too slow, the weld metal becomes lightly fluid and sags so there is lack of penetration at the bottom toe. Also there may be possible chances of incomplete fusion and future passes as the joint is filled.

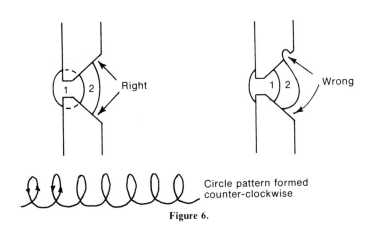

Circle pattern formed counter-clockwise

Figure 6.

7. Filler passes may be made with stringer bead technique or weave bead techniques. The choice of technique depends upon the requirements for the particular job.
8. The final weld pass should be approximately 3/32" high and cover half of the third pass. Weld to overlap 1/16" on each bevel edge. Over welding more than 1/16" will make a weld which is crack sensitive on this edge.

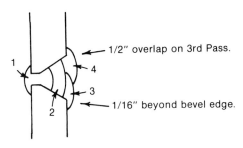

Figure 7.

Review Questions

1. What are the two procedures used for welding pipe with the GMAW process?
2. What other processes are commonly used to weld pipe?
3. Why is the GMAW process limited to non-critical piping?
4. What type of piping is welded with the downhill technique?
5. What type of piping is welded with the uphill technique?

Object:
To practice GMAW using a backing ring.

Equipment:
Lincoln "R3S" or DC-600 power source and LN-7, 8, or 9 wire feeder.

Material:
Lincoln L-50 .035″ electrode, CO_2 gas and the proper safety equipment. Roll or form a 1/8″ diameter piece of L-50 electrode into a 6″ diameter ring.

General Information

Some welding procedures require a backing ring to be used on the inside of the pipe. In this case the root opening normally should not be less than 3/16 of an inch, and the bevel feathered to a knife's edge. This provides for excellent fusion of the root bead to the backing ring.

The back-up ring used in pipe welding becomes somewhat easier for a skilled weldor to complete, because it gives the operator something besides thin air to weld on. These rings can be purchased in different diameters and thicknesses from any local welding supply company. For the purpose of practicing this lesson, roll or bend a section of L-50 1/8″ diameter wire to the same inside diameter as the pipe. The usual procedure is to carefully tack weld the ring to the inside of one coupon. Then proceed to fit both pieces of pipe together and re-tack (1/2″ long) in the same areas. Grind and prepare all tack welds before welding.

The usual practice when welding on a back-up ring is to utilize vertical-up techniques. In this practice weld the first pass vertical-up using a slight side-to-side weaving motion. Practice normal welding procedures — being careful of possible burn-through because of the thin "bottom" (root) ring. Refer to normal welding procedures to complete the pipe as in practice lesson 7.14 (120 amps, 18 volts, 18 c.f.h. CO_2).

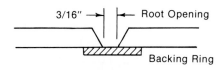

3/16″ →| |← Root Opening

Backing Ring

Job Instructions

1. Be sure the pipe is properly beveled and clean a small area on the inside of the pipe.

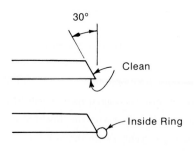

30°

Clean

Inside Ring

2. Tack weld the ring at four places to one side of the pipe.
3. Tack weld the pipe together with a 3/32, or 1/8 inch gap. Use four 1/2" long tack welds equally spaced around the pipe. (12, 6, 3, 9 o'clock.)

Groove Weld Positions

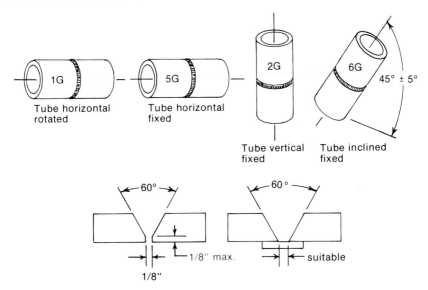

4. Clamp or tack weld the pipe in a 5G position and at a comfortable height and clear of all obstructions.
5. Feather the tacks by grinding, filing, or chiseling until they are just thick enough to hold the ring and the pipe coupons together while welding.

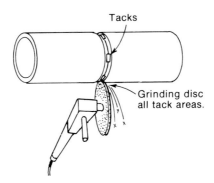

6. Set amperage, voltage, and gas the same as previous practice 7.14 (120 amps, 18 volts, 18 c.f.h. CO_2).
7. Weld the root pass with a stringer bead technique. Start at the 6 o'clock position and weld uphill to 12 o'clock. Use a side-to-side weave, as you move upward into the puddle, let the metal melt into the back-up ring and wash up against the sides of the groove for proper fusion.

8. Clean each pass thoroughly before running the next. Do not start and stop beads at the same spot as the previous pass. The second and intermediate passes may be made using a wider side-to-side weave technique.

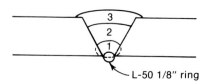

L-50 1/8" ring

9. All passes should be very neat and should have a contour as shown in Figure 1.
10. Make the cover pass like the filler pass. Be sure to pause briefly at each edge of the filler pass to obtain proper fusion. The bevel edges on each side should be your guide to determine the final width of the cover pass.
11. Clean and examine pipe for uniformity and proper penetration.

Job Instructions

1. What is the minimum gap when using a backing ring for GMAW pipe?

2. How should the pipe be prepared in terms of bevel and land?

3. Why is a back-up ring used?

4. What is a grinding disc used for?

LESSON 7.16

Object:
Weld 22 gage material using the Lincoln "Idealarc SP-200".

Equipment:
"Idealarc SP-200" welder with optional stitch/spot timer and gas solenoid. Gas regulator and the proper safety equipment.

Material:
24 gage sheet 2″ × 12″, Lincoln .030″ diameter L-50 electrode and C-25 shielding gas.

Figure 1. The SP-200 being used for auto-body repair.

General Information

The "SP-200" was described in Lesson 2.8 for Innershield welding. In just a few minutes the stitch/spot timer and gas solenoid can be added to increase its versatility for GMAW welding. Versatility is further enhanced for auto-body repair and other light gage applications with a variety of attachments available from you Lincoln welding distributor. The SP-200 can also easily be adapted to feed aluminum or stainless steel electrodes with the GMAW process. For details, contact your local Lincoln distributor.

Job Instructions

Load the SP-200 with the .030″ Lincoln L-50 electrode making sure the electrode will unwind in a clockwise manner. Grab the end of the electrode before you cut the last tie wire. Cut the wire, straighten the first 6 inches of electrode, insert it in the drive rolls, and depress the gun trigger. Hold the trigger until the wire is about 1/2" past the contact tip. Check the contact tip to be sure it is in good condition. Connect the work clamp to the workpiece with the machine set for DC(+) polarity. Check your welding procedures so that you have 85 inches per minute wire feed speed, 16 arc volts, and 20 — 25 cubic feet per hour of gas flow.

Set the "ON" and "OFF" dials on the stitch timer to 2, the burnback to 1, and the spot timer to 5. You are now ready to weld. Tack up the strips so that you have a lap weld and set the mode switch on the front of the machine to "STITCH". This will cause the arc and wire feed system to automatically pulse off and on according to the time intervals you have selected! Weld the 22 gage lap and notice how easy it is to control the weld puddle. Now flip the switch to continuous and try to make the same weld. It is almost impossible to not "burn through". For arc spot welds, flip the switch to spot and you can make consistent arc spot welds which are much stronger than those made with resistance welders.

If you have a large gap to fill, you may want to try METAL FILL. Here's how it works: Set the voltage range and fine tuning switches to their absolute minimum. Set the wire feed speed to 375 in/min. Hold the nozzle one inch away from the work and fill incredible gaps on very light material. To tie it in, come back and weld the edges with the stitch timer.

This technology makes gas and resistance welding obsolete for unibody vehicles. It is not only stronger but is easier and 3 to 10 times faster.

LESSON
7.17

Object:
To study the basics of the semi-automatic submerged arc process.

General Information

The submerged arc process is gaining popularity because there is no need to wear a welding helmet, protective leathers, or heavy welding gloves. The process is clean, comfortable, and produces virtually no welding fumes. This is all possible because the welding arc is buried under a "sand-like" granular material called flux. The arc melts the electrode, the base metal and flux into a common pool. The molten flux acts as a cleansing agent and floats to the top of the weld to form a protective slag while the weld solidifies. (Figure 1.) Submerged arc welds have a beautiful appearance and usually have excellent physical and mechanical properties. The slag is practically self-removing.

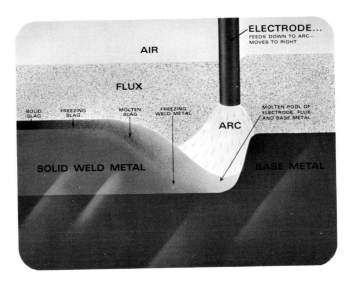

Figure 1. Schematic of the Submerged Arc Process.

Submerged arc fluxes and electrodes are made for a wide variety of applications. Lincolnweld fluxes and electrodes are made for mild steel, low-alloy, stainless, and hardsurfacing. For semiautomatic welding on mild steel over a wide range of procedures and application, Lincolnweld 980 flux and L-50 electrode is recommended. This provides the best combination of resistance to flash-through and arc blow porosity while maintaining very good slag control, bead shape, and slag removal. 980 is a relatively neutral flux so changing the welding procedures has little affect on the weld deposit chemistry. The L-50 electrode is copper coated mild steel to provide the finest quality.

Process Advantages

Semiautomatic submerged arc welding can produce consistent, high quality welds. Note the following advantages:

1. *Exceptional "Fast-Fill" ability* of submerged arc welding results in low cost welding. The deposition rate for 1/16" diameter electrode is about 16-18 lbs/hr while 5/64" diameter electrode may reach 22 lbs/hr with 1-3/4" ESO DC(-) (L-50/980 and LN-9, DC-600 CP Sub-arc mode).
2. *Outstanding "Fast-Follow" characteristics* make submerged arc welding an economical process for small welds. Welding travel speed is limited primarily by the operator's ability to follow a seam at high travel speeds — by adding a travel speed mechanism the "Fast-Follow" characteristics may be a greater advantage.
3. *Deep penetration* [DC(+)] minimizes the amount of weld metal required for full strength and sometimes reduces joint preparation requirements.
4. *Greater operator comfort* results because of reduced exposure to smoke, spatter, glare and heat.
5. *Excellent slag removal* (with proper procedures) means little or no chipping and, since there is no spatter and the beads are smooth and ripple-free, they require minimum cleaning time. Overall appearance is virtually unsurpassed when compared to other semiautomatic processes.
6. *Consistent quality* weld metal when using proper procedure:
   a. Mechanical properties are equal to or better than the base metal.
   b. Low hydrogen deposits are dense, crack resistant and free of inclusions.
   c. X-ray and code quality welds are easily made with standard procedures.

Required Equipment

Lincoln LN-8 and LN-9 semiautomatic wire feeders are recommended for submerged arc welding. The LN-7 may also be used.

The Idealarc DC-600, combination variable voltage and constant voltage DC power source, is the recommended power source for semiautomatic, submerged arc welding. The constant voltage output characteristic is recommended.

Other power sources such as the R3S-400, R3S-600, SAF-600, SA-800, SAM-400 and SAM-650 welders are also satisfactory for semiautomatic submerged arc welding.

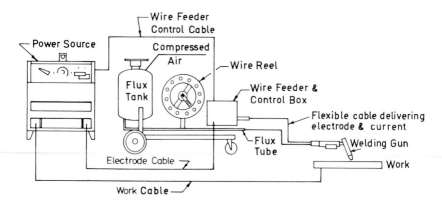

Figure 2. Schematic of Required Equipment.

Choice of Proper Welding Gun

The following three Squirtguns™ and 15-foot cable assemblies are available for semiautomatic submerged arc welding.

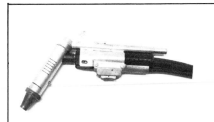

K-112 'SQUIRTGUN' AND CABLE: For LN-4, -5, -6, -7, -8 and -9. Gun and cable capacity 500 amperes, 60% duty cycle. Designed for 1/16 electrode. Gun includes one 1/16" contact tip and one each flux cone tip with 1/2" and 3/4" opening. This gun does not have flux valve or receptacle for mechanized travel attachment. Cannot be used on ML-2 or ML-3 machines.

FLUX CONE ASSEMBLY
Fits Squirtguns K-112 & K-113. Hopper type flux feeding replaces the continuous flux feed system.

K-113 'SQUIRTGUN' AND CABLE: For LN-4, -5, -6, -7, -8 and -9. Gun and cable capacity 600 amps., 60% duty cycle. Designed for 5/64" or 3/32" electrode. Gun includes 5/64" nozzle contact tip, and one each flux cone tip with 5/8 and 3/4" opening. This gun does not have flux valve or receptacle for mechanized travel attachment. For 2-1/4" electrical stickout order S-13027-1 extension and S-12957-15/16 flux cone tip if required.

K-114 'SQUIRTGUN AND CABLE: For LN-4, -5, -6, -8 and -9. Gun and cable capacity 600 amps., 60% duty cycle. Designed for 3/32" electrode (may also be used on 5/64" electrode). This gun has a flux valve, and receptacle for mechanized travel attachment. Gun includes one 3/32" nozzle contact tip, and one each flux cone tip with 5/8 and 3/4" opening. For 2-1/4" electrical stickout order S-12891-1 and S-12957-15/16 flux cone tip if required.

Figure 3.

Flux Feeding System

In addition to the K-119 flux cone assembly, Lincoln supplies a "Continuous Flux Feeding System" as standard equipment. The system consists of the following components: A 100-pound capacity steel flux tank which meets ASME Boiler Code specifications. The tank has a large screw cap type opening for quick and easy loading of flux. An internal screen at the tank input prevents large foreign particles from getting into the interior of the tank. (Used flux should be pre-screened through a screen opening.) A large drain orifice at the bottom of the tank permits quick and easy discharge of the flux for cleaning purposes and for changing to different fluxes.

Figure 4. The LN-9 wire feeder with pressurized flux tank and undercarriage is recommended for semiautomatic submerged arc welding.

The second part of the flux feeding system consists of the flux tank air system. The air, which provides a positive pressure inside the flux tank, enters first through a fine mesh screen cup and then through the air line filter which will remove normal amounts of moisture present in the air from the plant system. If excess moisture is present, a primary strainer or trap may be required in addition to the air line filter. Next, the air will enter the pressure regulator which reduces the pressure to 28 pounds. The 28-pound pressure is satisfactory for feeding flux through an 18' flux tube, which is a standard hose used under normal situations. When a 60' flux hose is used, it is recommended that the air pressure in the tank be raised to 50 or 60 psi. The tank is protected from over-pressure by a safety valve.

The "Continuous Flux Feeding System" normally supplies a sufficient amount of flux to cover the arc. On very rare occasions stoppages may occur from pieces of paper (from flux bags) or other objects which were picked up by reclaiming used flux.

Basic Requirements for Good Welds

Cleanliness

Organic contaminants, (oil, grease, paint, and so forth), rust and scale, or moisture can cause porosity. Therefore:
1. Use only clean, rust-free electrode.
2. Screen used flux to remove large particles of slag or other debris. If used flux is contaminated with excess fine mill scale, remove the mill scale with a Lincoln Magnetic Separator (K-58).

3. Always remove heavy rust or scale from the joint and clean off oil, grease or moisture. If any contaminants are present, welding speeds slower than maximum must be used to permit gas to bubble out of the weld before it solidifies. Therefore, it is often most economical to degrease the joint area or drive off moisture with a preheating torch.

Joint Designs and Fitup

Submerged arc welding is a deep-penetrating process. To avoid burn through, the plates being welded are generally either butted tight together, or a back-up strip is used. Gaps of any kind increase penetration and may cause burn through. As a rule of thumb, if the gap is large enough for loose flux to spill through, either a back-up or a manual seal bead is required to support the flux.

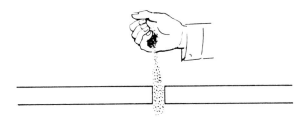

Figure 5. If flux spills through the gap, support is needed.

Review Questions

1. Why is a welding helmet and protective leathers not needed for submerged arc welding?

2. List six advantages of the submerged arc process.

3. Describe Lincoln's two flux feeding systems for getting flux to the welding arc.

4. What is a good way to check if a back-up is necessary for a butt weld with the submerged arc process?

Object:
To make a fillet weld with the submerged arc process.

Equipment:
Lincoln "R3S or DC-600" power source, LN-7, 8, or 9 wire feeder equipped for submerged arc welding with a K-113 gun.

Material:
Mild steel plate 1/4" thick, 3" × 18"; Lincoln 5/64" L-50 electrode and 980 flux as well as the proper safety equipment.

General Information

With the submerged arc process, once the procedures are set, welding is as easy as dragging the gun along the joint at the appropriate travel speed. Wire feeders such as the LN-8 and LN-9 have an interlock device that permits releasing the gun trigger and the arc is maintained until the gun is rapidly pulled away. This aids in weldor training. In just a few hours individuals who have never welded are able to make consistent quality welds with the submerged arc process.

Making the Weld

Tack weld the plates to form a "T" for fillet welding. Use a Lincoln K-113 gun with 5/8" flux cone. The size of the flux cone determines the volume of flux which will cover the arc. Too little flux will cause flash-through and porosity in the weld. Too much flux will cause a poor bead shape. Using the proper flux cone and travel speed helps assure uniform quality welds.

Set the wire feeder at 165 in/min wire feed speed (340 amps) and 32 to 34 volts DC negative polarity. Make sure the work clamp is firmly attached to the workpiece and that you have a 5/64" contact tip which is in good condition, in the K-113 gun. Check to see that the air is on if you are using the pressurized tank and that it has plenty of 980 flux.

Starting the Arc

With a pair of diagonal or side cutters, clip the end of the electrode to a sharp point close to the end of the flux cone. Improperly clipped electrode may result in poor starts and arcing of the contact tip. Do not let the clipped end fall back into the gun.

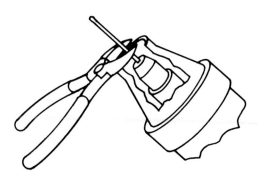

Figure 1.

Position the gun over the joint as described under "Gun Operating Positions". Allow the mound of flux to form, press the trigger and touch the electrode to the work by lightly scratching through the flux. A slow acceleration start with the LN-7, LN-8 and LN-9 improves most starts and reduces flash through. Allow the arc to become firmly established before beginning travel.

If the electrode hits the work, pushing the gun up without starting the arc, immediately release the trigger, raise the gun and turn the nozzle up. The welding arc probably has not been established because of a poor electrical circuit. The electrical circuit may be partially open because of (1) loose mill scale or dirt under the electrode tip, (2) a loose work lead connection, (3) worn or damaged welding cables, or (4) trying to arc on slag or flux. Be sure the work lead is properly connected and the work is clean at the starting point, clip the electrode end and try again.

Gun Operating Positions

Hand Held "Squirt" Guns

Hold the gun handle parallel to the joint and with the gun barrel not greater than 45° from the vertical. With the flux cone lightly touching the work, be sure an adequate supply of flux surrounds the striking area, press the trigger and proceed with the weld, lightly dragging the flux cone over the work.

Hold the trigger in until the weld is finished. Release the trigger to stop the arc. At the same time, lift the gun from the work and turn the nozzle up to stop the flux flow. Always set the gun down with the nozzle tipped up to avoid wasting flux and losing the back-up pressure which provides proper flux feeding.

The LN-8 and LN-9 wire feeders are equipped with a Trigger Interlock switch. When the switch is turned "on", the trigger can be released after the arc has started. An optional burn back kit, K-202, may be desirable for contactor dropout delay to prevent sticking the electrode in the crater when using high WFS.

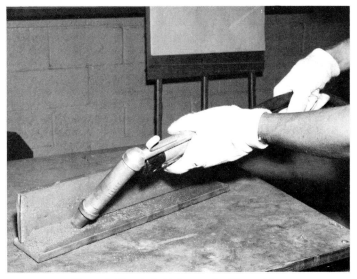

Figure 2. How to hold the gun for fillet welds.

Electrode Position

Most submerged arc welds are made by maintaining a 15° to 30° drag angle between the vertical and the welding gun axis. The drag angle is the angle seen when looking at the side view of the nozzle. Increasing the drag angle causes a small increase in the arc force back into the puddle. However, changing the drag angle to correct welding defects should be used only as a fine adjustment after voltage, wire feed speed, travel speed and electrode work angle are adjusted.

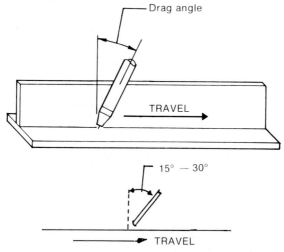

Figure 3. Drag Angle.

The electrode angle to the joint is measured from the bottom plate, therefore, on horizontal fillets the electrode angle is between 45° and 60° from the horizontal member. The electrode drag angle is maintained at 15-30°. (See Figure 4.)

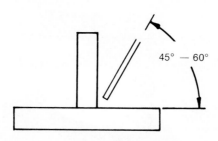

Figure 4.

Nozzle location in Lincoln submerged arc guns is fixed so the electrode exits at the center of the flux cone tip. This allows the operator to aim for good weld placement. Different diameter cone tips shipped with each gun minimize flash through and flux consumption regardless of weld size.

A weld with a 3/16″ leg should be easily made with a travel speed of 32 to 34 inches per minute. Upon completing the weld, the slag should be virtually self-removing as it

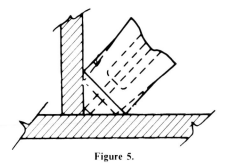

Figure 5.

cools. Do not be too eager to remove red hot flux while it is still glowing. It will be difficult to remove and weld quality may be reduced. Practice until you are able to make uniform, consistent welds.

Review Questions

1. Why do we need to cut the wire before starting to weld?

2. What is the importance of selecting the proper size flux cone?

3. What are the two most important factors the welding operator must learn to control?

Object:
To make a butt weld with the submerged arc process.

Equipment:
Lincoln "R3S or DC-600" power source, LN-7, 8, or 9 wire feeder equipped for submerged arc welding, with a K-112 gun.

Material:
Mild steel plate 10 gauge 2″ × 24″; Lincoln 1/16″ L-50 electrode and 980 flux as well as the proper safety equipment.

General Information

After completing lesson 7.17 you should be familiar with the basics of the submerged arc process. On plate less than 3/16″ thick, a steel backing bar is recommended for one pass butt welding from one side. Using DC(+) polarity produces outstanding penetration for a sound weld into the backing bar. Heavier plate can be welded from both sides and beveled if necessary. Full penetration butt welds have been made from one side on steel up to 3/8″ thick by using a gap and a steel or grooved copper back-up bar. See Figure 1. When using a copper back-up bar it is not a part of the finished weldment but only helps to form the bead shape of the back side of the weld.

The Lincoln Electric Company has been making some innovative advances at welding much heavier plate from one side with a specially built automatic submerged arc welder. This looks very promising and should permit tremendous cost saving potential for the ship building industry.

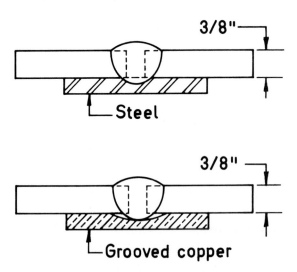

Figure 1. Submerged arc can be a very deeply penetrating process making full penetration welds on 3/8″ plate from one side.

Figure 2. Butt Weld — End View. Gun in Position.

Making the Weld

Tack three of the plates together so that you have a butt joint with a 5/64" gap and the third plate serves as a backing bar. Set the wire feeder so you have a wire feed speed of 210 in/min (375 amps), 28-30 volts, DC(+) polarity and a 1/2" flux cone. With the 1/16" electrode and 5/64" gap you should be able to make commercial quality welds with a travel speed of 35 to 40 inches per minute. See Figure 2.

Practice until you are able to produce uniform consistent welds.

Review Questions

1. Why is a backing bar used for butt welds?

2. What function would a copper backing bar provide?

LESSON
7.20

Object:
To learn the basics of mechanized travel with the submerged arc process.

General Information

After becoming familiar with the submerged arc process, it becomes apparent that to make good uniform welds, the travel speed of the gun is of prime importance. If a constant travel speed can be maintained, several improvements can be made to yield even higher deposition rates.

By selecting the K-114 welding gun, 3/32″ wire can be used. This permits higher deposition rates than the 5/64″ electrode.

For highly repetitive applications, mechanized travel may be desirable. Hold the gun in the position shown in the photos with the electrode perpendicular to the joint. Additional details for arranging the joints are given in the LN-8 and LN-9 wire feeder operating manuals. Although the gun is designed to be traveled at a preset travel speed on the motor driven wheel, it can also be hand traveled. For proper flux feeding the same gun position should be maintained when it is hand carried. The mechanized travel unit works well on any joint where the wheel has space for tracking. A fillet and butt weld are shown in Figure 2.

For even higher deposition rates, the electrical stickout can be increased from the normal 3/4″ to 2-1/4″ with an extension nozzle. This "nozzle" is called a LINC-FILL™ guide and the increased stickout causes preheating of the electrode for up to 50% higher deposition rates.

Figure 1. The K-114 gun with the optional K-110 mechanized travel unit.

BUTT WELD   FILLET WELD
Figure 2. The K-110 mechanized travel unit in action.

Review Questions

1. After becoming familiar with the submerged arc process, what is of prime importance for the operator to control?

2. Name 2 ways that deposition rates can be dramatically increased with the submerged arc process.

Object:
To learn the effect of operating variables so that you can develop submerged arc procedures for a variety of applications.

Effect of Operating Variables

Wire Feed Speed (WFS)

If the other variables are held constant, changing WFS changes the current and also has the following effects:
1. Increasing WFS increases penetration and deposition rate.
2. Excessively high WFS produces an erratic arc, undercut or a high narrow bead.
3. Excessively low WFS produces an unstable arc.

Voltage

Voltage is primarily used to control bead shape. If the other variables are held constant, changing voltage has the following effects:
1. Increasing voltage:
   a. Produces a flatter and wider bead.
   b. Improves slag removal on square edge butts and fillets.
   c. Increase flux consumption.
   d. Increases resistance to porosity caused by rust or scale.
   e. Helps bridge gaps when fitup is poor.
2. Excessively high voltage:
   a. Produces a "hat shaped" bead which is subject to cracking.
   b. Produces poor slag removal.
   c. Produces a concave fillet weld which will be subject to cracking.
   d. Reduces resistance to arc blow porosity.
3. Lowering the voltage produces a stiffer arc needed for getting penetration in a deep groove and to resist arc blow on high speed or multiple pass work. It also improves slag removal in deep groove welds.
4. An excessively low voltage produces a high, narrow bead with poor slag removal.

Travel Speed

Changing the travel speed, like changing the WFS, will change weld size and penetration. Basically:
1. In single pass welds, set the WFS and travel speed as high as possible and still get the correct weld size and desired penetration without burn through.
2. For multiple pass welds, set the travel speed to get the desired bead size.

If the other variables are held constant, changing travel speed has the following effects:
1. Excessively high travel speeds decrease wetting action and increase the tendency for undercut, arc blow, porosity and uneven bead shapes.
2. Slower travel speeds give gaseous material time to boil out of the molten weld, reducing porosity.
3. Excessively slow speeds produce:
   a. "Hat shaped" bead that is subject to cracking. (See Figure 1.)
   b. Excessive flash through which is uncomfortable for the operator.

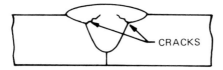

Figure 1.

   c. A large molten pool that flows around the arc resulting in a rough bead, spatter and slag inclusions.
   d. Less penetration.

Electrode Size

Guns, cables drive rolls and guide tubes will utilize a limited range of electrode sizes. Therefore, changing the electrode size often requires installation of parts proper for the size being used.

Only three different electrode sizes are commonly used:

1. The 5/64 diameter electrode is the most versatile size electrode. This electrode is used for single and multiple pass positioned fillets and butt welds. The 5/64 diameter electrode can also be used for many smaller single pass welds.
2. The 1/16 diameter electrode is normally used for, but not restricted to, small (1/4 and under) single pass welds where maximum penetration is required and for maximum operator appeal on single pass and multiple pass welds. This size offers the greatest cable flexibility.
3. The 3/32 diameter electrode is used mostly for mechanized semiautomatic welding with the K-110 Hand Travel Unit or the K-62 Squirtmobile, and in installations where the gun is mounted rather than hand held.

Deposition Rates

The stickouts listed are the approximate stickouts which result when a drag technique is used with the recommended flux cone or the recommended flux cone with the extension guide.

SINGLE WIRE DC(+) POLARITY

	Wire Feed Speed (in/min)	Approximate Current (amps)	Weld Metal Deposition Rate (lbs/hr)
1/16" Diameter 7/8" Electrical Stickout	85 150 235	200 300 400	4.3 7.5 12.0
5/64" Diameter 1" Electrical Stickout	85 125 170	300 400 500	6.8 10.0 13.5
Weight of Electrode (lbs/ft)			
1/16" — .010 5/64" — .016			

SINGLE WIRE DC(-) POLARITY

	Wire Feed Speed (in/min)	Approximate Current (amps)	Weld Metal Deposition Rate (lbs/hr)
1/16" Diameter 7/8" Electrical Stickout	105 215 330	200 300 400	5.3 11.0 16.5
5/64" Diameter 1" Electrical Stickout	135 215 265	300 400 500	11.0 17.0 21.0
5/64" Diameter 2-1/4" Electrical Stickout	160 240 335	300 400 500	13.0 19.0 27.0
Weight of Electrode (lbs/ft)			
1/16" — .010 5/64" — .016			

SUBMERGED ARC TROUBLE SHOOTING GUIDE

Semiautomatic, Single Electrode		
Joint	Problem	Corrective Action (In Order of Importance)
Any	Low Penetration	1. Increase welding current. 2. Use electrode positive. 3. Lower voltage on fillets or V-joints. 4. Use short stickout. 5. Decrease arc speed. 6. Increase included angle on V-joints.
Fillet	Cracking	1. Use EM-12K electrode. 2. Use electrode negative. 3. Lower voltage. 4. Decrease welding speed. 5. Preheat joint. 6. Increase electrode diameter and lower voltage.
Root Pass in Groove	Cracking	1. Lower current and voltage. 2. Use electrode negative. 3. Increase root opening or included angle. 4. Preheat joint. 5. Make sure back gouging is not narrow and deep.
Multiple Pass Weld	Transverse Cracking	1. Increase interpass temperature. 2. Decrease welding speed. 3. Decrease voltage. 4. Decrease current and voltage.
Square Butt Weld	Cracking	1. Check fixture for plate movement. 2. Decrease welding speed. 3. Check for proper pick-up from backup.
Fillet Lap or Square Butt	Pock Marking or Slag Sticking	1. Use EM-13K electrode. 2. Increase voltage. 3. Decrease current. 4. Decrease speed. 5. Position fillet, if possible. 6. Heavier plate than normal will cause pocking. 7. Clean all mill scale, rust and oil off plate.

Semiautomatic, Single Electrode		
Joint	**Problem**	**Corrective Action (In Order of Importance)**
Deep Grove	Slag Sticking	1. Decrease voltage. 2. Decrease current and voltage.
Any	Undercutting	1. Use electrode negative. 2. Decrease voltage. 3. Decrease current. 4. Increase electrode diameter and lower voltage. 5. Decrease speed.
Any	Porosity Caused by Rust	1. Use EM-13K electrode. 2. Increase voltage. 3. Lower current. 4. Use electrode positive. 5. Use torches in front of arc. 6. Clean joint completely (butting edges also). 7. Decrease speed.
Any	Porosity Caused by Organic Contaminants	1. Use electrode positive. 2. Decrease speed. 3. Degrease joint and dry completely.
Any	Porosity Caused by Arc Blow	1. Use electrode positive. 2. Lower voltage. 3. Lower current and voltage. 4. Increase electrode diameter and lower voltage. 5. Use lower silicon electrode.
Any	Back Side Porosity	1. Usually caused by improper tie-in. 2. Increase welding current to tie-in. 3. Decrease welding speed to tie-in. 4. If 100% joint not required, then decrease penetration.
Any	Surface Metal Spots	1. Lower voltage. 2. Use electrode negative. 3. Decrease current and voltage. 4. Increase arc speed.
Out of Position	Metal Spillage	1. On roundabouts, move further off center opposite to direction of travel. 2. Lower voltage. 3. Lower current and voltage. 4. Increase speed on horizontal fillets. 5. On roundabouts, increase speed — lower current and voltage.
Any	Bead Shape	1. Increase voltage to get wider, flatter bead. 2. Decrease current to get flatter bead. 3. Decrease speed to get flatter bead on fillets. 4. Use electrode diameter that is proper for welding current. 5. Use electrode positive on square butt welds and fillets smaller than 1/4.

SECTION VIII

TIG (Tungsten Inert Gas) WELDING

Object:
To study the TIG (tungsten inert gas) arc-welding process.

General Information

TIG welding is an arc-welding process in which the heat needed for fusion is generated by an arc between a nonconsumable tungsten electrode and the work. Since both the molten puddle and the hot tungsten electrode are susceptible to contamination from the air, an inert gas atmosphere or shield (usually argon or helium) is used to exclude air from the arc area. An especially designed torch or electrode holder is used for this welding process. Filler metal may or may not be used depending upon the type of weld and thickness to be welded. When filler metal is used, it is normally added manually with a filler "rod".

Some of the features that make TIG welding appealing are:

1. It produces high-quality welds in most metals and alloys, including many of the "space-age" materials.
2. It may be used on a wide range of thicknesses, from very thin up to several inches.
3. The arc and weld puddle are clearly visible to the operator.
4. There is no spatter, since no metal crosses the arc stream.
5. It is usable in all positions.
6. It requires little or no post-weld cleaning.
7. It has a puddle that is very easy to control once basic skills are acquired.

Equipment for TIG Welding

The basic equipment (Figure 1) for manual TIG welding consists of the following:

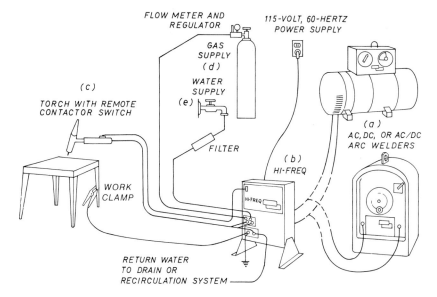

Figure 1. Schematic of the TIG process.

1. A suitable welding power source, either AC or DC, depending upon the type of welding to be done.
2. A special TIG torch with hose assembly, either air or water-cooled, depending upon the amount of current to be used.
3. A supply of inert gas (usually cylinders) with a regulator and flowmeter to furnish a measured adjustable flow to the torch.
4. The correct size and type of filler metal for the job.
5. A supply of the right type and size of tungsten electrodes.
6. Protective equipment and accessories including:
   (a) Welding helmet with proper shade filter lens
   (b) Suitable gloves
   (c) Stainless steel cleaning brush
   (d) Other protective clothing required by the specific job
7. A high-frequency generating unit, mandatory for AC welding of aluminum or magnesium, and highly desirable for DC welding of all metals.
8. An adequate supply of clean, cool water — if water-cooled torches are required.
9. Proper fittings and hoses to connect water and gas lines.
10. Work cable with suitable clamp.

Referring to Figure 1, the power supply (a) must be variable-voltage, but may be a DC motor generator, DC three-phase rectifier, single-phase AC-DC rectifier, or single-phase transformer, depending upon metals welded. The high-frequency unit (b), which is mandatory for AC welding, may have gas and water solenoid valves, intensity control, post flow timers, and remote control switch. Input usually requires 110 or 220-volts, single-phase AC. These high-frequency units with accessories are built into machines designed specifically for TIG welding.

The torch (c) may or may not be water-cooled, depending upon application. It is usually purchased with 8' to 16' sheathed cable, including water, gas, and power leads. Water-cooled torches may have the power lead in the water return line, with fusible links to protect the torch from insufficient water flow.

The gas supply (d) is usually provided by cylinders or bulk sytems. There are various types of gauge and gaugeless regulators used with flowmeters. Make sure the regulator-flowmeter combination you choose has capacity and scale for the gas or gases you will use.

Water (e) should be clean and cool. Make sure lines, fittings, and pressure are adequate to supply sufficient volume for the torch and currents to be used. Cooler-recirculators are sometimes used where water lines or drains are not handy or where mineral deposits could plug up torch.

Other features may be desirable or necessary to obtain the best welds on some jobs or materials. These are either built into TIG welding equipment or are available as accessories.

The choice of the basic types and size of a welding machine for TIG welding is for the most part determined by the type and thickness of metal to be welded. If aluminum or magnesium are the only metals to be welded, the choice is almost certain to be an AC machine with a high-frequency unit. On the other hand, if stainless and carbon steel are to be welded, the choice would normally be a DC machine with a high-frequency unit to eliminate touch starts. If stainless and aluminum or magnesium are to be welded, the best choice would be an AC-DC welding machine with a high-frequency unit. This latter choice would give the optimum power source for any type of welding material. The accompanying table will help in the selection of type of welder.

GUIDE TO SELECTION OF PROPER TYPE OF WELDING CURRENT FOR TIG WELDING

	Direct Current		Alter-nating Current		Direct Current		Alter-nating Current
	DC(−)	DC(+)			DC(−)	DC(+)	
Aluminum up to 3/32"	P	G	E	High-Alloy steels	E	P	G
Aluminum over 3/32"	P	P	E	High-carbon steels	E	P	G
Aluminum bronze	P	G	E	Low-alloy steels	E	P	G
Aluminum castings	P	P	E	Low-carbon steels	E	P	G
Beryllium copper	P	G	E	Magnesium up to 1/8"	P	G	E
Brass alloys	E	P	G	Mg over 1/8"	P	P	E
Copper base alloys	E	P	G	Magnesium castings	P	G	E
Cast iron	E	P	G	Nickel & Ni-alloys	E	P	G
Deoxidized copper	E	P	P	Stainless steel	E	P	G
Dissimilar metals	E	P	G	Silicon bronze	E	P	P
Hardfacing	G	P	E	Titanium	E	P	G
P = Poor G = Good E = Excellent							

From *Welding Data Book,* printed by *Welding Design and Fabrication* Magazine.

When standard hand welders are used for TIG welding, they should be selected carefully to see if they have the range and control necessary to do the job. Most hand welders either do not have low enough range or fine enough controls to do the best light-gauge TIG welding.

Since much TIG welding is done under 150 amperes and very little over 300 amperes, special machines have been designed for this process giving special consideration to very fine control down to as low as 2 amperes and incorporating high frequency along with many or all of the other desirable features helpful to the TIG weldor.

Current Flow and Arc Characteristics

Some discussion of the passage of current in the TIG arc (Figure 2) may be helpful in understanding its variables. First of all, as in any other arc, the passage of current is supported by electrons flowing in one direction or another across the arc in an ionized gas medium. In the case of the DC arc, the electron flow is from the work to the electrode on electrode positive (DCRP), and from the electrode to the ground on electrode negative (DCSP). When TIG welding in an argon atmosphere the positive side of the arc generates much more heat than the negative side.

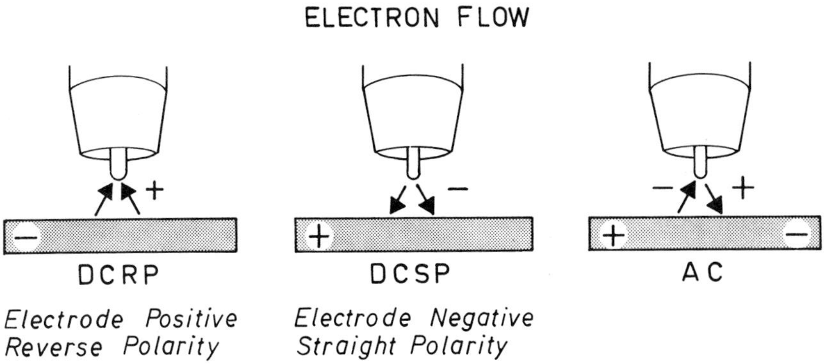

ELECTRON FLOW

DCRP — *Electrode Positive Reverse Polarity*

DCSP — *Electrode Negative Straight Polarity*

A C

Figure 2.

In an AC arc, the electron flow reverses itself 120 times a second on 60-hertz power, traveling toward the electrode for the first half cycle and away from it in the next half cycle.

When DC current is used for TIG welding, it is almost always used with electrode negative (DCSP). The reason for this is that on electrode positive, (DCRP), the high-density electron flow bombards the end of the tungsten electrode. This bombardment is so strong that even though the tungsten has a high melting point (6170°F), it still melts off and contaminates the weld. In the few cases where electrode positive is used on TIG, the electrode must have a much larger diameter to avoid melting. A 1/4" electrode is required to carry the same current on electrode positive as a 1/16" electrode can carry on electrode negative. Because of the direction of electron flow and electrode size, the penetration on electrode positive is more shallow and wider than that on electrode negative, with AC being between these two (see Figure 3).

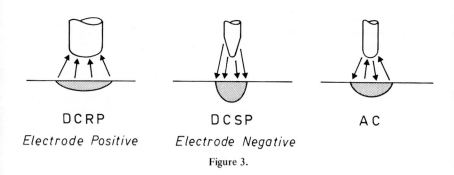

DCRP

Electrode Positive

DCSP

Electrode Negative

AC

Figure 3.

These arcs and their penetration characteristics are additionally modified by the choice of shielding gas. The essentially unusable reverse polarity arc does have one very useful characteristic that is advantageous on metals such as aluminum and magnesium that have refractory oxides. The oxides of these metals have a higher melting point than the metal itself and consequently would make welding difficult if they were not removed. Mechanical methods are only effective for a short time, since these oxides form very rapidly ahead of the arc. The reverse polarity half cycle of the AC arc imposes an excellent cleaning action on these oxides. This cleaning action is assumed to be caused by a combination of electrons escaping from the plate plus a bombardment of the plate by the heavy ions of the shielding gas. This apparently breaks up these high refractory oxides and scale, promoting sound welds. The AC arc, with its good cleaning characteristic, does need help in another area to make it useful in TIG welding. The 60-hertz AC power wave goes through zero volts 120 times every second and, at these times, the arc has a tendency to go out. In order to keep the arc lit during these zero voltage periods, a high-frequency, high-voltage, low-current wave must be superimposed on the welding circuit.

This is usually accomplished by a spark-gap generator, which can be bought separately or is built into the standard TIG machine. This high-frequency unit does the following jobs:

1. It ionizes a path to start the arc without touching the tungsten to the work.

2. It prevents the AC arc from going out at zero voltage.

3. It gives greater arc stability and cleaning action.
4. It assures longer tungsten life due to reduced contamination.
5. It permits a wider range of currents with a given tungsten size.

Derating Hand Welding Machines for TIG Welding

When standard AC hand welding machines are used for TIG welding of aluminum and magnesium, they must be derated to compensate for a rectification effect that takes place on the oxide surfaces of these metals. These oxides and the metals themselves are not as good emitters of electrons as tungsten, which prevents part of the current from flowing in the reverse polarity side of the AC wave. This so-called DC component, saturates the transformer iron, and more exciting current is required from the AC line. This abnormally high current in turn generates more heat. If a standard transformer welder is used as a TIG power source to the maximum of its hand welding rating, it could be seriously damaged or burnt out. A 60% duty-cycle hand welding machine must be derated to 70% of its rated amperage to give adequate protection from this DC component in aluminum or magnesium TIG welding. The chart below gives the maximum currents that should be drawn from 60% and 30% duty-cycle machines of various ratings:

Hand Weld Rating		TIG Rating		TIG Rating @ 100% Duty Cycle
500 Amp. 60%	→	350 Amp. 60%	→	280
400 Amp. 60%	→	280 Amp. 60%	→	225
300 Amp. 60%	→	210 Amp. 60%	→	168
250 Amp. 30%	→	175 Amp. 30%	→	88

Most welding machines designed specifically for TIG welding need not be derated in this manner, since this problem has already been handled by internal circuitry.

Tungsten Electrodes

The electrodes used for TIG welding are made of pure or alloyed tungsten. Tungsten is an elemental metal that has a very high melting point ($6170°$F) and is a good emitter of electrons. Pure tungsten electrodes are most frequently used for aluminum and magnesium, because of their tendency to assume an efficient ball-shaped tip on AC current.

The 1% and 2% thorium-alloy electrodes are designed to carry more current, give easier starting, and resist contamination better than pure tungsten. They do not assume a "ball shape" readily in the arc and are normally used on materials other than aluminum and magnesium.

The 1% zirconium-alloy, as well as "striped" electrodes, are designed to combine the good characteristics of pure tungsten. Striped electrodes are made of pure tungsten with a narrow strip of thorium alloy running down one side of the electrode.

Although these alloy electrodes are more costly to buy, they may actually save money by reason of their ability to give easier arc starting, carry more current, and resist contamination better than pure tungsten.

Most of these electrodes are manufactured in "cleaned" or "ground" types in diameters from .020" to 1/4" from 3" to 24" long.

Proper electrode size is important in TIG welding and should be carefully considered. Guides for the proper size of electrode for different applications are given in the tables at the end of this lesson.

These electrodes are expensive and fragile. They should be stored in a safe place free from any contaminating materials. If they are exposed to the air or touched to another surface at red heat or higher, contamination will result. When this happens the electrode end will have to be broken off and reballed or repointed, since poor welding action will result. Most TIG machines and high-frequency units have after-flow water and gas timers built into them to prevent contamination when welding is interrupted.

Proper Electrode Shape

At this point, it might be well to illustrate the difference between the tips of the tungsten electrode for DCSP and AC welding. See Figures 4 and 5.

In DCSP, the stream of electrons is continuously leaving the electrode and traveling to the work. For this mode of operation, the best shape for the electrode tip is a taper with a sharp point on the end.

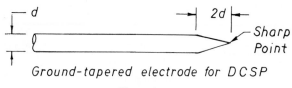

Ground-tapered electrode for DCSP

Figure 4.

When electrodes are ground to this shape, it should be done carefully with a very fine grit wheel used for no other purpose. Some authorities maintain that a tungsten electrode should not be taper-ground and that a better answer is to use a smaller tungsten.

In the case of AC welding, the situation is different; the electrode is receiving and emitting electrons every half cycle. For this condition, the half-ball shape is the most desirable end condition. Pure tungsten electrodes normally will ball themselves in this manner; however, the thoriated type, designed to carry higher currents, must be ground or balled electrically to get the desired shape. Balling electrically is done by striking an arc on a piece of copper with the high frequency on "start only" at a very low amperage setting in reverse polarity with gas and water flowing. When the electrode changes from orange to a very bright white color, it is time to break the arc immediately. This may take a very short time, and extreme care should be taken not to overheat the torch. The melted ball end formed should be no larger than the diameter of the electrode. If the balling operation does not take place fairly rapidly, the current must be increased until it does.

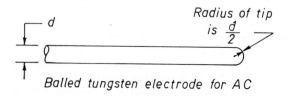

Balled tungsten electrode for AC

Figure 5.

The Shielding Gas

The TIG process requires an envelope or shield of some inert gas. The gas most frequently used for this process is argon, although helium and mixtures of these two gases are also used for special applications.

Argon is normally chosen for most TIG welding because of its arc characteristics, density, cost, high purity, and availability. It is a product of the distillation of liquid air and is sold in high-pressure cylinders similar to oxygen. Argon is heavier than air and has less thermal conductivity than helium. Some of argon's other advantages over helium are:

1. Better cleaning action on AC welding of aluminum and magnesium.
2. Lower flow rates, which mean less welding cost.
3. Quieter, smoother arc action.
4. Better resistance to drafts, since it is heavier than air.
5. Lower arc voltage for a given current and arc length, giving less susceptibility to arc wander.
6. Normally available in slightly higher purity than helium, insuring sounder welds.

Because of its lower thermal conductivity, argon has a more dense arc column than helium and shows different penetration characteristics.

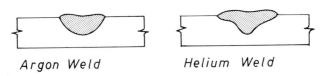

Argon Weld   *Helium Weld*

Figure 6.

Helium, a gas lighter than air, has high thermal conductivity and consequently tends to expand in the arc plasma. It runs at higher arc voltages and produces a wider bead than argon. Because helium's arc can carry higher thermal energy, it is frequently used when welding heavier thicknesses of high conductivity material or when high-speed automated applications are involved. Consult the tables at the end of this lesson for the correct selection of gas for specific applications.

The correct amount of gas flow depends upon the joint, the material, the position, the cup size, and the type of gas used. Needless to say, excess gas flow, over and above that required to protect the tungsten and the weld puddle, is costly and can cause other welding problems such as porosity. Gas flow rates that are too low or an incorrect cup size can cause oxidation of the tungsten electrode and the weld metal. Oxidized weld metal caused by insufficient shielding or moisture in the shielding gas usually has a black residue on or adjacent to the weld. Oxidized electrodes usually show a dull gray pitted end instead of the usual smooth, bright finish. The pitted, rough end indicates that small pieces of tungsten have gone across the arc and are undoubtedly included in the weld. When this occurs, the oxidized tip must be broken off and repointed or reballed before welding is resumed.

The Welding "Torch"

The "torch" or electrode holder for TIG welding is designed specifically for this process. It may be air or gas-cooled for low-current applications or it may be water-cooled for higher-current or high duty-cycle operations. These torches may vary in size from no larger than a marking pen to up to fairly large, weighty, water-cooled units for high-current applications. Some have adjustable angle nozzles to reach "hard-to-weld" locations. All of them have replaceable cups of different diameters. The cups, made of ceramic, high-temperature glass or copper, have a great deal to do with the effectiveness of the gas shielding. For TIG welding over 150 amperes, water-cooled torches and ceramic cups are usually used. Over 250 amperes, water-cooled torches with copper cups are normally used.

If the proper-diameter cup is used, the electrode should stick out from one and one-half to two times the electrode diameter beyond the end of the cup. This would give the proper extension for butts, laps, and corner welds. There are special torches in which the extension can be considerably more, because of the laminar gas-flow characteristics of such torches. Fillet welds require more extension in order to give cup clearance. The usual extension is from 3/16" to 5/16". See Figure 7.

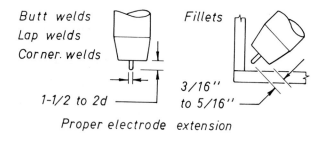

Proper electrode extension

Figure 7.

A cracked or broken cup can enable air to contaminate the electrode and the weld metal. Gas connections all the way back to the cylinder should be thoroughly checked to make sure that air cannot be aspirated into the gas stream. On water-cooled torches, all water connections should be carefully inspected, including the "O" rings on the torch itself. Very small amounts of water leaking in the torch head will cause porosity and black-surfaced welds. Your TIG torch should be handled carefully and checked from time to time to make sure all gas ports and water passages are clear. The collet on the torch holds the tungsten in its proper location and transfers current from the power lead to the tungsten. It should be clean and snug. Proper transfer of current from the power lead to the tungsten is aided by using ground tungsten electrodes.

Filler Metals

Filler metals for TIG welding are available in a wide range of sizes and types for all of the common metals welded by this process. As is the case of other welding processes, the filler metal may not always match base metal chemistry. More often than not, it will be chosen for its "as-welded" physical properties and weldability first, and secondly for its ability to match chemistry. If chemistry, as-welded physicals, and weldability are all available in the same filler metal, this one, of course, would be the proper choice. Some applications, of course, demand exact chemistry match.

Care should be exercised in selecting not only the proper type of filler metal but also the proper size, since this also has a bearing on the weld quality of a specific joint.

Regardless of what metals are welded, the filler metals should be clean and dry. Many critical welds have been rejected because some foreign material entered the weld via the "dirty-glove" or "dirty-filler-metal" route. When not in use, filler metals for TIG welding should be stored in closed containers in a warm, dry location.

Preparation and Cleaning of Joints

Joints for TIG welding are prepared by a wide variety of fabricating processes and therefore are subject to many contaminants that can affect the quality of the weld. It must be remembered here that since no fluxes are normally used with the process and the amount of deoxidizers in the filler rod are limited, great care should be taken to make sure that the areas to be welded are clean and dry. Mechanical methods, including stainless-steel brushes, are very effective for removal of oxides on aluminum. These brushes should not be used on any other job. Organic contaminants, such as grease or oil, can be removed by chemical means. Never use an organic solvent not specifically prescribed for this purpose and always follow good safety and ventilating procedures.

Special Safety Precautions for TIG Welding

The safety precautions that apply to all forms of arc welding also apply to TIG welding; however, because of the special nature of the process, it would be well here to emphasize the special precautions that are peculiar to this process:

- The arc is completely exposed and reflected very strongly by the molten pool; consequently, all bare skin should be shielded from its rays. As in other processes, the proper shade filter lens should be chosen for the currents and metals involved.

FILTER GLASSES FOR TIG WELDING

Glass No.	Welding Current
6 — 8	Up to 30 amperes
8 — 10	30 to 75 amperes
10 — 12	75 to 200 amperes
12 — 13	200 to 400 amperes
14	Over 400 amperes

- Since high frequency is used in most TIG welding operations, special note should be taken of its characteristics:
  1. It can jump through a gloved finger, if that finger is placed on or near the electrode tip when high frequency is on. This can cause irritating, pinpoint-size burns.
  2. Since it can jump approximately 1/4" or more in open air, all connections should be thoroughly insulated.
  3. Any water leaks should be corrected immediately, since water is a good ground path for high-frequency and welding current.
  4. It can interfere with radio and television transmission; consequently, it should be connected with strict adherence to the manufacturer's recommendations.

5. The high-frequency intensity switch should be set no higher than necessary to get good arc starting and stability, since the higher the setting, the higher the chance of radiated interference.

6. When hand-welding power sources are used for TIG welding, they require protection from high frequency. Most high frequency units have this protection built in, but it is a good idea to make sure. If not, it can be inexpensively added to the output terminals of the power source.

• This process uses gases stored in high-pressure cylinders. These cylinders should be stored in a safe, cool place with the valve caps on. They should not be moved about without the valve caps in place. They should be chained or supported in an upright position so that they cannot fall over. They should be at a sufficient distance from the welding operation so they cannot receive any spatter or accidental arcing. Since the hoses and jackets are usually made of synthetic materials that melt rather easily if placed on something hot, they should be kept off the floor and work when possible. Valves should be opened very slowly to prevent damage.

How to Use the Following Tables

The next two pages are made up of tables giving data on the TIG welding of aluminum and stainless steel. The tables are from "How to Do TIG (Heliarc) Welding", published by the Linde Division, Union Carbide Corporation. In the tables, under "weld", numbers are given. These numbers refer to the diagrams of types of weld joints shown at the bottom of this page.

DIAGRAMS OF WELD JOINTS REFERRED TO IN THE FOLLOWING TABLES

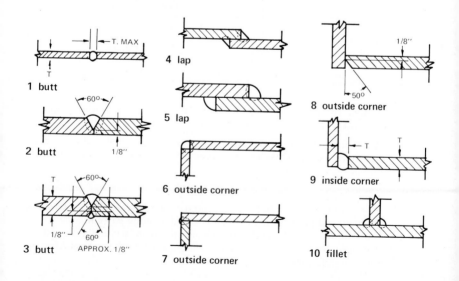

ALUMINUM, Manual Welding, High-Frequency Stabilized AC

WORK thickness, inches	WELD type	WELD number	tungsten electrode, diameter	CUP ORIFICE diameter	FILLER ROD (if any) diameter	CURRENT (flat welding) type	amperes●	GAS type	GAS flow cfh	GAS psi	SPEED inches per minute	REMARKS:
1/16	butt	1	1/16	1/4-3/8	1/16	AC	△ 60- 80	argon	15	20	12	
	lap	4, 5					△ 70- 90				10	
	corner	6,7					△ 60- 80				12	
	fillet	10					△ 70- 90				10	
1/8	butt	1	3/32	3/8-7/16	3/32 or 1/8	AC	△125-145	argon	17	20	12	use 1/8 filter rod, two passes
	lap	4, 5			3/32		△140-160				10	vertical and overhead
	corner	6,7			3/32		△125-145				12	
	fillet	10			3/32 or 1/16		△140-160				10	
3/16	butt	1	1/8	7/16-1/2	1/8	AC	△190-220	argon	21	20	11	
	lap	4, 5					△210-240				9	
	corner	6,7					△190-220				11	
	fillet	10					△210-240				9	
1/4	butt	1	3/16	1/2-3/4	1/8 or 3/16	AC	□260-300	argon	25	20	10	use 1/8 filter rod two passes
	lap	4, 5					□290-340				8	vertical and overhead
	corner	9					□280-320				10	use 1/8 filler rod vertical
	fillet	10					□280-320				8	
3/8	butt	2	3/16 or 1/4	5/8	3/16 or 1/4	AC	□330-380	argon	29	20	★	two passes
	lap	5					□330-380					two passes
	corner	8					□350-400					two passes
	fillet	10					□330-380					two or three passes
1/2	butt	2	3/16 or 1/4	5/8	3/16 or 1/4	AC	□400-450	argon	31	20	●	three passes
	lap	5					□400-450					three passes
	corner	8					△420-470					three passes
	fillet	10					□400-450					three passes

● Reduce currents 10% to 20% for vertical and overhead.
△ Ceramic or glass cup should be used for currents to 250 amps.

□ Water-cooled cup should be used for currents above 250 amps.
★ Welding speed for multiple passes cannot be accurately predicted.

WELDING ALUMINUM

The use of TIG welding for aluminum has many advantages for both manual and automatic processes. Filler metal can be either wire or rod and should be compatible with the base alloy. Filler metal must be dry, free of oxides, grease, or other foreign matter. If filler metal becomes damp, heat for 2 hours at 250°F before using. Although AC high-frequency stabilized current is recommended, DC reverse polarity has been successfully used for thicknesses up to 3/32".

STAINLESS STEEL, Manual Welding, Straight Polarity DC

WORK thickness, inches	WELD type	WELD number	tungsten electrode, diameter	CUP ORIFICE diameter	FILLER ROD (if any) diameter	CURRENT (flat welding) type	CURRENT amperes•	GAS type	GAS flow cfh	GAS psi	SPEED inches per minute	REMARKS:
1/16	butt	1	1/16	1/4-3/8	1/16	DC	△ 80-100	argon	11	20	12	
	lap	4, 5					△100-120				10	
	corner	6, 7, 9					△ 80-100				12	
	fillet	10					△ 90-100				10	
3/32	butt	1	1/16	1/4-3/8	1/16 or 3/32	DC	△100-120	argon	11	20	12	
	lap	4, 5					△110-130				10	
	corner	6, 7, 9					△100-120				12	
	fillet	10					△110-130				10	
1/8	butt	1	1/16	1/4-3/8	3/32	DC	△120-140	argon	11	20	12	
	lap	4, 5					△130-150				10	
	corner	6, 7, 9					△120-140				12	
	fillet	10					△130-150				10	
3/16	butt	1	3/32	1/4-3/8	1/8	DC	△200-250	argon	13	20	10	
	lap	5	3/32or1/8				□225-275				8	
	corner	6, 7, 9	3/32				△200-250				10	
	fillet	10	3/32or1/8				□225-275				8	
1/4	butt	1, 2	1/8	1/2	3/16	DC	□275-350	argon	13	20	5	one or two passes
	lap	5					□300-375					one or two passes
	corner	6, 7, 8					□275-350					one pass
	fillet	10					□300-375					
1/2	butt	2, 3	1/8 or 3/16	1/2	1/4	DC	□350-450	argon	15	20	★	two or three passes
	lap	5					□375-475					three passes
	corner	8					□375-475					three passes
	fillet	10					□375-475					three passes

• Reduce currents 10% to 20% for vertical and overhead.

△ Ceramic or glass cup should be used for currents to 150 amps.

□ Water-cooled cup should be used for currents above 250 amps.

★ Welding speed for multiple passes cannot be accurately predicted.

WELDING STAINLESS STEEL

In TIG welding of stainless steel, welding rods having the AWS-ASTM prefixes of E or ER can be used as filler rods. However, only bare uncoated rods should be used. Stainless steel can be welded using AC high-frequency stabilized current. However, for DC straight polarity current recommendations must be increased 25%. Light-gauge metal less than 1/16" thick should always be welded with DC straight polarity using argon gas. Follow the normal precautions for welding stainless such as: clean surfaces, dry electrodes, use only stainless steel tools and brushes, carefully remove soap from welds after pressure testing, keep stainless from coming into contact with other metals.

LESSON 8.2

Object:
To learn to operate TIG welding equipment and the variables that affect technique and weld quality.

Equipment:
The units for TIG welding as shown in Figure 1, Lesson 8.1.

Have a qualified electrician connect the input leads to the input line contactor in accordance with the National Electrical Code, all local codes, and the wiring diagram located inside the machine.

Setting Up Equipment for TIG Welding

1. Locate welding power source close to power access or fuse box, but allow enough room around machine for proper cooling air to circulate.
2. Connect machine with proper input wire size per manufacturer's instructions, making sure disconnect is "off" and fuses are "out."
3. Install ground wire from welder case to earthen ground per manufacturer's recommendations.
4. If a separate high-frequency unit is used, locate or mount it on or near welder (make sure its case is also grounded). Connect it to the welder and power supply per manufacturer's instructions.
5. Locate inert gas cylinder with its regulator and flowmeter near welding machine and high-frequency unit. Make sure it is supported or tied in an upright position and cannot fall.
6. Connect gas line from flowmeter to welder or high-frequency unit per instructions with these units. (If a high-frequency unit is not used on DC machine, connect gas line to a gas saver valve and then to flowmeter.)
7. Connect input water line (if used) to welder or high-frequency unit per manufacturer's instructions. Water recirculators using drums or coolers are sometimes used where water supply or drains are unavailable or where local water is not suitable. Mineral deposits from some water supplies can plug up cooling passages in the torch.
8. Connect water-in, water-out, gas, and power leads from torch to welding machine or high-frequency unit per manufacturer's instructions. (If your torch has thermal links, make sure that the "water-out" lead with these links is not connected to the water coming in from the machine, since connected in this manner they will not afford the protection intended.)
9. Connect work cable and clamp to welding machine or high-frequency unit. Make sure all cables, both work and electrode, are no longer than necessary. Do not coil unused cable. Use natural rubber-jacket cable for best containment of high frequency.
10. Connect work clamp to welding table or work. Make sure table is not too close to cylinder and welding equipment.
11. Review all work done with the following questions in mind:
    (a) Are all electrical connections tight and well insulated where required? Are they correctly wired?
    (b) Are all gas and water connections tight?
    (c) Are all of these electrical, gas, and water lines located in a safe place and of proper size and length so that no one may trip over or run into them?
    (d) Can welding be done in the indicated area without draft interference from welder fan or other sources?

12. Install proper size and type of tungsten with suitable cup for the job to be done. See tables at end of Lesson 8.1 for recommendations. Make sure electrode sticks out 1-1/2 to 2 times its diameter beyond end of cup. When torch is not in use, it should be placed in a safe, insulated holder or hanger to prevent accidental shorting and breakage.

13. Now, make the following tests:

    (a) Replace fuses, turn on main power-disconnect, and turn on welding machine.

        (1) If it's a rectifier or transformer − is the fan running? − is pilot light on?

        (2) It it's a motor generator − is it running in the right direction?

        (3) If the high-frequency unit has a separate input line − is this plugged in or wired in properly to welder's fan leads per manufacturer's instructions?

    (b) Turn on water supply valve or recirculator. If TIG machine or high frequency with solenoids is used, no water will circulate through torch at this time. Recommendations for water flow rates are given in the tables.

    (c) Open cylinder valve and regulator of gas supply with flowmeter turned "off." If no high-frequency unit or solenoid valves are used, gas will flow when flowmeter is opened to correct flow rate. If a high-frequency unit with solenoid valves is used, no gas will flow at this time even though flowmeter is opened.

    (d) Turn high frequency "on" and set for "continuous" position, depress starting switch on torch or foot control, holding torch in the hand but not attempting to strike an arc. At this time:

        (1) High frequency should come on, making a "hissing" sound at the unit.

        (2) Water and gas should flow (this is a good time − while purging air from the line − to adjust flowmeter to correct rate).

        (3) The contactor should come in on TIG machine, making a "thump" in the power source. If no contactor is used, electrode will be "hot to work at all times machine is running.

Now set the welding machine for the right current and polarity, put the right filter lens in your hood, and you are ready to weld.

Striking the Arc

If your machine has built in high frequency or if you have a separate high-frequency unit, striking the arc is a very simple task.

On DC, the high-frequency switch would normally be positioned on "start only", whereas on AC (aluminum or magnesium) the switch usually would be on "continuous." With this switch in the proper position, the torch is brought into a practically vertical position an inch over the work at the point where the weld is to begin. If your equipment is equipped with a torch start switch or foot control, depress this switch and slowly bring the torch down to with 1/4" of the work. The high-frequency, gas, and water should immediately come on and the arc initiate within a second thereafter. In the case where a high-frequency torch switch or foot switch is not used, the high frequency will be on all the time, and the torch should be brought down gradually. The arc will start as soon as the electrode is within "jumping" distance. A hot tungsten electrode will enable the high-frequency spark to jump farther than a cold one, possibly starting the arc before good gas coverage is attained.

Where a high frequency unit is not used for starting, the tungsten (with gas flowing) is brought into a momentary light scratching contact with the work and raised up quickly about one-eighth of an inch to establish the arc. The position of the torch for this arc starting is practically vertical, with possibly a very slight (10° to 15°) angle in the direction of welding.

Making the Weld

After the arc is struck, the torch is moved in a tight circular motion for a few seconds to establish a bright puddle from which the weld begins. The arc length should be equal to or slightly greater than the diameter of the electrode. In some cases, on very light material or certain types of welds, filler metal may not be used and the welding technique consists merely of maintaining the proper arc length at the right speed throughout the length of the weld with no hesitation or weave of any kind.

In most cases, however, filler metal is added in a manner similar to oxy-acetylene welding. The most important thing to remember about adding filler metal in TIG welding is that the filler metal is to be dipped into and melted by the pool. Filler metal should not be thrust into the arc stream or touched to the tungsten. The progression of the torch and the proper addition of filler metal constitute a type of rhythm that is the most difficult part of TIG welding to learn.

Once this rhythm is mastered and the reaction of the different metals to the arc is understood, the operator will make rapid progress. The back and forth movement of the torch is normally done with wrist movement, while the arm is resting on some support other than the work. The other hand, which is feeding rod, is usually resting on the work. Frequently the rod is fed by the thumb pushing it through the gloved fingers. Any method of feeding rod and moving the torch that works best for you is the one to use. Many operators, after acquiring a knowledge of metal flow characteristics, replace the backing up movement of the torch with a slight hesitation.

Regardless of the manipulating methods used, the following points should be kept in mind.

A. Major increases in arc length should be avoided, since this decreases the current and could cause a loss of gas shielding.

B. Do not angle the torch too much, since it is possible to aspirate air under the arc.

C. Do not touch the tungsten electrode with filler rod, since this will contaminate the tungsten and require break-off and possible redressing.

D. Do not touch the electrode to the puddle; this will also contaminate the tungsten.

Arc Wander

One problem that the beginning TIG weldor might encounter immediately is "arc wander." Arc wandering is the shifting of the points where the arc leaves the electrode and strikes the work. It can be disconcerting to the operator, but, fortunately in most cases, can be eliminated. The most common causes of arc wander are:

1. **Current too low — electrode too large —**

If the current is too low for a given size of electrode, the answer, of course, is to increase current or reduce electrode size to increase current density.

2. **Electrode or work contamination —**

Tungsten electrodes contaminated with any number of materials can cause wandering and spitting. The remedy is to break off and repoint or reball the electrode. In some cases, changing to alloy electrodes that are more resistant to contamination may be an answer. Base metals with heavy scale, oxides, or other contaminants may also affect arc stability.

3. Magnetic arc blow —

Magnetic arc blow, a term very familiar to the hand weldor, is caused by the arc and workpiece. Magnetic materials and DC current, of course, are the biggest offenders here. The normal solutions, such as changing the work clamp location and removing magnetic materials from the immediate arc area, usually help considerable.

4. Unstable gas shield —

An unstable gas shield can be caused by external drafts or air being aspirated into the gas stream. The solution to this problem is to remove or block the source of the drafts and make sure that all gas connections, fittings, and hoses are sound. Too long a stickout or too long an arc may leave the cup too high off the work. Make sure that cup size and gas flow rates are correct for the job.

5. Improper tungsten shape.

Penetration

One important feature of a good weld is properly controlled, uniform penetration. In TIG welding, the important parameters that control penetration are:

1. Current or Amperage —

Generally speaking, the higher the current, the deeper the penetration. Since we are using variable-power sources, the shorter the arc with a given machine setting, the higher the current and the deeper the penetration. This characteristic of the power source can be used to some limited extent to throttle the heat up and down to control penetration. The same current used on two sizes of tungsten electrode would tend to give deeper penetration on the smaller, since the current density is higher.

2. Thickness and Type of Base Metal —

Thinner materials tend to be penetrated more rapidly than thicker ones because they have less mass to absorb or "sink" the heat of the arc. The physical and chemical properties of the base metal have a profound effect upon penetration. Copper, for instance, is a good thermal conductor and requires a great deal of amperage because the heat of the arc is carried away so rapidly. Aluminum, also a good conductor but with a low melting point, has a tendency to form a high-temperature refractory oxide or "skin" that melts at a much higher temperature than the aluminum itself. Without the "cleaning effect" of the reverse polarity side of the AC arc, this metal would be very difficult to weld successfully with the TIG process. Stainless steel has very poor thermal conductivity, and the heat of the arc tends to "stay put" and overheat. Because of this property, stainless steel is normally welded with lower currents to slow the whole process down to a manageable situation.

3. Forward Speed or Progress of Welding —

The forward speed of the welding process with a given current and thickness determines how much power or "heat" has been put into each lineal inch or foot of weld. This, in turn, has a great deal to do with the penetration pattern and width of the weld. Dwelling on the front side of the puddle tends to increase penetration.

4. Size of the Filler Rod —

This variable is sometimes not considered to be very important but can have considerable effect on the penetration pattern. Every time the filler material is dipped into the molten metal, two things happen that tend to cool the pool and reduce penetration: The first is that the melting of the filler metal "sucks" considerable heat from the molten pool; the second is that some heat travels up into the cold filler rod and is dissipated. The size or diameter of the filler metal, consequently, determines how much heat is removed from the puddle with each dipping motion.

5. Dipping Technique of Filler Metal —

In addition to the size of the filler rod, the dipping technique and frequency play an important part in the penetration of the weld. If the rod is dipped too frequently or left in the pool too long with low heat, the weld will probably have poor penetration and tie-in with the base metal. Since the number of times the rod is dipped determines the number of ripples in the weld, a proper balance of dipping and current must be achieved to produce good uniform welds of the proper size. Since complete penetration is required on many sheet-metal jobs, the operator must acquire a "feel" for the melting characteristics of each metal he works with. Even though aluminum has a low melting point, it is easier to control burnthrough with it than with most other metals. This stems from the fact that the puddle with aluminum is larger than with stainless or mild steel and consequently the visible motion of "sagging" before burnthrough is much more obvious.

Once this "sagging" motion is recognized by the operator, he will learn to use it as a signal to add filler metal. This, of course, cools the pool, limits penetration, and builds up the weld.

6. Preheat —

Preheat of the base metal affects the penetration gained by a specific procedure by reducing the amount of heat required from the arc to achieve melting. It is especially helpful in welding heavier sections of the materials with high thermal conductivity, such as copper and aluminum.

7. Shielding Gas —

Although argon is used on most TIG welding applications because of its desirable characteristics, there are a few cases in which helium or mixtures of helium and argon are preferred. This stems from the fact that helium is capable of delivering more thermal energy or heat to the work than argon.

Finishing the Weld

If a TIG weld is suddenly terminated by pulling the torch away from the work, several things tend to happen that produce a crater crack, or hole, or both.

The sudden removal of heat usually leaves an unfilled hollow crater that is, in itself, crack-sensitive. In addition to this, the metal is "hot short" and has low tensile strength as it shrinks rapidly in the crater. Also, the shielding gas may have been removed before the metal was at a cool enough temperature to prevent contamination from the air.

If a foot or hand current control is employed, the crater is filled and the heat reduced slowly to allow the puddle to shrink under the influence of slow cooling and gas shielding. This current reduction usually continues until a low enough temperature is reached to prevent contamination. Some codes and specifications require that TIG machines be equipped with crater-filling devices or remote controls to prevent crater defects.

Where crater filling or remote current controls are not used, the technique must be different. If the crater is as full as possible, the arc is broken and restarted several times, each of shorter duration than the last to slowly cool the puddle. During this "down pumping" of the arc, the shielding gas stream must constantly be on the puddle and remain there until the puddle is sufficiently cool to prevent contamination.

THE LINCOLN IDEALARC TIG 300/300

General Information

The "Idealarc TIG" will handle any kind of manual welding job that comes along, whether it is done with stick electrodes or with inert gas. "Idealarc TIG" welders are equipped with high frequency for inert gas welding and also have rectifiers to provide DC welding power.

For manual welding with coated electrodes, the high frequency part of the machine is turned off. Then the machine operates very similar to the "Idealarc TM" welders described in Lesson 2.1. It has a polarity selector switch that sets the machine's output for AC, DC(+) or DC(−) welding power. There is also a current range selector that divides the machine's current range into five overlapping parts. Finally, a fine tuning control adjusts the current to the value required for the job being done.

Remote current controls, called "Amptrols" are available in hand or foot operated models. These remote controls provide instantaneous current response and are suitable for tapering off the current in crater filling operations.

When welding thin sections of stainless or welding aluminum or some of the new unusual metals, inert gas welding is preferred. In inert gas welding the arc is maintained between a non-consumable tungsten electrode and the work. The welding torch is connected to a supply of inert gas and feeds the gas around the arc to keep out impurities in the air which would otherwise harm the weld. Filler metal is hand fed into the arc in a manner similar to that used in gas welding.

Some types of metals, such as stainless steel, are best welded with DC. To use the "Idealarc TIG" for this type of welding, first set the polarity switch to DC [usually DC(−)], then turn the high frequency on-off switch ON. This assures control of gas and water flow into the torch.

There is a choice of the type of high frequency spark for DC welding. The spark can be left off, or it can be used just for starting where it automatically cuts off after the arc is established, or it can be left on all the time the arc is established. Usually the spark is used for starting only on DC welding.

The dial on the afterflow timer is keyed to electrode size and should be set for the size of tungsten electrode being used.

Figure 1. The Idealarc TIG 300/300.

Aluminum is usually welded with AC and continuous high frequency. The machine is set as described above except that the spark control is always set to the ON position. Also it is necessary to set the high frequency intensity control. It should be set high enough to assure a smooth steady arc, yet not so high that it makes pock marks on the weld.

The Arc Polarizer is an optional feature that improves operation on AC high frequency welding. It consists of three automotive batteries that can be put in or taken out of the welding circuit with a quickly detached connector. It should be in the circuit when welding with AC and high frequency and out at all other times.

Though the "Idealarc TIG" has many switches and controls, it is actually very easy to use. Its versatility in application has made the "Idealarc TIG" machine popular in small maintenance and repair shops that must be equipped to handle any kind of welding job that comes in the shop. These machines are also used in production shops that do nothing but inert gas welding.

Job Instructions

1. Familiarize yourself with all the controls on the machine. Note that all commonly used current and polarity selection controls are on the front of the machine.

2. Set the machine for welding with manual electrodes. Set the current and polarity switches for the electrode being used. Be sure the high frequency is turned OFF and the Arc Polarizer is disconnected. For remote control plug in the Amptrol and switch the remote switch ON. Weld with several sizes and types of electrodes to become familiar with the machine's operation and controls.

3. Set the machine for welding stainless. Turn the high frequency switch ON and set the spark control on the OFF or START ONLY position. Make torch, gas and water connections. Adjust current and afterflow timer. Plug in the output contactor remote switch. To start the arc depress the contactor remote switch after the torch is lined up over the work. The arc and gas and water flow will start simultaneously and remain until the arc is broken. Weld several samples to get the feel of the straight DC tungsten arc.

4. Set the machine for welding aluminum. Switch the spark control switch to ON. Adjust the spark intensity to about halfway through its range. Connect the Arc Polarizer. Weld to get the feel of an AC with high frequency arc. Adjust spark intensity to minimum and maximum to note its effect on the arc. Use the remote control to see how it reduces arc heat.

Object:
To learn some of the general principles involved in TIG welding of aluminum alloys and to "get ready" for practice work.

Equipment:
The units for TIG welding as shown in Figure 1, Lesson 8.1.

General Information

Although many metals are TIG welded, the metal most frequently associated with the process is aluminum, especially in the lighter thicknesses. Aluminum, of course, can be joined by other processes, but in the lighter gauges the most acceptable process is TIG.

Although the process is well suited for aluminum, there are a few characteristics of the metal that bring up points that must be considered if this material is to be welded with consistent ease and quality.

The pure metal has a melting point less than 1200°F and does not exhibit the color changes before melting so characteristic of most metals. For this reason, aluminum does not tell you when it is hot or ready to melt. The oxide or "skin" that forms so rapidly on its surface has a melting point almost three times as high (3200°+F). To add to the confusion, aluminum even boils at a lower temperature (2880°F) than this oxide melts. The oxide is also heavier than aluminum and, when melted, tends to sink or be trapped in the molten aluminum. For these reasons, it is easy to see why as much as possible of this oxide "skin" must be removed before welding. We are fortunate, indeed, that the reverse polarity half of the AC arc does an outstanding job of cleaning off quantities of this oxide ahead of the weld.

Although not as good as copper, aluminum nevertheless is an excellent conductor of heat. It requires large heat inputs when welding is begun, since much heat is lost in heating the surrounding base metal. After welding has progressed for awhile, however, much of this heat has moved ahead of the arc and preheated the base metal to a temperature requiring less welding current than the originally cold plate. If the weld is continued farther on to the end of two plates where there is nowhere for this preheat to go, it can pile up to such a degree as to make welding difficult unless the current is decreased. The foregoing explanation illustrates why many TIG welding machines are equipped with remote foot or hand current controls that enable the operator to change current while welding.

Some of the aluminum alloys exhibit "hot short" tendencies and are crack-sensitive. This means that at the range of temperatures where the liquid alloy is slushy (part solid and part liquid) or just turned solid, it has not quite enough tensile strength to resist the shrinkage stresses that are occurring from cooling and transformation. The proper choice of filler metal and welding procedures along with smaller beads can help eliminate many problems of this kind. Some experts recommend backstepping the first inch or so of each aluminum weld before finishing in the normal direction.

Filler Metals for Welding Aluminum Alloys

The metal produced in the weld pool is a combination of metals that must have the strength, ductility, freedom from cracking, and the corrosion resistance required by the application. Correct choice of filler alloy minimizes the presence

RECOMMENDED FILLER METALS FOR VARIOUS ALUMINUM ALLOYS

Base Metal	Recommended Filler Metal[1]	
	For Maximum As-Welded Strength	For Maximum Elongation
EC	1100	EC, 1260
1100	1100, 4043	1100, 4043
2219	2319	(2)
3003	5183, 5356	1100, 4043
3004	5554, 5356	5183, 4043
5005	5183, 4043, 5356	5183, 4043
5050	5356	5183, 4043
5052	5356, 5183	5183, 4043, 5356
5083	5183, 5356	5183, 5356
5086	5183, 5356	5183, 5356
5154	5356, 5183	5183, 5356, 5654
5357	5554, 5356	5356
5454	5356, 5554	5554, 5356
5456	5556	5183, 5356
6061	4043, 5183	5356[3]
6063	4043, 5183	5356[3]
7005	5039	5183, 5356
7039	5039	5183, 5356

Notes:
1. Recommendations are for plate of "0" temper.
2. Ductility of weldments of these base metals is not appreciably affected by filler metal. Elongation of these base metals is generally lower than that of other alloys listed.
3. For welded joints in 6061 and 6063 requiring maximum electrical conductivity, use 4043 filler metal. However, if both strength and conductivity are required, use 5356 filler metal and increase the weld reinforcement to compensate for the lower conductivity of 5356.

of intermetallic compounds and brittleness in aluminum fusion welds. The table below gives recommended filler metals for various aluminum alloys. Note that filler alloys 5356 and 5183 can be used for most aluminum welding applications.

Straight lengths of bare aluminum wire in EC, 1100, 4043, 5039, 5654, 5183, 5356, and 5556 alloys are available in diameters of 1/16", 3/32", 1/8", 5/32', 3/16', and 1/4". This bare rod stock is used primarily for TIG welding.

Maximum rate of deposition is obtained with filler wire or rod of the largest practical diameter while welding at the maximum practical welding current. Wire diameter best suited for a specific application depends upon the current that can be used to make the weld. The current, in turn, is governed by the available power supply, joint design, alloy type and thickness, and the welding position.

Quality of Weld Deposit: Good weld quality is obtained only if the filler wire is clean and of high quality. If the wire is not clean, a large amount of contaminant may be introduced into the weld pool, because of the relatively large surface area of the filler wire with respect to the amount of weld metal being deposited.

Contaminants on the filler wire are most often an oil or a hydrated oxide. The heat of welding releases the hydrogen from these sources, causing porosity in the weld. High-quality aluminum welding wire is manufactured under rigorous control to exacting standards and is packaged to prevent contamination during storage. Since filler wire is alloyed, or diluted, with base metal in the weld pool, the compositions of both the filler wire and the base metal affect the quality of the weld.

Need for Cleaning: Pieces to be welded are usually formed, sheared, sawed, or machined prior to the welding operation. Complete removal of all lubricants from these operations is a prerequisite for high-quality welds. Particular care must be taken to remove all oil, other hydrocarbons, and loose particles from sawed or sheared edges prior to welding. Sheared edges should be clean and smooth, not ragged. For ease of cleaning, lubricants used in fabrication should be promptly removed.

To reduce the possibility of porosity and dross in welds, cleanliness of the welding surfaces cannot be overemphasized. Hydrogen can cause porosity, and oxygen can cause dross in welds. Oxides, greases, and oil films contain oxygen and hydrogen that, if left on the edges to be welded, will cause unsound welds with poor mechanical and electrical properties. Cleaning should be done just prior to welding. A summary of general cleaning procedures is given in the accompanying table.

COMMON METHODS FOR CLEANING ALUMINUM SURFACES FOR WELDING

Compounds Removed	Type of Cleaning	
	Welding Surfaces Only	**Complete Piece**
Oil, grease, moisture, and dust. (Use any method listed.)	Wipe with mild alkaline solution. Wipe with hydrocarbon solvent, such as acetone or alcohol. Wipe with proprietary solvents. Dip edges, using any of above.	Vapor degrease. Spray degrease. Steam degrease. Immerse in alkaling solvent. Immerse in proprietary solvents.
Oxides (Use any method listed.)	Dip edges in strong alkaline solution, then water, then nitric acid. Finish with water rinse. Wipe with proprietary deoxidizers. Remove mechanically, such as by wire-brushing, filing, or grinding. For critical applications, scrape all joint and adjacent surfaces immediately prior to welding.	Immerse in strong alkaline solution, then water, then nitric acid. Finish with water rinse. Immerse in proprietary solutions.

Get-Ready Instructions for Aluminum Welding

The following instructions apply to Lessons 8.4 through 8.12, and should be checked prior to each of these lessons after a shutdown.

1. Have clean area and table to work on.
2. Make sure welding machine and torch are properly connected. Check fittings and electrical connections to see that they are tight.
3. Have proper protective clothing: Apron, gloves, helmet with proper shade lens (No. 12), cap, and leg protection if needed.
4. Have stainless-steel wire brush and a pair of pliers at weld location.
5. Check tungsten electrode in torch: It should be 3/32" pure tungsten (green end), and it should extend 1-1/2 to 2 times the diameter of the

electrode beyond the end of the gas cup. If electrode extension is improper, collet cut or cap must be loosened to obtain proper distance. The electrode should be bright and shiny with a half ball on the end if it has been used before. If it has been used before and has a rough, eroded, or match-head appearance it should be broken off and a new, half ball established.

6. Check diameter of the cup: It should be 3/8" I.D. for these lessons. It should be clean, even, and have no cracks or badly burned areas.
7. Turn on welding machine.
8. Set welding machine for AC.
9. Set "spark" switch to ON.
10. Set "current range" to medium (35-165).
11. Set fine adjustment to No. 7.
12. Set spark intensity to No. 7.
13. Set switch at remote control receptacle to "remote control."
14. Set "afterflow timer" to 3/32.
15. Set "soft start" switch to ON.
16. Set weld control switch to inert gas position.
17. Open argon cylinder valve slowly but completely to seal packing. Always stand clear of gauge front when opening valve.
18. Adjust gas flowmeter after stepping on foot Amptrol briefly. Set for 15 cubic feet per hour flow rate.
19. Make sure main water valve to machine is on. Step on foot Amptrol again to see if water comes out outlet on drain.
20. Make sure you understand the operation of the foot Amptrol before proceeding. A brief explanation follows:

Operation of the Foot Amptrol

The foot or hand Amptrol varies the current between the minimum for the "Current Range Selector" setting and the maximum established by the "Fine Adjustment Current Control." If the "Fine Adjustment Current Control" is set on No. 10, the Amptrol can then vary the current over the entire range of the "Current Range Selector" setting.

The "Fine Adjustment Current Control" should be set at the maximum current you wish to use in the "Current Range Selector" setting you have chosen. This maximum current would then be obtained when the foot control is pushed all the way down.

Slightly depressing the foot Amptrol closes the output contactor, starts the water and gas flow, energizes the high-frequency unit, and provides a current setting equal to the minimum on the "Current Range Selector" setting.

As the foot is further depressed the current is increased, and, when the foot is raised, the current is decreased to the point where, when it is all the way up, the internal switch again turns off the contactor and high frequency while the water and gas continue to flow until timed out by the "Afterflow Timer" setting.

General Shutdown Instructions

The following instructions should be followed whenever welding practice or lessons are completed.

1. Place torch in hanger or location where it cannot arc or fall.
2. Close main argon-cylinder valve.

3. Press foot Amptrol once to release pressure on flowmeter and bleed gas line.
4. Close flowmeter-adjusting valve.
5. Turn off welding machine.
6. Turn off main water valve to machine.
7. Clean up welding table and area. (Put hot work or scrap in a safe area or container.)

LESSON 8.4

Object:
To strike an arc, establish a puddle, and make a stringer weld on aluminum in the flat position – without filler metal addition.

Equipment:
Lincoln TIG 300-300 with foot Amptrol, TIG torch, and other required accessories.

Material:
Pieces of aluminum approximately 1/8" thick, sheared or saw-cut into plates 1-1/2" to 2" wide and 4" to 6" long.

Job Instructions

1. Follow get-ready instructions for aluminum welding in Lesson 8.3.

2. Wire-brush area to be welded on aluminum plates thoroughly with stainless brush.

3. Place torch about 5/8" off work, tilted at about 60° from the horizontal opposite to the direction of travel.

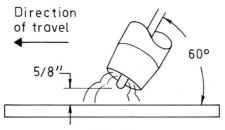

Direction of travel

5/8"

60°

Figure 1.

4. Lower hood and depress foot Amptrol about half way. (High frequency, gas flow, and water flow will now come on.)

5. Lower torch gently toward work – when the electrode is between 3/16" and 5/16" away from work the arc should ignite.

6. When arc ignites, establish arc length at about twice the diameter of the electrode. Do not touch electrode to work.

7. Raise angle slightly to about 75° and depress foot Amptrol to form a puddle approximately 1/4" in diameter. Small circular motions may be used to help accomplish this.

8. When a shiny 1/4"-diameter puddle is formed, start forward motion while maintaining constant arc length. When current and travel speed are correct, the bead width will be about twice the diameter of the electrode. This bead should penetrate but not fall through to the other side.

9. Repeat the arc striking, forming a puddle and traveling until you can consistently make a stringer bead about 3/16" to 1/4" wide with full penetration

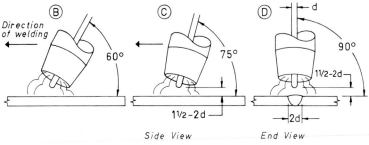

Figure 2.

at about 12 inches per minute. Watch specifically for the telltale signs of the puddles sagging prior to fall-through. Even though the color of aluminum does not change considerably, other signs will be noticed that are signals of imminent burnthrough. Try varying the current with the foot Amptrol and notice its effect on bead width, penetration, and travel speed. Notice that with aluminum much less heat is needed at the end of the weld than at the beginning to get the same penetration.

10. Check stringer beads for —

    a. Consistent bead width
    b. Smooth edges
    c. Consistent penetration
    d. Even ripple
    e. Clean appearance (no black areas)

LESSON

8.5

Object:
To make a stringer-bead weld on aluminum in the flat position with the addition of filler metal.

Equipment:
Lincoln TIG 300-300 with foot Amptrol, TIG torch, and other required accessories.

Material:
Pieces of 1/8" aluminum plate; 3/32" 1100 filler rod.

Job Instructions

1. Ready machine as indicated in last lesson.

2. Clean aluminum thoroughly with stainless wire brush.

3. Strike an arc in the manner learned in last lesson.

4. After the arc is struck and a bright fluid puddle about twice the diameter of the filler metal is established, the torch is moved to the back side of the puddle (away from the direction of welding).

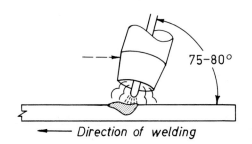

Figure 1.

5. The filler metal is slowly added to the front side of the puddle with the other hand at an angle of 10 to 20° from the horizontal. Filler metal, torch, and direction of travel should all be in the same plane with no side angle.

Make sure that the filler metal is not thrust into the arc stream, but does stay in the envelope of the shielding gas. Do not touch the tungsten to the filler metal or puddle.

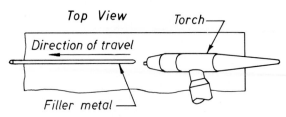

Figure 2.

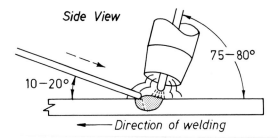

Figure 3.

6. Withdraw the filler metal from the puddle.

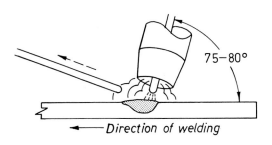

Figure 4.

7. Move torch (and arc) to front side of puddle – hesitate to penetrate and melt base metal. Wait until the puddle is bright and fluid again.

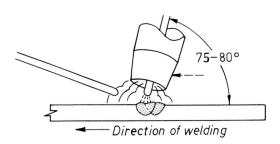

Figure 5.

8. Move torch to the rear of the crater again.

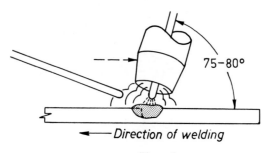

Direction of welding

Figure 6.

9. Add filler metal in the same manner as before.

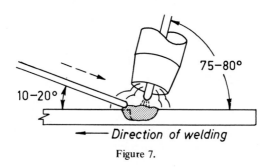

Direction of welding

Figure 7.

10. Repeat cycle over and over again to form weld bead.

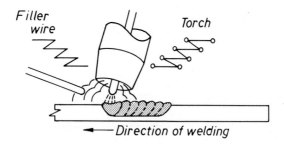

Direction of welding

Figure 8.

11. Finish the bead by filling up the crater and slowly tapering the current off with the foot Amptrol. Leave the torch in position over the crater even after the arc has gone out so that the crater will still have gas coverage while it cools.

12. Repeat this stringer-bead welding practice over and over again until it is mastered. It is the heart of all TIG welding jobs. Special attention should be paid to the following points while practicing these welds:

  a. Keep arc length constant (equal to the diameter of the tungsten electrode).
  b. Keep torch angle approximately the same (75-80° from horizontal).
  c. Keep bead width constant (about twice the tungsten diameter).
  d. Keep penetration uniform (a function of current, travel, and filler addition).
  e. Finished bead width should be 3/16" to 1/4".

13. Inspect finished welds for the following:

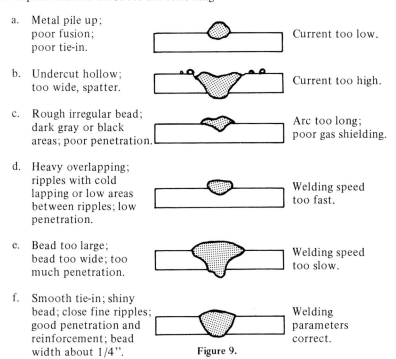

  a. Metal pile up; poor fusion; poor tie-in.
     Current too low.

  b. Undercut hollow; too wide, spatter.
     Current too high.

  c. Rough irregular bead; dark gray or black areas; poor penetration.
     Arc too long; poor gas shielding.

  d. Heavy overlapping; ripples with cold lapping or low areas between ripples; low penetration.
     Welding speed too fast.

  e. Bead too large; bead too wide; too much penetration.
     Welding speed too slow.

  f. Smooth tie-in; shiny bead; close fine ripples; good penetration and reinforcement; bead width about 1/4".
     Welding parameters correct.

Figure 9.

14. Shut down equipment per general shutdown instructions.

Object:
To make a butt weld on aluminum in the flat position with filler metal addition.

Equipment:
Lincoln TIG 300-300 with foot Amptrol, TIG torch, and other required accessories.

Material:
Pieces of 1/8" aluminum with sheared or sawed edges; 3/32" 1100 filler metal.

Job Instructions

1. Clean area on aluminum with stainless wire brush where weld is to be made. File edges to be butt-welded if they are dirty or irregular. Fit with 1/16" gap between plates.

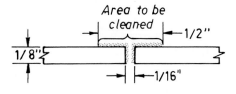

Figure 1.

2. Tack-weld one end by starting arc, melting into each side and adding a small amount of filler material to bridge gap and hold plates.

3. Turn work around, make sure 1/16" gap is maintained, and tack other end about 1/2" in from the end.

4. Restart arc on the end of joint in front of tack. Melt into both sides of joint and add filler metal in the same manner as in previous lesson.

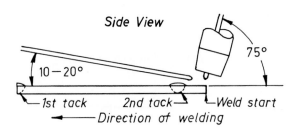

Figure 2.

5. Continue weld in same manner as stringer bead in last lesson. Make sure fusion is complete into both sides of plate and that sufficient filler metal is added to bring weld up to slightly over flush. Welding current and filler

metal addition is very important here to assure complete penetration and proper buildup without fall-through. Notice that less heat will be required as weld progresses and preheat has preceded arc.

6. Finish weld by following proper crater-filling technique described in previous lesson.

7. Inspect finished weld for the following:

    a. Smooth clean welds
    b. Even width of bead — approximately 1/4"
    c. Proper penetration and reinforcement without excessive fall-through
    d. Even ripple
    e. No undercut or spatter
    f. Properly filled crater with no cracks

8. Repeat practice until this weld is mastered.

9. Shut down per general shutdown instructions.

**LESSON
8.7**

Object:
To make a lap weld on aluminum in the horizontal position without filler metal.

Equipment:
Lincoln TIG 300-300 with foot Amptrol, TIG torch, and other required accessories.

Material:
1/8" aluminum plate with sheared or saw-cut edges.

Job Instructions

1. Clean with stainless wire brush areas that are to be welded.
2. Fit and hold securely for tacking. Tack indicated corners (4) on both ends without filler metal, Figure 1.

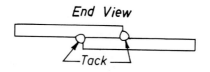

End View

—Tack—

Figure 1.

3. Hold torch at approximate angle in sketch to obtain best results in welding.

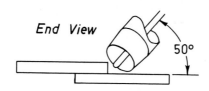

End View

50°

Figure 2.

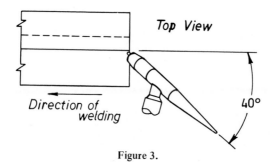

Top View

Direction of welding

40°

Figure 3.

4. Strike arc on bottom plate in corner. When fluid pool has formed, move up so that edge of electrode is just over upper edge of lap corner. Maintain arc length at about the diameter of the electrode to prevent undercut and give complete penetration.

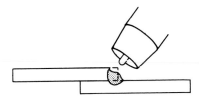

Figure 4.

5. Proceed down the joint. Observe that a V-shaped pool forms and that forward travel speed is determined by how fast the notch of the vee travels. If the notch is not completely filled, lack of penetration and poor fusion will result. Bead face should be about 1/4" wide. Fill crater in proper manner.

6. Inspect work for the following:

    a. Undercut on top edge — too long arc
    b. Insufficient penetration into corner — too long arc or too fast travel
    c. Too wide bead face — too slow travel

7. Repeat practice until good welds are mastered.

8. Shut down equipment per general shutdown instructions.

LESSON

8.8

Object:
To make a horizontal lap weld on aluminum with the addition of filler metal.

Equipment:
Lincoln TIG 300-300 with foot Amptrol, TIG torch, and other required accessories.

Material:
Small 2" x 4" aluminum plates 1/8" thick; 3/32" 1100 filler metal.

Job Instructions

1. Clean, fit, and tack plates as in previous lesson.

2. Hold torch at same angles as described in previous lesson. Hold filler wire as shown in Figure 1.

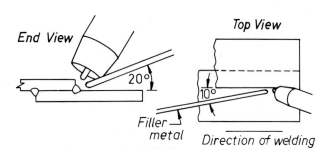

Figure 1.

3. Start arc and initiate puddle in same manner as in previous lesson. When plates are joined and V-shaped pool has formed, add filler metal to the top front side of the pool. Maintenance of the proper arc length (approximately the diameter of the tungsten electrode) and addition of filler metal to the top of the pool will prevent undercut of the top plate.

4. Proceed down joint at a speed consistent with good penetration into the bottom corner and giving a generous convex bead with a face width between 2 and 3 times the tungsten diameter. Fill crater in proper manner.

5. Inspect weld for undercut, penetration, and bead shape.

6. Repeat practice and make corrections in technique to eliminate faults.

7. Shut down equipment per general shutdown instructions.

LESSON

8.9

Object:
To make a horizontal fillet on aluminum with the addition of filler metal.

Equipment:
Lincoln TIG 300-300 with foot Amptrol, TIG torch, and other required accessories.

Material:
1/8" aluminum plates approximately 2" x 3"; 3/32" 1100 filler metal.

Job Instructions

1. Fit and tack T section with two pieces of aluminum.

2. Thoroughly clean (with stainless wire brush) areas where fillets are to be made.

3. Torch and filler rod angles should be maintained as shown in the sketch. You may prefer to extend tungsten electrode for fillet welding, but do not exceed 3 times the tungsten diameter beyond the cup.

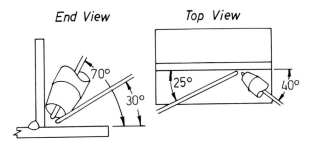

Figure 1.

4. Travel and deposit metal in a manner similar to the previous lesson on lap welding. Hold arc length at about twice the diameter of the tungsten and add filler metal on the high front side of the pool. Undercut and underwash are controlled by arc length, current, travel speed, and filler addition. Bead shape should be flat to slightly convex with fine ripples. Bead width should be about 3 times the diameter of the tungsten. Fill crater in proper manner.

5. Inspect finished weld for:

   a. Undercut or underwash on top side — too long arc, arc too much on the vertical plate, too much current, too little filler added.

   b. Incomplete penetration into corner — arc too long, current too low, travel too fast.

   c. Bead face too large on bottom side — too slow travel, too much current.

6. Repeat practice until fillet is mastered.

7. Shut down equipment per general shutdown instructions.

LESSON 8.10

Object:
To make an outside corner weld on aluminum in the flat position without filler metal.

Equipment:
Lincoln TIG 300-300 with foot Amptrol, TIG torch, and other required accessories.

Material:
2" x 4" pieces of aluminum.

Job Instructions

1. Ready machine according to general instructions.

2. Clean, fit, and tack two pieces of aluminum in the manner shown in sketch. Tack on inside corners away from weld and position as shown.

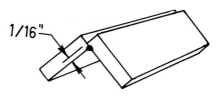

Figure 1.

3. Strike and hold an arc approximately 5/32" long. With no side angle, traverse torch as shown in sketch. Favor high side of the joint slightly. Watch for corners to melt and flow into center of groove, giving good penetration.

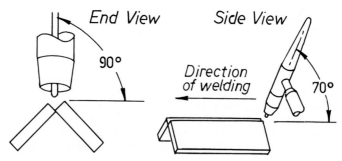

Figure 2.

4. If weld is not bright and clean, gas flow may have to be slightly increased.

5. Bead should have a smooth, even rippled face about 3/16" to 1/4" wide and be penetrated through back side. Crater should be properly filled.

6. Repeat welding operation until consistently good welds with even back-side penetration are made.

7. Shut down per general shutdown procedures.

LESSON 8.11

Object:
To make vertical stringer beads on aluminum with and without filler metal. Also to make a vertical butt weld with the addition of filler metal.

Equipment:
Lincoln TIG 300-300 with foot Amptrol, TIG torch, and other required accessories.

Material:
Pieces of 1/8" aluminum approximately 2" x 6"; 3/32" 4043 filler metal.

General Information

Although TIG welding on aluminum can be done either vertically up or down, we will concentrate here on vertical-up since it is easier for the beginner to see the penetration and filler metal action. Care must be taken, however, to see that the added filler metal does not touch the tungsten as it flows to the bottom of the pool.

Job Instructions — Part I

1. Clean and tack two pieces of aluminum to form an angle with long legs. Clamp or hold down this angle on edge of table or upright so that vertical face can be welded and there is sufficient clearance for the torch.

2. Hold torch at angle shown in sketch, strike an arc, and run several stringers up the plate from bottom to top without filler wire. Watch melting pattern

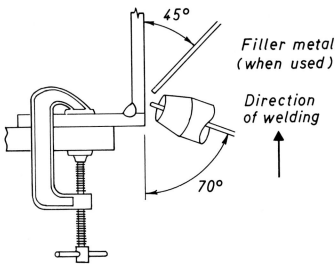

45°

Filler metal
(when used)

Direction
of welding

70°

Figure 1.

and hold 5/32" arc during upward progress. Forward progress is determined by current, penetration, and freezing pattern under arc. Bead should penetrate completely through sheet.

3. After observing the action of the TIG arc and melting characteristics of aluminum in this position, try the same weld with the addition of filler metal. The filler metal should be held at the angle shown in the sketch. No side angles are involved with torch or filler metal. Add filler metal frequently, in small amounts, so that the puddle doesn't become too large and the bead shape can be carefully controlled as upward movement progresses. Make sure to fill crater at finish.

4. Inspect welds for:

    a. Penetration through back side.
    b. Bead shape not overly convex and with tight ripples — bead face should be about 5/16" wide.

5. Shut down equipment per general shutdown instructions.

Job Instructions — Part II

1. Clean and tack two plates together with a tight fit to form a butt-weld joint. Tack this assembly vertically on another plate to make an angle similar to the one used in Part I. Secure this angle to the table with the vertical butt joint facing you.

2. Strike an arc, progress upward, and add filler metal in the same manner as in Part I. Keep arc length at approximately 5/32", watch penetration pattern, and add filler when needed. Make sure finish crater is filled properly.

3. Inspect for:

    a. Appearance — not overly convex; not too wide; clean, smooth tie-in; close ripple.
    b. Penetration through to the back side and even.

4. Repeat weld as many times as necessary to become proficient.

5. Shut down equipment per general shutdown instructions.

Object:
To study and practice the welding of stainless steel by the TIG process.

Equipment:
Lincoln TIG 300-300 with foot Amptrol, TIG torch, 1/16" electrode, and accessories.

Material:
Pieces of 16-gauge, type 304 stainless steel; 1/16" ER308 filler rod.

General Information

"Stainless steel" is the term generally applied to several families of alloys all having corrosion or heat-resisting properties derived from the addition of chromium. The stainless steels that we will discuss here are what are called the "300" series materials of the austenitic or nonmagnetic variety. These types (304, 309, 312, 316, and 310) probably encompass at least 90% of all stainless steel welding applications.

These materials for the most part all have good strength, good ductility, and good welding properties. They do not harden when quenched, but cannot be cut with normal fuel-gas cutting equipment. They work-harden fairly rapidly and require higher pressures for shearing, bending, and forming than mild steel. They all have poor electrical and thermal conductivity and their coefficient of expansion is almost double that of mild steel. These last two characteristics tell us that heat travels very slowly in these materials and can cause more distortion than in mild steel.

Typical procedures for TIG welding of stainless steels are given in the table on the following page.

Most jobs are done with DC(−), straight polarity, because it produces excellent quality and good fusion at very low currents. AC can be used on thin materials.

Lessons for the welding of stainless steel have not been included in this text because the technique is so similar to that of aluminum.

The basic lessons used for aluminum can be applied to stainless steel with the following exceptions:

Follow "Get Ready Instructions" in Lesson 8.3 and make the following changes −

No. 3. You may wish to use a slightly lighter lens for stainless welding, since the currents are lower and the arc is smaller.

No. 5. The electrode for stainless welding should be 1/16", 1 or 2% thoriated (yellow or red end), with a ground taper end described earlier in the text.

No. 6. The gas cup for stainless welding could be reduced in size to 5/16" I.D., although the 3/8" cup will still perform satisfactorily.

No. 8. Set welding machine to DC negative, straight polarity.

No. 9. Set "spark" switch to "start only" position.

TYPICAL PROCEDURES FOR TIG WELDING OF STAINLESS STEEL

Plate Thickness, T (in.)	Current, DCSP	Electrode Diameter (in.)	Gas Flow, Argon (cfh)	Filler-Rod Diameter (in.)	Arc Speed (ipm)	Total Time (hr/ft of weld)
	Less than 0.1 T					
1/16	80 – 100	1/16	10	1/16	12	0.0167
3/32	100 – 120	1/16	10	1/16	12	0.0167
1/8	120 – 140	1/16	10	3/32	12	0.0167
3/16	200 – 250	3/32	15	1/8	10	0.0200
1/16	90 – 110	1/16	10	1/16	10	0.0200
3/32	110 – 130	1/16	10	1/16	10	0.0200
1/8	130 – 150	1/16	10	3/32	10	0.0200
3/16	225 – 275	3/32	15	1/8	8	0.0250

For vertical-up and overhead, decrease the current 10 to 20%.

No. 10. Set current range switch to low (8-93 amp).
Set fine adjustment rheostat to No. 8.

No. 13. Set afterflow timer to 1/16".

No. 17. The gas flow can be reduced to about 12 cu.ft./hr. or 10 cu.ft./hr. if 5/16" cup is used. It would not be decreased for outside corner welds.

The differences in welding stainless steel and aluminum are:

a. Lower heats are used to weld stainless steel (40 – 70 amp).

b. Less heat is required to get the initial puddle formed.

c. There is less difference in the starting and finishing currents with stainless-steel welds.

d. Smooth penetration through to the back side is more difficult to acquire with stainless steel welds.

e. Welding speeds are less than with aluminum.

f. The molten puddle is smaller than with aluminum and somewhat more difficult to judge.

g. In fillet and lap welds, the puddle seems to require more "pushing" and will not move until the arc is moved.

h. Arc lengths are shorter and puddle widths are narrower than with aluminum.

With the foregoing differences in mind it should be reasonably easy to use the same lesson plan for stainless steel (300 series) as for aluminum.

LESSON 8.13

Object:
To consider other uses for the TIG welding process.

TIG Welding of Carbon and Low-Alloy Steels

The TIG welding process is frequently used on light-gauge mild steel and low-alloy material, especially where it can be automated or no filler metal is required. It is possible with the TIG process to make excellent welds on very light material (21 gauge or less).

When the gauge is heavier than 16, other processes are usually more economical unless the special characteristics of the TIG process are required.

When TIG welds are made on mild steel with no filler metal added, the steel base metal must be of good quality to preclude a "rimming action" in the puddle. This rimming action can cause considerable porosity in the welds. When filler metal is added to make welds on steels of poorer quality, some help can be obtained in limiting porosity by the use of what are called triple deoxidized filler metals. However, whenever possible fully killed (deoxidized) steels should be used where TIG welding is involved.

One of the characteristics of TIG welding has been useful at times in certain pipe-welding applications. This characteristic is the ability of the TIG process to penetrate and melt through on the first or stringer pass on pipe without leaving undercut or slag on the back side of the joint and with a minimum of reinforcement. This technique, of course, requires a high degree of skill. It is usually accompanied by special pipe-joint preparation and sometimes special consumable backing rings. Since the bead is normally small compared to the cross section of the pipe and has a tendency to be concave, care must be taken to prevent cracks in this pass. Sometimes these cracks may be very difficult to see and will even avoid X-ray detection if subsequent passes are put over them prior to inspection.

As in the case of stainless steel, practice lessons have not been put in this book for carbon or low-alloy steels. However, the basic guides for stainless can be used on mild or low-alloy steels.

The one minor difference in the setup for mild steel is that slightly more current can be used and that the "fine current adjustment" rheostat should be set to No. 10.

If anything, the TIG welding of mild steel is more easily accomplished than with stainless because distortion is not so great a problem. For this reason, many beginners will go from aluminum to mild steel and then on to stainless. Of course, when you are dealing with higher-carbon or low-alloy materials, the same principles of metallurgy and thickness apply as do in all other processes of welding, and so proper procedures, including preheat and postheat, must be adhered to.

Other Metals

Many other metals, both ferrous and nonferrous, can be welded with the TIG process. These include cast iron and copper and nickel-base materials, as well as most of the "space age" alloys. Specific procedures and techniques should be obtained from the manufacturers of these materials.

The Idealarc TIG 250/250.

SECTION IX

SUPPLEMENTARY DATA

INTRODUCTION

The information in this section is included to help the weldor advance his career. To move forward with the industry, the weldor must be amenable to the acceptance of new ideas, new techniques, new processes, and new equipment. Welding technology is a relatively young industrial science. New developments are coming into being constantly. The progressive weldor will keep up with these developments and make use of them to further his own career. Many of the improved ways for handling jobs come directly from the men working in the shops; others come from the research laboratories of equipment and material manufacturers. The weldor who uses his personal observations to help his employer reduce costs and improve products is playing an important role in advancing welding technology and in furthering his career in a dynamic field of industrial science.

Welding technology has been expanding at a rapid rate since World War II. This rate is constantly increasing — given impetus by such factors as the increased cost of materials and labor, the development of new weldable metal compositions, the improvement of equipment and processes, and advances in engineering that enable designers to make fuller use of the strength and other properties of materials. In fact, almost all of the economic and social changes since World War II have been favorable to the increased use of weldments in metal-product manufacturing. As an example, problems of energy supply have made weldments more desirable than castings in assemblies, since much less energy is required in joining prefashioned steel materials than in remelting vast amounts of iron or steel for castings. As another example, the trend to high-rise buildings with their need for improved transfer of the strength of materials in the framing has been a boost for weld joining. Similar examples could be cited for bridge building, machinery and machine-tool manufacture, and even in home and farm products, where unitized structures save the number of parts, the weight of materials, and the amount of assembly labor.

The weldor — even in the final quarter of the Twentieth Century — is in a growth industry. Not all skilled workmen and technicians have such a favorable outlook.

There are many reasons why welding technology is dynamic and will continue to be so. All of these reasons, however, resolve down to one underlying fact — namely, WELDING ENABLES THE REDUCTION OF COSTS. Whether weld fabrication eliminates patterns for castings, unnecessary parts, unnecessary weight, or unnecessary assembly operation, everything boils down to reduced costs. The weldor who adjusts his thinking to the use of his skills to reduce costs is in tune with the future.

What can the individual weldor do to help his employer reduce costs — and, thus, further the technology and his own career?

First, he can make the highest quality welds within his capabilities. Since quality welds are almost always stronger than the parts they join, good welding means a product that will win a reputation for reliability in service. One poor weld can mean a dissatisfied and lost customer for the weldor's employer.

Second, the weldor should be receptive to new methods, processes, and equipment that reduce welding costs and increase weld quality. He should be willing to "go along" with his employer on any innovation that will be beneficial to the company — and, in time, to himself. This means continued learning — a requirement in any skill or profession.

Third, the weldor should be on the look-out for ways of reducing welding costs or improving the product — and should not hesitate in revealing his ideas to management. As noted previously, the worker on the job is an ally of the research man in the laboratory or the designer at his drawing table.

Finally, the weldor should follow instructions on the prints — unless he has reason to suspect an error, in which case deviation from instructions should be undertaken only after consultation with appropriate authorities. Weldors, as a rule, generally err in not following instruction by deviating on what seems to be the "better side". Thus, a 5/16" fillet may be placed where a 3/16" fillet is specified "to make the joint stronger". While the intention of the weldor here is commendable, what he may not know is that the designer has gone to extensive calculations to establish that a 3/16" fillet is adequate — with a large margin of safety. Since the amount of weld metal in a fillet increases with the square of the leg size, a small "reasonable addition for assured safety" may actually double the welding costs. Also, any extra welding done with good intentions by the weldor might cause a distortion problem that the designer has been careful to avoid.

The weldor should always remember that he is the executor of a highly involved branch of industrial science. Weld design and welding engineering are exceedingly complex subjects, involving mathematics, metallurgy, physics, and chemistry. Many of the jobs that the weldor will work on today and tomorrow — a bridge girder, for example — could not have come into existence without mathematical computations so complex that they can be solved economically only with computers and highly developed computer programs.

Figure 1. This weldor — and his company — are keeping up with welding technology. Here, the semiautomatic Innershield process (plus the simple fixture) has resulted in a significant production increase.

LESSON 9.1

Metals:
Their Identification, Classification, Manufacture, and Weldability.

When planning a career in welding, some provision must be made for spending time and effort to follow a definite program of self-improvement in the technical and scientific aspects of welding. An all-around weldor must know more than just how to deposit weld metal correctly.

It is necessary to know something about the characteristics and identification of metals, their chemical and physical structure, and the effects of heat on them. A knowledge of the metal classifications and specifications as used on working drawings and purchase orders is a necessity in many types of welding jobs.

It is often necessary to first identify the general type of metal used in a part before selecting or working out the proper welding procedure in a maintenance or construction job. This means that the weldor should have one or more dependable, accurate, and rapid methods of identifying metals. Most of the metals encountered by the weldor engaged in general construction and repair work will be some type of ferrous metal. A ferrous metal is one that contains a predominant amount of iron, such as carbon-steel, low alloy-steels, and cast iron. Nonferrous metals are those that contain no iron or very little iron. Emphasis in metal identification, classification, and manufacturing methods, therefore, will be placed on the ferrous metals.

Identifying Metals Using a Magnet — A small permanent magnet will help identify metals. Of the magnetic metals iron, nickel, and cobalt, only iron is likely to be encountered in the welding shop. If the piece is nonmagnetic, iron and steel can be ruled out. If the piece is magnetic, it is likely to be carbon-steel, low-alloy steel, or one of the 400-series stainless steels.

Identifying Metal by Surface Appearance — The shape, texture, and color of a metal will help to classify it. An experienced weldor can often immediately identify a metal by visible means.

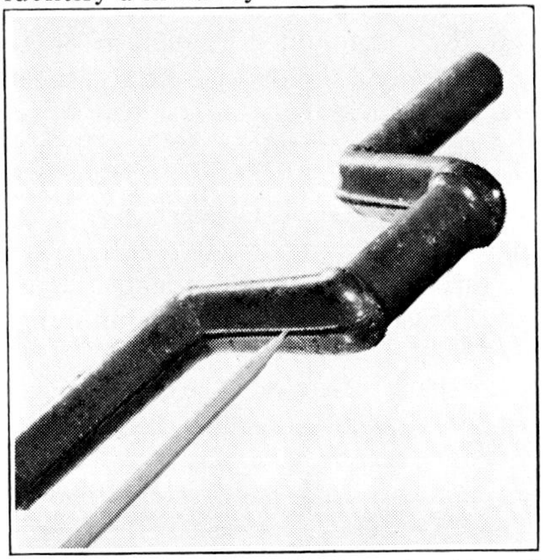

Figure 1. Ridges are left along the sides of drop-forged parts at points where the two dies overlap. The surface is rough due to iron scales that form on the dies during the forging operation.

Figure 2. Gates are present on sides of parts that are cast in molds. Cast-steel parts have large gates as compared with cast iron.

Most castings are made by pouring molten metal into a mold cavity made by withdrawing a wood or metal pattern from the sand that has been rammed around it. Metal cast in sand has a rough, "grainy" appearance, due to the imprint of the sand grains.

Castings have a ridge, called a "flashing", along the edge where the two halves of the mold come together. This may be ground off flush, but its method of removal or a small portion of the flashing will usually be visible. There may also appear one or more enlarged areas along the flashing, called "gates". These are formed by openings cut into the sand mold to allow the metal to flow into the mold cavity during the casting process. On the surface, a gate appears as though it were fractured, but may have been smoothed by grinding.

Forgings are made by placing pieces of steel heated to a forging temperature in a die, where they are forced into the die under pressure of a heavy hammer or press.

Pieces that have been drop-forged may have a rather rough, scaly surface appearance, while others are tumbled or shot-peened to give an even-grained effect. There is usually a flashing left along the edge of the piece where the two dies come together. This is usually sheared and sometimes ground smooth. The parts numbers stamped on the part during the drop-forging operation appear sharp and distinct as compared with those found on castings. Forgings are usually made of medium-carbon or low-alloy steels.

Identifying Metal by Sound — Identification may be made by rapping the metal with a hammer in order to hear the sound given off. It is difficult to explain a sound in words, so it is necessary for each individual to compare the sound from different types of metal a number of times to establish a dependable standard. For example, when one strikes rolled or forged steel with a hammer, it resounds with a tone higher pitched than that given off by cast metal. Gray castings, malleable castings, and white castings may be compared by sound. Gray castings have a dull, chalky tone, while malleable castings have a higher, clearer-pitched tone, and white cast iron an even higher pitch.

Identifying Metals Using the Spark Test — Most ferrous metals may be roughly classified by observing the sparks given off when the surface or edge of the metal is touched against a grinding wheel. To classify the unknown metal, the sparks given off are compared to those of a known metal. Either a portable or stationary grinder may be used. A wheel of medium grit, such as 40 to 60-grain, gives the most satisfactory results. The wheel should operate at a speed of 7,000 to 8,000 surface feet per minute. An 8-inch-diameter grinding wheel turning at a rate of 3,600 R.P.M. provides a surface speed of 7,500 feet per minute.

The wheel should be dressed before testing a metal. This removes glazing, sharpens the wheel, and removes traces of metals ground previously.

Sparks can be observed more easily in a diffused light. Avoid bright sunlight or a darkened room. If the sparks are given off against a dark background, it is easier to distinguish the spark characteristics.

Different elements in the steel influence spark behavior. The presence of carbon causes a bursting stream of sparks; the higher the carbon content, the more plentiful the spark bursts (Figure 5). An exception to this is when the metal has alloys such as silicon, chromium, nickel, and tungsten, which tend to suppress the carbon bursts. As the manganese content is increased, the sparks tend to follow the surface of the wheel. Chromium gives off sparks that are orange in color. Difficulty is experienced in getting a spark stream. When nickel is added to a metal, forked tongues are produced on the end of the spark streams.

The core wire of Fleetweld 5P contains about .10% carbon, .40% manganese, and very small amounts of silicon, sulfur, and phosphorus. Keep a piece of this handy to use as a standard for low-carbon steel.

Heat treatment also changes spark patterns. The undersurface as well as the surface should be tested, since some metals may have a low or high-carbon surface due to surface treatment, while the underneath composition is different.

It will take practice to classify metals by the spark test. Spend time observing sparks from known metals, carefully noting the length, color, and end shape of the spark from the time it leaves the wheel until it disappears. It is advisable to keep samples of known metals by the grinder to use in making comparative tests. The color of the spark stream is important. It will vary from white, yellow, orange, and straw. Various terms are used to describe the pattern of the spark stream. The sketches in Figure 5 illustrate the common patterns and terms.

Identifying Metals by Fracture — Looking at the broken edge of the part is one of the first steps in metal identification. The fractured surface reveals such items as nature of the break, type of grain, and color.

Figure 3. A bench grinder is used to grind metal for identifying sparks. A medium grain, 8-inch-diameter wheel turning at 3600 R.P.M. is used. Sparks are easier to observe if seen against a slate-colored background.

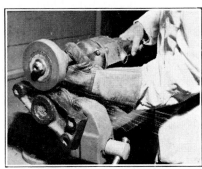

Figure 4. A portable grinder is used to spark-test pieces before welding operation is begun. It is easier to identify sparks given off in a diffused light.

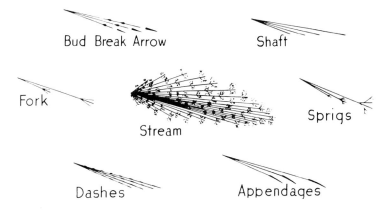

Bud Break Arrow   Shaft

Fork   Sprigs

Stream

Dashes   Appendages

Figure 5. Illustrations of terms used in spark testing.

The surface of a fracture on a piece of gray cast iron is dark gray and will usually rub off black (graphite) on the finger tip. White cast iron has a silvery white appearance. Malleable cast iron shows a dark center with a light outer skin, due to its surface treatment.

The way in which the part breaks is of interest. Malleable cast-iron parts exhibit more ductility than gray or white cast iron. The metal along the edge of the break will indicate this characteristic by showing some distortion. Gray and white cast irons are brittle and make a clean break.

The fractured surface of steel provides a definite grain pattern. Low-carbon steel is bright gray, while high-carbon is a little darker, but still light gray.

The fractured edge of a steel axle or rod has a distinctive grain pattern. The metal checks at a point of stress and, as the break continues across the piece, the friction of the two surfaces smooths the fractured grain pattern. When the part finally breaks, the portion of metal that broke last has had no rubbing action and shows a crystalline surface. In the presence of oil or grease, this surface will often be free of grease, and the older portion of the break will be darkened by it.

Identifying Metals by Chipping and Filing — It is sometimes impossible to observe a clean fracture in the metal, because it is oxidized, dirty, or the metal is still in one piece. The use of a file and chisel may help the weldor in several ways. The oxidized or dirty surface is removed, exposing the true color of the metal, as was discussed when observing a fracture. The relative hardness of the metal can be determined by comparing its resistance to the cutting edge and the type of chip it yields with that of mild steel. A soft metal will cut easily, giving a continuous chip. A tough metal will also give a continuous chip, but will present more resistance to the cutting edge. A brittle metal will give a series of broken chips. A hardened metal will resist the cutting of file or chisel. Mild steel yields a continuous chip, and increases in toughness and hardness as the carbon content is increased. Gray and white cast irons tend to chip off in a series of small pieces, with white cast iron being more resistant to the cutting edge. Malleable cast iron will give a continuous chip, because of the annealed surface.

Identifying Nonferrous Metals — Although there are many nonferrous metals and alloys in use today, they are not encountered as often by the general construction and maintenance weldor as those metals in the ferrous category. A weldor should be able to identify the common nonferrous metals, as most of them will be confined to a few basic metals or families of metals. The copper family, ranging from pure copper through varying alloys of brass and bronze, aluminum and its alloys, and the nickel alloys are probably the most common. Many other categories such as magnesium, lead, "white metal", and titanium are commercially available and useful, but price, certain physical properties, or their recent development prohibits all but specialized uses.

Most of these metals are formed in the same way as ferrous metals, so that surface appearance will often show the type and form of metal being identified. The same distinguishing marks will identify cast and forged metal, and that which has been formed by rolling. The brasses and bronzes, however, are not usually hot-worked. They are known as "hot-short", which means that they have little strength above their critical temperatures and cannot be hammered or rolled, because they break or crumble rather than hold their shape under pressure of a hammer or rolls.

Weight is often a distinctive characteristic of the nonferrous groups. Aluminum, although it is only slightly whiter in color than low-carbon steel and the nickel alloys, is much lighter in weight. It is approximately one-third the weight of steel, and also approximately one-third the weight of "white metal" or "pot metal", for which it is sometimes mistaken. Alloys high in copper and nickel are slightly heavier than steel, and everyone is familiar with the comparatively heavy weight of lead.

The spark test is not very revealing on these materials. Nonferrous metals and alloys do not yield a spark on the grinding wheel, except for a very small wavy spark from nickel.

Looking at the fracture on nonferrous metals is a good way to identify them. If the fracture is fresh, the color of the metal is quite true and free of oxides. If the fracture is old, or the metal has not come apart, it may be necessary to take a file or chisel and remove the surface of the metal to observe the undersurface. Many nonferrous metals quickly lose their true color when exposed to the atmosphere or by handling. Aluminum has a white color. Copper is red. When it is alloyed with zinc to make brass, it becomes yellow, and with the addition of tin or aluminum to make bronze it has a lighter yellow or gold color. Nickel has a nearly white color, which turns to a light gray as it is alloyed in Monel and Inconel.

Filing or using a chisel to remove chips is a help in identifying nonferrous metals and to check their hardness. Aluminum cuts easily with the chisel giving a continuous chip, but when it is alloyed for strength the color becomes more gray and the metal is tougher to cut. A file removes aluminum and its alloys easily, and, unless the file is very coarse or has curve-cut teeth, the soft aluminum tends to clog and cause "pinheads' in the teeth. Copper and its alloys cut rather easily with the file and chisel, giving a continuous chip, although they are not quite as soft and yielding as aluminum. Nickel is tough and its alloys are tougher. It will cut with the file, and the chisel will give a continuous chip, but it will take more pressure to force the cutting edge through the metal. Lead is the softest of all the common metals and will cut easily with a chisel, showing a bright gray-white surface. It will quickly clog up other than a special file made for it.

Care must be exercised when welding or working nonferrous metals in the molten state. The fumes given off by these metals or their fluxes are often toxic and should not be breathed.

Melting Points for Metals and Alloys — A weldor should know the relative melting points of common metals and alloys. In addition to this, it is important to know the temperatures the metal passes through when becoming solid. In repair work, the weldor is often required to join two different metals, such as mild steel and cast iron. It is well to know that there is a difference in the melting points of these two metals of about 500 degrees Fahrenheit (F), cast iron having the lower melting point. A general rule to remember is that as the carbon content is increased, the melting point is decreased.

Bronze is an alloy that melts at a comparatively low temperature. When bronze is applied to steel in the brazing operation, the bronze is molten at 1600 to 1650 F, whereas the steel is heated only to a bright red.

Pure aluminum and copper, as other pure metals, have precise melting points. Alloys of these metals, being "chemically impure" solids, melt at varying temperatures dependent on their compositions. Solder is an example of an alloy of this type. The melting points of some industrial metals and alloys, however, have a melting-point range narrow enough to be considered a single temperature. These are shown in the left-hand column of the chart[1] (Figure 6). The melting points of various alloys having a wider range appear in the right-hand column. The color scale in the center shows the approximate temperatures at which color

---

[1] Industry and Welding, August, 1946.

changes appear. The right-hand column with both Centigrade and Fahrenheit scales can be used as a general conversion table between these scales.

The color scale is purposely indefinite as to the border line between colors, because of differences of opinions as to color names, and because the amount of light present affects the visible color. The colors for the temperatures indicated can be seen only in a dark location. In a well-lighted shop, faint red may not appear until the metal has reached a temperature of 1100 or 1150 degrees F.

The Effect of Welding on Grain Structure of Metal — During the arc-welding process, when metal in the crater is molten, such changes in the metal may take

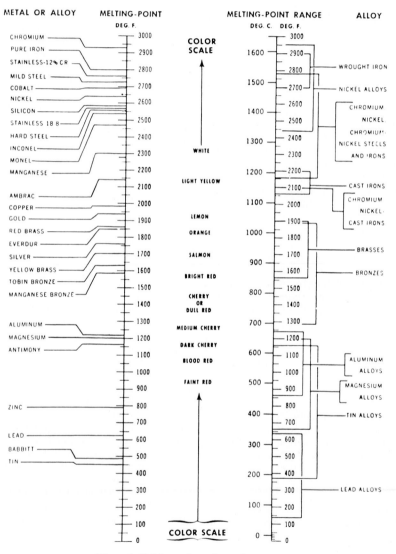

Figure 6. Melting points of metals and alloys.

place as removal or introduction of gases and formation of oxides. When the metal cools and solidifies, a grain structure is formed that influences the hardness, strength, toughness, and impact resistance of the metal. The rate of cooling influences grain size, as well as composition of the grains. Information about the changes that take place in that part of the metal that is heated and cooled during the welding cycle is important. This information is helpful when undertaking new welding applications or in understanding the added precautions necessary when welding certain common metals, such as hardenable steels.

Grain structure of metal changes when the second pass of a double-vee butt weld is made. Observe the effects on the grain structure in the magnified sections of the parent metal and the weld metal after the first and second pass is made (Figure 7). The annealed metal of the first weld pass has a fine grain and characteristics that make it tough. Preheating and postheating will often give a weld added strength and toughness as well as prevent cracking and stress concentration.

Grain Structure — Metals in the molten state take on a precise geometric grain pattern as they cool and solidify. This results from atomic arrangement into the crystalline form characteristic of the metal. Iron takes a cubic form. This basic cube has one atom at each corner and one at the exact center of the body, and is called body-centered-cubic. These cubes are the building bricks that fit together and form the grain or crystalline structure of the metal. Many grains, in turn, form the bar or plate of iron with which we are familiar in the shop. The diagram in Figure 8 is provided as an explanation of the effect of heating on grain growth.

The structure and physical properties of steel are modified or changed entirely when the metal is heated and cooled. The most significant changes take place

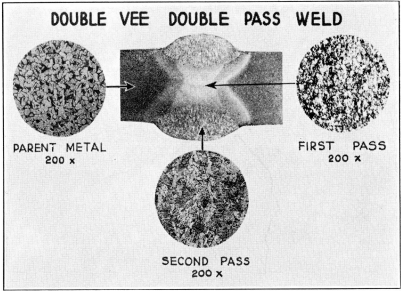

Figure 7. The annealing effects of a two-pass weld are shown by comparing the grain structures of parent metal with those of first and second-pass welds in a double-vee built joint.

at temperatures known as critical points (or critical range). The critical point is the point where steel recrystalizes from body-centered-cubic to face-centered-cubic on a rising temperature. At this point, iron becomes nonmagnetic, so that the iron may be roughly checked in the shop with a magnet to see when the point is reached. Grain size increases and decreases depending on the heat treatment given the metal. The circles drawn on the diagram in Figure 8 illustrate the effect of heating on low and high-carbon steel grain growth.

When low-carbon steel is heated, grain refinement commences at approximately 1325 degrees F (line A, Figure 8). Grain size continues to diminish until the metal is heated to a bright red color (line B). When the metal is heated beyond this point, the grain begins to grow in size. This continues until the melting temperature is reached.

Grain size in high-carbon steel changes immediately when reaching the critical temperature of heating (1325 degrees F, line A). At this point, grain size is very small. The size then increases slowly as the temperature of the metal is increased.

The size of grain in steel may be coarse, medium, or fine before heating is begun, depending upon the previous heat treatment given the metal. Regardless of grain size previously obtained, the grain will be fine when the steel is heated to the temperature shown on the chart as line B. It is important that this grain growth be understood and the temperatures be recognized for purposes of weld-

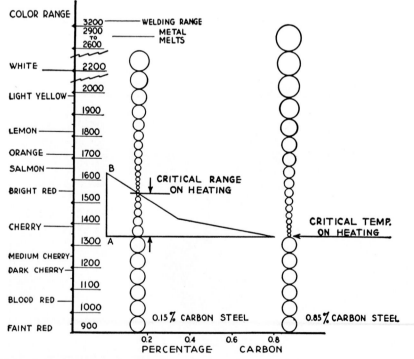

Figure 8. Steel temperature and grain-growth chart. The temperature of heat-treated steel is estimated by observing the color. Grain growth increases or decreases depending upon the heat treatment given the steel.

Figure 9. A comparison of grain structure is observed when two pieces of a high-carbon, fine-grain file are welded together with a butt weld.

ing and heat treating. To obtain maximum strength and impact resistance, a refined grain is necessary.

A fine-grain structure is reached in low or high-carbon steel when the metal is heated to the temperature indicated by line B. Fast or slow cooling will hold this fine-grain structure so that it will be present in either a hardened or annealed piece of metal. Rapid cooling of metal from this temperature zone to a temperature of 200 degrees or lower causes the metal to harden. Full hardness in steel, however, is not obtained unless the carbon content exceeds approximately 60 points (0.6%). A piece of steel cannot be hardened and used as an edge tool unless there is sufficient carbon or alloy content.

Steel is annealed by first heating to a temperature of 50 to 100 degrees F above that shown by line B. The steel is allowed to cool slowly to room temperature by packing it in sand or some other insulating material, or allowing it to cool in a furnace after shutting the furnace off. Annealing is used to completely soften steel, relieve internal stresses due to previous heat treatment or mechanical working, and refine the grain. Normalizing is similar to annealing, except that the metal is allowed to cool down from above the critical temperature by leaving it in the air. The resultant metal is softened enough for machining and stress relief.

Manufacture of Ferrous Metals — It may prove helpful to individuals working with metals to have some knowledge of the manufacturing processes used in producing them.

Iron is not found in the free state (except as meteoric iron), but is combined with other elements as an ore. The ore when removed from the mine is mixed

Figure 10. A view of an open-pit iron-ore mine of U.S. Steel's Oliver Iron Mining Company, at Hibbing, Minnesota.

Figure 11. This iron-ore carrier is shown being loaded at an upper lake port.

with dirt and impurities. Iron ore has the appearance of ordinary reddish soil. Some iron ores are found in surface veins and are mined from open-pit mines after the overburden of soil and rock has been stripped off. Deeper veins are mined by underground methods. The iron ore from the Mesabi Range in northern Minnesota is loaded on railroad cars at the mine and transported to lake ports, where it is loaded on boats and shipped through the Great Lakes to blast furnace locations. The blast furnace reduces the ore to the pig iron necessary in the later processes to manufacture cast iron and steel.

The high-grade iron ores from the Mesabi Range had been the primary U.S. sources of iron for many years. These mines are rapidly becoming depleted, so a lower grade of ore, taconite, has become a major source. The taconite is crushed and concentrated magnetically. The concentrate is then pelletized, which results in a product that is better for blast-furnace use than the former high-grade ores.

The raw materials used in the blast furnace are iron ore, limestone, and coke. These materials are carefully weighed and charged by layers into the blast furnace. Iron ore as mined is high in iron oxides. The coke, derived from soft coal, provides heat and reduces the iron oxides to iron. Limestone forms a flux that unites with the nonmetallic content of the ore and forms a slag. Hot air is blown through the bottom of the blast furnace to intensify the heat of the burning coke. When the heating action has been completed, molten slag floats to the top and molten iron settles to the bottom of the furnace (Figure 12). The iron is tapped off and either transferred to the steel mill for immediate further processing, or poured into molds where it is left to chill and form "pigs" to be used at a later date or at another furnace location. The blast furnace process is continuous. As each layer of coke and limestone is consumed while reducing the layer of iron ore above it into molten metal, other layers follow into the smelting zone and more are charged into the top of the furnace.

Gray Cast Iron — The properties of gray cast iron, such as low cost, ease of machining, casting to shapes, and high compressive strength have long made it an important metal in machine construction, in spite of its low tensile strength of 18,000 to 30,000 psi (mild steel is about 65,000 psi). Cast iron is not a pure metal but a mixture of iron, carbon, silicon, manganese, sulphur, and phosphorus. Different foundries will vary these elements to obtain a casting suitable for

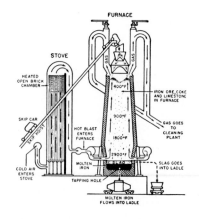

Figure 12. A view and cross-sectional diagram of a blast furnace. The "blast" comes in the form of heated air from stoves, the dome-shaped structures to the left of the furnace.

Fracture	Spark Test
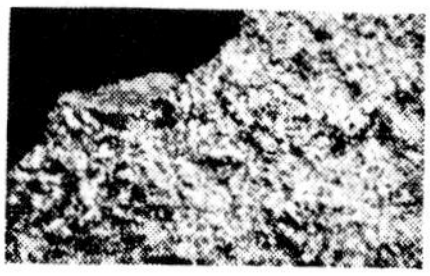	**Gray Cast Iron**
	} Color-red
	Color - straw yellow
Dark gray color rubs off black.	Average stream length with power grinder - 25 in.
Surface Appearance	Volume - small
Evidences of sand mold. Color, dark gray.	Many sprigs, small and repeating

Figure 13. Identification characteristics of gray cast iron.

Fracture	Spark Test
	White Cast Iron
	} Color-red
Very fine silvery white crystalline formation.	Color - straw yellow
Surface appearance	Average stream length with power grinder-20 in.
Evidences of sand mold. Color, dark gray.	Volume - very small
	Sprigs-finer than gray iron, small and repeating

Figure 14. Identification characteristics of white cast iron.

their particular product. Cast iron has a much higher carbon and silicon content than steel.

Cast iron is produced by melting a charge of pig iron and scrap steel with the necessary alloying ingredients in a cupola (similar to a small blast furnace) with limestone for a fluxing agent and coke for fuel. Cast irons may also be melted in an electric-arc furnace. Molten cast iron is poured into sand molds. Cover plates, gears, bases, brackets, and machinery housings are a few uses of gray cast iron. Gray iron is allowed to cool slowly in the mold. During this cooling period carbon separates from the iron in the form of tiny graphite flakes. It is this graphite that gives the casting its grayish appearance. The graphite provides sufficient lubrication so that gray cast iron may be drilled and machined dry without cutting oil.

Gray cast iron is very low in ductility and malleability, that is, it will not stretch or distort. Welding heat causes expansion and contraction forces that may result in excessive stress or fractures. The weldor must give special consideration to these factors when welding gray-iron castings.

Machinable and nonmachinable-type electrodes have been developed for use with arc-welding equipment. The machinable-type electrode is nickel or a high nickel alloy. The weld deposit is soft and easily machined, having characteristics similar to the metal in the casting. A low current setting is used to weld cast iron to reduce the fractures that result from heat stresses. This type electrode is used extensively for repairing broken parts, filling up defects in castings, repairing machining errors, building up worn parts, and filling holes that must be drilled and tapped. The nonmachinable electrode is a low-carbon steel electrode with a special covering for cast iron. It may be ground to shape. The skin of the casting, formed by the sand mold, should be ground off in the weld area, exposing clean metal.

Bronze welding may be used to weld gray cast iron, using either the carbon-arc or the oxyacetylene torch. In most cases, the casting will have to be preheated to prevent localized stresses. The weld area must be brought to a red heat so that the bronze flux and rod will flow and "tin" the surface.

White Cast Iron — This is also known as "chilled" cast iron, due to its method of manufacture. It is produced in the same manner as gray cast iron, except that the molten metal is cooled rapidly in the mold. In some cases the iron and carbon content may be varied to assist in making white cast iron. The sudden cooling or correct balance between iron and carbon causes the carbon to remain in combination with iron instead of separating in a graphitic form. This results in a metal that is harder and more brittle, a fact that must be kept in mind when white cast iron is welded. Due to its brittleness, white cast is not used extensively in machinery, except for parts that require a wearing surface that will withstand abrasion. A white cast-iron surface is sometimes put on a gray-iron casting by chilling the surface of a heavier casting. This gives a more abrasion-resistant surface. Although it can be repaired by arc welding under special conditions, the repair of white cast iron by the welding process is not recommended. Heating and cooling during the welding process tend to change the characteristics of the metal in the weld area. Generally, the type of part made of white cast iron is not worth repairing when it is broken or worn out.

Malleable Iron — Many uses have been made of malleable iron castings in the production of machinery during the last century. It is much more impact-resistant than gray iron and will withstand some bending without breaking. Its tensile strength ranges from 38,000 to 55,000 psi.

Malleable-iron castings are manufactured by further processing hard, brittle white cast iron. These white-iron castings are packed in annealing boxes buried

Fracture	Spark Test
	Malleable Iron
	Color – straw yellow
Color, dark gray except for light outer layer.	Average stream length with power grinder – 30 in.
	Volume-moderate
Surface appearance Evidences of sand mold. Color, dark gray.	Longer shafts than gray iron ending in numerous small, repeating sprigs

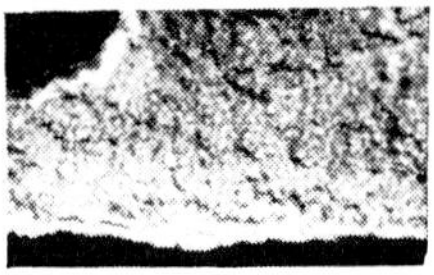

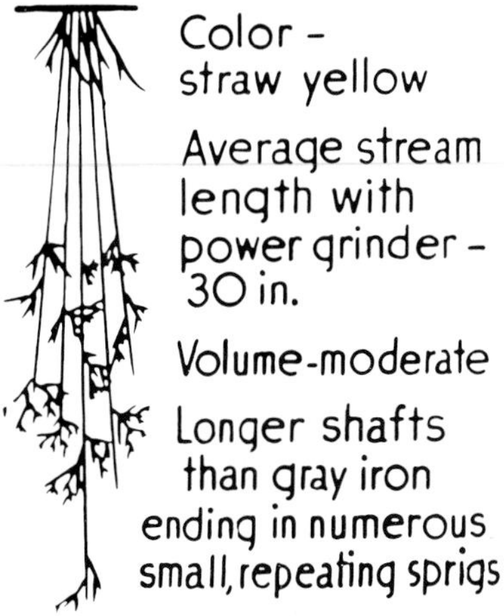

Figure 15. Identification characteristics of malleable cast iron.

in furnace slag, mill scale, or sand and annealed in a furnace at a temperature of about 1600 degrees F for a period of 40 to 60 hours. The temperature is lowered slowly to room temperature. After this operation, the castings are cleaned by blasting or tumbling. The weldor must understand that there is a critical temperature when white cast changes to malleable. Whenever malleable iron is heated above this critical temperature (1325 degrees F), the metal reverts to one having some of the original characteristics of white cast. Since the desirable physical properties of malleable iron are dependent upon the heat treatment or malleable-izing process, heat from fusion welding has a tendency to change the physical properties of the metal unless the critical temperature is observed. The following two methods are commonly used to repair broken malleable parts.

Bronze welding has been one of the standard methods of repairing malleable iron parts. This application is made with either the oxyacetylene or carbon-arc torch. The fracture is veed out if the base metal is 3/16″ or thicker. The metal is heated to a dull red color, and a brazing flux is applied with the bronze rod to "tin" the surface. Additional bronze is applied to build the joint up to the desired height.

Arc welding with nickel-type electrodes is also used on malleable castings. These electrodes give a machinable deposit. The temperature is kept low enough so that the hand can be placed on the casting after each pass. It is important not to overheat the casting to prevent it from reaching the temperature where stresses are developed. This makes the electric-arc process ideal for this metal, as the arc heat is concentrated, the puddle is instantaneous, and the filler metal may be deposited quickly and the heat removed. Little difficulty is encountered at the hard fusion zone, which forms at the line where the alloy electrode deposit and casting join. Postheating is applied to provide an annealing action to the casting if the weldor believes that the critical temperature of the metal has been reached.

Special Cast Irons — In an effort to overcome the disadvantages of low-tensile strength and impact resistance, many types of cast irons have been tried. Alloy gray castings are coming in for more frequent use. These castings contain the basic elements of gray iron, with the addition of nickel, chromium, molybdenum, and vanadium being the most common alloying elements. The alloys raise the tensile strength up to the 40,000 to 60,000-psi range, and increase the price of the casting two to five times over gray iron.

With the addition of special alloys and mixtures, a change may be effected in the form of the carbon within the casting. Instead of being in flake form, as in gray cast iron, the carbon is in small spheres with the iron. This is called "ductile iron" or "nodular cast iron". The resultant castings are nearly comparable in tensile strength with alloy steels, and possess even higher impact resistance. The term "semi-steel" is also used for these castings.

These castings will not be encountered too often. Special alloy electrodes are available for welding them. Repairs may usually be made using the nickel electrode, although the strength of the weld may not be as high as the base metal. The same care should be exercised as when working on gray iron.

Wrought Iron — Wrought iron is the oldest form of structural ferrous metal, and is made from pig iron, iron oxide, and silica. Modern manufacturing processes mix and work these ingredients together. After the pig iron has been melted and purified, it is carried to the processing machine, where the molten pig iron is poured into a ladle that contains a predetermined amount of silicate slag. A reaction takes place between the slag and molten metal, and the resulting

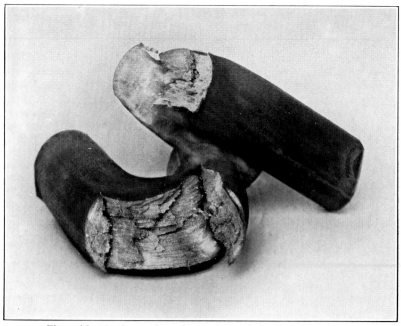

Figure 16. A broken surface of wrought iron has a fibrous appearance.

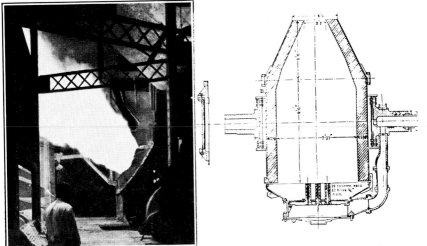

Figure 17. Bessemer converter furnace. Liquid pig iron is poured into the mouth of the converter while it is turned on its side. An air blast is blown through holes in the bottom when the converter is turned in upright position. The oxygen burns out impurities. Flames and sparks belch forth from the mouth of the converter, producing the spectacular sights of a steel mill.

product is a sponge-like ball or mass of metal. This sponge-like mass is then worked in a heavy press. The action of the press removes the surplus slag and welds the various particles of slag-coated plastic iron into a solid bar or "bloom". This bloom is rolled into plates, sheets, or bars, depending upon the use to be made of the metal. When wrought iron is bent so the surface is fractured, it appears to have many fibers running the length of the stock.

The chief advantages of wrought iron are its corrosion resistance and its ability to resist breakage when exposed to sudden or excessive shock. Its corrosion resistance is attributed to the pure iron that is used as a base metal and the presence of glass-like fibers embedded in the metal.

The arc-welding procedures used when welding wrought iron are similar to those followed when welding mild steel. A mild-steel electrode, such as the E6013, will give satisfactory results. The speed of travel is reduced slightly in order to keep a molten pool of metal in the crater for a longer period of time. This permits the excess slag present in the base metal to flow out on top of the bead. A slightly lower current is used to provide only sufficient penetration to bond the weld and base metal. Excessive penetration results in freeing large amounts of slag present in the base metal. A minimum amount of base metal should be removed during the joint preparation, so that additional filler metal is kept to a minimum.

Steel — Carbon steel is a mixture of iron and carbon with inherent small amounts of manganese, sulphur, and phosphorus. Over 99 per cent of carbon steel may be iron. The carbon content varies from 0.05 per cent to 1.5 per cent. The amount of carbon, while relatively small, has a very important part in determining the property of the metal. Steel differs from gray cast iron in that the carbon in the steel is all in a chemical combination with the iron and none exists in the free state. Other alloying elements that are sometimes added, depending upon the use to be made of the steel, are manganese, nickel, chromium, and molybdenum. These alloys provide additional strength and impact resistance. The steels are usually termed "low-alloy" or "high-tensile", and are used where extra strength is needed. They may be welded with special high-tensile electrodes for maximum weld strength. Mild-steel electrodes will join them, but the weld tends to be a lower tensile strength than the base metal.

Pig iron, the raw product turned out of the blast furnace, is used as one of the ingredients in the manufacture of steel. Large quantities of scrap steel may also be used in the manufacturing process. The first step in steel making is the removal of impurities in the pig iron by the process of oxidation. The most common steel-making processes are the basic oxygen furnace, electric-arc furnace, Bessemer converter and open-hearth furnace.

Steel-Making Processes — In the Bessemer process, molten pig iron is refined by blowing unheated air through the furnace. The Bessemer converter, named after an Englishman who developed it, is an egg-shaped vessel having a capacity of 15 to 25 tons of metal (Figure 17). Heat is generated from oxidation of the impurities in the charge. The blowing of the charge causes an intense heat in the mouth of the converter reducing the silicon, manganese, and carbon content. Blowing continues until the correct chemical content is reached. The furnace is then tipped forward, and the charge is poured off. This process cannot produce a steel as closely controlled in composition as other methods of refining.

The open-hearth process uses a larger saucer-like hearth to hold the charge of pig iron (solid or molten), scrap steel, and limestone (Figure 18). It is this furnace that makes use of the tons of scrap iron collected through salvage yards. Heat is supplied by preheated gas and air. The charge is heated from 6 to 14 hours. Carbon, manganese, and other elements are added during the heat. The slow heating procedure increases the possibility of controlling the refining action, and samples are taken and tested on the spot during the heat. Many

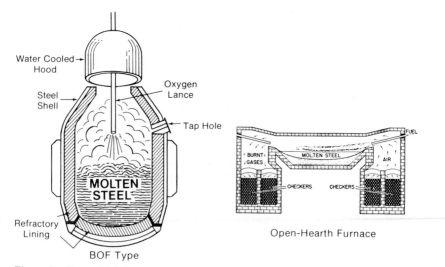

Figure 18. Two widely used steel making processes: The Basic Oxygen Furnace, which is becoming more and more popular, and the Open-Hearth Furnace. The BOF can produce steel at a much faster rate.

DIAGRAM OF
ELECTRIC FURNACE

ELECTRODES

TILTED POSITION
FOR TAPPING FURNACE

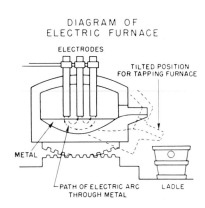

METAL

PATH OF ELECTRIC ARC
THROUGH METAL

LADLE

Figure 19. Electric furnace. The entire furnace tilts forward to spill its molten load into the ladle. Note at the top of the furnace the three carbon electrodes that furnish the intense heat.

Figure 20. Tapping a 30-ton heat of alloy steel made with the electric furnace. Impurities are removed and alloying elements added at different stages during the heating process.

different grades and qualities of steels are made by this process.

The technology for making pure oxygen has advanced so that now large quantities can be made at a low cost. This has led to the use of oxygen in the manufacture of steel and the basic oxygen furnace process, commonly referred to as the BOF process. This is the most common steel making process today.

Scrap steel and molten iron from the blast furnace are charged into a vessel. An oxygen lance is lowered into the vessel so that a stream of pure oxygen can be blown directly on the surface of the slag of the molten bath. This agitates the bath and oxidizes the slag, which in turn transfers the oxygen to the molten iron. Reactions take place that quickly refine the molten iron to a low-carbon steel. The time required to complete the refining is only a fraction of the time required by the open-hearth process, and the quality of the steel is comparable. The success of the process depends on a large supply of low-cost oxygen, so the oxygen-processing facility is built on the site of the steel mill. (Figure 18.)

The electric-arc furnace is used primarily in the manufacture of special steels. The heat for the electric-arc process is supplied through the use of three large carbon electrodes placed in the chamber, which has been charged with graded scrap steel, pig iron, alloys, and fluxing materials (Figure 19). Heat is generated by the flow of electricity, and purification of the metal is brought about through the action of iron oxide and flux. The process works quickly and its popularity is also increasing.

Cast Steel — Cast-steel machinery parts are formed by pouring molten steel into molds similar to those used in making gray-iron castings. When the metal solidifies it is the desired shape and further forming is not necessary. The exterior surface of a steel casting resembles gray cast iron; however, this is the extent of the similarity. Cast steel, as compared to cast iron, is more ductile and has fine grain structure after proper heat treatment. A fracture shows its color as bright gray, rather than dark gray as in the cast iron.

Figure 21. Steel ingots are reheated in the soaking pit in preparation for rolling. The hot ingots are first rolled in the blooming mill to reduce them to desired size.

Techniques followed when welding cast steel are similar to those used when welding mild steel in structural shapes. Carbon in steel castings generally runs around 0.3 per cent, although steel castings may be made with various carbon contents, as well as with alloy steels. No special precautions are needed when welding cast steel unless the carbon content is high or it is an alloy steel. The spark test should be used to determine what type of steel has been used in the casting. If the part has a high-carbon content, preheat to control localized heating and rate of cooling. The sand mold edge or casting skin is removed as recommended for cast iron. Parts are not to be overheated when welded. It is a good plan to cool parts slowly after welding and protect them from drafts. If underbead cracking results after a pass has been run, this is an indication that the carbon content is high. More satisfactory results are obtained if low-hydrogen electrodes are used.

Steel Forgings — Forgings are steel that is worked hot or rolled. Many common machinery parts are made by the "drop-forging" process. A large hammer, operated by steam, air, hydraulic, mechanical force, or gravity, is "dropped" down on a piece of hot steel that has been placed on a die. The force of the hammer forms the part. Examples of forged parts are ball-peen hammers, pliers and wrenches, rock guards for a mower, and mower knife heads. Most of these parts are made by the "closed die" method for maximum accuracy. The characteristics that help the weldor distinguish forged parts from castings were discussed in a previous paragraph. Forgings are used for pieces that are expected to have a rather high strength and withstand shock and vibration. This calls for medium-carbon steels, in some instances high-carbon and alloy steels.

Hot and Cold-Rolled Steel — Large chunks of steel, called "billets", are heated and rolled into various shapes such as squares, angles, channels, flats, etc. Many different types of rollers and hydraulic presses are used for these processes. Hot-rolled steel is usually identified by the black oxide on the surface. This is due to the formation of oxides as the metal is exposed to the air at a red

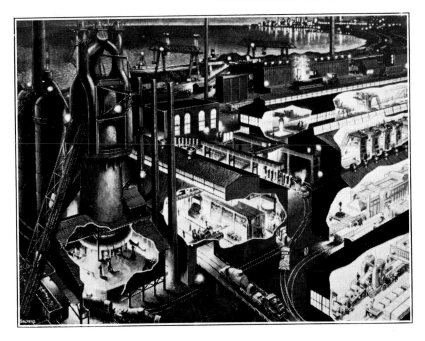

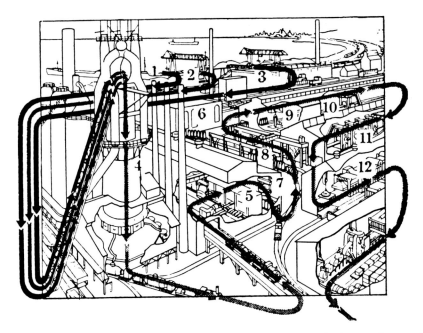

Figure 22. A cut-away and cross-sectional diagram showing the steps in the manufacture of steel in a steel mill.

heat. Hot-rolled stock is usually slightly lower in price than cold-rolled shapes, although the carbon content may be the same.

Spark Test Characteristics

Low-Carbon Steel*	High-Carbon Steel	Alloy Steel**
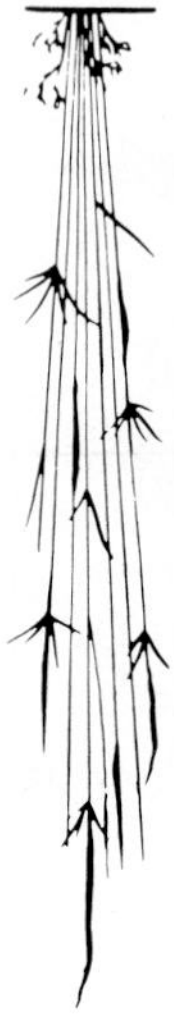 Color-white Average length of stream with power grinder - 70 in. Volume - moderately large Shafts shorter than wrought iron and in forks and appendages Forks become more numerous and sprigs appear as carbon content increases	 Color-white Average stream length with power grinder - 55 in. Volume - large Numerous small and repeating sprigs	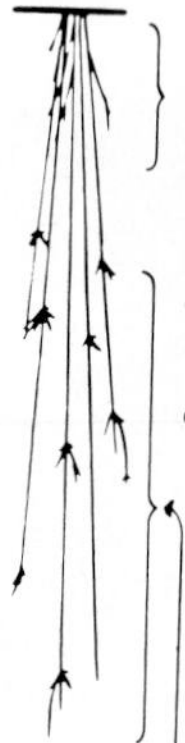 Color - straw yellow Stream length varies with type and amount of alloy content Shafts may end in forks, buds or arrows, frequently with break between shaft and arrow. Few, if any, sprigs Color - white
Fracture Bright gray	**Fracture** Light gray	**Fracture** Medium gray
Surface Appearance Dark gray—rolling or forging marks are present. Evidence of sand mold on cast steel.	**Surface Appearance** Dark gray—rolling or forging lines may be noticeable.	**Surface Appearance** Dark gray—smooth.

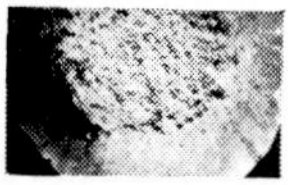

*These sparks also apply to cast steel.
**Spark shown is used to identify stainless steel.

Figure 23. Identification characteristics used to determine low-carbon, high-carbon, and alloy steel. The spark test is used to distinguish types of steel. An increase in carbon content results in a short spark with luminous bursts. The addition of alloying elements tends to suppress the spark bursts given off from alloy steel.

Figure 24. Hot plastic steel is passed between two horizontal rolls to reduce size and to shape the steel to the desired type, such as angle, channels and "I" beams.

Cold-rolled steel is produced by descaling hot-rolled steel in an acid pickling solution. The steel is then passed through several sets of rolls or drawn through dies while cold. Cold-rolled metal is used whenever close tolerances or metals of smooth finish are needed. Cold-rolled metals have a surface that is harder and smoother than hot-rolled stock, due to the cold-working.

Classification of Steel for Construction Purposes — Weldors and operators of welding and metalworking shops use new stock in steel construction and repair operations. It is necessary to order or keep a supply of commonly used types of steel on hand for use as the need arises. Classifications and size specifications

Figure 25. A hot-rolled strip runs swiftly down the runout table. The strip is immersed in a pickling tank containing hot sulphuric acid to remove the oxide scale, after which it is cold-rolled to convert the hot-rolled strip into a smooth-surface, cold-rolled sheet of steel.

must be designated correctly for the various shapes when placing orders to insure correct stock. Manufacturers of steel and distributors can supply catalogs of available stock. Stock sizes, together with weight per foot, classifications, alloy contents, working qualities, and heat treatment may also be listed in these catalogs. It makes a helpful reference for anyone using steels.

The American Society for Testing and Materials writes specifications for steels used in a wide area of construction and manufacturing. ASTM Standards, Part 1 contains specifications for steel tubing, piping and fittings. Part 3 covers sheet steel, strip, bar, wire, chain, and spring. Construction steels, reinforcing bars, pressure vessls, and rails and steel forgings are specified in Part 4.

The Society of Automotive Engineers (SAE) has set up a 4-digit (sometimes 5) number classification for SAE steels. The first digit of the number refers to the type or alloy category of the steel: 1, carbon steels; 2, nickel steels; 3, nickel-chromium; 4, molybdenum; 5, chromium; 6, chrome-vanadium, etc. The second digit refers to the series within that category, and the last two digits tell the average carbon content in points (.01%). The classification numbers may or may not have prefix letters designating the melting process used for the steel, such as "C" for basic open-hearth carbon, or "A" for basic open-hearth alloy. These were set up by the American Iron and Steel Institute (AISI).

A common type of steel used for general repair and construction work is the C1020. One could specify this steel when ordering angles or flat stock and know that he would get: C, a basic open-hearth carbon steel; 1, within the carbon-steel category; 0, plain carbon steel containing no important alloys; 20, having 18 to 23 points (.18-.23%) of carbon. For forging a chisel or punch, a steel classified as C1085 might be used.

Steel is sold on a per-hundred-weight basis. It may also be ordered by the running foot, however, the cost is usually billed for weight. The stock lengths of angles, rounds, and bars are standardized at 16, 18, and 20 feet. Extra charge is made when stock is cut to special lengths.

Method of Estimating Weight Per Foot of Steel

Welding operators need to know the weight per foot in estimating costs of contruction jobs or selling prices of finished projects. The following procedure uses a formula as a method of estimating weight per foot, which can be used when charts are not available. All that is necessary is to multiply thickness times width times 10 and divide by 3. The operator will have to substitute size of stock into formula. Sample problems follow:

Sample Problem: Flat plate (48" wide, 96" long, 1/4" thick)

Thickness (1/4") x Width (48") = 12 square inches.

12 square inches x 10 = 120

120 ÷ 3 = 40 (pounds per linear foot of plate)

40 pounds x 8 feet (length of plate) = 320 pounds (approximate weight of plate)

Sample Problem: Flat bar iron (1/4" thick, 2" wide)

Thickness (1/4") x width (2") = .5 square inch

.5 square inch x 10 = 5.0

5 ÷ 3 = 1.6 pounds (approximate weight of bar per linear foot)

Sample Problem: Angle (width 1", width 1", thickness 3/16")

Consider one flange 1" long and the other 13/16" long. Add the two flanges (1" + 13/16" = 1-13/16") and solve the problem as if it were a flat bar.

1-13/16" x thickness (3/16") = .34 square inch

.34 x 10 = 3.4

3.4 ÷ 3 = 1.13 pounds (approximate weight per linear foot)

Sketches illustrating commonly used steel stock are shown. Methods of designating stock sizes accompany each type of steel stock.

Bars (Square)	Size Specifications (thickness x width)

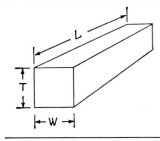

W = Width

T = Thickness
1/4" to 2-3/4", in graduations of 1/16" and 1/8".

L = Length — 16', 20', 36'.

Flats (Hot and Cold-Rolled)	Size Specifications (thickness x width)

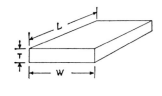

T = Thickness
1/4" to 1/2" in graduations of 1/16".
1/2" to 1-1/4" in graduations of 1/8".
1-1/4" to 2' in graduations of 1/4".
(3/16" and lighter, see Strips)

W = Width — 3/8" to 6" in graduations of 1/8" to 1/4".

L = Length — 16', 36'.

H Beams (Structural)	Size Specifications (height and width of beam)

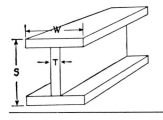

S = Size — 3", 4", 6" and larger.

W = Width of flange.

T = Thickness of web.

L = Length — 5' to 60'.

Strips (Hot-Rolled) **(3/16″ or less in thickness)**	**Size Specifications** **(thickness x width)**

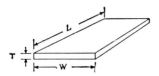

T = Thickness — (thickness measurement expressed in fractions of an inch and gauge number).
3/16″ (.1875″)
No. 10 (.134″); 1/8″ (.125″);
No. 12 (.109″); No. 14 (.083″);
No. 16 (.065″); No. 18 (.049″);
No. 20 (.035″); No. 22 (.028″).

W = Width
3/8″ to 2″ in graduations of 1/8″.
2″ to 3-1/2″ in graduations of 1/4″.
3-1/2″ to 6″ in graduations of 1/2″.
6″ to 12″ in graduations of 1″.

L = Length — 14′ to 16′.

Sheets (Hot and Cold-Rolled)	**Size Specifications** **Rolled steel 3/16″ or less is classified as sheet;** **over 3/16″, plate.**

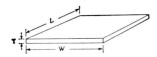

F = Thickness — 3/16″ and less expressed according to gauge number.
3/16″
No. 8 (.1644″);   No. 10 (.1345″);
No. 11 (.1196″);   No. 12 (.1046″);
No. 14 (.0747″);   No. 16 (.0598″);
No. 18 (.0478″);   No. 20 (.0359″);
No. 22 (.0299″);   No. 24 (.0239″);
No. 26 (.0179″);   No. 28 (.0149″).

W = Width — measurements given in inches —
30″, 36″, 42″, 48″, 54″, 60″, 72″, 84″.

L = Length — measurements given in inches —
96″, 120″, 144″, 156″, 240″.

Angles (Bar and Structural)

**Size Specifications
(width x width x thickness)**

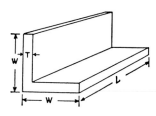

W = Width
1/2" to 1-1/2" in graduations of 1/8" of flange.
1-1/2" to 2-1/2" in graduations of 1/4".
3" and over structural steel.

T = Thickness of flange 1/8" to 1/2" in graduations of 1/16".

Angle stock is manufactured in unequal width of flanges, example: 2-1/2" x 1-1/2".

L = Length — 16', 18', 20'.

Tees (Bar and Structural)

**Size Specifications
(flange width x stem x thickness)**

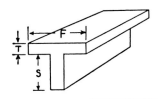

F = Flange width
3/4" to 2-1/2" in graduations of 1/4".

S = Stem width
3/4" to 2-1/2" in graduations of 1/4".

T = Thickness
1/8" to 3/8" in graduations of 1/16".

I Beams (Structural)

**Size Specifications
(height and width of beam)**

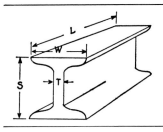

S = Size
4 x 4
5 x 5
6 x 6

W = Width of flange — same as S

T = Thickness of web.

L = 5' to 60'.

Channels — Bar Size

**Size Specifications
(depth x width of flange x thickness of web)**

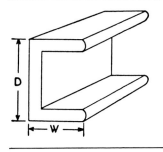

D = Depth
1/2" to 3/4" in graduations of 1/16".
3/8" to 1-1/4" in graduations of 1/8".
1-1/4" to 2 " in graduations of 1/4".

W = Width (of flange) —
164, 5/16, 3/8, 6

W = Width (of flange) —
1/4", 5/16", 3/8", 7/16", 1/2", 9/16", 3/4", 1".

T = Thickness of web — 1/8", 3/16", 1/4".

Channels — Structural	Size Specifications (depth of channel)
	Common sizes are 3″, 4″, 5″, 6″, 7″, and 8″.

Half Ovals (Hot Rolled)	Size Specifications (thickness x width)

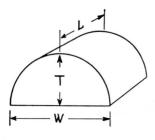

T = Thickness
3/8″ to 1/2″ in graduations of 1/16″.

W = Width
1/8″ to 1-1/4″ in graduations of 1/8″.
1-1/4″ to 2″ in graduations of 1/4″.
2″ to 3″ in graduations of 1/2″.

L = Length — 16′.

Rounds (Hot and Cold-Rolled)   **Size Specifications**

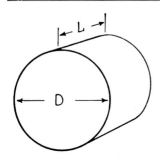

D = Diameter 3/8″ to 2″ or larger in graduation increases of 1/16″ and 1/8″.

L = Length — 16′, 18′ and 20′.

Many commercial users of welding are, at times, confronted with the problem of how to determine welding costs. A cost analysis may be required in advance of actual welding – in which case the results would constitute a cost estimate – or the cost analysis may be made after welding is in progress for various evaluation or management purposes. The reasons for costing welding are varied, but most often are to:

provide data needed for bidding on a job

compare the economics of welding with some other method of fabricating or manufacturing

establish information required in making a decision between alternate designs

evaluate proposed changes in procedures

compare the economic advantages of competing welding processes.

Students, designers, shop foremen, and others tend to be apprehensive about the task of cost estimation because of the many factors that must be taken into account and the possibility for errors. Also, the mathematical formulas that have been developed for cost determination look forbidding – even though they only involve simple arithmetic processes. It is the intent here to give practical methods for costing welding that can be applied by anyone and that will lead to usable results.

A word of caution, however, is desirable. Although the techniques for determining or estimating welding costs are sound and have been proved in practice, the results of an analysis will only be as good as the data inserted in the cost equations. Some of the data to be used will be dependent on the human factor; other data will be dependent upon corporate accounting practices. Where unrealistic figures are assigned – say, to welding speeds or to the operating factor – the cost formulas will give unrealistic results.

Rightfully, every operation made necessary by the decision to use welded assembly could be charged as a welding cost. Thus, the cost of joint preparation, such as cutting or machining, could be added to the cost of welding if these operations are not necessary for alternative fabrication methods. Similarly, the preweld and postweld cleaning and any preheating and postheating, straightening, or other operations made necessary by welding are part of the total costs of welding. However, these incidental consumers of time, materials, and power are often included in the operating factor assigned to welding if the weldor performs any of these operations. Some operations such as radiographic inspection, ultrasonic testing, and stress relieving are costed separately and are not included in the welding cost. Rather than get involved with complex cost equations of doubtful application to the accounting system of a company, the discussion here will be limited primarily to the cost of actually depositing weld metal.

Welding processes are fairly consistent. The time and material required to produce a certain length of weld by a given process on one job are good indications of the time and material required to produce the same type of weld on a similar job. Most of the methods described in this section make use of this fact; that is, they provide an estimate of costs by utilizing tables and curves obtained from welding experience. The methods presented, designed to determine costs from test welds, can be used where no prior figures are available, or where a particularly accurate forecast of costs is needed.

The Approach To Cost Calculations

The cost of producing a weld is basically the combined costs of material and labor. Material cost for shielded metal arc welding consists of the cost of the electrode. Labor costs include the normal costs of manpower, plus in most accounting systems, an allowance for overhead. Overhead may take care of many expenses not immediately apparent: the cost of supervision, janitorial and maintenance services, equipment amortization and repair, the cost of heating and lighting, and so on. The electric power costs directly required for welding are usually lumped in the overhead.

For convenience in welding cost computations, it is desirable to use a common reference for both material and labor. Both can conveniently be expressed in dollars per foot of weld.

Calculations Based On Handbook Data

The procedure tables of this text list the data needed for cost estimates for the more commonly used welds. The tables list: 1) Time required to produce a foot of the weld. 2) Amount of electrode consumed.

Cost computations for welds listed are simple and straightforward, because the basic information required can be selected directly from the procedures tables. The only other information required is the electrode cost per pound, determined by its cost when purchased; labor and overhead costs per hour, established by the company's accounting system; and an estimated operating factor. Costs can then be calculated by simple formulas.

Materials: The cost of electrode consumed per foot of weld is found by multiplying the weight of electrode in pounds consumed per linear foot by the electrode cost in dollars per pound.

Labor, Overhead, Operating Factor: Direct labor rates plus all overhead factors, as established by the individual company, may be represented by (CR) in dollars per hour. The labor and overhead cost per linear foot of weld (CL) then becomes:

$$\text{Time required per linear foot of weld} \times \frac{\text{Cost of labor and overhead, \$/hr}}{\text{Operating factor}}$$

The denominator is the operating factor, which needs explanation.

Actual arc time is considered only during the time the weldor is applying productive weld metal. While assembling, positioning, and tacking, the weldor is "preparing" to join. When removing an assembly from the positioner or cleaning a weld, he is executing necessary "follow-up" operations. When changing electrodes, moving from one location to another, or taking a coffee break, he is not joining. The total hours he works are always more than the hours he welds, and the ratio of the hours spent in welding to the total hours worked is known as the operating factor. This factor is one of the most basic factors in cost formulas, and must be determined accurately in order to make sound evaluations of costs.

The operating factor may be defined as:

$$\frac{\text{Arc Time}}{\text{Total Time}}$$

where total time is arc time plus the time the weldor spends in operations other than welding, including time for personal purposes. Since arc time is always divided by a larger number, the ratio is always less than 1.0, and thus a decimal. For convenience in referring to operation factors, the ratio is multiplied by 100 and expressed as a percentage. Thus, one speaks of an operating factor of 30, 40, or 50%. When using an operating factor in a cost formula, however, it must be kept in the decimal form. Thus, a 40% operating factor would be written .40 in a cost formula. Values for operating factor usually range from 0.2 to 0.6, but may be higher for automated welding or lower for construction field welding. However, the operating factor should be carefully determined since it has considerable bearing on the final estimated welding cost.

Multiplying the cost per linear foot by the number of feet of weld gives the calculated cost of welding. The accuracy of the value obtained will depend upon the accuracy of the factors used.

Calculations For Welds Not Listed

When the weld under consideration is not listed in a procedure table, the same cost equations apply, but the values for the weight of the electrode consumed per linear foot of weld and the time required per linear foot of weld must be determined by computation or by measurement from test welds. Other equations are required for such computations.

At this point, it becomes necessary to make a distinction between the weight of electrode consumed, and the weight of weld metal deposited. In most welding processes (the notable exception is the submerged-arc process), not all of the electrode ends up as a useful deposit of weld metal. Some is lost as spatter and vaporization, and a substantial portion of the weight of the electrode may be made up of materials for providing an arc shield and a protective slag. Consequently, the weight of electrode required to produce a given length of weld is usually greater than the weight of metal required for the weld.

The proportion of the electrode that ends up as weld metal, however, is fairly constant for each welding process, and the weight of electrode required can be calculated if the weight of weld metal is known. The weight of electrode can also be measured directly from a test weld, in which case a computation for the weight of the weld metal is not required.

A similar distinction must be made between the two quantities that can be used to compute welding time. One of these is the melt-off rate in pounds per hour at which the electrode is melted during welding. The other quantity is the deposition rate in pounds per hour at which weld metal is actually deposited. These two quantities usually differ for the same reason that the weight of electrode consumed does not necessarily equal the weight of weld metal deposited.

Direct Measurement of Electrode Consumption: The weight of electrode required can be determined from direct measurements (usually on test welds), either on the basis of weld length or time. If computations are being made on the basis of length (pounds per foot of weld), the measured weight of electrode consumed is divided by the length of the weld to provide a value for weight of electrode consumed per foot of weld.

Shielded metal arc welding electrode consumption is easily measured directly. The most common method is to weigh more than enough electrode to make the test weld. After completing the test weld, the unused electrode is weighed. The difference in weight, before and after, is the measured weight of the electrode consumed for the length of the test weld.

Making a test weld using less than one complete electrode usually is not accurate and is not recommended. However, if it is necessary to make a test weld using less than one length of electrode, the weight of the electrode consumed must be increased a proportional amount to include the stud-end loss. Stub ends are usually 1-1/2 to 3" long.

Calculating Electrode Consumption: Most methods of calculating weight of electrode consumed per foot of weld are based on an estimate of the weight of weld metal deposited. There are, in turn, several ways in which the weight of the metal deposited can be found. The most direct method is to select values from the included tables. If the weld is not listed in these tables or in the welding procedures, the weight of the metal deposited can be calculated from the volume of weld metal required for the given weld cross sectional area.

TABLE 1 — WEIGHT OF STEEL WELD METAL FOR FILLET JOINTS

Size of Fillet (in.)	Weight of Metal (lb/ft)		
	Flat	Convex	Concave
1/8	0.032	0.039	0.037
3/16	0.072	0.087	0.083
1/4	0.129	0.155	0.147
5/16	0.201	0.242	0.230
3/8	0.289	0.349	0.331
7/16	0.394	0.475	0.451
1/2	0.514	0.620	0.589
9/16	0.651	0.785	0.745
5/8	0.804	0.970	0.920
3/4	1.16	1.40	1.32
7/8	1.58	1.90	1.80
1	2.06	2.48	2.36
1-1/8	2.60	3.14	2.98
1-1/4	3.21	3.88	3.68
1-3/8	3.89	4.69	4.45
1-1/2	4.62	5.58	5.30
1-5/8	5.43	6.55	6.22
1-3/4	6.29	7.59	7.21
1-7/8	7.23	8.72	8.28
2	8.23	9.93	9.43

Note: Values are for leg size 10% oversize, consistent with normal shop practices.

After the weight of the deposited metal has been determined, the weight of the electrode consumed per foot of weld is calculated:

$$\frac{\text{Weight of deposited metal}}{\text{Deposition efficiency}}$$

TABLE 2 — WEIGHT OF STEEL WELD METAL FOR BUTT JOINTS

Joint Configuration			
Plate Thickness (in.)	Weight of Weld Metal (lb/ft)		
	Included Angle (deg)		
	60	20	20
1	1.81	2.24	1.82
1-1/8	2.17	2.61	2.17
1-1/4	2.61	2.99	2.52
1-3/8	3.09	3.37	2.88
1-1/2	3.57	3.76	3.27
1-5/8	4.12	4.18	3.65
1-3/4	4.67	4.59	4.05
2	5.93	5.44	4.87
2-1/8	6.58	5.88	5.28
2-1/4	7.32	6.34	5.72
2-3/8	8.05	6.80	6.16
2-1/2	8.87	7.28	6.63
2-5/8	9.67	7.76	7.10
2.3/4	10.5	8.26	7.75
3	12.4	9.27	8.55
3-1/8	13.3	9.80	8.90
3-1/4	14.5	10.3	9.40
3-1/2	16.5	11.2	10.6
3-3/4	18.8	12.5	11.6
4	21.2	13.7	12.9
4-1/2	26.4	16.2	15.2
5	32.3	18.8	17.8
5-1/2	38.7	21.6	20.5
6	45.7	24.6	23.4
6-1/2	53.3	27.8	26.4
7	61.4	30.4	29.6
7-1/2	70.0	34.3	32.9
8	79.5	37.9	36.4
9	99.9	45.5	43.9
10	122.6	53.8	52.0

Note: Reinforcement is +10% width of groove.

The deposition efficiency for shielded metal arc welding is typically 0.65. This factor compensates for the loss of material as slag, shielding gas, spatter, and stub ends.

Determining Weight of Weld Metals: Estimates of weld metal required to predict electrode consumption can be made by first finding the cross-sectional

TABLE 2 – WEIGHT OF STEEL WELD METAL FOR BUTT JOINTS (Cont'd.)

Plate Thickness (in.)	Weight of Weld Metal (lb/ft)		
	Included Angle (deg)		
	0	20	0
1		1.54	
1-1/8		1.89	
1-1/4		2.27	
1-3/8		2.65	
1-1/2		3.07	
1-5/8		3.50	
1-3/4		3.94	
2		4.91	
2-1/8		5.40	
2-1/4		5.94	
2-3/8		6.50	
2-1/2		7.06	
2-5/8		7.65	
2-3/4		8.25	
3		9.54	
3-1/8		10.2	10.2
3-1/4		10.8	10.8
3-1/2		12.3	12.1
3-3/4		13.8	13.3
4		15.4	14.7
4-1/2		18.9	17.2
5		22.6	19.8
5-1/2	20.4	26.7	22.3
6	23.0	31.0	25.0
6-1/2	25.4	35.6	27.0
7	28.1	40.5	30.1
7-1/2	30.6	46.0	32.8
8	33.3	51.7	35.3
9	38.4	63.9	40.4
10	43.5	77.4	45.6

area of the weld in square inches. This value is then multiplied by an appropriate conversion factor (3.4 for steels and 1.2 for aluminum) to determine weight of weld metal in pounds per linear foot of weld. The factor (3.4) is approximate for most alloy steels, including stainless steels.

Tabular data, such as found in the tables on page(s) 9.34 to 9.38, give weight of steel weld metal directly. Thus, Table 1 gives the weight of weld metal in pounds per foot for various sizes of flat, convex, and concave fillet welds. Table 2 gives similar values for weight of weld metal for commonly used butt joints.

A butt joint, however, may be shaped so the tabular data in Table 2 does not apply. In that case, Table 3 may be helpful. With its use, the weights of portions of the weld's cross section can be determined one by one, and those weights totaled to give the weight of weld metal in pounds per foot for that configuration of cross section. In Table 3, segments that can be scribed by straight lines through the cross section of the butt weld are indicated by drawings labeled A, B, C, and D in Figure 1. The values for the weight of the segments are read from the columns, using the applicable dimensions for (d) and (t) or the applicable included angle.

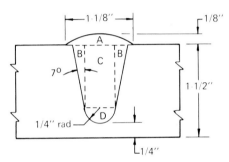

Figure 1. Weld cross section used to illustrate procedure for calculating weight of weld metal by Table 3.

For example, it is necessary to know the weight of weld metal per linear foot for the groove weld shown in Figure 1 in order to use that value in a cost equation. Divide the cross section into the A, B, C, and D segments illustrated by the dotted lines. These segments are shapes that match the shapes illustrated in Table 3. By using given dimensions for the weld and reading from the table, the weights of weld for the individual segments are determined. Thus —

Segment	Given Dimensions or Included Angle	Weight of Deposited Metal of Each Segment from Table 3 (lb/ft)
A	t = 1/8 in. d = 1-1/8 in.	0.318
B	included angle — 7° + 7° = 14° d = 1-1/2 − (1/4 + 1/4) = 1 in.	0.417
C	t = 1/4 + 1/4 = 1/2 in. d = 1-1/2 − (1/4 + 1/4) = 1 in.	1.700
D	r = 1/4 in.	0.334
TOTAL for the joint		2.769 lb/ft

TABLE 3 — WEIGHT OF STEEL WELD METAL FOR BUTT JOINT SEGMENTS (lb/ft)

Dimension d (in.)	Dimension t (in.)* 1/16	1/8	3/16	1/4	Included Angle, θ° 14	20	60	70	90	Dimension t (in.) 1/16	1/8	3/16	1/4	3/8	1/2	Dimension d (in.)
1/8	0.027				0.0065	0.0094	0.031	0.037	0.054	0.027	0.053	0.080	0.106	0.159	0.212	0.083
3/16	0.035				0.0147	0.021	0.069	0.084	0.120	0.040	0.080	0.119	0.159	0.239	0.318	0.188
1/4	0.044				0.026	0.037	0.123	0.149	0.212	0.053	0.106	0.159	0.212	0.318	0.425	0.334
5/16	0.053				0.041	0.059	0.192	0.232	0.332	0.066	0.133	0.199	0.265	0.390	0.531	0.531
3/8		0.106			0.059	0.084	0.276	0.334	0.478	0.080	0.159	0.239	0.318	0.478	0.637	0.750
7/16	0.062	0.124	0.186		0.080	0.115	0.376	0.456	0.652	0.091	0.186	0.279	0.371	0.557	0.743	1.02
1/2	0.071	0.142	0.212		0.104	0.150	0.491	0.595	0.850	0.106	0.212	0.318	0.425	0.637	0.849	1.33
9/16	0.080	0.159	0.239		0.132	0.190	0.621	0.753	1.08	0.119	0.239	0.358	0.478	0.716	0.955	
5/8	0.089	0.177	0.266		0.163	0.234	0.766	0.930	1.33	0.133	0.265	0.398	0.531	0.796	1.06	
11/16	0.097	0.195	0.292	0.389	0.197	0.283	0.927	1.13	1.61	0.146	0.292	0.438	0.584	0.876	1.17	
3/4	0.111	0.212	0.318	0.424	0.234	0.337	1.11	1.34	1.91	0.159	0.318	0.478	0.637	0.955	1.27	
13/16	0.124	0.230	0.345	0.460	0.275	0.396	1.30	1.57	2.24	0.172	0.345	0.517	0.690	1.04	1.38	
7/8	0.133	0.248	0.372	0.490	0.319	0.459	1.50	1.82	2.60	0.186	0.371	0.557	0.743	1.11	1.49	
15/16	0.142	0.266	0.398	0.530	0.367	0.527	1.73	2.07	3.00	0.199	0.398	0.597	0.796	1.19	1.59	
1		0.282	0.418	0.566	0.417	0.599	1.96	2.38	3.40	0.212	0.425	0.627	0.849	1.25	1.70	
1-1/16	0.150	0.301	0.451	0.602	0.471	0.676	2.22	2.68	3.84	0.226	0.451	0.677	0.902	1.35	1.80	
1-1/8	0.159	0.318	0.477	0.637	0.528	0.758	2.48	3.02	4.30	0.239	0.478	0.716	0.955	1.43	1.91	
1-3/16	0.168	0.336	0.505	0.672	0.588	0.845	2.77	3.36	4.80	0.252	0.504	0.756	1.01	1.51	2.02	
1-1/4	0.177	0.354	0.531	0.706	0.651	0.936	3.07	3.72	5.32	0.265	0.531	0.796	1.06	1.59	2.12	
1-5/16	0.186	0.372	0.557	0.743	0.718	1.03	3.38	4.10	5.86	0.279	0.557	0.836	1.11	1.67	2.23	
1-3/8	0.195	0.389	0.584	0.777	0.789	1.13	3.71	4.50	6.42	0.292	0.584	0.876	1.17	1.75	2.34	
1-7/16	0.203	0.407	0.610	0.814	0.836	1.24	4.05	4.91	7.02	0.305	0.610	0.915	1.22	1.83	2.44	
1-1/2	0.212	0.425	0.636	0.849	0.938	1.35	4.42	5.36	7.64	0.318	0.637	0.955	1.27	1.91	2.55	
1-9/16	0.221	0.442	0.664	0.884	1.02	1.46	4.79	5.81	8.30	0.332	0.664	0.995	1.33	1.99	2.65	
1-5/8	0.230	0.460	0.690	0.920	1.10	1.58	5.18	6.29	8.98	0.345	0.690	1.04	1.38	2.07	2.76	
1-11/16	0.239	0.477	0.716	0.956	1.19	1.71	5.59	6.80	9.68	0.358	0.716	1.07	1.43	2.15	2.87	
1-3/4	0.249	0.495	0.743	0.990	1.28	1.84	6.01	7.29	10.4	0.371	0.743	1.11	1.49	2.23	2.97	
1-13/16	0.257	0.513	0.770	1.03	1.37	1.97	6.45	7.81	11.1	0.385	0.769	1.15	1.54	2.31	3.08	
1-7/8	0.266	0.531	0.796	1.06	1.47	2.10	6.90	8.36	11.9	0.390	0.796	1.19	1.59	2.39	3.18	
1-15/16	0.274	0.549	0.823	1.10	1.56	2.25	7.36	8.94	12.8	0.411	0.822	1.23	1.65	2.47	3.29	
2	0.283	0.566	0.849	1.13	1.67	2.40	7.85	9.52	13.6	0.425	0.849	1.27	1.70	2.55	3.40	

Note 1: For 45° angle use one half of 90°.

*Reinforcement d is +10% the width of the groove.

Estimates of Welding Time: Values of welding time can be found by several methods. The estimate can be projected from a direct measurement of the time to deposit one foot of a test weld. Or, if the electrode type and welding current are known, the time can be calculated from the deposition rate. Deposition rates for the various types of shielded metal arc welding electrodes are given in Figure 2. When the weight of the weld metal can be selected from a table or computed from the cross-sectional area, then the welding time in hours per foot of weld can be computed from:

$$\frac{\text{Weight of the weld metal, pounds/ft}}{\text{Deposition rate, pounds/hr}}$$

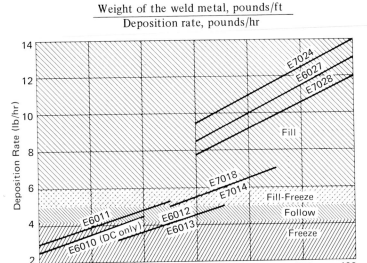

Figure 2. Deposition rates for various mild-steel electrodes.

Welding Procedures

All welding codes and specifications that cover critical work require the contractor to prepare a written procedure specification and demonstrate that the work done in conformance with that procedure will produce satisfactory joints. These procedures are used by the weldors and their supervisors and other authorized personnel such as inspectors.

Much of the welding being done does not require the high quality specified in the codes. For example, welds that need not be pressure-tight or welds subject to very low stress can tolerate some degree of defects and still be satisfactory. Even with this lower quality, welding should be documented. After a satisfactory end product has been produced the data should be recorded and filed for future use. This information is valuable if the same job or a similar job occurs at a later date.

For economical, high-speed welding of carbon-steel plate, the composition of the steel should be within the "preferred-analysis" ranges indicated in Table 4. If one or more elements varies from the ranges shown, cost-increasing methods are usually required to produce good welding results. Thus, steels within these ranges should be used whenever extensive welding is to be done unless their properties do not meet service requirements. Published welding procedures generally apply to normal welding conditions and to the more common

PREFERRED ANALYSES FOR STEELS TO BE ARC-WELDED

Element	Composition (%)	
	Preferred	High*
Carbon	0.06 to 0.25	0.35
Manganese	0.35 to 0.80	1.40
Silicon	0.10 or less	0.30
Sulfur	0.035 or less	0.05
Phosphorus	0.030 or less	0.04

*Additional care is required in welding of steels containing these amounts of the elements.

preferred-analysis mild steels. Low-hydrogen electrodes and processes will generally tolerate a wider range of the elements than shown in Table 4.

If the chemical specification of a steel falls outside of the preferred-analysis range, it is usually not necessary to use special welding procedures based on the extremes allowed by the specification. The chemistry of a given heat of steel, under average mill-production conditions, may be considerably below the top limits indicated in the specification. Thus, for maximum economy, welding procedures for any type of steel should be based on actual rather than allowed chemistry values. A mill test report* can be obtained that gives the analysis of a heat of steel. From this information, a welding procedure can be established that ensures production of quality welds at lowest possible cost.

The ideal welding procedure is the one that will produce acceptable quality welds at the lowest over-all cost. So many factors influence the optimum welding conditions that it is impossible to write procedures for each set of conditions. In selecting a procedure, the best approach is to study the conditions of the application and then choose the procedure that most nearly accommodates them. The procedures given here are typical, and it may be necessary to make adjustments for a particular application to produce a satisfactory weld.

Weldability of Material

Weldability of a steel has a considerable effect on the welding procedure. For some joints, more than one procedure is offered because of the marginal weldability of the steel.

Good weldability indicates a steel with a composition that is within the preferred range — one whose chemistry does not limit the welding speed.

Fair weldability indicates a steel with one or more elements outside the preferred range or one that contains one or more alloys. These steels require a lower welding speed or a mild preheat, or both, to minimize defects such as porosity, cracking, and undercut.

Poor weldability steels are those with compositions outside the preferred range, alloy additions, segregations, previous heat-treatment, or some other condition that makes them difficult to weld. These steels require still lower welding speeds, preheat, possibly a postheat, and careful electrode selection to obtain a satisfactory weld.

---

*A mill test report is usually based on a ladle analysis and is an average for an entire heat. Some low-carbon steels are rimmed steels, used because of their excellent forming and deep-drawing properties. The analysis of a rimmed steel varies from the first ingot to the last ingot of a single heat and also from the top to the bottom of a single ingot. Thus, a mill test report is an average and should be interpreted as such.

The addition of alloys to steel that enhance the mechanical properties or hardenability usually have an adverse effect on weldability.

Code-Quality Procedures

Code-quality procedures are intended to provide the highest level of quality and appearance. To accomplish this, conservative currents and travel speeds are recommended.

These procedures are aimed at producing welds that will meet the requirements of the commonly used codes: AWS Structural, AISC Buildings, ASME Pressure Vessels, AASHTO Bridges, and others. Code-quality welds are intended to be defect-free to the extent that they will measure up to the nondestructive testing requirements normally imposed by these codes. This implies crack-free, pressure-tight welds, with little or no porosity or undercut.

The specific requirements of codes are so numerous and varied that code-quality procedures may not satisfy every detail of a specific code. Procedure qualification tests are recommended to confirm the acceptability of chosen procedures.

All butt welds made to code quality are full-penetration; fillet welds are full-size, as required by most codes. (The theoretical throat, rather than the true throat, is used as the basis of calculating strength.)

Commercial-Quality Procedures

Commercial quality implies a level of quality and appearance that will meet the nominal requirements imposed on most of the welding done commercially. These welds will be pressure-tight and crack-free. They will have good appearance, and they will meet the normal strength requirements of the joint.

Procedures for commercial-quality welds are not as conservative as code-quality procedures; speeds and currents are generally higher. Welds made according to these procedures may have minor discontinuities that would be objectionable to the more demanding codes.

It is recommended that appropriate tests be performed to confirm the acceptability of the selected procedure for the application at hand prior to putting it into production.

Procedure Notes

The procedure data given will have been developed to provide the most economical procedures for various applications. In some cases, more than one type or size of electrode is recommended for the same joint. In small shops, electrode selection may depend on the available power source; consequently, some joints have procedures for either AC or DC welders.

With some joints, procedures for two different types of electrodes are given – for example, E7018 or E7028. This allows a choice of electrodes so the one with the better usability characteristics can be selected.

Any procedure for a poor or fair welding quality steel may be used on a steel of a better welding quality.

Travel speed is given as a range. The electrode required and the total time are based on the middle of the range.

Unless otherwise indicated, both members of the joint are the same thickness.

Pounds-of-electrode data include all ordinary deposition losses. These values are in terms of pounds of electrode needed to be purchased.

Total time is the arc time only and does not allow for operating factor.

After a satisfactory welding procedure has been established, all the data should be recorded and filed for future reference. This information is invaluable if the same job or a similar job occurs at a later date.

The presented procedures are offered as a starting point and may require changes to meet the requirements of specific applications. Because the many variables in design, fabrication, and erection or assembly affect the results obtained in applying this type of information, the serviceability of the product or structure is the responsibility of the builder.

Butt Weld Procedures

Square-Edge Butt Welds

For square-edge butt welds, the procedures can vary considerably the amount of penetration that will be obtained. Even a very shallow molten pool under the arc will form an insulating layer and absorb some of the penetrating power of the arc force. The molten pool under the arc also tends to cause the operator to raise the tip of the electrode to keep it out of the molten metal, and the resulting longer arc dissipates more of its heat into the air and, in flaring out, tends to widen the bead. The operator should, therefore, hold a short arc with the electrode at the proper angle. This will automatically tend to force the molten pool from under the electrode tip, especially when aided by rapid arc-travel speed. With the heavily covered electrodes recommended, the correct arc length will be obtained when the electrode is dragged along the joint with the covering touching the plates. See Figure 3.

Vee Butt Welds

For vee butt welds, still greater variation in penetration exists between slow and fast travel speeds. The penetration can be increased as much as 40% by proper speed and arc length as compared with a slow speed.

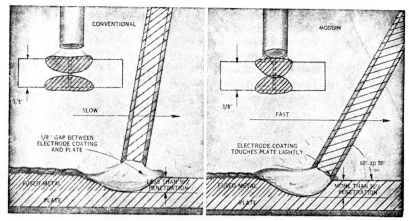

Figure 3. On square-edge butt welds made with an E6010-type electrode, high speed, with electrode covering dragging gives better penetration than long arc and slow speed.

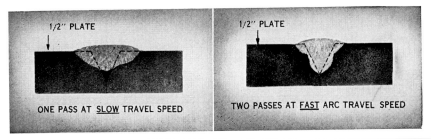

Figure 4. Two V-butt welds made at same current, the left-hand one run slowly in one pass, the right-hand one run in two fast passes.

Figure 4 shows two welds made at the same current, one run slowly in one pass and the other in two fast passes. By going slow and weaving, the molten metal and slag got under the arc and left an unpenetrated section at the root of the joint. By merely using faster arc-travel speed and keeping the molten pool from under the arc, this can be avoided. Notice the two pass weld has a larger throat and is stronger even though the arc time is approximately the same.

The tip of the electrode should be held down in the groove so that the covering touches both sides of the joint lightly. Travel as fast as possible on the first pass with good slag coverage. A slight undercut on any but the last pass will not be objectionable, as the succeeding passes will fill in the undercut.

For the last few passes on heavy plate with wide grooves, weaving is permissible, but is necessary only where fusion at both edges cannot be obtained with a straight bead. For multiple-pass butt welds, the surface will be much smoother if enough room is left on the next-to-last pass so that the last pass will be slightly above flush with the plate. This also assures the ideal cross section for the weld.

In General

(1) Use the electrode, plate preparation, and current recommended in procedures. (2) In welding first pass, hold the electrode as shown in Figure 3. The arc should be so short the covering drags lightly on the surface of the plates. In welding succeeding passes, hold a short arc, if desired, but dragging of covering is preferred. (3) Keep just ahead of the molten pool, traveling as fast as possible, still maintaining uniform slag coverage to assure good appearance and watching for undercut. Weaving is not recommended except on wide beads.

Selection of Joint — Flat Position

Four welding procedures are included for butt welds in the flat position. Factors that determine which procedure should be used include:
1. Plate thickness.
2. Equipment available for preparing and fitting up the edges of the joint.
3. Whether or not the joint can be welded from only one side:
    (a) With backup strip.
    (b) Without backup strip.

Wherever possible, it is recommended that the joint be welded from both sides, because the welding speeds generally are higher and the costs lower.

If the joint must be welded from one side, the procedure for welding on a backup strip is recommended, beacause less care is required for fitting-up and the welding speeds are higher than for joints without backup strip.

Fitup

In order to obtain maximum welding speeds, proper fitup is important. Except when the joint must be welded from one side only, a gap of 1/16" or less is recommended.

If the gap exceeds 1/16", one or more beads should be deposited with 3/16" electrode to seal the gap.

If the gap can be sealed with one pass, the welding time per foot of joint will be increased by 2 or 2-1/2 minutes above that required with a gap of 1/16" or less. Correspondingly more time will be required if more than one bead is necessary to seal the gap.

Edge Preparation for Single-V Butt Weld

The 1/8" root face is preferred to the feather edge from the standpoint of welding economy. Therefore, the procedures are based on the preparation with the 1/8" root face. If the feather-edge preparation is used, it is recommended that the first pass, or passes required to seal a gap, be welded at approximately 150 amperes with 5/32" E6011. For structural work, E7018 is often preferred over E6011.

Electrode

The electrodes recommended for butt joints welded in the flat position are indicated in tables for specific procedures.

Technique

When the joint preparation and fitup are as recommended, weld the first pass by dragging the tip of the covering in the groove and pointing the electrode as shown in Figure 3. The travel speed or arc speed should be governed to keep the electrode just ahead of the molten pool. A small ball of molten slag or metal rolling ahead of the electrode may be encountered, but will cause no difficulty.

When a sealing bead or beads must be run with E6010 or E6011, it may be necessary to whip the electrode back and forth along the seam to prevent burn-through.

Iron-Powder Technique – Iron-powder electrodes are contact electrodes, and the best results generally will be obtained by using this technique. However, if the slag follows too closely, as may be true in the case of initial passes on deep groove welds or under some arc-blow conditions, holding a very short arc will usually give better results.

To obtain the full advantage of this type electrode in deep-groove welding:
1. The weldment should be flat – not uphill or downhill.
2. Use recommended current, which is generally somewhat higher than with other types.
3. Travel should be such as to insure complete slag coverage.
4. Use contact technique – don't hold an arc.
5. Use stringer beads – don't use a wide weave.
6. Tilt the electrode in the direction of travel, as in Figure 3.
7. AC welding current is recommended – it will invariably produce the best results.
8. Because of the greater covering diameter and tendency for slag interference, it is generally necessary to use one size smaller than the conventional electrode.

This procedure will improve the cover-pass appearance with any electrode, but, with iron-powder electrodes, the results will be excellent — comparable to automatic welds.

Back gouging normally is not required to obtain a joint as strong as the plate when welding in flat position. If it is necessary to use currents lower than those recommended in the procedure pages for the 1st pass made on either side of the joint, back gouging is recommended. Currents lower than those recommended may be required by variation in fitup or where certain corrective measures must be used. When welding butt joints, if complete fusion is required, back gouging is recommended for all positions.

Back gouging may also be required because it is specified as part of a code requirement.

Position: Flat
Weld Quality Level: Code
Steel Weldability: Good
Welded From: One side

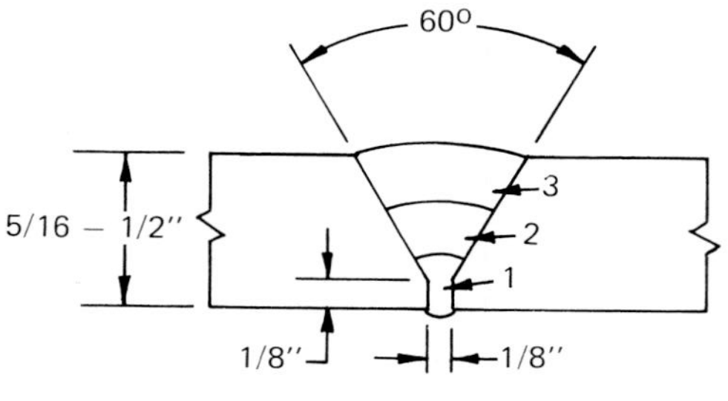

Plate Thickness (in.)	5/16		3/8		1/2		
Pass	1	2	1	2 & 3	1	2	3
Electrode Type	Fleetweld 35	Jetweld 2	Fleetweld 35	Jetweld 2	Fleetweld 35	Fleetweld 35	Jetweld 2
Size	5/32	5/32	5/32	5/32	5/32	1/4	1/4
Current (amp) AC	135	240	135	240	135	275	400
Arc Speed (in./min)	5.5-6.5	12.0-14.0	5.5-6.5	12.0-14.0	5.5-6.5	8.0-10.0	10.0-12.0
Electrode Req'd (lb/ft)	0.168	0.142	0.168	0.284	0.168	0.228	0.354
Total Time (hr/ft of weld)	0.0487		0.0641		0.0717		

Figure 5. Shielded Metal-Arc (Manual).

Position: Flat
Weld Quality Level: Code
Steel Weldability: Good
Welded From: One side

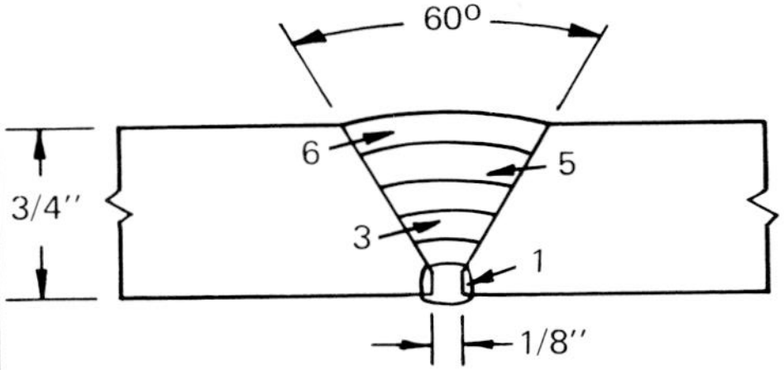

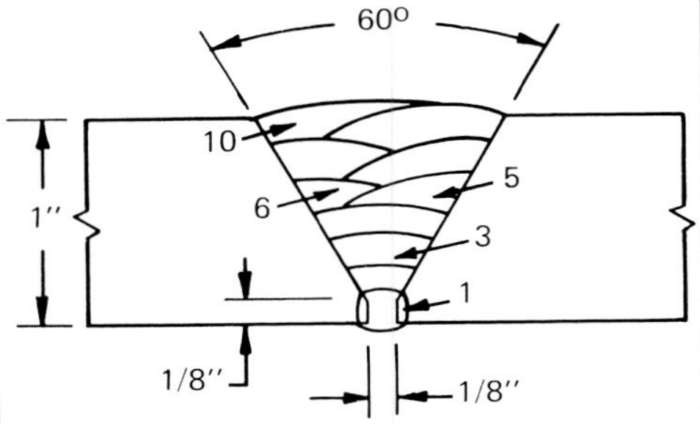

Plate Thickness (in.)	3/4			1		
Pass	1	2	3 – 6	1	2	3 – 10
Electrode Type	Fleetweld 35	Fleetweld 35	Jetweld 2	Fleetweld 35	Fleetweld 35	Jetweld 2
Size	5/32	1/4	1/4	5/32	1/4	1/4
Current (amp) AC	135	275	400	135	275	400
Arc Speed (in./min)	5.5 – 6.5	8.0 – 10.0	11.0 – 13.0	5.5 – 6.5	8.0 – 10.0	11.0 – 13.0
Electrode Req'd (lb/ft)	0.168	0.228	1.47	0.168	0.228	2.94
Total Time (hr/ft of weld)			0.122			0.189

Figure 6. Shielded Metal-Arc (Manual).

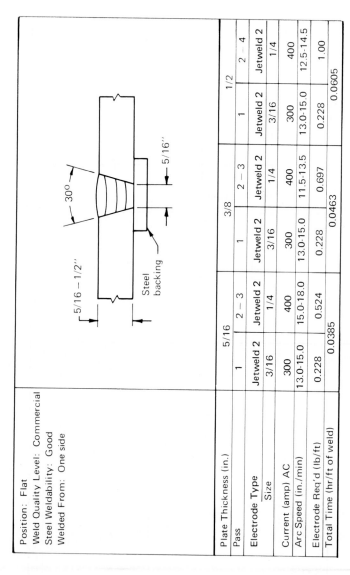

Position: Flat
Weld Quality Level: Commercial
Steel Weldability: Good
Welded From: One side

Plate Thickness (in.)	5/16		3/8		1/2	
Pass	1	2 – 3	1	2 – 3	1	2 – 4
Electrode Type	Jetweld 2	Jetweld 2	Jetweld 2	Jetweld 2	Jetweld 2	Jetweld 2
Size	3/16	1/4	3/16	1/4	3/16	1/4
Current (amp) AC	300	400	300	400	300	400
Arc Speed (in./min)	13.0-15.0	15.0-18.0	13.0-15.0	11.5-13.5	13.0-15.0	12.5-14.5
Electrode Req'd (lb/ft)	0.228	0.524	0.228	0.697	0.228	1.00
Total Time (hr/ft of weld)	0.0385		0.0463		0.0605	

Figure 7. Shielded Metal-Arc (Manual).

Position: Flat
Weld Quality Level: Commercial
Steel Weldability: Good
Welded From: One side

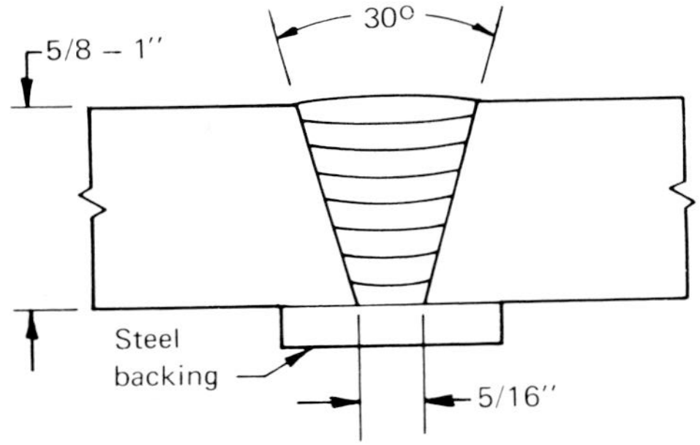

Plate Thickness (in.)	5/8		3/4		1	
Pass	1	2 – 5	1	2 – 6	1	2 – 8
Electrode Type	Jetweld 2	Jetweld 2	Jetweld 2	Jetweld 2	Jetweld 2	Jetweld 2
Size	3/16	1/4	3/16	1/4	3/16	1/4
Current (amp) AC	300	400	300	400	300	400
Arc Speed (in./min)	13.0-15.0	12.5-14.5	13.0-15.0	12.5-14.5	13.0-15.0	12.5-14.5
Electrode Req'd (lb/ft)	0.228	1.35	0.228	1.69	0.228	2.37
Total Time (hr/ft of weld)	0.0759		0.0913		0.122	

Figure 8. Shielded Metal-Arc (Manual).

Position: Flat
Weld Quality Level: Code
Steel Weldability: Good
Welded From: Two sides

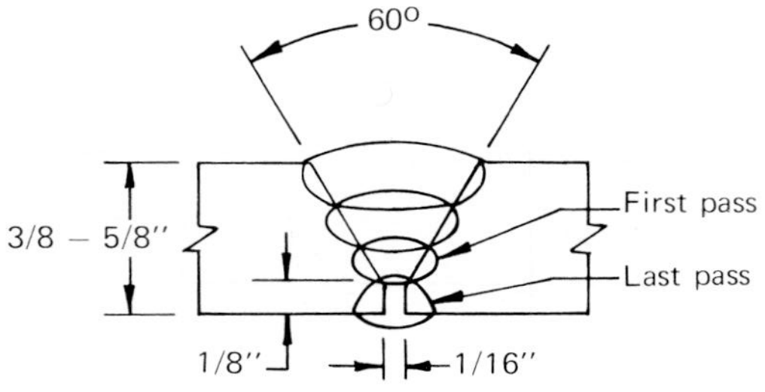

Plate Thickness (in.)	3/8		1/2		5/8		
Pass	1	2 & 3	1	2 & 3	1	2 & 3	4
Electrode Type	Fleetweld 35	Jetweld 2	Fleetweld 35	Jetweld 2	Fleetweld 35	Jetweld 2	Jetweld 2
Size	3/16	3/16	1/4	7/32	1/4	1/4	7/32
Current (amp) AC	175	280	275	340	275	375	340
Arc Speed (in./min)	8.0-10.0	14.5-17.5	7.0-9.0	13.5-15.5	7.0-9.0	12.5-14.5	11.5-13.5
Electrode Req'd (lb/ft)	0.148	0.366	0.239	0.480	0.241	0.795	0.235
Total Time (hr/ft of weld)	0.0472		0.0526		0.0706		

Back gouge first pass before welding last pass.

Figure 9. Shielded Metal-Arc (Manual).

Position: Flat
Weld Quality Level: Code
Steel Weldability: Good
Welded From: Two sides

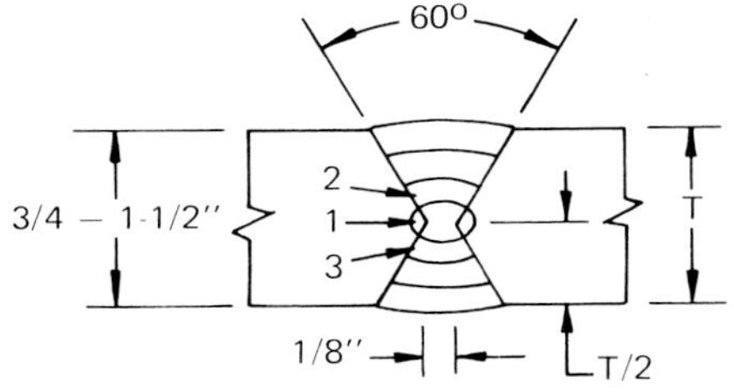

Plate Thickness (in.)	3/4			1			1-1/2		
Pass	1	2 & 3	4 & 5	1	2 & 3	4 – 7	1	2 & 3	4 – 10
Electrode Type	Fleetweld 35		Jetweld 2	Fleetweld 35		Jetweld 2	Fleetweld 35		Jetweld 2
Size	3/16	1/4	1/4	3/16	1/4	1/4	3/16	1/4	1/4
Current (amp) AC	135	275	400	135	275	400	135	275	400
Arc Speed (in./min)	5.5-6.5	8.0-10.0	11.0-13.0	5.5-6.5	8.0-10.0	11.0-13.0	5.5-6.5	8.0-10.0	9.5-11.5
Electrode Req'd (lb/ft)	0.190	0.400	0.728	0.190	0.400	1.45	0.190	0.400	3.04
Total Time (hr/ft of weld)	0.111			0.144			0.211		

Back gouge first pass before welding third pass. Complete third pass side before turning over.

Figure 10. Shielded Metal-Arc (Manual).

SHIELDED METAL-ARC (MANUAL)
Special Procedures for ASTM A203 and A537 Steels

Position: Flat
Weld Quality Level: Code
Steel Weldability: Poor
Welded From: Two sides

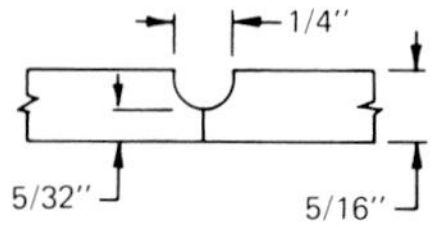

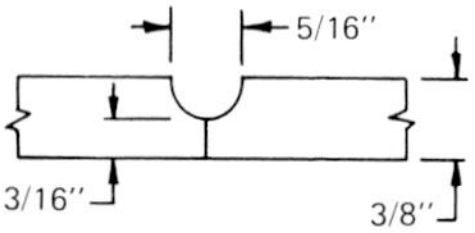

Plate Thickness (in.)	5/16		3/8	
Pass	1 & 2	3 & 4*	1 – 3	4 – 6*
Electrode Type	Jet-LH 8018-C1		Jet-LH 8018-C1	
Size	5/32	5/32	5/32	5/32
Current (amp) DC(+)	150	150	150	150
Arc Speed (in./min)	9 – 11	8 – 10	9 – 11	8 – 10
Electrode Req'd (lb/ft)	0.48		0.65	
Total Time (hr/ft of weld)	0.0844		0.127	
Interpass Temperature, Max. (°F)	150		150	

Position: Flat
Weld Quality Level: Code
Steel Weldability: Poor
Welded From: Two sides

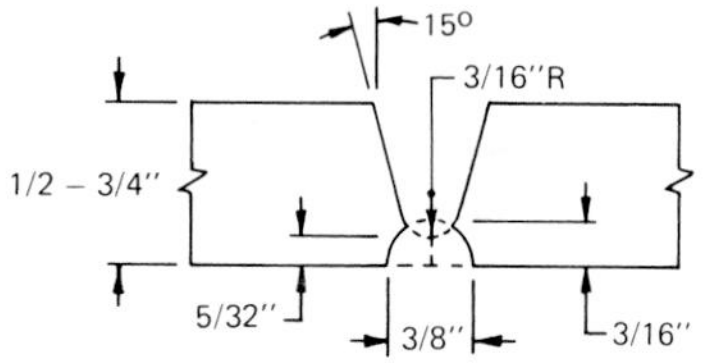

Plate Thickness (in.)	1/2		5/8		3/4	
Pass	1 – 5	6 – 8*	1 – 7	8 – 10*	1 – 10	11 – 13*
Electrode Type	Jet-LH 8018-C1		Jet-LH 8018-C1		Jet-LH 8018-C1	
Size	5/32	5/32	5/32	5/32	5/32	5/32
Current (amp) DC(+)	150	150	150	150	150	150
Arc Speed (in./min)	7 – 9	8 – 10	7 – 9	8 – 10	7 – 9	8 – 10
Electrode Req'd (lb/ft)	1.40		1.79		2.25	
Total Time (hr/ft of weld)	0.188		0.238		0.313	
Interpass Temperature, Max. (°F)	175		200		225	

* Second side is gouged after first side is completed.

Figure 11. Shielded Metal-Arc (Manual). Special Procedures for ASTM A203 and A537 Steels.

Position: Vertical up
Weld Quality Level: Code
Steel Weldability: Good
Welded From: One side

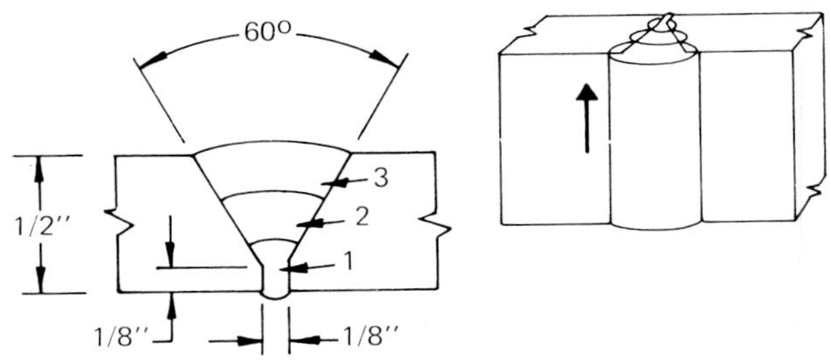

Plate Thickness (in.)	1/4	5/16	3/8	1/2
Pass	1 & 2	1 & 2	1 & 2	1 – 3
Electrode Type	Fleetweld 5P	Fleetweld 5P	Fleetweld 5P	Fleetweld 5P
Size	5/32	5/32	3/16	3/16
Current (amp) DC(+)	110	120	150	170
Arc Speed (in./min)*	5.2-5.8	3.8-4.2	4.8-5.3	3.8-4.2
Electrode Req'd (lb/ft)	0.323	0.440	0.586	0.990
Total Time (hr/ft of weld)	0.0901	0.118	0.130	0.152

* First pass only. Vary speed on succeeding passes to obtain proper weld size.

Figure 12. Shielded Metal-Arc (Manual).

Position: Vertical up
Weld Quality Level: Code
Steel Weldability: Good
Welded From: One side

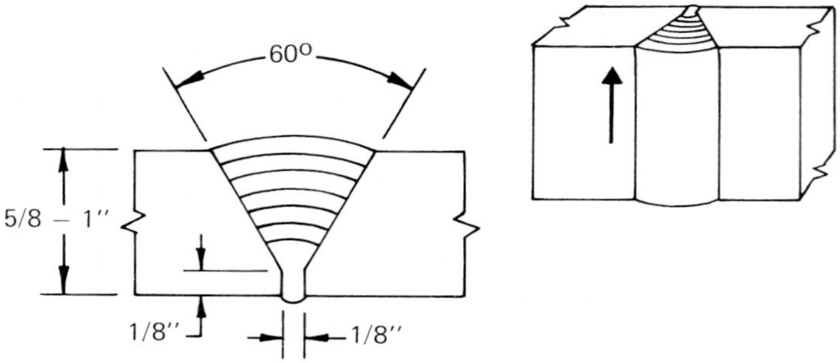

Plate Thickness (in.)	5/8	3/4	1
Pass	1 – 4	1 – 6	1 – 10
Electrode Type	Fleetweld 5P	Fleetweld 5P	Fleetweld 5P
Size	3/16	3/16	3/16
Current (amp) DC(+)	170	170	170
Arc Speed (in./min)*	3.8 – 4.2	3.8 – 4.2	3.8 – 4.2
Electrode Req'd (lb/ft)	1.48	2.08	3.56
Total Time (hr/ft of weld)	0.228	0.318	0.547

* First pass only. Vary speed on succeeding passes to obtain proper weld size.

Figure 13. Shielded Metal-Arc (Manual).

Position: Vertical up
Weld Quality Level: Code
Steel Weldability: Fair
Welded From: One side

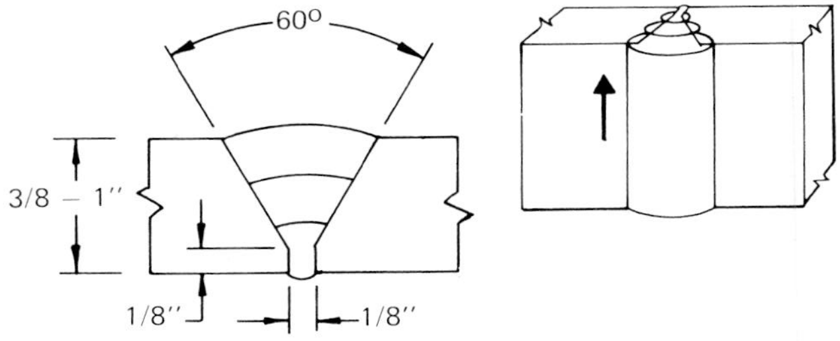

Plate Thickness (in.)	3/8		1/2		3/4		1	
Pass	1	2	1	2 – 3	1	2 – 7	1	2 – 11
Electrode Type	Fleetweld 5P	Jetweld LH-72	Fleetweld 5P	Jetweld LH-72	Fleetweld 5P	Jetweld LH-72	Fleetweld 5P	Jetweld LH-72
Size	5/32	5/32	5/32	5/32	5/32	5/32	5/32	5/32
Current (amp) DC(+)	160	160	160	160	160	160	160	160
Arc Speed (in./min)	4.3 – 4.7	3.2 – 3.5*	4.3 – 4.7	3.2 – 3.5*	4.3 – 4.7	3.2 – 3.5*	4.3 – 4.7	3.2 – 3.5*
Electrode Req'd (lb/ft)	0.281	0.341	0.281	0.758	0.281	1.93	0.281	3.52
Total Time (hr/ft of weld)	0.104		0.176		0.381		0.659	

*Second pass only. Vary speed on succeeding passes to obtain proper weld size.

Figure 14. Shielded Metal-Arc (Manual).

Position: Vertical up
Weld Quality Level: Code
Steel Weldability: Good
Welded From: Two sides

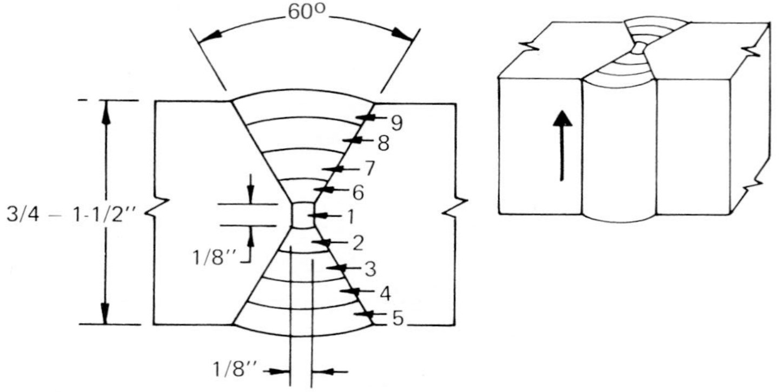

Plate Thickness (in.)	3/4		1		1-1/4		1-1/2	
Pass	1	2 – 5	1	2 – 7	1	2 – 7	1	2 – 9
Electrode Type	Fleetweld 5P	Jetweld LH-72	Fleetweld 5P	Jetweld LH-72	Fleetweld 5P	Jetweld LH-72	Fleetweld 5P	Jetweld LH-72
Size	5/32	5/32	5/32	5/32	5/32	5/32	5/32	5/32
Current (amp) DC(+)	140	160	140	160	140	160	140	160
Arc Speed (in./min)	3.5 – 4.1	4.1 – 4.9	3.5 – 4.1	3.5 – 4.1	3.9 – 4.1	2.3 – 2.9	3.5 – 4.1	2.4 – 3.0
Electrode Req'd (lb/ft)	0.240	0.900	0 0.240	1.66	0.240	2.40	0.240	3.16
Total Time (hr/ft of weld)	0.230		0.367		0.514		0.645	

Gouge out seam for first pass on second side.

Figure 15. Shielded Metal-Arc (Manual).

Position: Horizontal
Weld Quality Level: Code
Steel Weldability: Fair
Welded From: One side

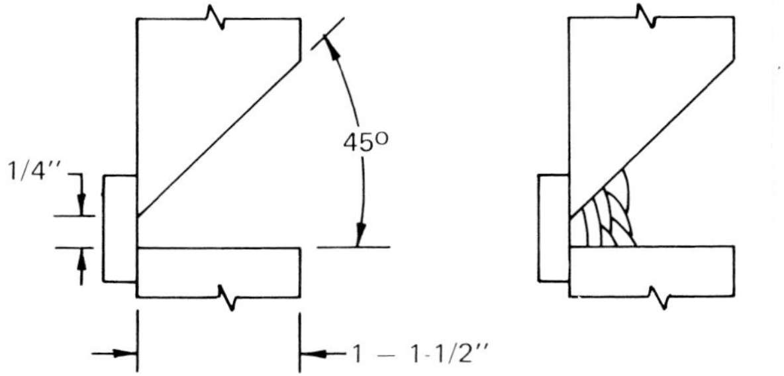

Plate Thickness (in.)		1		1-1/4		1-1/2	
Pass	1*	2 – 13	14 – 19†	2 – 17	18 – 24†	2 – 22	23 – 31†
Electrode Type				Jetweld LH-70			
Size (in.)	3/16	7/32	3/16	7/32	3/16	7/32	3/16
Current (amp) DC(+)	240	280	240	280	240	280	240
Arc Speed (in./min)	5 – 6	6.2-6.8	9.5-10.5	5.7-6.3	9.5-10.5	5.2-5.8	9.5-10.5
Electrode Req'd (lb/ft)		3.39	.994	4.82	1.23	6.40	1.60
Total Time (hr/ft of weld)		0.526		.714		1.00	

* First pass for all thicknesses

† Cover passes.

Figure 16. Shielded Metal-Arc (Manual).

Position: Horizontal
Weld Quality Level: Commercial
Steel Weldability: Fair
Welded From: Two sides

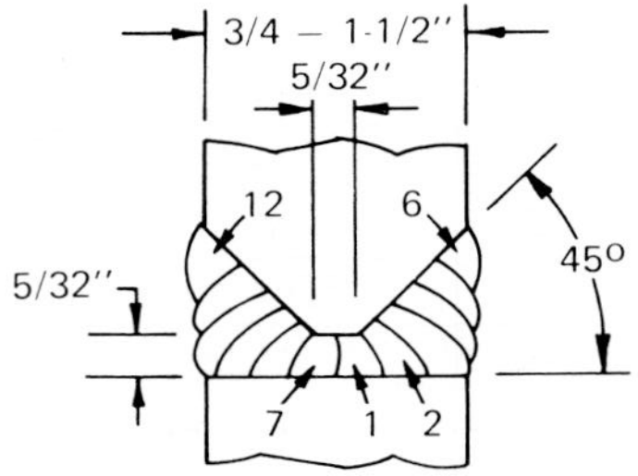

Plate Thickness (in.)	3/4		1		1-1/4		1-1/2	
Pass	1	2 – 6	1	2 – 10	1	2 – 10	1	2 – 12
Electrode Type	Jetweld LH-70		Jetweld LH-70		Jetweld LH-70		Jetweld LH-70	
Size	3/16	3/16	3/16	3/16	3/16	3/16	3/16	3/16
Current (amp) DC(+)	240	240	240	240	240	240	240	240
Arc Speed (in./min)	5.5-6.5	9.0-11.0	4.4-5.2	8.5-10.5	3.8-4.6	5.5-6.5	3.7-4.3	4.6-5.4
Electrode Req'd (lb/ft)	0.956		1.47		2.60		3.84	
Total Time (hr/ft of weld)	0.133		0.230		0.347		0.490	

Fill first pass side. Back gouge as required before welding second side.

Figure 17. Shielded Metal-Arc (Manual).

Position: Overhead
Weld Quality Level: Code
Steel Weldability: Fair
Welded From: One side

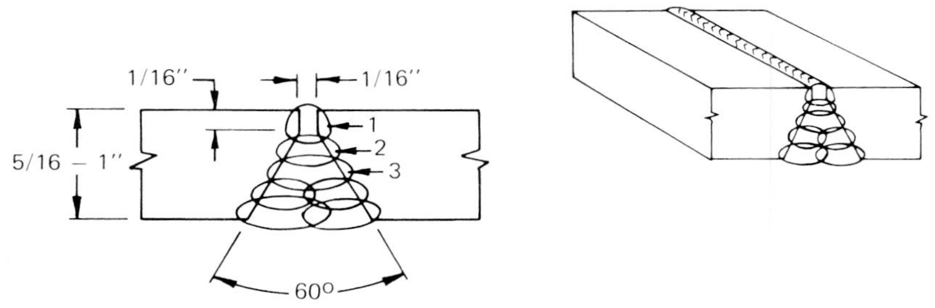

Plate Thickness (in.)	5/16		3/8		1/2		3/4		1	
Pass	1	2	1	2 – 3	1	2 – 5	1	2 – 9	1	2 – 13
Electrode Type	Fleetweld 5P	Jetweld LH-72	Fleetweld 5P	Jetweld LH-72	Fleetweld 5P	Jetweld LH-72	Fleetweld 5P	Jetweld LH-72	Fleetweld 5P	Jetweld LH-72
Size	1/8	5/32	1/8	5/32	1/8	5/32	1/8	5/32	1/8	5/32
Current (amp) DC(+)	110	170	110	170	110	170	110	170	110	170
Arc Speed (in./min)	4.3 – 4.7	3.4 – 3.8	4.3 – 4.7	3.3 – 3.7	4.3 – 4.7	3.6 – 4.0	4.3 – 4.7	4.3 – 4.7	4.3 – 4.7	3.6 – 4.0
Electrode Req'd (lb/ft)	0.155	0.327	0.155	0.671	0.155	0.918	0.155	2.08	0.155	3.70
Total Time (hr/ft of weld)	0.0999		0.158		0.202		0.399		0.575	

Split layers after third pass, as shown in sketch.

Figure 18. Shielded Metal-Arc (Manual).

Fillet and Lap Weld Procedures

The American Welding Society defines fillet-weld size, for equal-leg fillet welds, as the leg length of the largest isosceles right triangle that can be inscribed within the fillet-weld cross section. For unequal-leg fillet welds, the size is the leg length of the largest right triangle that can be inscribed within the fillet-weld cross section. The theoretical or effective throat thickness is the distance from the beginning of the root of the joint perpendicular to the hypotenuse of the inscribed right triangle. (The effective throat thickness of an equal leg, 45°-fillet weld is 0.707 times the normal leg size of the weld.)

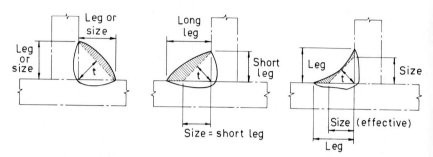

Figure 19. (Left) Equal leg-size convex fillet. (Center) Unequal leg-size convex fillet. (Right) Unequal leg-size concave fillet.

Although a concave fillet weld produces a smooth change in section at the joint, it is more susceptible to shrinkage cracks, especially in higher-carbon steels. Because it is concave, the critical dimension that must be maintained is the throat size. Concave fillets are measured with gauges that measure the theoretical throat section of the weld. See Figure 20.

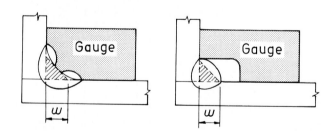

Figure 20. Gauges for measuring fillet size.

A convex fillet weld will have much less tendency to crack as a result of shrinkage upon cooling. It is relatively free from undercut. However, excessive convexity will result in excessive weld metal, which will decrease welding speed and add nothing to the strength of the weld. Because it is convex, the critical dimension that must be maintained is the leg size. Convex fillets are measured with gauges that measure the length of the smallest leg.

The ideal fillet weld would be a flat or slightly convex 45° fillet.

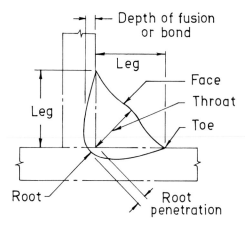

Figure 21. Ideal fillet weld shape.

For a number of years, the maximum allowable shear stress in fillet welds was 13,600 psi for E60XX electrodes. In 1961, a value of 15,800 was added for E70XX electrodes. In 1969 these values were increased to .30 of the nominal tensile strength of the weld metal or .30 EXX. In the table below are the present allowable loads for the various sizes of fillet welds.

TABLE 5 — ALLOWABLE LOAD FOR VARIOUS SIZES OF FILLET WELDS

Strength Level of Weld Metal (EXX)						
60	70	80	90	100	110	120
Allowable Shear Stress on Throat, 1000 psi of Fillet Weld or Partial-Penetration Groove Weld						
18.0	21.0	24.0	27.0	30.0	33.0	36.0
Allowable Unit Force on Fillet Weld, 1000 pounds/linear inch						
12.73	14.85	16.97	19.09	21.21	23.33	25.45

Leg Size	Allowable Unit Force for Various Sizes of Fillet Welds 1000 pounds/linear inch						
1″	12.73	14.85	16.97	19.09	21.21	23.33	25.45
7/8″	11.14	12.99	14.85	16.70	18.57	20.41	22.27
3/4″	9.55	11.14	12.73	14.32	15.92	17.50	19.09
5/8″	7.96	9.28	10.61	11.93	13.27	14.58	15.90
1/2″	6.37	7.42	8.48	9.54	10.61	11.67	12.73
7/16″	5.57	6.50	7.42	8.35	9.28	10.21	11.13
3/8″	4.77	5.57	6.36	7.16	7.95	8.75	9.54
5/16″	3.98	4.64	5.30	5.97	6.63	7.29	7.95
1/4″	3.18	3.71	4.24	4.77	5.30	5.83	6.36
3/16″	2.39	2.78	3.18	3.58	3.98	4.38	4.77
1/8″	1.59	1.86	2.12	2.39	2.65	2.92	3.18
1/16″	.795	.930	1.06	1.19	1.33	1.46	1.59

The AWS Structural Welding Code has restrictions on the size of fillets. In table 6 are shown the minimum-size fillet welds permitted for various thicknesses of material. In 1975 this table was cut off at "over 3/4 inch plate" and "5/16 inch fillet weld".

TABLE 6 — MINIMUM FILLET-WELD SIZE

Material Thickness of Thicker Part Joined (inches)	Minimum Size (inches)
to 1/4 incl.	1/8
over 1/4 to 1/2	3/16
over 1/2 to 3/4	1/4
over 3/4 to 1-1/2	5/16
over 1-1/2 to 2-1/4	3/8
over 2-1/4 to 6	1/2
over 6	5/8

Techniques — Where possible fillet welds should be made using iron-powder electrodes specifically designed for making fillets. The following techniques used with these electrodes will produce the best results:

1. In general, use one size smaller-diameter electrode than is used with conventional techniques for a particular job. However, if the same size can be used, still greater savings can be effected.
2. These are AC-DC electrodes, but AC is recommended over DC because greater speeds can be obtained.
3. These are contact electrodes. The covering touches the plate and the weld is made using a simple drag technique. The electrode should be held into a fillet with light pressure so that the electrode covering is pressing against both legs of the fillet. The electrode is held at an angle of approximately 45° to the horizontal and leans in the direction of welding at an angle approximately 60° (Figure 22). If the electrode leans back towards the bead, slag will run under the arc causing slag holes.
4. Too low current will permit slag to follow too closely. Excessive current will adversely affect bead appearance and slag removal.

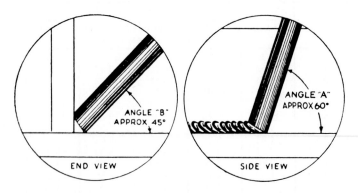

Figure 22. Angle of electrode for maximum speed.

5. Maintain a travel speed such that the arc is 1/4" to 3/8" ahead of the slag. The natural leg sizes for fillets resulting from this technique are: 3/16" electrode produces 1/4"-leg fillet, and 1/4" electrode produces 5/16"-leg fillet. The bead shape will be flat or slightly convex. If the bead appears to have an overhang, increase the travel speed.

6. Slag will be almost self-removing, if most favorable conditions are created: smooth, uniform head; reasonable quench effect; use of moderate current.

7. When welding on short sections, traveling toward the ground will help keep the slag from under the arc. This is especially true of the 1/4" electrode.

8. Correct welding currents are very important to obtaining maximum results with iron-powder electrodes. Since machine efficiency varies and conditions, such as cable length, vary, current should be determined by a tong meter, if possible. The following currents will produce excellent results at maximum speeds:

5/32"	225 amps. AC	30-31 arc volts
3/16"	275 amps. AC	31-32 arc volts
1/4"	350 amps. AC	34-36 arc volts

If a meter is not available, current can be determined by melt-off. If the melt-off rate of a given electrode is known, the current and amount of electrode deposited in a minute can be correlated. A typical electrode produces the following:

5/32"	225 amps. AC	13.4 inch/minute
3/16"	275 amps. AC	12.1 inch/minute
1/4"	350 amps. AC	9.5 inch/minute

Melt-off rates will give close approximation of correct welding current, and the amount of current indicated by the machine dial should be disregarded.

Another way of approximating current is by observing slag formation. At the proper welding current with an electrode angle as indicated in Figure 22, slag formation should begin from 1/8" to 3/8" behind the electrode. Melt-off determination is more accurate, however, since the variable of travel speed influences slag formation.

The reason for the current variation with iron-powder electrodes is because the electrode core burns high inside the covering, thus producing a relatively high arc voltage (10 to 20% higher than conventional electrodes used for fillet welding). Many machines in use are calibrated for conventional E6012 and E6010 electrodes, which operate at substantially lower voltages. Electrodes with lower voltages for a given machine setting will receive more current than those operating at higher voltages.

Multiple-Pass Horizontal Fillets

Multiple-pass fillets are made with either E6012, E7014, E7024, or E7028 electrodes.

The first bead is laid in the corner with a fairly high current and speed and with little attention paid to undercutting. Subsequent beads should be made with the electrode held at an angle of $70°$ to $80°$ with the horizontal plate and line of weld, except the beads against the vertical plate, in which case, the

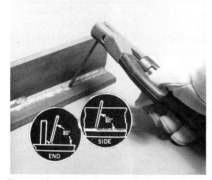 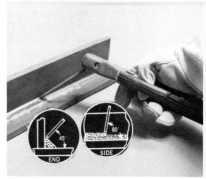

Figure 23. Angle of electrode for beads not against vertical plate.

Figure 24. Angle of electrode for beads against vertical plate.

electrode should be at about a 45° angle. See Figures 23 and 24. The beads are laid from the bottom upward, as shown in Figure 25. The idea here is to provide a flat horizontal surface upon which to place succeeding beads, permitting higher currents, resulting in faster welding.

When a weld of two passes is required, the first bead can be put in as shown in Figure 27. Here, the first bead is deposited mostly on the bottom plate, then the second bead is applied, holding the electrode at about 45° and fusing into vertical plate and the first bead.

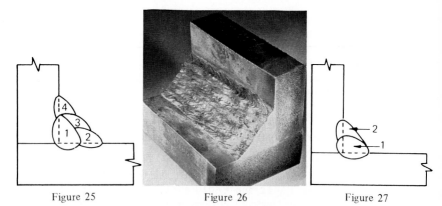

Figure 25   Figure 26   Figure 27

Figure 25. Sequence of placing beads for a four-pass fillet weld.
Figure 26. A 16-pass fillet weld made with E6012 electrode. Plate 1-1/4" thick.
Figure 27. Location of beads for two-pass fillet.

Position: Flat
Weld Quality Level: Code
Steel Weldability: Good

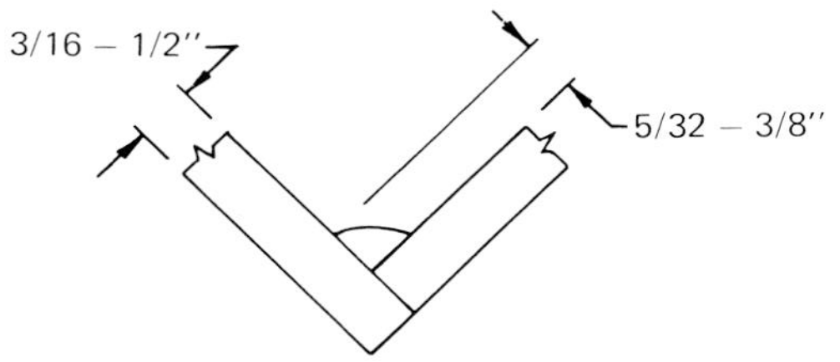

Weld Size, L (in.)	5/32	3/16		1/4		9/32	5/16	3/8
Pass	1	1	1	1	1	1	1	1
Electrode Type	Jetweld 2	Jetweld 2	Jetweld 2	Jetweld 2	Jetweld 2	Jetweld 2	Jetweld 2	Jetweld 2
Size	5/32	5/32	3/16	3/16	7/32	1/4	1/4	1/4
Current (amp) AC	210	220	260	270	335	380	390	400
Arc Speed (in./min)	15.5-17.0	13.5-15.0	15.5-17.0	12.5-14.0	14.5-16.0	14.0-15.5	11.0-12.0	9.5-10.5
Electrode Req'd (lb/ft)	0.119	0.146	0.167	0.215	0.228	0.269	0.343	0.428
Total Time (hr/ft of weld)	0.0123	0.0140	0.0123	0.0151	0.0131	0.0136	0.0174	0.0200

Figure 28. Shielded Metal-Arc (Manual).

Position: Flat
Weld Quality Level: Code
Steel Weldability: Good

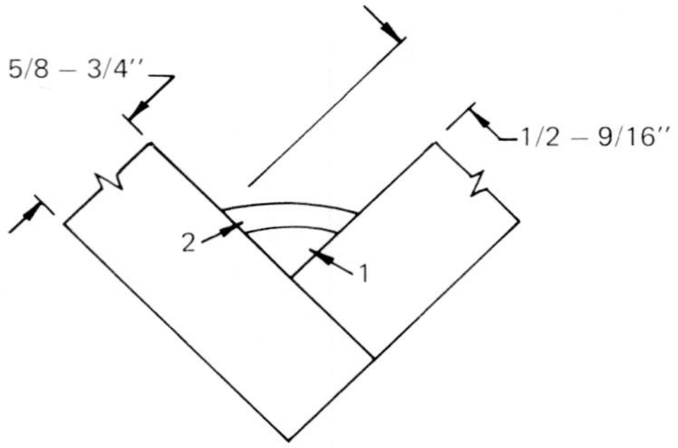

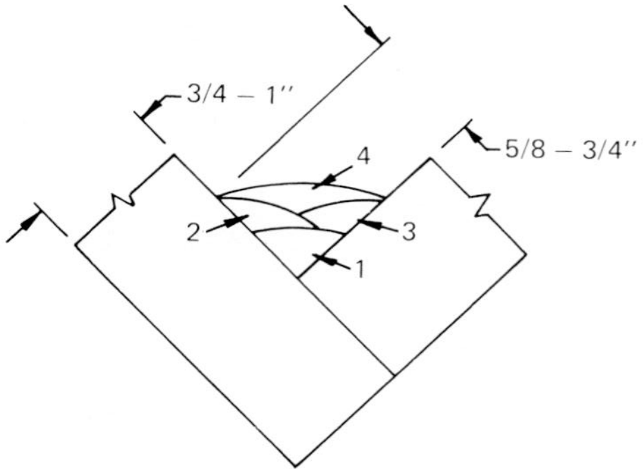

Weld Size, L (in.)	1/2		9/16		5/8		3/4	
Pass	1	2	1	2	1	2 & 3	1	2 – 4
Electrode Type	Jetweld 2	Jetweld 2	Jetweld 2	Jetweld 2	Jetweld 2	Jetweld 2	Jetweld 2	Jetweld 2
Size	1/4	1/4	1/4	1/4	1/4	1/4	1/4	1/4
Current (amp) AC	400	400	400	400	400	400	400	400
Arc Speed (in./min)	11.5-12.5	11.5-12.5	11.5-12.5	7.5-8.5	11.5-12.5	11.0-12.0	11.5-12.5	10.0-11.0
Electrode Req'd (lb/ft)	0.727		0.936		1.12		1.58	
Total Time (hr/ft of weld)	0.0333		0.0417		0.512		0.0737	

Figure 29. Shielded Metal-Arc (Manual).

Position: Flat
Weld Quality Level: Commercial
Steel Weldability: Good

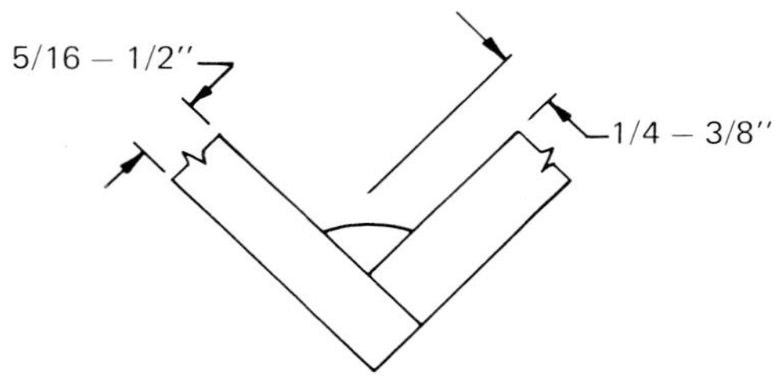

Weld Size, L (in.)	1/4	1/4	9/32	5/16	3/8
Pass	1	1	1	1	1
Electrode Type	Jetweld 1	Jetweld 1	Jetweld 1	Jetweld 1	Jetweld 1
Size	3/16	7/32	1/4	1/4	5/16
Current (amp) AC	275	325	375	375	475
Arc Speed (in./min)	14.0-16.0	16.0-18.0	17.0-19.0	14.0-15.0	11.0-12.0
Electrode Req'd (lb/ft)	0.19	0.20	0.22	0.29	0.38
Total Time (hr/ft of weld)	0.0133	0.0118	0.0131	0.138	0.174

Figure 30. Shielded Metal-Arc (Manual).

Position: Flat
Weld Quality Level: Commercial
Weldability: Good

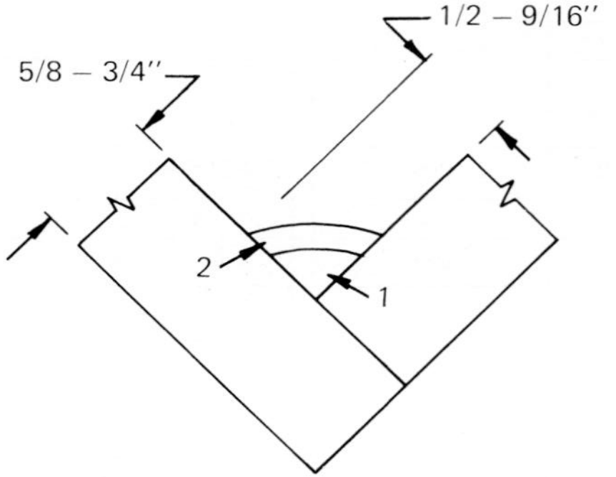

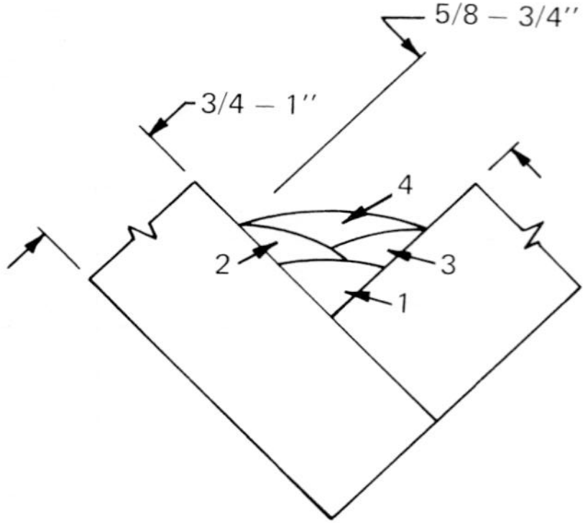

Weld Size, L (in.)	1/2		9/16		5/8		3/4	
Pass	1	2	1	2	1	2 & 3	1	2 – 4
Electrode Type	Jetweld 3	Jetweld 3	Jetweld 3	Jetweld 3	Jetweld 3	Jetweld 3	Jetweld 3	Jetweld 3
Size	5/16	5/16	5/16	5/16	5/16	5/16	5/16	5/16
Current (amp) AC	475	550	475	550	475	550	475	550
Arc Speed (in./min)	13.0-15.0	14.0-16.0	13.0-15.0	10.0-11.0	13.0-15.0	14.0-15.0	13.0-15.0	13.0-14.0
Electrode Req'd (lb/ft)	0.67		0.85		1.07		1.46	
Total Time (hr/ft of weld)	0.0276		0.0333		0.0429		0.587	

Figure 31. Shielded Metal-Arc (Manual).

Position: Flat
Weld Quality Level: Code
Steel Weldability: Poor

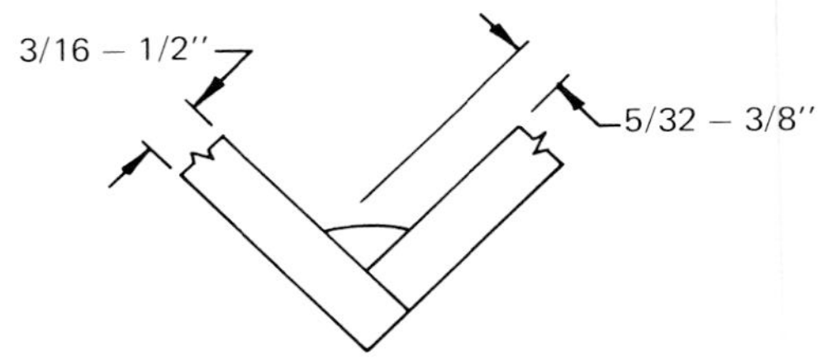

Weld Size, L (in.)	5/32	3/16	1/4	5/16	3/8
Pass	1	1	1	1	1
Electrode Type	Jetweld LH-3800				
Size	5/32	3/16	3/16	7/32	1/4
Current (amp) AC	215	260	280	330	400
Arc Speed (in./min)	13.5-15.0	13.5-15.0	11.0-12.0	10.0-12.0	8.5-9.5
Electrode Req'd (lb/ft)	0.104	0.147	0.208	0.285	0.437
Total Time (hr/ft of weld)	0.0140	0.0140	0.0175	0.0175	0.222

Preheat may be necessary depending on plate material.

Figure 32. Shielded Metal-Arc (Manual).

Position: Flat
Weld Quality Level: Code
Steel Weldability: Poor

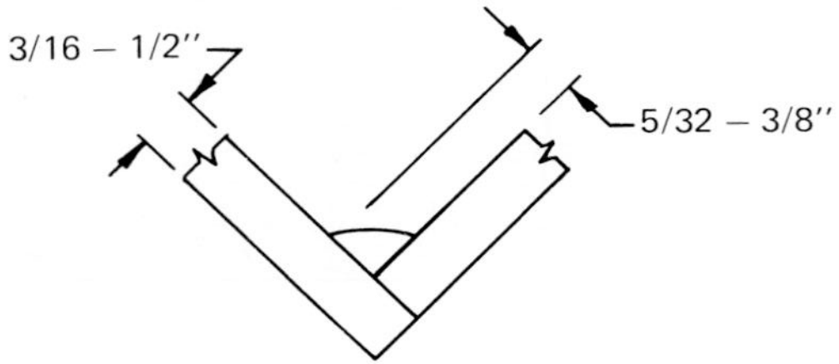

Weld Size, L (in.)	5/32	3/16	1/4	5/16	3/8
Pass	1	1	1	1	1
Electrode Type		Jetweld LH-70			
Size	3/16	7/32	7/32	1/4	1/4
Current (amp) AC	240	275	275	350	350
Arc Speed (in./min)	13.5-15.0	13.0-14.0	9.0-10.0	7.0-8.0	6.0-6.8
Electrode Req'd (lb/ft)	0.109	0.132	0.195	0.272	0.409
Total Time (hr/ft of weld)	0.0140	0.0149	0.0202	0.0270	0.0313

Preheat may be necessary depending on plate material.

Figure 33. Shielded Metal-Arc (Manual).

Position: Horizontal
Weld Quality Level: Commercial
Steel Weldability: Good

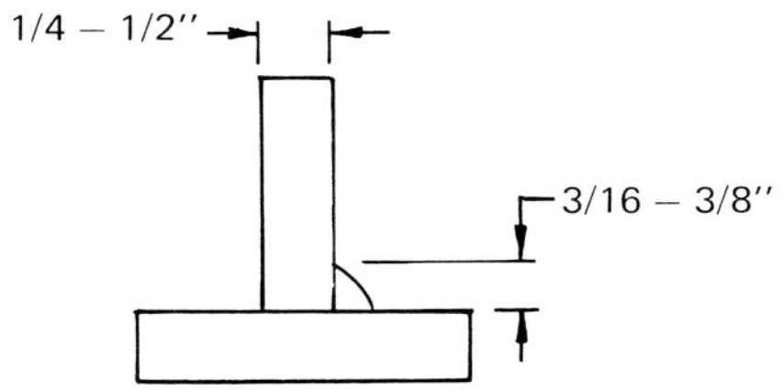

Weld Size, L (in.)	3/16		1/4		9/32	5/16	3/8
Pass	1	1	1	1	1	1	1
Electrode Type	Jetweld 1	Jetweld 1	Jetweld 1	Jetweld 1	Jetweld 1	Jetweld 1	Jetweld 1
Size	5/32	3/16	3/16	7/32	1/4	1/4	1/4
Current (amp) AC	230	270	275	325	375	375	375
Arc Speed (in./min)	13.5-15.0	15.0-17.0	14.0-15.0	16.0-18.0	16.0-18.0	13.0-14.0	10.5-11.5
Electrode Req'd (lb/ft)	0.150	0.166	0.20	0.21	0.23	0.30	0.41
Total Time (hr/ft of weld)	0.0141	0.0125	0.0138	0.0118	0.0118	0.0148	0.0182

Figure 34. Shielded Metal-Arc (Manual).

Position: Horizontal
Weld Quality Level: Commercial
Steel Weldability: Good

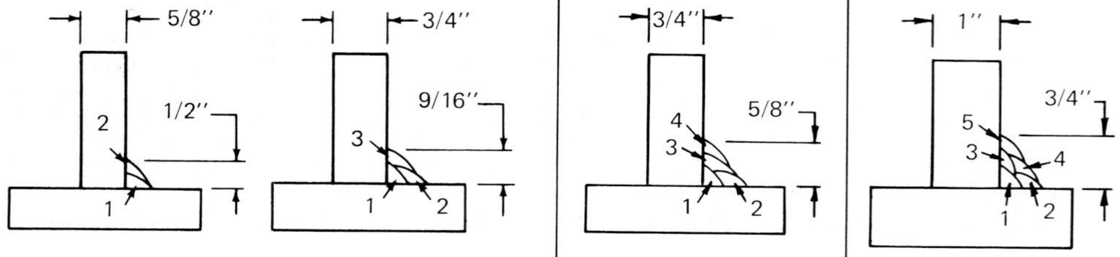

Weld Size, L (in.)	1/2		9/16		5/8		3/4	
Pass	1	2 & 3	1	2 & 3	1	2 – 4	1	2 – 5
Electrode Type	Jetweld 1	Jetweld 1	Jetweld 1	Jetweld 1	Jetweld 1	Jetweld 1	Jetweld 1	Jetweld 1
Size	1/4	1/4	1/4	1/4	1/4	1/4	1/4	1/4
Current (amp) AC	375	375	375	375	375	375	375	375
Arc Speed (in./min)	10.5-11.5	11.0-12.0	10.5-11.5	14.0-16.0	10.5-11.5	14.0-16.0	10.5-11.5	12.0-13.0
Electrode Req'd (lb/ft)	0.73		0.92		1.15		1.62	
Total Time (hr/ft of weld)	0.0356		0.0449		0.0582		0.0822	

Figure 35. Shielded Metal-Arc (Manual).

Position: Horizontal
Weld Quality Level: Code
Steel Weldability: Good

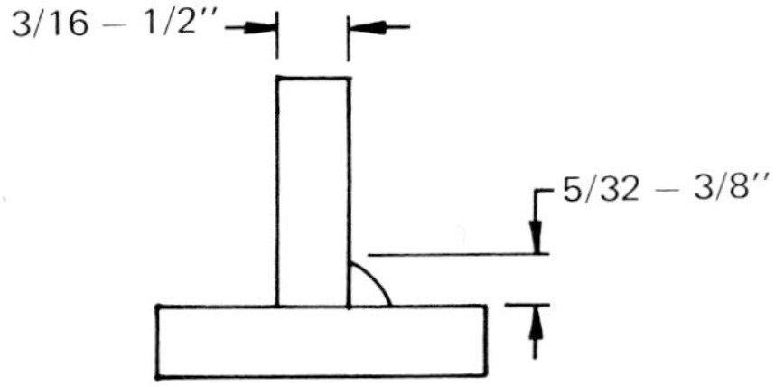

Weld Size, L (in.)	5/32	3/16		1/4		9/32	5/16	3/8
Pass	1	1	1	1	1	1	1	1
Electrode Type	Jetweld 2	Jetweld 2	Jetweld 2	Jetweld 2	Jetweld 2	Jetweld 2	Jetweld 2	Jetweld 2
Size	5/32	5/32	3/16	3/16	7/32	7/32	7/32	1/4
Current (amp) AC	210	220	250	260	320	325	335	360
Arc Speed (in./min)	14.5-16.0	13.0-14.5	14.5-16.0	11.5-12.5	13.0-14.5	11.5-12.5	9.5-10.5	7.5-8.5
Electrode Req'd (lb/ft)	0.128	0.151	0.173	0.224	0.241	0.281	0.356	0.463
Total Time (hr/ft of weld)	0.0131	0.0145	0.0131	0.0167	0.0145	0.0167	0.0200	0.0250

Figure 36. Shielded Metal-Arc (Manual).

Position: Horizontal
Weld Quality Level: Code
Steel Weldability: Poor

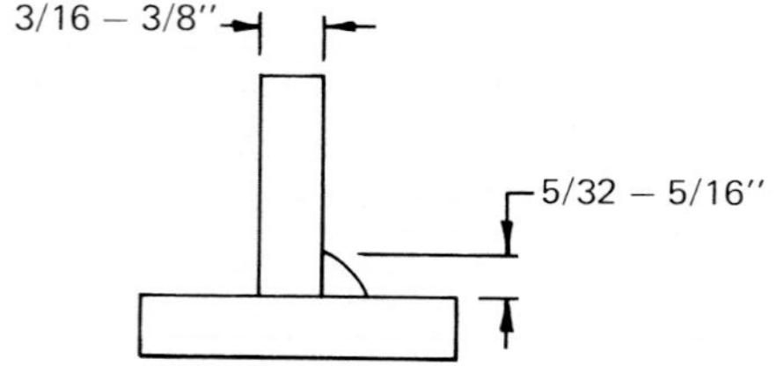

Weld Size, L (in.)	5/32	3/16	1/4		5/16	
Pass	1	1	1	1	1	1
Electrode Type	Jetweld LH-3800					
Size	5/32	3/16	3/16	7/32	7/32	1/4
Current (amp) AC	215	260	280	335	335	390
Arc Speed (in./min)	12.5-13.5	11.5-12.5	9.5-10.5	12.0-13.0	9.5-10.5	11.5-12.5
Electrode Req'd (lb/ft)	0.112	0.157	0.235	0.236	0.320	0.330
Total Time (hr/ft of weld)	0.0152	0.0167	0.0200	0.0160	0.0200	0.0167

Preheat may be necessary depending on plate material.

Figure 37. Shielded Metal-Arc (Manual).

Position: Vertical
Weld Quality Level: Code
Steel Weldability: Good

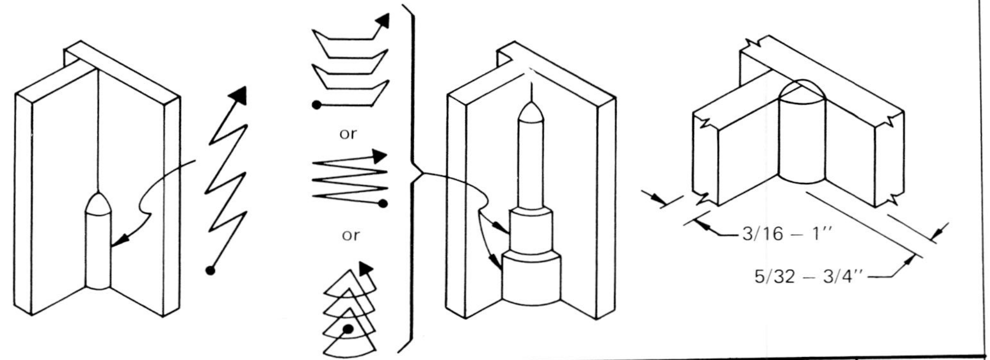

Weld Size, L (in.)	5/32	3/16	1/4	5/16	3/8	1/2	5/8	3/4
Pass	1	1	1	1	1	1 – 2	1 – 3	1 – 4
Electrode Type	Fleetweld 5P	Fleetweld 5P	Fleetweld 5P	Fleetweld 5P	Fleetweld 5P	Fleetweld 5P	Fleetweld 5P	Fleetweld 5P
Size	5/32	3/16	3/16	3/16	3/16	3/16	3/16	3/16
Current (amp) DC(+)	120	150	155	155	155	160	160	160
Arc Speed (in./min)	10.5-11.5	7.4-8.2	5.0-5.5	3.0-3.3	2.0-2.2	4.3-4.7*	4.3-4.7*	4.3-4.7*
Electrode Req'd (lb/ft)	0.0712	0.137	0.211	0.346	0.514	0.850	1.31	1.93
Total Time (hr/ft of weld)	0.0182	0.0256	0.0381	0.0635	0.0952	0.147	0.227	0.333
Direction of welding	Down	Up	Up	Up	Up	Up	Up	Up

* First pass only. Vary speed on succeeding passes to obtain proper weld size.

Figure 38. Shielded Metal-Arc (Manual).

Position: Vertical
Weld Quality Level: Code
Steel Weldability: Fair

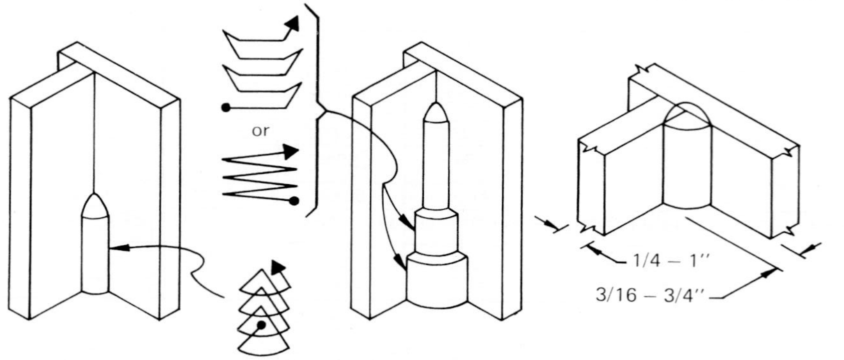

Weld Size, L (in.)	3/16	1/4	5/16	3/8	1/2	5/8	3/4
Pass	1	1	1	1	1	1 – 2	1 – 3
Electrode Type	Jetweld LH-72						
Size	1/8	1/8	1/8	5/32	5/32	5/32	5/32
Current (amp) DC(+)	135	140	140	150	150	150	150
Arc Speed (in./min)	5.4-5.8	3.8-4.2	2.3-2.5	1.8-2.0	1.1-1.3	1.9-2.1*	1.9-2.1*
Electrode Req'd (lb/ft)	0.155	0.231	0.371	0.556	0.925	1.41	2.11
Total Time (hr/ft of weld)	0.0357	0.0500	0.0833	0.105	0.167	0.261	0.389

* First pass only. Vary speed on succeeding passes to obtain proper size.

Figure 39. Shielded Metal-Arc (Manual).

Position: Overhead
Weld Quality Level: Code
Steel Weldability: Good

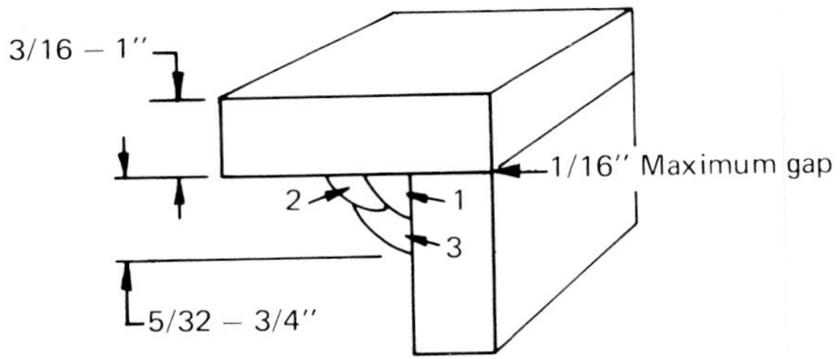

1/16" Maximum gap

3/16 — 1"

5/32 — 3/4"

Weld Size, L (in.)	5/32	3/16	1/4	5/16	3/8	1/2	5/8	3/4
Pass	1	1	1	1 – 2	1 – 3	1 – 6	1 – 10	1 – 15
Electrode Type				Fleetweld 5P				
Size	5/32	3/16	3/16	3/16	3/16	3/16	3/16	3/16
Current (amp) DC(+)	130	170	170	170	170	170	170	170
Arc Speed (in./min)*	7.0-7.7	8.5-9.4	4.8-5.3	6.6-7.3	6.6-7.3	6.6-7.3	6.6-7.3	6.6-7.3
Electrode Req'd (lb/ft)	0.100	0.145	0.253	0.369	0.532	0.945	1.48	2.13
Total Time (hr/ft of weld)	0.0272	0.0223	0.0396	0.0567	0.0820	0.145	0.228	0.328

On 1/2 in. plate and thicker, place the first pass of each layer on the top plate.

* First pass only. Vary speed on succeeding passes to obtain proper weld size.

Figure 40. Shielded Metal-Arc (Manual).

Position: Overhead
Weld Quality Level: Code
Steel Weldability: Fair

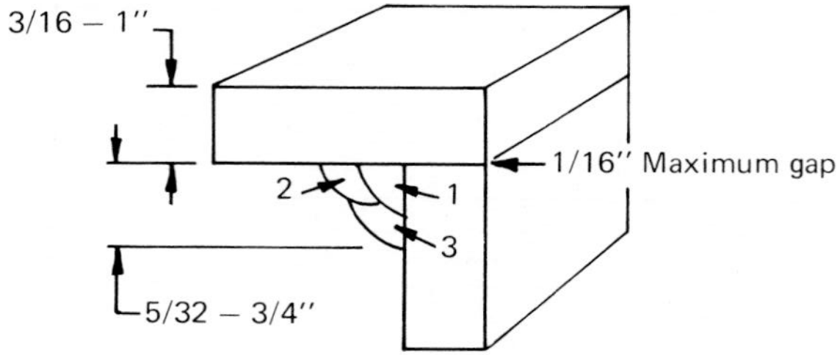

3/16 – 1"

1/16" Maximum gap

5/32 – 3/4"

Weld Size, L (in.)	5/32	3/16	1/4	5/16	3/8	1/2	5/8	3/4
Pass	1	1	1 – 2	1 – 3	1 – 4	1 – 6	1 – 10	1 – 15
Electrode Type					Jetweld LH-72			
Size	5/32	5/32	5/32	5/32	5/32	5/32	5/32	5/32
Current (amp) DC(+)	170	170	170	170	170	170	170	170
Arc Speed (in./min)*	10.5-11.5	7.2-8.0	8.2-9.1	8.2-9.1	8.5-9.4	7.0-7.7	7.2-8.0	8.1-8.9
Electrode Req'd (lb/ft)	0.107	0.155	0.277	0.394	0.570	1.01	1.59	2.29
Total Time (hr/ft of weld)	0.0182	0.0264	0.0463	0.0670	0.0967	0.172	0.269	0.388

On 3/8 in. plate and thicker place the first pass of each layer on the top plate.

* First pass only. Vary succeeding passes to obtain proper weld size.

Figure 41. Shielded Metal-Arc (Manual).

Position: Flat
Weld Quality Level: Commercial
Steel Weldability: Good
Welded From: One side

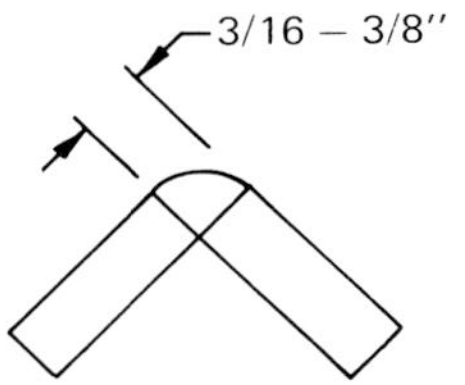

		3/16 – 3/8"			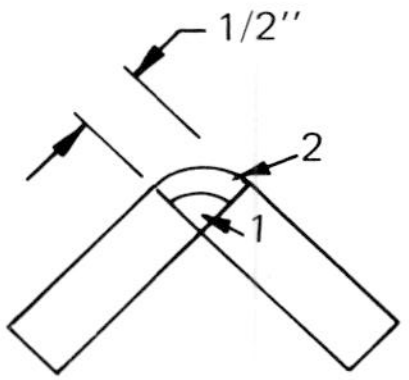 1/2"
Weld Size, L (in.)	3/16	1/4	5/16	3/8	1/2
Plate Thickness (in.)	3/16	1/4	5/16	3/8	1/2
Pass	1	1	1	1	1 & 2
Electrode Type	Jetweld 1	Jetweld 1	Jetweld 1	Jetweld 1	Jetweld 1
Size	3/16	7/32	7/32	1/4	1/4
Current (amp) AC	250	320	350	400	410
Arc Speed (in./min)	21.0 – 25.0	18.0 – 22.0	14.5 – 17.5	13.0 – 16.0	11.5 – 14.5
Electrode Req'd (lb/ft)	0.101	0.133	0.198	0.240	0.530
Total Time (hr/ft of weld)	0.00870	0.0100	0.0125	0.0139	0.0308

Figure 42. Shielded Metal-Arc (Manual).

Position: Flat
Weld Quality Level: Commercial
Steel Weldability: Good
Welded From: One side

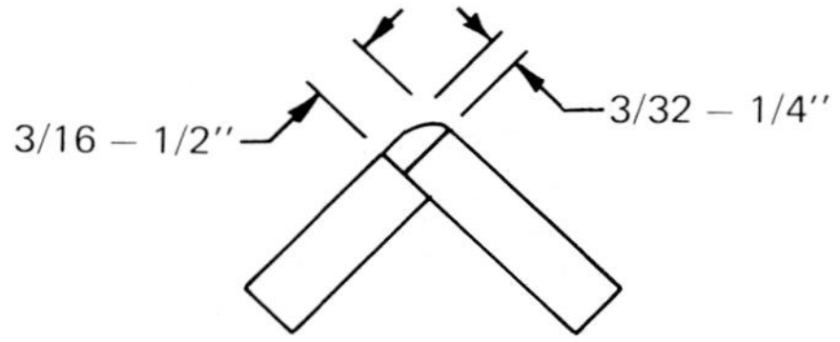

3/32 – 1/4"

3/16 – 1/2"

Weld Size, L (in.)	3/32	1/8	5/32	3/16	1/4
Plate Thickness (in.)	3/16	1/4	5/16	3/8	1/2
Pass	1	1	1	1	1
Electrode Type	Jetweld 1	Jetweld 1	Jetweld 1	Jetweld 1	Jetweld 1
Size	5/32	3/16	7/32	7/32	1/4
Current (amp) AC	215	275	350	360	410
Arc Speed (in./min)	22.0-27.0	19.0-23.0	18.5-22.5	16.5-19.5	14 – 17
Electrode Req'd (lb/ft)	0.0750	0.114	0.152	0.175	0.250
Total Time (hr/ft of weld)	0.00820	0.00952	0.00975	0.0111	0.0130

Figure 43. Shielded Metal-Arc (Manual).

Sheet-Metal Procedures

The following are the main factors governing the speed of sheet-metal welding:
1. Type and size of electrode.
2. Current.
3. Fitup of joint.
4. Position in which the joint is welded.

General

Hold a short arc with the electrode covering almost touching the plate. In the flat position, it may be desirable to lightly touch the covering against the plate for greater ease of welding. Angle of electrode should be about the same as in welding heavier plate for the same type of joint.

Current, Speed, and Fitup

Within the limits of good weld appearance, the speed of welding will increase as the current is increased. As the gap in the joint becomes greater, the current must be decreased to prevent burnthrough and the welding speed will be reduced. Hence, it is important to fit up the joints as closely as possible in order to obtain maximum welding speeds. A clamping fixture is a practical aid in maintaining fitup of sheet-metal joints, and, on production runs, such equipment soon pays for itself. Such clamping fixtures, if equipped with a copper backing strip, will result in easier welding by decreasing the tendency to burn through. Such a fixture also aids materially in reducing time for aligning joints and tacking, and in minimizing warpage.

The current values on the sheet-metal procedure sheets are given merely as a guide in choosing the proper current. The actual current used should be determined by trial, using the highest current possible without burning through or melting away the edges of the joint.

The speeds given in the sheet-metal procedures are for high-speed production welding where uniform tight fitup can be maintained. A few hour's training on a specific joint in a production setup will enable an experienced operator to obtain these speeds.

The decrease in speed resulting from poor fitup is shown on the graph of Figure 44. The current will also have to be reduced to prevent burnthrough.

Feet of Joint Welded per Hour is based on actual welding time only. No allowance has been included for setup, electrode changing, cleaning, or other factors, which will vary greatly with the type of work to be done. In order to use the figures in this column in cost calculations, they must be divided by an operating factor, which can be estimated or determined by trial for the job in question.

Control of Welding Current

It is desirable to have some means by which the operator can regulate current while actually welding, preferably a foot-controlled device that leaves both hands free. The operator then will be able to lower his current when he comes to a section of the joint with poor fitup to prevent burning through, and then raise the current again when he comes to a section with good fitup. Thus, instead of setting his current at a low value that will not burn through at the joint with the poorest fitup and handicapping his travel speed on the entire joint, he can use the highest practical current at all times.

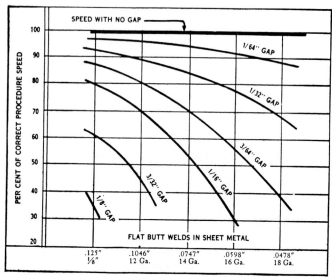

Effect of joint fit-up on welding speed.

Figure 44.

Position in Which the Joint Is Welded

The sheet-metal procedures have been set up in the assumption that, at times, sheet metal must be welded in all positions. However, for maximum welding speeds, to minimize distortion, and for low electrode consumption, sheet-metal joints should be welded downhill about 45° with the same or slightly higher currents that are used in the flat procedures. By welding downhill, it is generally possible to increase the speed of welding over the speed obtainable when welding in the flat position. Welding downhill also decreases the tendency to burn-through a joint that has poor fitup and generally produces a flatter and better-appearing weld.

Experience of Operator

Because of small electrodes and light currents, the molten pool behind the arc is small and the beads are narrow. Therefore, the speed at which a joint can be made depends a great deal on the operator's ability to stay on the seam and travel at a uniform rate. Welds made with the procedures outlined will have good mechanical properties and good appearance when made by a reasonably good operator after a few days' experience in the specialized field of light-gauge welding.

Pinholes in Sheet Metal Welds

On watertight joints, difficulty with small pinholes in the welds is sometimes encountered — these are due to foreign matter in the joint and will usually be eliminated by removing the rust, scale, or other foreign material from the edges of the joint.

Position: Flat
Weld Quality Level: Commercial
Steel Weldability: Good
Welded From: One side

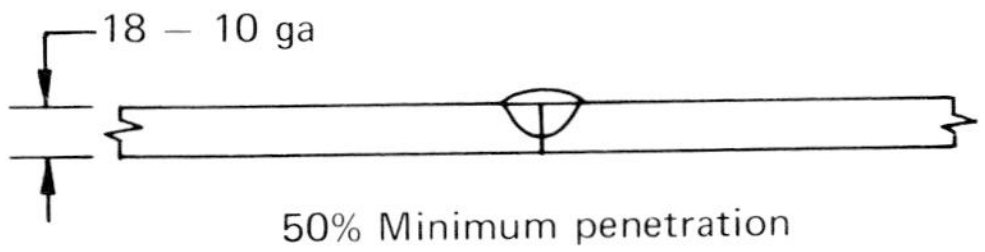

18 – 10 ga

50% Minimum penetration

Plate Thickness (in.)	0.048 (18 ga)	0.060 (16 ga)	0.075 (14 ga)	0.105 (12 ga)	0.135 (10 ga)*
Pass	1	1	1	1	1
Electrode Type	Fleetweld 5P	Fleetweld 5P	Fleetweld 5P	Fleetweld 5P	Fleetweld 5P
Size	3/32	1/8	1/8	5/32	3/16
Current (amp) DC(+)	40†	70†	80	120	135
Arc Speed (in./min)	22 – 26	30 – 35	25 – 30	20 – 24	17 – 21
Electrode Req'd (lb/ft)	0.0244	0.0287	0.0262	0.0487	0.0695
Total Time (hr/ft of weld)	0.00833	0.00615	0.00727	0.00909	0.0105

* Use 1/16 in. gap and whip the electrode.

† DC(−)

Figure 45. Shielded Metal-Arc (Manual).

Position: Flat
Weld Quality Level: Commercial
Steel Weldability: Good
Welded From: One side

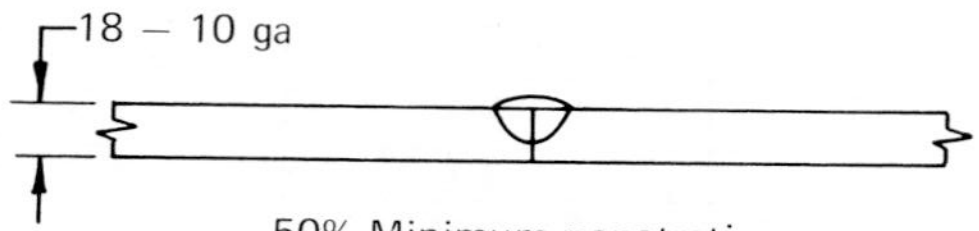

|---18 — 10 ga

50% Minimum penetration

Plate Thickness (in.)	0.048 (18 ga)	0.060 (16 ga)	0.075 (14 ga)	0.105 (12 ga)	0.135 (10 ga)*
Pass	1	1	1	1	1
Electrode Type	Fleetweld 35	Fleetweld 35	Fleetweld 35	Fleetweld 35	Fleetweld 35
Size	3/32	1/8	1/8	5/32	3/16
Current (amp) AC	50	100	105	130	145
Arc Speed (in./min)	20 – 24	28 – 33	26 – 31	24 – 29	22 – 27
Electrode Req'd (lb/ft)	0.0251	0.0326	0.0367	0.0527	0.0648
Total Time (hr/ft of weld)	0.00909	0.00656	0.00702	0.00755	0.00817

* Use 1/16 in. gap and whip the electrode.

Figure 46. Shielded Metal-Arc (Manual).

Position: Horizontal
Weld Quality Level:Commercial
Steel Weldability: Good

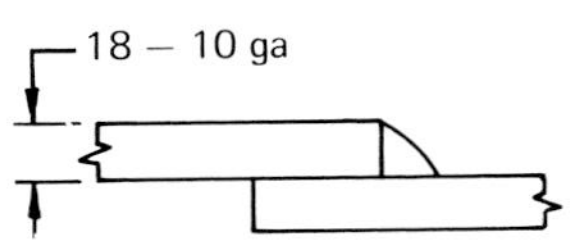

18 — 10 ga

	0.048 (18 ga)	0.060 (16 ga)	0.075 (14 ga)	0.105 (12 ga)	0.135 (10 ga)
Plate Thickness (in.)	0.048 (18 ga)	0.060 (16 ga)	0.075 (14 ga)	0.105 (12 ga)	0.135 (10 ga)
Pass	1	1	1	1	1
Electrode Type	Fleetweld 37	Fleetweld 7	Fleetweld 7	Fleetweld 7	Fleetweld 7
Size	3/32	1/8	5/32	3/16	3/16
Current (amp) DC(−)	70	105	145	200	210
Arc Speed (in./min)	19 — 23	21 — 26	20 — 24	18 — 22	14 — 18
Electrode Req'd (lb/ft)	0.0339	0.0427	0.0717	0.101	0.134
Total Time (hr/ft of weld)	0.00953	0.00851	0.00910	0.0100	0.0125

Figure 47. Shielded Metal-Arc (Manual).

Position: Horizontal
Weld Quality Level: Commercial
Steel Weldability: Good

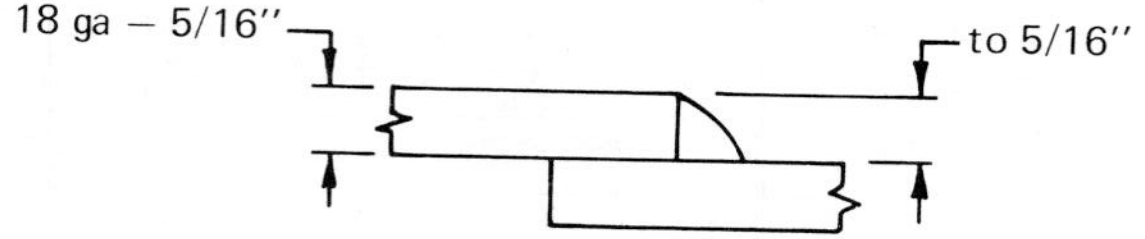

18 ga – 5/16" to 5/16"

Weld Size, L (in.)								
Plate Thickness (in.)	0.048 (18 ga)	0.060 (16 ga)	0.075 (14 ga)	0.105 (12 ga)	0.135 (10 ga)	3/16	1/4	5/16
Pass	1	1	1	1	1	1	1	1
Electrode Class	Fleetweld 37	Fleetweld 37	Fleetweld 37	Fleetweld 37	Fleetweld 37	Jetweld 1	Jetweld 1	Jetweld 1
Size	3/32	1/8	5/32	5/32	3/16	3/16	7/32	7/32
Current (amp) AC	75	115	160	165	215	290	360	360
Arc Speed (in./min)	15 – 19	16 – 20	16 – 20	14 – 18	13 – 17	14 – 17	14 – 16	12 – 14
Electrode Req'd (lb/ft)	0.0389	0.0490	0.0667	0.0773	0.103	0.170	0.211	0.253
Total Time (hr/ft of weld)	0.0118	0.0111	0.0111	0.0125	0.0133	0.0129	0.0133	0.0155

Figure 48. Shielded Metal-Arc (Manual).

Position: Vertical down
Weld Quality Level: Commercial
Steel Weldability: Good

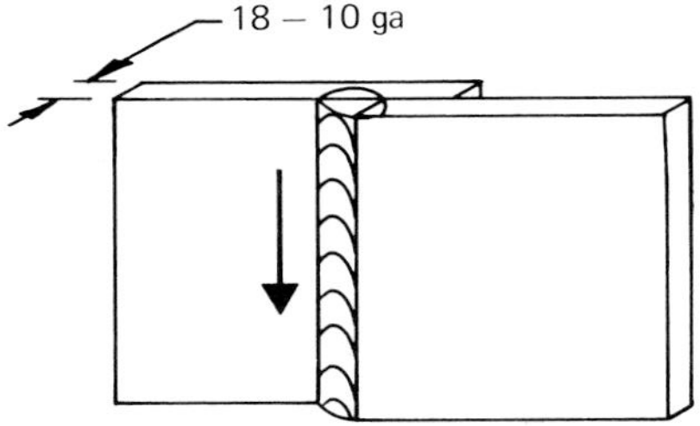

18 – 10 ga

Plate Thickness (in.)	0.048 (18 ga)	0.060 (16 ga)	0.075 (14 ga)	0.105 (12 ga)	0.135 (10 ga)
Pass	1	1	1	1	1
Electrode Type	Fleetweld 37	Fleetweld 7	Fleetweld 7	Fleetweld 7	Fleetweld 7
Size	3/32	1/8	5/32	3/16	3/16
Current (amp) DC(−)	75	115	155	210	220
Arc Speed (in./min)	22 – 27	27 – 32	27 – 32	25 – 30	22 – 27
Electrode Req'd (lb/ft)	0.0316	0.0375	0.0576	0.0781	0.0930
Total Time (hr/ft of weld)	0.00817	0.00678	0.00678	0.00728	0.00817

Figure 49. Shielded Metal-Arc (Manual).

Position: Vertical down
Weld Quality Level: Commercial
Steel Weldability: Good

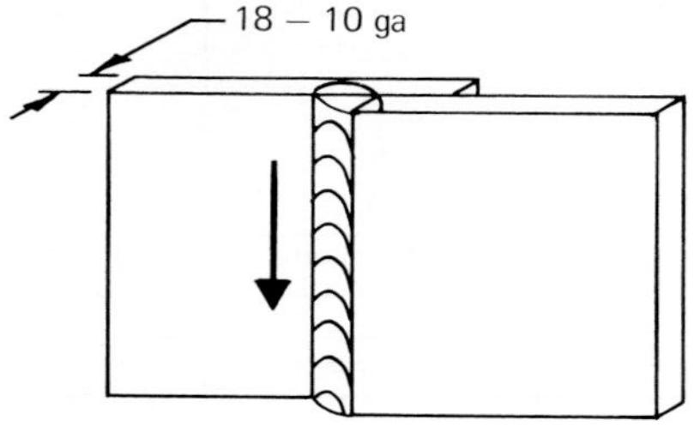

Plate Thickness (in.)	0.048 (18 ga)	0.060 (16 ga)	0.075 (14 ga)	0.105 (12 ga)	0.135 (10 ga)
Pass	1	1	1	1	1
Electrode Type	Fleetweld 37	Fleetweld 37	Fleetweld 37	Fleetweld 37	Fleetweld 37
Size	3/32	1/8	5/32	5/32	3/16
Current (amp) AC	85	125	170	175	225
Arc Speed (in./min)	19 − 23	20 − 24	21 − 26	19 − 23	16 − 20
Electrode Req'd (lb/ft)	0.0358	0.0444	0.0546	0.0631	0.0922
Total Time (hr/ft of weld)	0.00953	0.00910	0.00850	0.00953	0.0111

Figure 50. Shielded Metal-Arc (Manual).

Position: Flat
Weld Quality Level: Commercial
Steel Weldability: Good
Welded From: One side

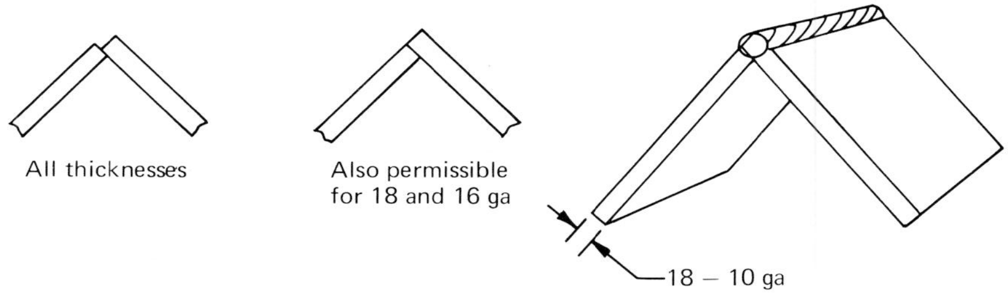

All thicknesses

Also permissible for 18 and 16 ga

18 — 10 ga

Plate Thickness (in.)	0.048 (18 ga)	0.060 (16 ga)	0.075 (14 ga)	0.105 (12 ga)	0.135 (10 ga)
Pass	1	1	1	1	1
Electrode Type	Fleetweld 5P	Fleetweld 5P	Fleetweld 5P	Fleetweld 5P	Fleetweld 5P
Size	3/32	1/8	1/8	5/32	3/16
Current (amp) DC(−)	45	80	85	110	155*
Arc Speed (in./min)	30 − 35	35 − 40	35 − 40	33 − 38	27 − 32
Electrode Req'd (lb/ft)	0.0197	0.0282	0.0300	0.0432	0.0505
Total Time (hr/ft of weld)	0.00616	0.00533	0.00533	0.00563	0.00678

* Use DC(+)

Figure 51. Shielded Metal-Arc (Manual).

Position: Vertical down
Weld Quality Level: Commercial
Steel Weldability: Good
Welded From: One side

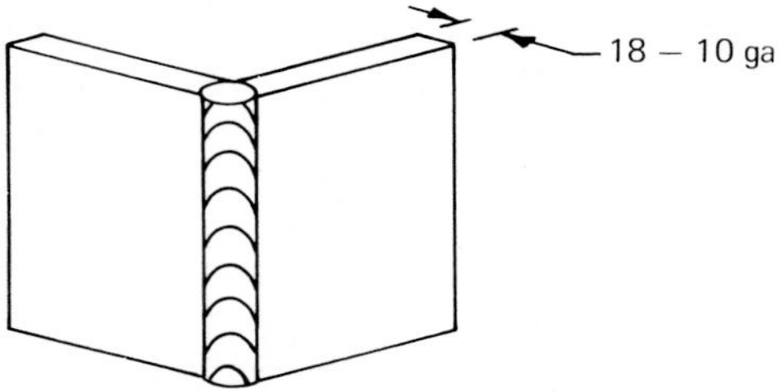

18 – 10 ga

Plate Thickness (in.)	0.048 (18 ga)	0.060 (16 ga)	0.075 (14 ga)	0.105 (12 ga)	0.135 (10 ga)
Pass	1	1	1	1	1
Electrode Type	Fleetweld 5P	Fleetweld 5P	Fleetweld 5P	Fleetweld 5P	Fleetweld 5P
Size	3/32	1/8	1/8	5/32	3/16
Current (amp) DC(−)	50	90	95	120	170*
Arc Speed (in./min)	35 – 40	40 – 45	40 – 45	37 – 42	33 – 38
Electrode Req'd (lb/ft)	0.0184	0.0278	0.0293	0.0436	0.0461
Total Time (hr/ft of weld)	0.00533	0.00471	0.00471	0.00507	0.00563

* DC(+)

Figure 52. Shielded Metal-Arc (Manual).

Position: Flat and horizontal
Weld Quality Level: Commercial
Steel Weldability: Good

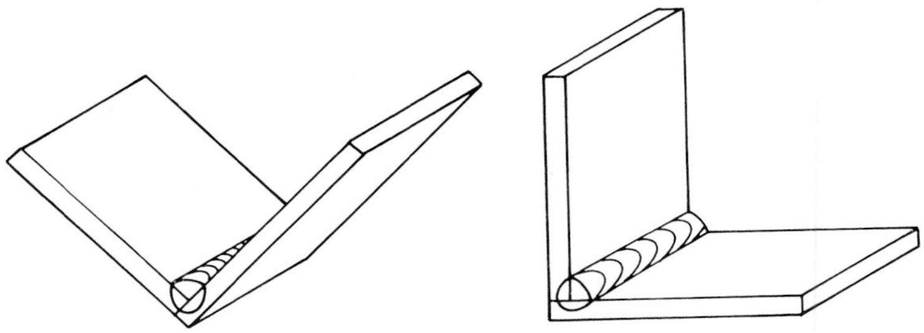

18 – 10 ga

Plate Thickness (in.)	0.048 (18 ga)	0.060 (16 ga)	0.075 (14 ga)	0.105 (12 ga)	0.135 (10 ga)
Pass	1	1	1	1	1
Electrode Type	E6013	E6012	E6012	E6012	E6012
Size	3/32	1/8	5/32	3/16	3/16
Current (amp) DC(−)	70	95	140	190	200
Arc Speed (in./min)	14 – 18	15 – 19	16 – 20	20 – 24	16 – 20
Electrode Req'd (lb/ft)	0.0413	0.0583	0.0848	0.0865	0.112
Total Time (hr/ft of weld)	0.0125	0.0118	0.0111	0.00910	0.0111

Figure 53. Shielded Metal-Arc (Manual).

Position: Flat and horizontal
Weld Quality Level: Commercial
Steel Weldability: Good

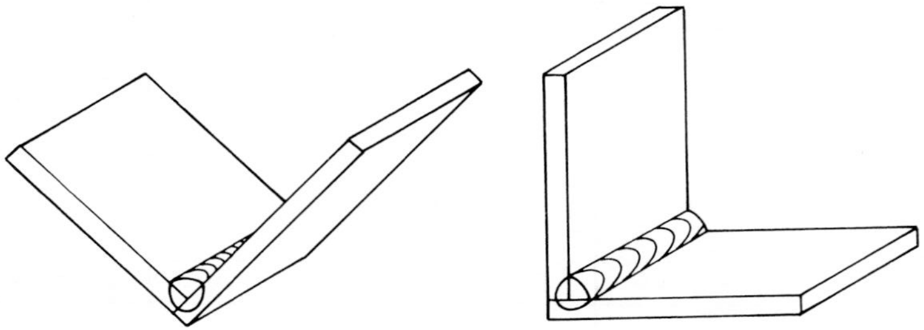

18 – 10 ga

Plate Thickness (in.)	0.048 (18 ga)	0.060 (16 ga)	0.075 (14 ga)	0.105 (12 ga)	0.135 (10 ga)
Pass	1	1	1	1	1
Electrode Type	E6013	E6013	E6013	E6013	E6013
Size	3/32	1/8	5/32	5/32	3/16
Current (amp) AC	70	105	155	160	210
Arc Speed (in./min)	14 – 18	14 – 18	15 – 19	14 – 18	14 – 18
Electrode Req'd (lb/ft)	0.0413	0.0495	0.0670	0.0742	0.0926
Total Time (hr/ft of weld)	0.0125	0.0125	0.0118	0.0125	0.0125

Figure 54. Shielded Metal-Arc (Manual).

Position: Flat
Weld Quality Level: Commercial
Steel Weldability: Good

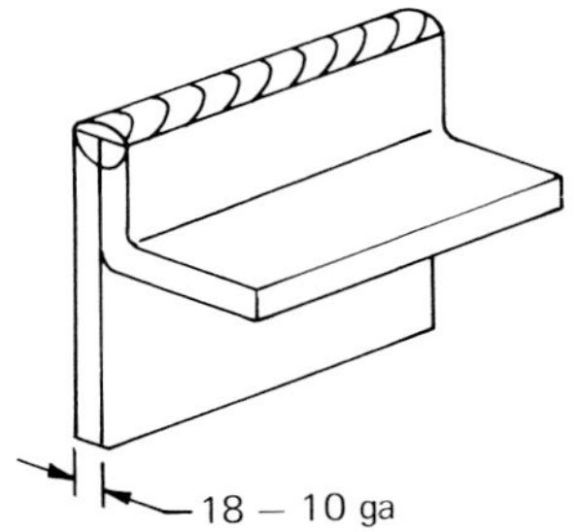

18 – 10 ga

Plate Thickness (in.)	0.048 (18 ga)	0.060 (16 ga)	0.075 (14 ga)	0.105 (12 ga)	0.135 (10 ga)
Pass	1	1	1	1	1
Electrode Type	E6010	E6010	E6010	E6010	E6010
Size	3/32	1/8	1/8	5/32	3/16
Current (amp) DC(−)	50	80	85	115	140
Arc Speed (in/min)	45 – 50	43 – 48	40 – 45	40 – 45	37 – 42
Electrode Req'd (lb/ft)	0.0145	0.0232	0.0263	0.0382	0.0476
Total Time (hr/ft of weld)	0.00421	0.00439	0.00471	0.00471	0.00505

Figure 55. Shielded Metal-Arc (Manual).

Position: Vertical down
Weld Quality Level: Commercial
Steel Weldability: Good

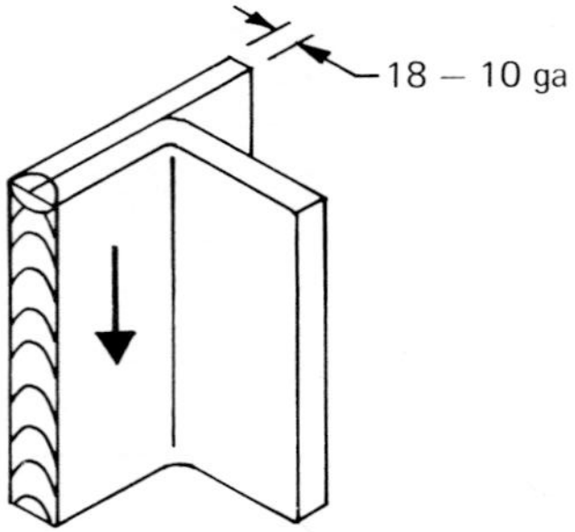

Plate Thickness (in.)	0.048 (18 ga)	0.060 (16 ga)	0.075 (14 ga)	0.105 (12 ga)	0.135 (10 ga)
Pass	1	1	1	1	1
Electrode Type	E6010	E6010	E6010	E6010	E6010
Size	3/32	1/8	1/8	5/32	3/16
Current (amp) DC(−)	55	90	95	125	155
Arc Speed (in./min)	53 – 58	50 – 55	47 – 52	47 – 52	43 – 48
Electrode Req'd (lb/ft)	0.0141	0.0225	0.0251	0.0358	0.0473
Total Time (hr/ft of weld)	0.00361	0.00381	0.00404	0.00404	0.00439

Figure 56. Shielded Metal-Arc (Manual).

Plug-Weld Procedures

These are a special type of welds made by fusing the metal of one plate to the side of a hole (generally round) in another plate, the plates being held closely together.

Two common types of plug welds are as follows:
1. Round hole in one plate. Here the diameter of the hole is up to 2-1/4 times the plate thickness. See Figure 57.

Figure 57.

2. Scarfed hole in one plate. The scarfing corresponds to a backed-up butt joint with more than usual root opening, as shown in Figure 58.

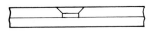

Figure 58.

Plug welds are used to advantage primarily in cases where access to the work is from one side only, such as flooring, in cover plates for girders, additions to existing structures, or to provide additional strength or stiffness in cases where there is not sufficient space or accessibility available to use the usual fillet welds. An example of the latter case is a lap joint welded from one side only, as shown in Figure 59.

Figure 59.

It is to be noted that plug welds cause practically no distortion and are, therefore, particularly useful in cases of plate fabrication where distortion is encountered.

The procedure for plug welds is unique, inasmuch as the direction of welding changes constantly. The corner all around must be completely fused. For any given instant, the electrode position is approximately standard, or as near 30° – 60° as the hole will permit.

The inside corner all around is generally welded first. For plug welds made in the flat position, the arc is carried around the root of the joint and then carried along a spiral path to the center of the hole, fusing and depositing a layer of weld metal in the root and bottom of joint. This welding in a circle should continue without breaking the arc until the plug is filled in. If the arc is broken or slag interference occurs, then the weld must be cleaned by chipping to remove the slag. If the arc is not broken, the slag will float to the surface and may be cleaned after the plug is completed. E7018 electrodes with AC are best.

Positon: Flat
Weld Quality Level: Commercial
Steel Weldability: Good

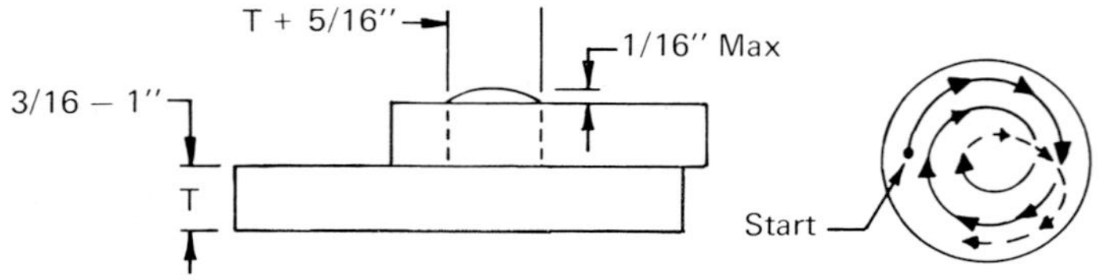

T + 5/16″

1/16″ Max

T

3/16 − 1″

Start

Plate Thickness (in.)	3/16	5/16	3/8	1/2	3/4+	1+
Electrode Type			Jetweld LH-70			
Size	1/8	3/16	3/16	7/32	1/4	1/4
Current (amp) AC	140	250	250	300	350	350
Arc Speed (in./min)						
Electrode Req'd*	0.0154	0.0440	0.0642	0.113	0.300	0.605
Total Time* (hr)	0.00417	0.00500	0.00731	0.0118	0.0236	0.0475

Weld with spiral motion and continue as long as slag can be kept molten or until the weld is completed.

* Per weld

+ Thickness of these welds may be reduced to 5/8″ per AWS Structural Welding Code 2.8.8.

Figure 60. Shielded Metal-Arc (Manual).

Corrective Suggestions

Every weld should be a good weld. This means that it should be made at the lowest possible cost to adequately perform the function for which it is designed. A weld that is expensively overwelded is almost as bad as a weld that is underwelded.

To make a good weld requires not only a knowledge of the proper procedures, but also a knowledge of how to recognize a good weld and how to recognize faults in a weld and how to correct them. Failure at this point can be harmful to the quality of welding and substantially increase its cost.

Inspection

If standard procedures are used as specified, the end result, the weld, can usually be predicted. To get the best results, therefore, the best time to inspect a weld is while it is being made. A check as to edge preparation, electrode type and size, welding current and travel speed used, and surface appearance of the computed weld can tell a qualified inspector most of the information he needs to know about the strength of the weld.

A good surface appearance is determined by the following factors: no cracks; no serious undercut, overlap, surface holes, or slag inclusions. The ripples and width of bead should be uniform, with butt welds flush or slightly above the plate surface without excessive buildup. Fillet welds should have equal legs on each plate. If there is more than a slight variation from these standards, a check should be made on plate preparation, gap limits, polarity, current, speed, electrode angle, and other factors of welding.

Training the Inspector

To employ visual inspection effectively, some training is necessary, both to be able to observe during welding, as well as after welding. The method: Maintain all conditions fixed except one and note the effect of variation of that one condition. The conditions are: (1) welding current; (2) arc length; and (3) arc speed, for a certain plate thickness, type of joint, and size of electrode. The results to be observed are:

1. Consumption of electrode. How it melts off – smoothly or evenly.
2. Crater. Its size, shape, and appearance of surface.
3. Bead. Its size, shape, and fusion.
4. Sound of the arc.

Observing these four items and noting the effect of variation of one of the three conductors, the initial observation is made under normal conditions. (See Figure 1).

Observation A is made with:

```
(1) arc current  =  100% normal
(2) arc length   =  100% normal
(3) arc speed    =  100% normal
```

Observation B is made with:

    (1) arc current = 50% normal
    (2) arc length = 100% normal
    (3) arc speed = 100% normal

Observation C is with:

    (1) arc current = 150–250% normal
    (2) arc length = 100% normal
    (3) arc speed = 100% normal

Observation D is with:

    (1) arc current = 100% normal
    (2) arc length = 50% normal
    (3) arc speed = 100% normal

Observation E is with:

    (1) arc current = 100% normal
    (2) arc length = 150–200% normal
    (3) arc speed = 100% normal

Observation F is with:

    (1) arc current = 100% normal
    (2) arc length = 100% normal
    (3) arc speed = 50% normal

Observation G is with:

    (1) arc current = 100% normal
    (2) arc length = 100% normal
    (3) arc speed = 150–250% normal

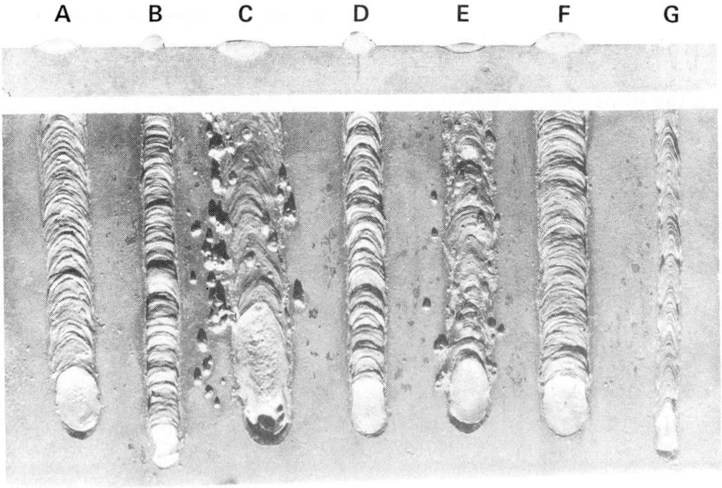

Figure 1. Plan and elevation views of welds made with an E6010-type electrode under various conditions. Conditions are accentuated to illustrate differences. Iron-powder-type electrodes when used minimize variations shown here. (A) Current, arc length, and speed normal. (B) Current too low. (C) Current too high. (D) Arc length too short. (E) Arc length too long. (F) Speed too low. (G) Speed too high.

The effects of variation in conditions were more apparent when bare electrodes were used. Modern shielded-metal-arc electrodes are less sensitive to adverse conditions, but the results in Figure 1 can be observed. The newer iron-powder electrodes still further minimize the effect of variations. Arc-length control is automatic when the contact technique is used. Control of variables is designed into the electrode itself.

Careful observation of the operations by *actual performance* in the shop will enable a good observer to become a trained welding inspector. This training and experience will be of great assistance to the inspector in judging welds both during and after welding.

Inspection During Welding

The method outlined above applies to the inspection of welds during their making.

Inspection After Welding

As in the inspection during welding, certain telltale signs will reveal considerable information to a qualified inspector after the welding is done. Items to consider in inspecting after welding include size and shape of bead, appearance of bead, appearance of slag, undercut, overlap, and location of craters (indicating where operator started and stopped welding). A study of the weld and proper interpretation of these telltale signs will disclose other conditions of welding. These conditions are illustrated in Figures 1 and in 2, 3 and 4 (A to I) for an E6012 type electrode. The illustrations show the appearance of beads deposited under different procedures; some good, some poor. A study of these will indicate clearly what normal conditions are and the comparison to abnormal conditions. Welds were *not* made with iron-powder-type electrodes. With an E7024 electrode, appearance would be improved and be less susceptible to the effects of variations.

Weld Spatter

Weld spatter is an appearance defect of no consequence to the structural function of the weld. Excessive spatter is not necessary, however, and its appearance on a weldment is not pleasing.

Cause. (1) Using too high a welding current. (2) Wrong electrode. (3) Wrong polarity. (4) Too large an electrode. (5) Wrong electrode angle. (6) Arc blow. (7) Too long an arc length.

Cure. (1) Select the proper current setting for the diameter electrode and plate thickness. (2) Be sure that the electrode does not have an inherent spatter-producing characteristic. (3) Check the polarity switch to determine that the polarity is correct for the electrode. (4) Use an electrode of the proper diameter for the plate thickness. (5) Correct electrode angle for procedure used. (6) See Lesson 1.14 for corrections for arc blow. (7) Shorten arc length.

Undercut

Undercut, unless it is serious, is more of an appearance defect than a structural detriment. Unfortunately, however, some inspection agencies will not accept undercut of any type and demand that it be chipped out and the joint rewelded. For this reason, undercut should be avoided.

Cause. (1) Welding current too high. (2) Improper electrode manipulation. (3) Arc blow. (4) Too long an arc length. (5) Incorrect direction of welding.

Tabulation of resultant weld characteristics obtained on fillet welds when proper welding procedure is used, except as indicated. This tabulation applies to welding of mild rolled steel with E6012 electrodes in the horizontal position, as shown in Figure 2, 3 and 4.

TABLE 1 – RESULTING WELD CHARACTERISTICS

	"A"	"B"	"C"	"D"	"E"	"F"	"G"	"H"	"I"
Arc current	Normal	Low	High	Normal	Normal	Normal	Normal	Normal	Normal
Arc length	Normal	Normal	Normal	Short	Long	Normal	Normal	Normal	Normal
Arc speed	Normal	Normal	Normal	Normal	Normal	Low	High	Normal	Normal
Electrode angle	Normal	Normal	Normal	Normal	Normal	Normal	Normal	Angle "A" too small	Angle "A" too large
Appearance of bead	Good surface. No undercut. Good slag coverage. Throat proper size.	Surface apt to be rough due to poor slag coverage. Not well fused to both plates. Throat much too small.	Rough surface. Bad undercut. Slag uneven.	On some steels, surface rough and slag may fall away from vertical plate or "island-out". On most mild steels, it is satisfactory. Surface holes on some plates.	Bad undercut. Too much metal on bottom plate. Surface rough because of poor slag coverage.	Too much metal on bottom plate. Slag may fall away from vertical plate.	Surface rough due to poor slag coverage. Bad undercut. Small surface holes. Throat too small.	Too much metal on bottom plate. Legs uneven. Throat too small.	Ridge down center of bead. Slag falls away from vertical plate. Undercut. Legs uneven.

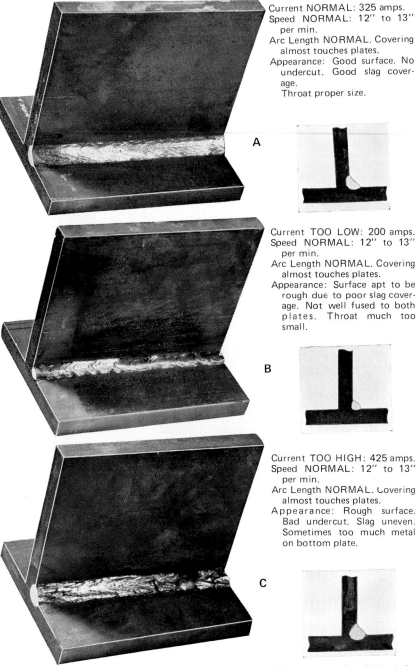

Current NORMAL: 325 amps.
Speed NORMAL: 12" to 13" per min.
Arc Length NORMAL. Covering almost touches plates.
Appearance: Good surface. No undercut. Good slag coverage.
Throat proper size.

A

Current TOO LOW: 200 amps.
Speed NORMAL: 12" to 13" per min.
Arc Length NORMAL. Covering almost touches plates.
Appearance: Surface apt to be rough due to poor slag coverage. Not well fused to both plates. Throat much too small.

B

Current TOO HIGH: 425 amps.
Speed NORMAL: 12" to 13" per min.
Arc Length NORMAL. Covering almost touches plates.
Appearance: Rough surface. Bad undercut. Slag uneven. Sometimes too much metal on bottom plate.

C

Figure 2 (A, B, C). Fillet-weld specimens made with E6012 electrode. See Table 1 for explanation. Current and speed values will be substantially different when iron-powder electrodes are used.

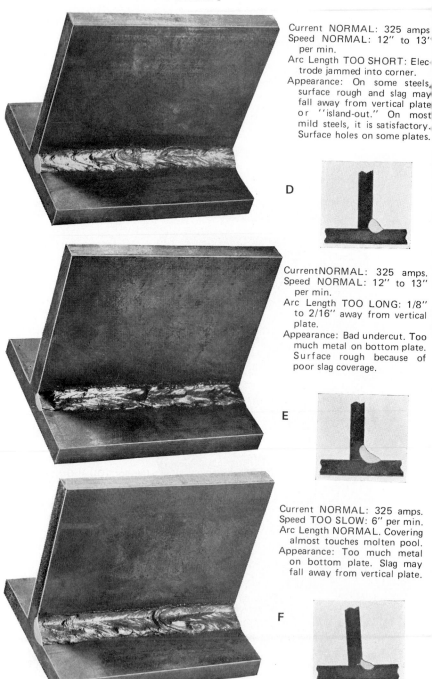

Current NORMAL: 325 amps
Speed NORMAL: 12" to 13" per min.
Arc Length TOO SHORT: Electrode jammed into corner.
Appearance: On some steels, surface rough and slag may fall away from vertical plate or ''island-out.'' On most mild steels, it is satisfactory. Surface holes on some plates.

D

CurrentNORMAL: 325 amps.
Speed NORMAL: 12" to 13" per min.
Arc Length TOO LONG: 1/8" to 2/16" away from vertical plate.
Appearance: Bad undercut. Too much metal on bottom plate. Surface rough because of poor slag coverage.

E

Current NORMAL: 325 amps.
Speed TOO SLOW: 6" per min.
Arc Length NORMAL. Covering almost touches molten pool.
Appearance: Too much metal on bottom plate. Slag may fall away from vertical plate.

F

Figure 3 (D, E, F). Fillet-weld specimens made with E6012 electrode. See Table 1.

Current NORMAL: 325 amps.
Speed TOO HIGH: 18" to 19"
    per min.
Arc Length NORMAL. Covering
    almost touches plates.
Appearance: Surface rough due
    to poor slag coverage. Bad
    undercut. Small surface
    holes. Throat too small.

G

Current NORMAL: 325 amps.
Speed NORMAL: 12" to 13"
    per min.
Arc Length NORMAL. Covering
    almost touches plates.
Electrode held TOO HIGH:
    Held at 80° to flat plate (in-
    stead of normal 45° - 60°).
Appearance: Too much metal
    on bottom plate. Legs un-
    even. Throat too small.

H

Current NORMAL: 325 amps.
Speed NORMAL: 12" to 13"
    per min.
Arc Length NORMAL. Covering
    almost touches plates.
Electrode held TOO LOW: Held
    at 30° to flat plate (instead
    of normal 45° - 60°).
Appearance: Ridge down center
    of bead. Slag falls away from
    vertical plate. Undercut. Legs
    uneven.

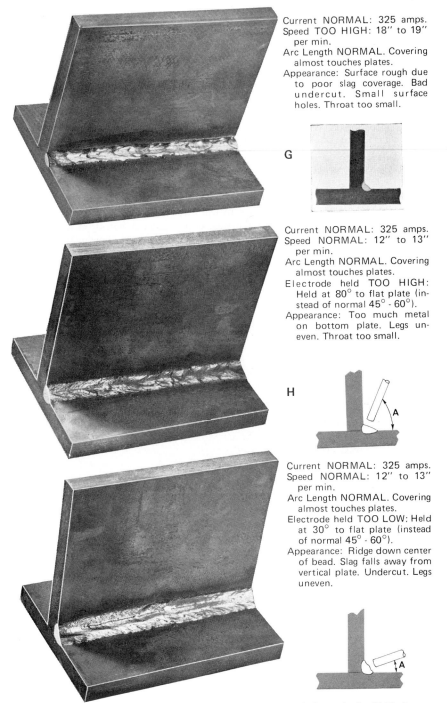

Figure 4 (G, H, I). Fillet-weld specimens made with E6012 electrode. See Table 1.

Cure. (1) Use correct welding current and correct travel speed. (2) Undercut may result from using too large an electrode. It may also result if the molten weld puddle is too large. A uniform weave of the electrode will tend to prevent undercutting when making butt welds. Excessive weaving will cause undercut and should be avoided. See Lesson 1.14 for corrections for arc blow.

Poor Fusion

Poor fusion is sometimes associated with incomplete penetration and can be a structural fault. Proper fusion is essential to making full-strength welds. It should be the concern of both weldor and inspector to assure that correct procedures are used to obtain the required fusion and penetration.

Cause. (1) Current setting improper. (2) Welding technique improper. (3) Failure to prepare joint properly. (4) Wrong size welding electrode used.

Cure. (1) Remember, heavier plates require more current for a given electrode than small plates. Be sure to use sufficiently high welding current to insure correct deposition of weld metal with a good penetration of the base metal. (2) In connection with welding technique, be sure to thoroughly melt the sides of the joint. (3) In preparing the joint, be sure the face of the groove is clean and free of foreign material. Deposit the weld metal in such a manner as to insure good fusion between the plates. (4) Use an electrode sufficiently small to reach the bottom of the groove in making the first pass.

Cracking – Causes and Cures

Except in some weld-surfacing operations, cracks are considered deleterious. Cracking can occur either in the deposited metal or in the heat-affected zone of the base metal adjacent to the weld. The major cause of cracking in the base metal or in the weld metal is a high-carbon or high alloy content that increases the hardenability. High hardenability, combined with a fast cooling rate, produces the brittle condition that leads to cracking. Other causes of weld cracking are: joint restraint that produces high residual stresses in the weld, improper shape of the surface of the weld bead, hydrogen pickup, and contaminants on the plate or electrode.

Factors Causing Underbead Cracking

Subsurface cracks in the base metal, under or near the weld, are known as underbead cracks. Underbead cracking in the heat-affected base metal is caused by: 1. A relatively high-carbon or alloy-content steel that is allowed to cool too rapidly from the welding temperature. 2. Hydrogen pickup during welding.

Underbead cracking seldom occurs with the preferred-analysis steels. With carbon steels above 0.35% carbon content and with the low-alloy structural-grade steels, underbead cracking can be minimized by using a low-hydrogen welding process. The problem is most severe with materials such as the heat-treated structural steels having tensile strengths of 100,000 psi and higher.

The second factor that promotes underbead cracking – the pickup and retention of hydrogen – is also influenced by the cooling rate from the welding temperature. During welding, some hydrogen – a decomposition product of moisture from the air, electrode covering, wire, flux, shielding gas, or the surface of the plate – can dissolve into the molten weld metal and from there into extremely hot (but not molten) base metal. If cooling occurs slowly, the process reverses, and the hydrogen has sufficient time to escape through the weld into the air. But if cooling is rapid, some hydrogen may be trapped in the heat-

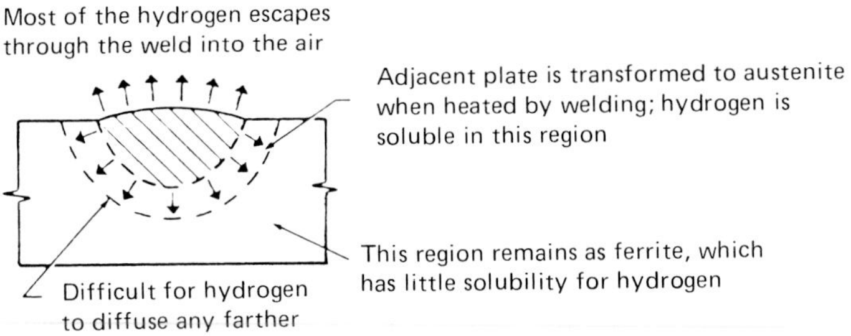

Most of the hydrogen escapes
through the weld into the air

Adjacent plate is transformed to austenite
when heated by welding; hydrogen is
soluble in this region

This region remains as ferrite, which
has little solubility for hydrogen

Difficult for hydrogen
to diffuse any farther

Figure 5. Austenitic heat-affected zone of a weld has high solubility for hydrogen. Upon cooling, the hydrogen builds up pressure that can cause underbead cracking.

affected zone next to the weld metal, as illustrated by Figure 5. The hydrogen is absorbed and produces a condition of low ductility known as hydrogen embrittlement.

One theory suggests that the hydrogen produces a pressure, which — combined with shrinkage stresses and any hardening effect from the chemistry of the steel — causes tiny cracks in the metal immediately under the weld bead (Figure 6). Similar cracks that appear on the plate surface adjacent to the weld are called "toe cracks."

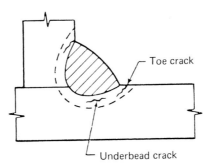

— Toe crack

— Underbead crack

Figure 6. Underbead cracking and toe cracks caused by hydrogen pickup in heat-affected zone of plate.

Slower cooling (by welding slower, or by preheating) allows more of the hydrogen to escape and helps control the problem. In addition, the use of low-hydrogen welding materials eliminates the major source of hydrogen and usually eliminates underbead cracking.

Rapid cooling rates occur when the arc strikes on a cold plate — at the start of a weld with no previous weld bead to preheat the metal. The highest cooling rates occur on thick plate and in short tack welds. The effect of weld length on cooling rate can be illustrated by the time required to cool welds for a particular welding procedure from 1600° to 200°F on a 3/4" steel plate:

2-1/2" weld	1.5 minutes
4" weld	5 minutes
9" weld	33 minutes

A 9"-long weld made on plate at 70°F has about the same cooling rate as a 3" weld on a plate that has been preheated to 300°F.

Welds with large cross sections require greater heat input than smaller ones. High welding current and slow travel rates reduce the rate of cooling and decrease the likelihood of cracking.

The Effects of Section Thickness

In a steel mill, billets are rolled into plates or shapes while red hot. The rolled members are then placed on finishing tables to cool. Because a thin plate has more surface area in proportion to its mass than a thick plate, it loses heat faster (by radiation) and cools more rapidly.

If a thick plate has the same chemistry as a thin one, its slower cooling rate results in lower tensile and yield strength, lower hardness, and higher elongation. In very thick plates, the cooling rate may be so low that the properties of the steel may not meet minimum specifications. Thus, to meet specified yield-strength levels, the mill may increase the carbon or alloy content of the steels that are to be rolled into thick sections.

In welding, cooling rates of thin and thick plates are just the opposite. Because of the larger mass of plate, the weld area in a thick plate cools more rapidly than the weld area in a thin plate. The heat input at the weld area is transferred, by conduction, to the large mass of relatively cool steel, thus cooling the weld area relatively rapidly. (Heat is transferred more rapidly by conduction than by radiation.) The thin plate has less mass to absorb the heat, and it cools at a slower rate. The faster cooling of the thicker plate produces higher tensile and yield strengths, higher hardness, and lower elongation.

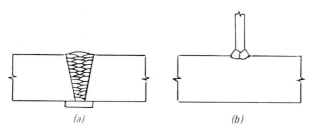

(a)   *(b)*

Figure 7. A groove-welded butt joint in thick plate (a) requires a higher preheat, because of joint restraint, than a fillet-welded joint of a thin member and a thick plate (b).

Welds in structural-steel shapes and plate under 1/2" thick have less tendency toward cracking than welds in thicker plate. In addition to the favorable (slower) cooling rate of thinner members, two other factors minimize causes of cracking: 1. Thinner plate weldments usually have a good ratio (high) of weld-throat-to-plate thickness. 2. Because they are less rigid, thinner plates can flex more as the weld cools, thus reducing restraint on the weld metal.

Thicker plates and rolled sections do not have these advantages. Because a weld cools faster on a thick member, and because the thick member probably has a higher carbon or alloy content, welds on a thick section have higher strength and hardness but lower ductility than similar welds on thin plate. If these properties are unacceptable, preheating (especially for the more critical root pass) may be necessary to reduce the cooling rate.

Because it increases cost, preheating should be used only when needed. For example, a thin web to be joined to a thick flange plate by fillet welds may not

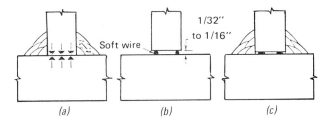

Figure 8. In a restrained joint in thick plates (1), all shrinkage stress must be taken up in the weld. Separating the plates with soft wires (b) allows the plates to move slightly during cooling. The wires flatten (c) and remove most of the stress from the weld metal.

require as much preheat as two highly restrained thick plates joined by a multiple-pass butt weld (Figure 7).

The Effect of Joint Restraint

If metal-to-metal contact exists between thick plates prior to welding, the plates cannot move — the joint is restrained. As the weld cools and contracts, all shrinkage stress must be taken up in the weld, as illustrated in Figure 8(a). This restraing may cause the weld to crack, especially in the first pass on the second side of the plate.

Joint restraints can be minimized by providing a space of 1/32" to 1/16" between the two members to allow some movement during cooling. Such spaces or gaps can be incorporated by several simple means:

1. Soft steel wire spacers may be placed between the plates, as in Figure 8(b). The wire flattens out as the weld shrinks, as shown in Figure 8(c).

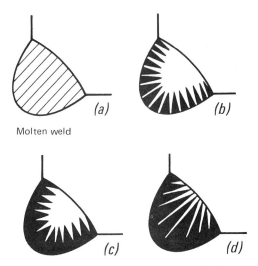

Figure 9. A molten fillet weld (a) starts to solidify along the sides next to the plate (b). Solidification proceeds as shown in (c) and (d).

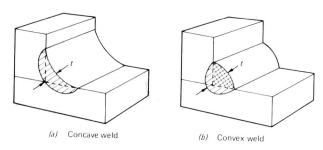

(a) Concave weld   (b) Convex weld

Figure 10. The leg size and the surface of a concave fillet weld (a) may be larger than that of a convex bead (b), but its throat, t, may be considerably smaller.

(Copper wire should not be used because it may contaminate the weld metal).

2. Rough flame-cut edges on the plate. The peaks of the cut edge keep the plates apart, yet can deform and flatten out as the weld shrinks.

3. Upsetting the edge of the plate with a heavy center punch. Results are similar to those of the flame-cut edge.

Provision for a space between thick plates to be welded is particularly important for fillet welds.

Fillet Welds: A molten fillet weld starts to solidify, or freeze, along the sides of the joint, as in Figure 9, because the heat is conducted to the adjacent plate, which is at a much lower temperature. Freezing progresses inward until the entire weld is solid. The last material to freeze is that at the center, near the surface of the weld.

Although a concave fillet weld may appear to be larger than a convex weld (Figure 10), it may have less penetration into the welded plates and a smaller throat than the convex bead. Thus the convex weld may be the stronger of the two, even though it appears to be smaller.

In the past, the concave weld has been preferred by designers because of the smoother stress flow it offers to resist a load on the joint. Experience has shown, however, that single-pass concave fillet welds have a greater tendency to crack during cooling than do convex welds. This disadvantage usually outweighs the effect of improved stress distribution, especially in steels that require special welding procedures.

When a concave bead cools and shrinks, the outer surface is in tension and

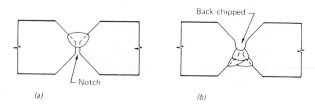

Figure 11. The root pass of a double-V joint is susceptible to cracking because of the notch effect (a). On high-quality work, the notch is minimized by back-chipping (b).

may crack. A convex bead has considerably reduced shrinkage stresses in the surface area, and the possibility of cracking during cooling is reduced.

When design conditions require concave welds for smooth flow of stresses in thick plate, the first bead (usually three or more passes are required) should be slightly convex. The others are then built up to the required shape.

Groove Welds: The root pass of a groove weld in heavy plate usually requires special welding procedures. For example, the root pass on the first side of a double-V joint is susceptible to cracking because of the notch, as illustrated in Figure 11(a), which is a crack starter. On high-quality work, this notch is back-gouged, as in Figure 11(b), to: 1) Remove slag or oxides from the bottom of the groove. 2) Remove any small cracks that may have occurred in the root bead. 3) Widen the groove at the bottom so that the first bead of the second side is large enough to resist the shrinkage that it must withstand due to the rigidity of the joint.

The weld metal tends to shrink in all directions as it cools, and restraint from the heavy plates produces tensile stresses within the weld. The metal yields plastically while hot to accommodate the stresses; if the internal stresses exceed the strength of the weld, it cracks, usually along the centerline.

The problem is greater if the plate material has a higher carbon content than the welding electrode. If this is the case, the weld metal usually picks up additional carbon through admixture with the base metal. Under such conditions, the root bead is usually less ductile than subsequent beads.

A concave root bead in a groove weld, as shown in Figure 12(a), has the same tendency toward cracking as it does in a fillet weld. Increasing the throat dimension of the root pass, as in Figure 12(b), helps to prevent cracking. Electrodes and procedures should be used that produce a convex bead shape. A low-hydrogen process reduces cracking tendencies; if not, preheating may be required.

Centerline cracking can also occur in subsequent passes of a multiple-pass weld if the passes are excessively wide or concave. This can be corrected by putting down narrower, slightly convex beads, making the weld two or more beads wide, as in Figure 13.

Width/Depth Ratio: Cracks caused by joint restraint or material chemistry usually appear at the face of the weld. In some situations, however, internal cracks occur that do not reach the surface. These are usually caused by improper joint design (narrow, deep grooves or fillets) or by misuse of a welding process that can achieve deep penetration.

If the depth of fusion is much greater than the width of the weld face, the surface of the weld may freeze before the center does. When this happens, the

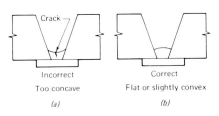

Incorrect — Too concave
(a)

Correct — Flat or slightly convex
(b)

Figure 12. A concave root pass (a) may crack because tensile stresses exceed the strength of the weld metal. A slightly convex root-pass bead (b) helps prevent cracking.

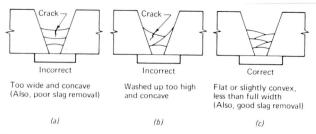

Figure 13. Wide, concave passes (a and b) in a multiple-pass weld may crack. Slightly convex beads (c) are recommended.

shrinkage forces act on the almost-frozen center (the strength of which is lower than that of the frozen surface) and can cause a crack that does not extend to the surface. Figure 14(a) is illustrative.

Internal cracks can also be caused by improper joint design or preparation. Results of combining thick plate, a deep-penetrating welding process, and a 45° included angle are shown in Figure 14(b). A similar result on a fillet weld made with deep penetration is shown in Figure 14(c). A too-small bevel, and arc-gouging a groove too narrow for its depth on the second-pass side of a double-V groove weld, can cause the internal crack shown in Figure 14(d).

Internal cracks are serious because they cannot be detected by visual inspection methods. But they can be eliminated if preventive measures are used. Penetration and volume of weld metal deposited in each pass can be controlled by regulating welding speed and current and by using a joint design that establishes

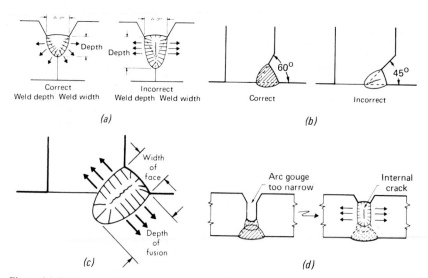

Figure 14. Internal cracking can occur when weld penetration is greater than width. Correct and incorrect proportions are shown in (a), (b), and (c). Arc-gouging a groove too narrow for its depth can cause a similar internal crack (d).

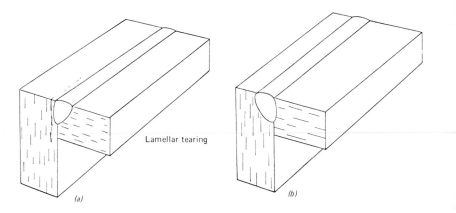

Figure 15. Lamellar tearing (a) and a suggested solution (b).

reasonable depth-of-fusion requirements. Recommended ratios of width of each individual bead to depth of fusion are between 1.2 to 1 and 2 to 1.

Lamellar cracking or tearing is illustrated in Figure 15. In (a), the shrinkage forces on the upright member are perpendicular to the direction in which the plate was rolled at the steel mill. The inclusions within the plate are strung out in the direction of rolling. If the shrinkage stress should become high enough, lamellar tear might occur by the progressive cracking from one inclusion to the next. A way to prevent this is illustrated in Figure 15(b). Here, the bevel has been made in the upright plate. The weld now cuts across the inclusions, and the shrinkage forces are distributed, rather than applied to a single plane of inclusions.

Porosity

Porosity in welds does not present too serious a problem from a strength standpoint, unless the weld is extremely porous. Surface holes in the weld bead are undesirable from an appearance standpoint. The other common forms of porosity, aside from surface holes, commonly referred to as blow holes, are gas pockets and slag inclusions.

Cause. (1) One of the major causes of porosity is poor base metal. (2) Improper welding procedure also results in porosity of weld metal. (3) Porosity may be an inherent defect of the welding electrode being used.

Cure. (1) Be sure the base metal is one that will produce a porosity-free weld. High-sulfur, phosphorus, and silicon steels sometimes produce gaseous combinations that tend to make blow holes and gas pockets. Nonferrous material, high in oxygen, also tends to result in porous welds. Base metal, containing segregations and impurities, contribute to porosity. (2) Change welding procedure. Do not use excessive welding currents, but be sure that each layer of weld metal is completely free of slag and flux before depositing another layer. Puddle the weld, keeping the metal molten sufficiently long to allow entrapped gases to escape. Decrease current and use a short arc. (3) Most low-hydrogen electrodes will be found helpful in eliminating porosity.

Moisture Pickup

Electrodes exposed to damp atmosphere may pick up moisture that, when excessive, may cause undercut, rough welds, porosity, or cracking. For electrodes other than low-hydrogen, this condition is usually corrected by storing the electrodes in a cabinet or room heated to about 10° F above the surrounding atmosphere. If the electrodes have become wet, they may be dried by removing from box and spreading out to dry at a temperature of 200° F for one hour. Some types may require a higher temperature.

For drying low-hydrogen electrodes see Lesson 3.5.

Preventive Inspection

In summary, it should be universally recognized that inspection after welding, while often essential, is somewhat too late. Any excessive weld cracks, undercuts, undersize welds, poor fusion or other defects detected that late will be expensive to correct. All parties concerned should insist on good welding, supervision, conscientious qualified weldors, and a thorough system of preventive inspection.

Preventive inspection, in which every one concerned should share responsibility, involves a systematic observation of welding practices and adherence to specifications before, during, and after welding in order to visually detect and stop any occurrences that may result in substandard welds. The check list that follows will aid in developing this pattern of operation.

Check List of Items That Influence Weld Quality (Points to be Visually Checked for Before, During and After Welding)

● O O	Check Before Welding	
O ● O	Check During Welding	
O O ●	Check After Welding	

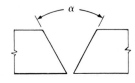

1. *Proper Included Angle*   ● O O
   The included angle must be sufficient to allow electrode to reach root of joint, and to ensure fusion to side walls on multiple passes. In general, the greater this angle the more weld metal will be required.

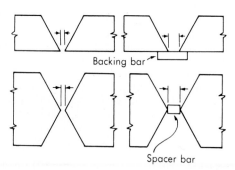

Backing bar

Spacer bar

2. *Proper Root Opening (Fit-Up)*   ● O O
   Without a backing bar, there is a possibility of burning through on the first pass; so, the root opening is reduced slightly. Lack of fusion of the root pass to the very bottom of the joint is no real problem because the joint must be back gouged before the pass may be made on the back side.

With a backing bar, the root opening is increased to allow proper fusion into the backing bar, since it will not be back gouged; also there is no burn-through.

With a spacer bar, it serves as a backing bar but must be back gouged before welding on the back side to ensure sound fusion.

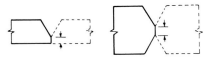

3. *Proper Root Face*   ● ○ ○

A root face is usually specified in joints welded by the submerged-arc process to prevent burn-through on the first or root pass; therefore, there is a minimum limit to this dimension. There is also a maximum limit so that the back pass, when made, will fuse with the first root pass to provide a sound joint. This fusion of root and back passes can be checked after welding, if the joint runs out to an exposed edge of the plate and onto run-off bars.

(a) Too small root face; (b) Too large root face; (c) Proper root face;
burn-through   lack of penetration   proper penetration

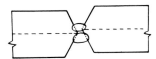

4. *Proper Alignment*   ● ○ ○

Misalignment of plates being joined may result in an unpenetrated portion between root and back passes. This would require more back gouging.

The previous items, included angle (1) and root opening (2), go hand in hand to ensure clearance for the electrode to enter the joint sufficiently for proper fusion at the root, and yet not require excessive weld metal.

In general, as the included angle is decreased to reduce the amount of weld metal, the root must be opened up to maintain proper fusion of weld metal at the joint root. For any given thickness of plate, there is a range in the combination of included angle and root opening that will result in a minimum amount of weld metal consistent with the required weld quality.

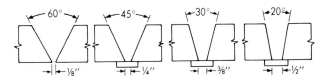

5. *Cleanliness of Joint* ● ● ●
Joint and plate surface must be clean of dirt, rust, and moisture. This is especially important on those surfaces to be fused with the deposited weld metal.

6. *Proper Type and Size of Electrode* ○ ● ○
Electrodes must suit the metal being joined, the welding position, the function of the weld, the plate thickness, the size of the joint, etc. Where standard procedures specify the electrodes, periodic checks should be made to ensure their use.

7. *Proper Welding Current and Polarity* ○ ● ○
Welding current and polarity must suit the type electrode used and the joint to be made.

8. *Proper Tack Welds* ○ ● ○
These should be small and long, if possible, so they won't interfere with subsequent submerged-arc welds. On heavy plates, low-hydrogen electrodes should be used.

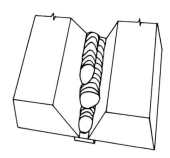

9. *Good Fusion* ○ ● ●
Each pass should fuse properly into any backing plate, preceding pass, or adjacent plate metal. No unfilled or unfused pockets should be left between weld beads.

10. *Proper Preheat and Interpass Temperature*
The need for preheat and required temperature level depends on the plate thickness, the grade of steel, the welding process, and ambient temperatures. Where these conditions dictate the need, periodical checks should be made to ensure adherence to requirements.

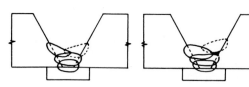

(a) No problem for next pass to fuse properly into side of joint and weld   (b) Not enough room left between side of joint and last pass; will not fuse properly; may trap slag

11. *Proper Sequencing of Passes* ○ ● ○
The sequencing of passes should be such that no unfused portion results, nor distortion.

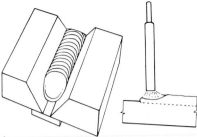

○ ● ○

12. *Proper Travel Speed*

If travel speed is too slow, molten weld metal and slag will tend to run ahead and start to cool; the main body of weld metal will run over this without the arc penetrating far enough, and the trapped slag will reduce fusion.

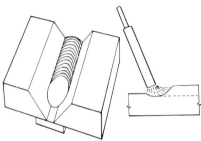

If travel speed is increased, good fusion will result because the molten weld metal and slag will be forced backward, with the arc digging into the plate.

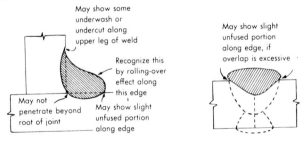

May show some underwash or undercut along upper leg of weld

Recognize this by rolling-over effect along this edge

May not penetrate beyond root of joint

May show slight unfused portion along edge

May show slight unfused portion along edge, if overlap is excessive

○ ● ●

13. *Absence of Overlap*

If speed of travel is too slow, the excessive amount of weld metal being deposited will tend to roll over along the edges, preventing proper fusion. This roll-over action is easily noticed during welding. The correction is very simple; increasing the travel speed will achieve the desired effect (below).

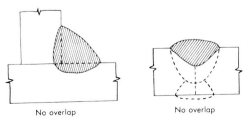

No overlap

No overlap

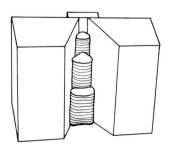

14. *In Vertical Welding, Tilt of Crater*   ○ ● ○

The crater position should be kept tilted slightly so slag will run out toward the front of weld and will not interfere. This will help ensure good fusion.

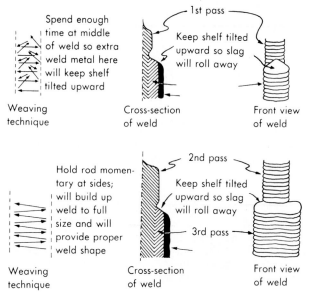

15. *Filled Craters*   ○ ● ●

It might be argued that craters are a problem if —

a. they are undersize, i.e. not full throat, and/or
b. they are concave, since they might crack upon cooling; of course, once they cool down to room temperature, this would no longer be a problem.

Normally, on continuous fillet welds, there is no crater problem because each crater is filled by the next weld. The weldor starts his arc at the outer end of the last crater and momentarily swings back into the crater to fill it before going ahead for the next weld.

For a single connection, it is important at the end of the weld not to leave the crater in a highly stressed area. If necessary to do so, extra care should be taken to carefully fill the crater to full throat.

Example: On a beam-to-column connection using a top connecting plate, the crater of the fillet weld joining the plate to the beam flange should be made full throat.

Example: In shop welding a flexible seat angle to the supporting column flange, the welding sequence should permit the weld to start at the top portion of the seat angle, and carry down along the edge, with the crater at the bottom; as shown.

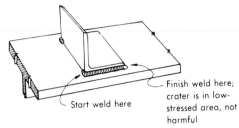

Finish weld here; crater is in low-stressed area, not harmful

Start weld here

On intermittent fillet welds, unfilled craters should normally be no problem because:

a. The additional strength obtained by filling the crater would not be needed in this low-stressed joint, for which intermittent fillet welds are sufficient.

b. Any notch effect of an unfilled crater should be no worse than the notch presented by the start end of the fillet weld; shown below. No matter what is done to the crater, it will still represent the termination of the weld, in other words an unwelded portion meeting a welded portion.

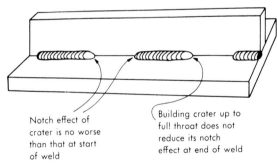

Notch effect of crater is no worse than that at start of weld

Building crater up to full throat does not reduce its notch effect at end of weld

16. *Absence of Excessive Undercut*   O ● ●

   a. The digging effect of the arc melts a portion of the base plate.

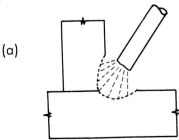

(a)

b. If the arc is too long, the molten weld metal from the end of the electrode may fall short and not completely fill this melted zone, thus leaving an undercut along the upper leg of the weld.

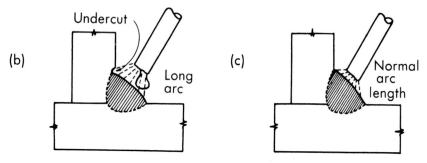

c. If the arc is shortened to the proper arc length, the molten weld metal from the end of the electrode will completely fill this melted zone and will leave no undercut.

Undercut should not be accepted on a recurring basis since it can be eliminated with proper welding procedure. If, however, undercut does occur, the question to be answered at this point is whether it is harmful and needs repair.

1. If the undercut results in a sizeable loss of net section that cannot be allowed.

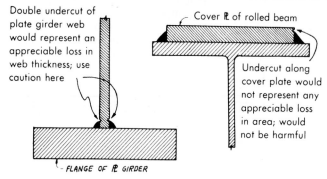

2. If a force must be transferred transverse to the axis of the undercut, which may then act as a notch or stress riser.
   a. Here the tensile force is applied transverse to the undercut and presents a stress riser. This *would be* harmful.
   b. Here the axial tensile stresses are applied parallel to the undercut and would not present a stress riser. This should *not* be harmful.
   c. Here the shear force is applied parallel to the undercut and would not present a stress riser. This should *not* be harmful.

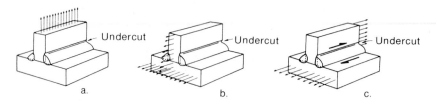

The AWS allows undercut up to 0.01″ in depth if it lies transverse to the applied force, and 1/32″ if it lies parallel to the force.

Although both undercuts in this tensile joint are transverse to the notch, the upper undercut undoubtedly has less effect upon producing a stress raiser because the stress flows smoothly below the surface of the root of the notch. On the other hand, the lower undercut does represent a stress raiser because the flow of stress is greatly disturbed as it is forced to pass sharply around the root of the notch.

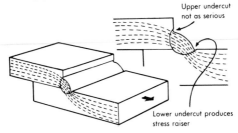

Upper undercut not as serious

Lower undercut produces stress raiser

In addition, any eccentricity would produce bending stresses in the region of the lower undercut.

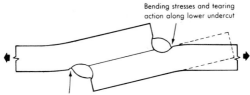

Bending stresses and tearing action along lower undercut

17. *Slight Reinforcement on Groove Welds* ○ ● ●

A nominal weld reinforcement (about 1/16″ above flush) is required. Any more than this is unnecessary and increases the weld cost.

Slight reinforcement

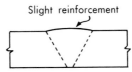

18. *Full Size on Fillet Welds* ○ ○ ●

Proper gaging of fillet welds is important to ensure adequate size.

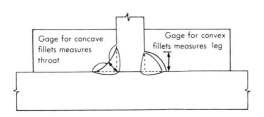

Gage for concave fillets measures throat

Gage for convex fillets measures leg

19. *Absence of Cracks* ○ ● ●

There should be no cracks of any kind, either in the weld or in the heat-affected zone of the welded plate.

General Information

Figure 1. Many welding applications require operator qualification and weld testing.

General Information

Various codes and specifications require that the welding procedures for a job be proved to give satisfactory welds by prescribed tests. In addition, the governing code or specification may demand that the weldors and welding-machine operators be proved by tests as qualified for the job. All such tests are referred to as welding qualification tests.

Although any code-writing body may prescribe its own welding qualification tests, most codes and specifications concerned with welded steel structures in the United States incorporate the welding qualification tests of the American Welding Society, the American Society of Mechanical Engineers, or the American Petroleum Insititute in their specifications. Thus, the American Association of State Highway Officials in its specifications for highway bridges incorporates the AWS welding qualification tests for procedures and personnel, as those qualification tests are given in the AWS Structural Welding Code. Many other code-writing organizations, including private companies, industrial groups, or governmental agencies, also refer to AWS, ASME, or API specifications for welding qualification tests.

AWS tests are most widely recognized, but are not universally applicable. In certain types of work, other qualification tests may be required. The contractor doing the welding must make certain that the qualification of procedures and personnel he uses meets the requirements of the governing code.

There are three different qualification tests:

1. A test to qualify the welding procedure to be used for a specific welding project.

2. A test of the welding proficiency of the operator with hand-held welding equipment (the stick-electrode holder or the semiautomatic welding gun). This is referred to as weldor qualification.
3. A test of the proficiency of the operator with fully automatic welding equipment — referred to as welding operator qualification.

Procedure Qualification

Welding *Procedures* for work under the STRUCTURAL WELDING CODE — AWS D1.1 (and most other codes) must be "qualified" before fabrication can begin.

If the procedures conform to the provisions of Section 2 — Design, Section 3 — Workmanship, Section 4 — Techniques and either Section 8 — Buildings, Section 9 — Bridges or Section 10 — Tubular Structures, they are "prequalified" and *no testing of the procedure is required.*

If the contractor wishes to deviate from these requirements, the procedures must be qualified in accordance with the testing requirements in the code. For a review of these requirements, see pages 9-126 to 9-130.

Operator Qualification

A universal operator qualification test for all types of welding in all locations does not exist. The AWS and other industry and governmental agencies, as listed below, issue specifications that cover certain types of work. Since the requirements of the *governing* code must be met, always be certain to select the tests required by the appropriate code.

In addition to the proper code, select the test details that will qualify for the type steel, plate thickness, joint and welding positions to be used on the job.

The AWS STRUCTURAL WELDING CODE test requirements for manual electrode and semiautomatic operators are reviewed on pages 9-122 to 9-126. Test requirements for fully automatic machine operators are reviewed on page 9-126.

How to Pass Qualification Tests

Purpose of Operator Qualification Tests

Operator qualification tests are designed to prove that each individual weldor on a job has the ability to produce sound welds. In other words, they separate the capable weldor from the amateur.

Unfortunately, however, professional weldors sometimes fail because of poor plate quality, improperly prepared samples or incorrect interpretation of the results. This is exasperating and expensive to both the weldor and his employer.

The following section provides information needed to minimize such failures.

Check the Plate

Face and root bend tests are designed so both plate and weld stretch during the test. If the plate has strength *substantially* higher than the weld metal (and this is possible with steel purchased as mild steel) the plate will not stretch sufficiently, thereby forcing the weld metal to stretch beyond its yield and crack.

Welding Techniques

To permit using manual electrode and semiautomatic weldors for a variety of work, most testing is done using the two positions that provide almost unlimited qualifications. See page 6 for a review of these positions and the other testing requirements for unlimited qualification for plate and structural pipe welding.

For unlimited manual electrode qualification, low hydrogen (usually Jetweld® LH-70 or Jet-LH® 72 — E-7018) is required. EXX10 or EXX11 electrodes are also frequently used, but do not qualify the operator for welding low hydrogen electrodes. Remember, low hydrogen electrodes require different techniques than EXX10 or EXX11. Train the weldors on these different techniques before testing, even if they are expert EXX10 weldors.

Critical to passing any of these tests is getting good penetration and sound weld metal in the root passes. To get good penetration, generally use the highest current you can handle within the recommended range for the electrode. Recommended ranges for making these tests with Lincoln low hydrogen and E-6010 and E-6011 electrodes are in the following table. Consult electrode data for current ranges for other electrodes.

Electrode Size	Jetweld® LH-70 and Jet-LH® 72	Fleetweld® 5-5P-35
1/8	100 — 130 amps	70 — 100 amps
5/32	120 — 160 amps	100 — 120 amps
3/16	210 — 240 amps*	160 — 180 amps

* 3/16 Jetweld LH-70 not recommended for vertical and overhead welding. Use 5/32 or smaller.

Many operators worry too much about appearance on the first beads. Appearance means nothing to the testing machine. But poor penetration and unsound weld metal cause most failures.

When vertical welding on the job, the operator must use the same direction, upwards or downwards, as he used in the qualification test. The AWS Structural Code specifies use of the vertical-up technique for plate welding with shielded metal arc welding electrodes.

Before starting to weld, be sure the test plates are at normal room temperature (at least 70° F). Use higher preheats when specified either by the procedures to be used in production or by Table 4.2 of D1.1-80. Always keep the weld area hot until welding is completed. Interpass temperatures of 300 — 400° F are ideal and usually easy to maintain at a normal welding pace. Never quench the plate or accelerate the cooling in any way.

Preparing the Specimen

Poor specimen preparation can cause sound weld metal to fail.

Specimen size, location and preparation are specified for each particular AWS test (see pages 9-123 thru 9-130).

The notch effect from even a slight nick across the sample may open up under the severe bending stress of the test, causing failure. Therefore, always grind or machine lengthwise on the specimen as indicated in Figure 2. Always grind or machine both faces of the specimen until the entire bend area is even, leaving no indentations or irregular spots.

Remove the reinforcement. This is required by the test because the reinforcement can cause failure of a good weld (see Figure 3). Be sure the edges are rounded to a smooth radius. This can quickly be done with a file and is good insurance against failure caused by cracks starting at the sharp corner.

When grinding specimens, do not water quench them when they are hot. Quenching may create tiny surface cracks that become larger during the bend test.

The jig for testing weld specimens is shown in Figure 4. Note that three plunger diameters are required, with the larger diameter used for the higher strength steels in recognition of their lower ductility. Alternate test jigs are shown in Figures 5 and 6.

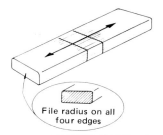

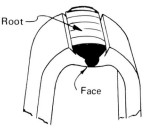

Figure 2. Grinding marks must be parallel with specimen edges. Otherwise they may have a notch effect which could cause failure.

Figure 3. If weld reinforcement is not removed, stretching is concentrated at the edge of the bead and faiure results.

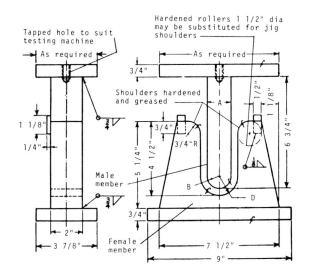

Jig Dimensions — in.	AWS TEST For Mild Steel Min. Yield Strength — psi			API Std. 1104 For All Pipe Grades
	50,000 & under	55,000- 90,000	90,000 & over	
Radius of plunger — B	¾	1	1¼	1¾
Radius of die — D	1¾/₁₆	1⁷/₁₆	1¹¹/₁₆	2⁵/₁₆

Figure 4. Jig for guided bend test used to qualify operators for work done under AWS and API specifications.

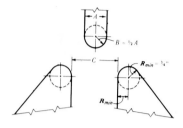

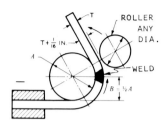

Figure 5. Alternative roller equipped test jig for bottom ejection.

Figure 6. Alternative wrap around test jig.

Figure 5				Figure 6	
A	**B**	**C**	**Yield Point — psi***	**A**	**B**
1½	¾	2⅜	50,000 & Under	1½	¾
2	1	2⅞	55,000 to 90,000	2	1
2½	1¼	3⅜	90,000 & Over	2½	1¼

* Minimum specified.

The Radiographic Examination of Welds

The AWS Structural Welding Code D1.1-80 permits radiographic examination of test plates for operator qualification in place of the guided bend test. Radiographic examination, in addition to being more fair (because it gives a more positive appraisal of the weld) can reduce the cost of qualification tests by eliminating the machining of test specimens. Furthermore, this option permits a weldor to be tested in the morning and put to work in the afternoon, avoiding the time delays that have frustrated employers and employees alike.

Fillet welds may be used in skewed T joints having a dihedral angle between 135° and 60°; beyond these angles they are considered to be groove joints and must be qualified as such (2.7.1.4).

Weldor Qualification (D1.1-80)

All manual electrode and semiautomatic welding operators working on projects covered by the AWS Structural Welding Code must prove their ability to make sound welds by passing the appropriate tests as specified in Tables 1 and 2. Note that the plate welding tests differ from the structural pipe welding tests. However, the requirements are often similar and sometimes overlap. They are reviewed below, see pages 9-124 thru 9-126. For complete information obtain a copy of the code.

Test Requirements

A weldor is qualified for all of the weldable structural steels in article 10.2 if he qualified for any one of them (5.16.1).

With manual shielded metal arc welding, qualification with any electrode identified in the following table will qualify for any other electrode in the same group designation and with any electrode listed in a numerically lower group designation (5.16.3).

Group	AWS Electrode Classification
F4	EXX15 EXX16 EXX18
F3	EXX10 EXX11
F2	EXX12 EXX13 EXX14
F1	EXX20 EXX24 EXX27 EXX28

A weldor qualified with an approved combination of electrode and shielding medium is also qualified for any other approved combination of electrode and shielding medium for the same semiautomatic process used in the qualification test (5.16.4).

Weldor qualification tests remain in effect indefinitely. (5.30) unless:
1. The weldor does not work with the welding process for which he is qualified for a period exceeding 6 months. In this case a requalification test is required only on 3/8" thick plate.
2. There is a specific reason to question his ability.

If a weldor fails his test he may retest (5.29) as follows:
1. An immediate retest shall consist of two test welds of each type he failed. All test specimens must pass.
2. A retest can be made if the weldor has had further training or practice. In this case, a complete retest shall be made.

Qualification for Plate Welding

A weldor can achieve qualification for making *any type* weld, in *any position,* on *any thickness* of plate, and on *any of the steels* listed in the code by satisfactorily completing just *two weld test plates.* Involved would be two groove welds joining 1" thick material of any of the listed steels using the process for which he is being tested. Make one weld in the vertical (3G) and one in the overhead (4G) position. Machining and bending can be determined by using radiographic inspection. *If no overhead welding will be required* on the job, make just one test plate in the vertical (3G) position.

Qualification for plate welding also gives the operator similar qualifications for welding rectangular tubing (5.17.3).

TABLE 1: Weld Type and Position Limitations (5.23)

F = Flat, H = Horizontal,
V = Vertical and OH = Overhead

Test Position	Qualifies for Plate and Pipe Welding — Grooves	Fillets
PLATE WELDING TEST		
1G	F**	F, H**
2G	F, H**	F, H**
3G	F*, H*, V*	F, H, V*
4G	F*, OH*	F, H*, OH*
3G & 4G	All*	All*, FH
1F	—	F
2F	—	F, H
3F	—	F*, H*, V*
4F	—	F*, H*, OH*
3F & 4F	—	All*
PIPE WELDING TEST		
1G	F	F, H
2G	F, H	F, H
5G	F, V, OH	F, V, OH
6G	All†	All†
2G & 5G	All†	All†
6GR	All	All

* Plate Welding Only.
† Except TYK connections.
** Qualified on pipe over 24" dia.

TABLE 2: Weldor Qualification Tests (5.26.1)

PLATE WELDING TEST

Type of Weld	Test Plate Thickness	Qualifies for Plate Thickness	Face Bend	Root Bend	Side Bend	Tee Joint Break	Macroetch
Groove	3/8"	3/4" Max.†	1	1			
Groove	Over 3/8", Under 1"	T/2 — 2T†			2		
Groove	1" & over	Unlimited†			2		
Fillet	Option 1, 1/2"	Unlimited				1	1
Fillet	Option 2, 3/8"	Unlimited		2			

PIPE WELDING TEST

Type of Weld	Test Type	Qualifies for Pipe Sizes (Wall & Dia.)	Visual Inspect	Face Bend	Root Bend	Side Bend
Groove	2" Sch. 80 or 3" Sch. 40	.063 — .674 Wall thru 4" Dia.	Yes	1*	1*	
Groove	Job size pipe Dia. ≤ 4"	.063 — .674 Wall 3/4" thru 4" Dia.				
Groove	6" Sch. 80 or 8" Sch. 120	.187 & thicker 4" Dia. & larger	Yes			2*
Groove	Job size pipe Dia. > 4"	.187 & thicker 1/2" Dia. or 4" Min.**				
Groove	With Restriction Ring	All Wall & Dia. T, K & Y Connections	Yes			4

* For pipe positions 5G or 6G, double the number of specimens listed here.
† Also fillet welding on unlimited plate thickness.
** Min. pipe size qualified shall not be less than 4" or 1/2d, whichever is greater.

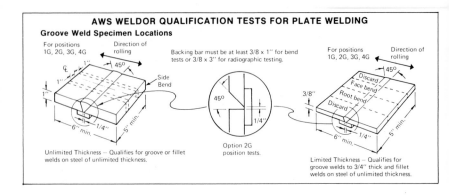

AWS WELDOR QUALIFICATION TESTS FOR PLATE WELDING

Groove Weld Specimen Locations

For positions 1G, 2G, 3G, 4G — Direction of rolling

Backing bar must be at least 3/8 x 1" for bend tests or 3/8 x 3" for radiographic testing.

For positions 1G, 2G, 3G, 4G — Direction of rolling

Side Bend

Option 2G position tests.

Discard / Face bend / Root bend / Discard

Unlimited Thickness — Qualifies for groove or fillet welds on steel of unlimited thickness.

Limited Thickness — Qualifies for groove welds to 3/4" thick and fillet welds on steel of unlimited thickness.

Qualification for Welding Pipe Structures

A weldor can achieve qualification for welding any type welding, in any position, on unlimited wall thickness, and on any of the steels listed in the code by satisfactorily completing either one test weld in the 6G position or two test welds — one in the 2G and one in the 5G position. For welding T, K or Y tubular connections, a restrictive ring in the 6G position must be used. The weldor is qualified to weld in the vertical position only in the direction (upward or downward) for which he was tested (5.16.7.).

Qualification for welding pipe structures also gives the operator the same qualifications for welding plate.

Welding Operator Qualification (AWS D1.1-80)

Qualification of the man who operates automatic welding equipment is covered by Part D of Section 5. Here also, the operator is qualified to weld any of the steels listed in 10.2 if he qualifies on any one of them (5.33.1). An operator qualified for any approved combination of electrode and shielding medium is also approved for any other approved combination of electrode and shielding medium for the same process and used in the qualification test (5.33.2). Qualification with multiple electrodes (5.33.3). A change in welding position requires requalification (5.33.5).

The welding operator may be qualified for fillet welding by only making either the tee test (Option 1) or weld soundness test (Option 2). These are the same as shown for the weldor test except the test plates and welds are 15 inches long (5.34.4).

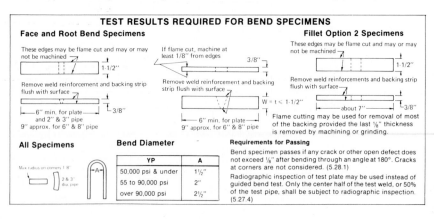

TEST RESULTS REQUIRED FOR BEND SPECIMENS

Face and Root Bend Specimens

These edges may be flame cut and may or may not be machined

Remove weld reinforcement and backing strip flush with surface

6" min. for plate and 2" & 3" pipe
9" approx. for 6" & 8" pipe

If flame cut, machine at least 1/8" from edges

Remove weld reinforcement and backing strip flush with surface

6" min. for plate
9" approx. for 6" & 8" pipe

Fillet Option 2 Specimens

These edges may be flame cut and may or may not be machined

Remove weld reinforcements and backing strip flush with surface

about 7"

Flame cutting may be used for removal of most of the backing provided the last 1/8" thickness is removed by machining or grinding.

All Specimens

Max radius on corners 1 8"

2 & 3" dia. pipe

Bend Diameter

YP	A
50,000 psi & under	1½"
55 to 90,000 psi	2"
over 90,000 psi	2½"

Requirements for Passing

Bend specimen passes if any crack or other open defect does not exceed ⅛" after bending through an angle at 180°. Cracks at corners are not considered. (5.28.1)

Radiographic inspection of test plate may be used instead of guided bend test. Only the center half of the test weld, or 50% of the test pipe, shall be subject to radiographic inspection. (5.27.4)

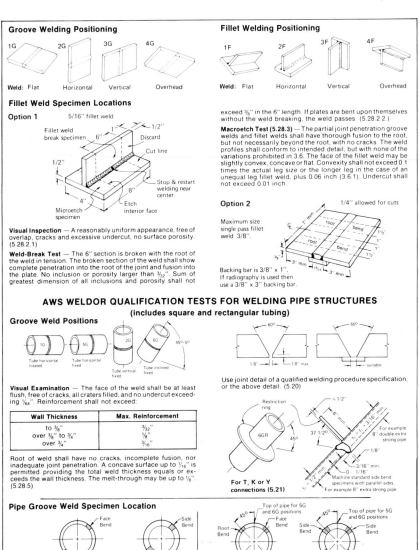

Groove Welding Positioning

1G   2G   3G   4G

Weld: Flat   Horizontal   Vertical   Overhead

Fillet Welding Positioning

1F   2F   3F   4F

Weld: Flat   Horizontal   Vertical   Overhead

Fillet Weld Specimen Locations

Option 1   5/16'' fillet weld

Fillet weld break specimen
1''
1/2''
6''
Discard
Cut line
1/2''
Stop & restart welding near center
8''
4''
Etch interior face
Microetch specimen

Visual Inspection — A reasonably uniform appearance, free of overlap, cracks and excessive undercut, no surface porosity. (5.28.2.1)

Weld-Break Test — The 6'' section is broken with the root of the weld in tension. The broken section of the weld shall show complete penetration into the root of the joint and fusion into the plate. No inclusion or porosity larger than $\frac{3}{32}$''. Sum of greatest dimension of all inclusions and porosity shall not

exceed $\frac{3}{8}$'' in the 6'' length. If plates are bent upon themselves without the weld breaking, the weld passes. (5.28.2.2.)

Macroetch Test (5.28.3) — The partial joint penetration groove welds and fillet welds shall have thorough fusion to the root, but not necessarily beyond the root, with no cracks. The weld profiles shall conform to intended detail, but with none of the variations prohibited in 3.6. The face of the fillet weld may be slightly convex, concave or flat. Convexity shall not exceed 0.1 times the actual leg size or the longer leg in the case of an unequal leg fillet weld, plus 0.06 inch (3.6.1). Undercut shall not exceed 0.01 inch.

Option 2   1/4'' allowed for cuts

Maximum size single pass fillet weld 3/8''.

Backing bar is 3/8'' x 1''. If radiography is used then use a 3/8'' x 3'' backing bar.

AWS WELDOR QUALIFICATION TESTS FOR WELDING PIPE STRUCTURES
(includes square and rectangular tubing)

Groove Weld Positions

1G   5G   2G   6G   45°, 5°

Tube horizontal rotated   Tube horizontal fixed   Tube vertical fixed   Tube inclined fixed

60°   60°

1/8''   1/8'' max   suitable

Use joint detail of a qualified welding procedure specification, or the above detail. (5.20)

Visual Examination — The face of the weld shall be at least flush, free of cracks, all craters filled, and no undercut exceeding $\frac{1}{64}$''. Reinforcement shall not exceed:

Wall Thickness	Max. Reinforcement
to $\frac{3}{8}$''	$\frac{3}{32}$''
over $\frac{3}{8}$'' to $\frac{3}{4}$''	$\frac{1}{8}$''
over $\frac{3}{4}$''	$\frac{3}{16}$''

Root of weld shall have no cracks, incomplete fusion, nor inadequate joint penetration. A concave surface up to $\frac{1}{16}$'' is permitted providing the total weld thickness equals or exceeds the wall thickness. The melt-through may be up to $\frac{1}{8}$''. (5.28.5)

Restriction ring
6GR
45°
37 1/2°
≤ 1/2''
6'' min
For example 8'' double extra strong pipe
1/8''
3/16'' min.
0 - 1/16''
Machine standard side bend specimens with parallel sides. For example 8'' extra strong pipe

For T, K or Y connections (5.21)

Pipe Groove Weld Specimen Location

Face Bend
Side Bend
Root Bend
Side Bend
Pipe wall 3/8'' and under
1G and 2G Positions

Pipe wall over 3/8''

Top of pipe for 5G and 6G positions
45°
Face Bend
Root Bend
Side Bend
Pipe wall 3/8'' and under

Top of pipe for 5G and 6G positions
45°
Side Bend
Root Bend
Face Bend
Side Bend
Pipe wall over 3/8''
5G and 6G Positions

The welding operator making and passing a procedure qualification test is also qualified for that process and test position for plates of thicknesses equal to or less than the thickness of the test plate welded. In the case of 1'' or over in thickness he will be qualified for all thicknesses (5.34.3). Qualification on plate in the 1G or 2G positions also qualify welding of pipe over 24 inches in diameter in similar positions. Qualification on pipe also qualifies for welding of plate.

The test welding procedure shall be the same as specified by the Procedure Specification (5.36).

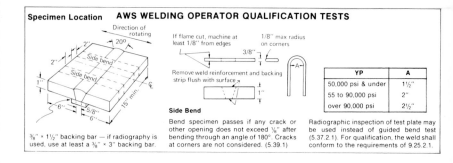

Specimen Location   **AWS WELDING OPERATOR QUALIFICATION TESTS**

If flame cut, machine at least 1/8" from edges   1/8" max radius on corners

Remove weld reinforcement and backing strip flush with surface

Side Bend

Bend specimen passes if any crack or other opening does not exceed 1/8" after bending through an angle of 180°. Cracks at corners are not considered. (5.39.1)

3/8" × 1½" backing bar — if radiography is used, use at least a 3/8" × 3" backing bar.

	YP	A
	50,000 psi & under	1½"
	55 to 90,000 psi	2"
	over 90,000 psi	2½"

Radiographic inspection of test plate may be used instead of guided bend test (5.37.2.1). For qualification, the weld shall conform to the requirements of 9.25.2.1.

Procedure Qualification (AWS D1.1-80)

Unless prequalified procedures are used (see page 9-121), the welding *procedures* for work done under the STRUCTURAL WELDING CODE — AWS D1.1-80 must be "qualified" before fabrication can begin.

The following three pages review *procedure* qualification testing. Obviously not all details are covered. Therefore, anyone responsible for actual qualification testing must have and understand the code to obtain full information.

Applicable Steels

Steels to be welded under the code are listed in Section 8.2 — Buildings, Section 9.2 — Bridges and Section 10.2 — Tubular Structures. 10.2 includes all steels listed in 8.2 and 9.2. Procedure qualification requirements for the steels listed in 10.2 are covered in Sections 5.5.1.1 thru 5.5.1.4 and are reviewed in Figure 9.

TABLE 3 — PROCEDURE QUALIFICATION TESTS (5.10.1.1)

COMPLETE JOINT PENETRATION GROOVE WELDS

Test Size		Qualifies for Plate Thickness or Pipe Size	No. of Sample Welds/ Pos.	NDT and Visual Inspec.	Number and Type of Tests Required			
					Reduced Tension	Root Bend	Face Bend	Side Bend
3/8" plate		3/4" max. plate	1	Yes	2	2	2	—
Over 3/8" but under 1" plate		Twice thickness of test plate	1	Yes	2	—	—	4
1" plate and over		Plate of unlimited thickness	1	Yes	2	—	—	4
2" Sch. 80 or 3" Sch. 40		.063 — .674 Wall 3/4" to 4" Dia.	2	Yes	2	2	2	—
6" Sch. 80 or 8" Sch. 120		.187 & thicker 4" Dia. & larger	1	Yes	2	—	—	4
Large dia. job size pipe	dia. < 24 in.	test dia. & over	1	Yes	2	—	—	4
	dia. ≥ 24 in.	24 in. dia. & over						
	t < 3/4 in.	1/2t to 2t						
	t ≥ 3/4 in.	3/8 & over						

Required Procedure Qualification Tests (See Table 3 on 9-128)

In addition to the standard required tests, the test plates shall be radiographically or ultrasonically tested (5.10.1.3).

To qualify procedures for welds in T or corner joints, weld butt joints having the same groove configurations as the T or corner joint to be used in construction (5.10.1.2).

A test joint for partial joint penetration groove welds shall be made for each type of joint and weld position except the depth of the groove does not have to exceed 1″. A temporary restrictive plate shall be used on the butt joint if this represents a T-joint. A macroetched cross section of the completed joint shall be made to show that the designated effective throat thickness is obtained and that the requirements of the procedure specification are met (5.10.2).

When required by the filler metal specification application to the weld metal being tests, aging at 200 to 220° F for 48 ±2 hours is allowed (5.10.4).

For some products (such as Innershield and some stick electrodes) where aging is allowed, aging is necessary to consistently pass the qualification tests.

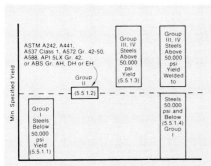

combination steels included in 10.2 having a specified yield the same or lower than the steel tested.

5.5.1.2 — Qualification using a steel in Group II shall qualify for welding all steels or combination of steels in this group and steels included in 10.2 having a lower minimum specified yield point.

5.5.1.3 — Qualification using a steel listed in 10.2 having a minimum specified yield point in excess of 50,000 psi only qualifies the procedure for welding steels of the same specification and grade or types having the same minimum yield. A reduction in yield point because of increase in thickness is permitted; for example, a procedure qualifies for 1″ thick 100,000 psi yield also qualifies for 3″ thick 90,000 psi yield steel of the same specification.

5.5.1.4 — Qualification using a steel included in 10.2 having a minimum yield point higher than 50,000 psi when welded to another steel having a minimum specified yield of 50,000 psi or less, qualifies the procedure for welding the higher strength steel to any of the other steels included in 10.2 having a minimum specified yield of 50,000 psi or less.

5.5.1.1 — Qualification using a steel included in 10.2 but not listed in 5.5.1.2 having a minimum specified yield below 50,000 psi qualifies that procedure for welding any other steels or

Figure 9. Procedure Qualification Requirements for the Listed Steels.

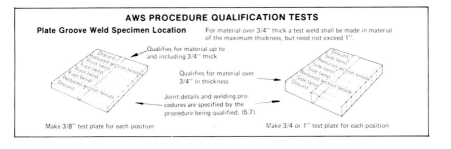

Pipe Groove Weld Specimen Location

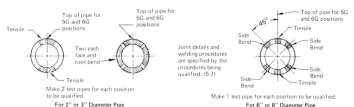

Make 2 test pipes for each position to be qualified.

For 2" or 3" Diameter Pipe

Joint details and welding procedures are specified by the procedures being qualified. (5.7)

Make 1 test pipe for each position to be qualified.

For 6" or 8" Diameter Pipe

Visual inspection requirements (5.12) are same as "Weldor Qualification" visual inspection requirements (see page 5).

Fillet Weld Specimens

When required:

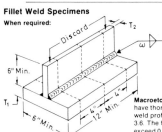

Weld Size ω	T₁ min.	T₂ min.
3/16	1/2	3/16
1/4	3/4	1/4
5/16	1	5/16
3/8	1	3/8
1/2	1	1/2
5/8	1	5/8
3/4	1	3/4
>3/4	1	1

Two test welds shall be made for each position to be used; one with the maximum size single pass fillet weld and one with the minimum size multiple pass fillet weld to be used.

Macroetch Test (5.28.3) — The partial joint penetration groove welds and fillet welds shall have thorough fusion to the root, but not necessarily beyond the root, with no cracks. The weld profiles shall conform to intended detail, but with none of the variations prohibited in 3.6. The face of the fillet weld may be slightly convex, concave or flat. Convexity shall not exceed 0.1 times the actual leg size, or the longer leg in the case of an unequal leg fillet weld, plus 0.06 inch (3.6.1). Undercut shall not exceed 0.1 inch.

TEST RESULTS REQUIRED — Procedure Qualification

Reduced Section Tensile

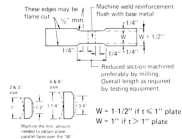

Machine weld reinforcement flush with base metal

Reduced section machined preferably by milling. Overall length as required by testing equipment.

W = 1-1/2" if t ≤ 1" plate
W = 1" if t > 1" plate

Machine the min. amount needed to obtain plane parallel faces over the "W" reduced section.

Tensile strength shall not be less than the minimum specified tensile strength of the base metal used. (5.12.1) It may break in the weld.

	YP	A
	50,000 psi & under	1½"
	55 to 90,000 psi	2"
	over 90,000 psi	2½"

Face & Root Bend

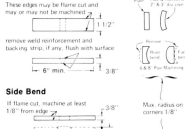

These edges may be flame cut and may or may not be machined

remove weld reinforcement and backing strip, if any, flush with surface

Side Bend

If flame cut, machine at least 1/8" from edge

Max. radius on corners 1/8"

For base materials differing markedly from weld metal in bending properties, longitudinal bend tests may be used in lieu of transverse bend test (5.10.1.5)

Cut along this edge when t exceeds 1-1/2". Edge may be flame cut and may or may not be machined.

NOTE: For 3/8 to 1½", W = T. For plates over 1½" thick, cut specimens into a minimum number of approximately equal strips between 3/4 and 1½" in width. Bend specimen passes if crack or other opening does not exceed 1/8" after bending through an angle of 180°. Cracks at corners are not considered. (5.12.2)

Sources of Information

AWS Structural Welding Code

Many state and local bridge and building codes accept the procedure and operator qualification provisions of the AWS STRUCTURAL WELDING CODE D1.1-81. The operator qualification requirements are also sometimes used by individual companies or agencies to prove the skill of their weldors. It includes two different tests — one for manual electrode and semiautomatic welding operators and the second for fully automatic welding equipment operators. These tests have been reviewed on pages 9-122 thru 9-126. For a copy of the code, order D1.1-80 from the American Welding Society, 2501 N.W. 7th St., Miami, Florida 33125.

AWS Piping and Tubing

A code of growing national importance is AWS D10.9-69 "Standard For Qualification of Welding Procedures and Welders for Piping and Tubing." This standard provides three levels of Acceptance Requirements as follows:

AR-1 is for highest weld quality applications including nuclear energy, outer space, cryogenics and certain chemical systems.

AR-2 is for high weld quality applications including pipelines and most pressure piping systems.

AR-3 is for pipe in less severe service such as domestic water and heating lines.

For a copy of this standard, write: The American Welding Society, 2501 N.W. 7th St., Miami, Florida 33125.

Cross-Country Pipelines

a. For a review of pipe welding procedures, techniques and electrodes, request Lincoln bulletins M640 and M642, available free.

b. For the actual code, get "Standard for Welding Pipelines and Related Facilities"... API 1104 ... $2.00 from the American Petroleum Institute, 2101 L Street, N.W., Washington, D.C. 20037.

Boilers, Pressure Vessels and Pipings

a. For a review of pipe welding procedures, techniques and electrodes, request Lincoln bulletin M640, available free.

b. For a readable version of the ASME code requirements get "The Qualification of Welding Procedures and Weldors" from Factory Mutual Public Relations & Publications, 1151 Boston-Providence Turnpike, Norwood, Massachusetts 02062.

c. For a detailed review of operator qualification tests for in-plant pipe welding, get "Pipefitter Welder's Review of Metallic Welding for Qualification under ASME Rules" from National Certified Pipe Welding Bureau, Suite 750, 5530 Wisconsin Ave., Washington, D.C. 20015.

LESSON
9.5
Automatic Welding

In applications where there is a high volume of identical or similar parts, a full automatic welding fixture will often be used. The welding operator loads parts into the fixture, hits a button which activates the welding equipment and positioners, waits for the welding to be completed, and then unloads the finished part. This operator is often paid piece work and can earn very good wages. The welding procedures and the fixture itself are often developed by a welding engineer. It is not unusual to spend many hours developing this material for a weld which will only take a few seconds to complete. It takes a lot of skill and many years of training to be good at doing this type of work.

To maintain precise procedures on a consistent basis, Lincoln has developed the NA-5 wire feeder. The NA-5 permits digital setting of the welding procedures for each phase of the weld. Separate procedures can be entered for striking, starting, welding, crater, and burnback as well as timers which precisely regulate the amount of time each mode is activated. Once set, the NA-5 has the ability to automatically adjust the power source and drive motor so that the preset procedures are maintained. If for some reason the procedures cannot be maintained, the feeder will "shut-down" and not allow a weld to be made which is not according to the set procedures.

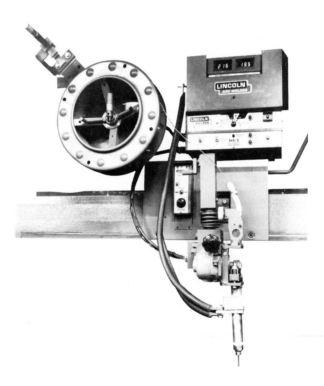

Figure 1. The NA-5 automatic wire feeder.

SECTION X

APPENDIX

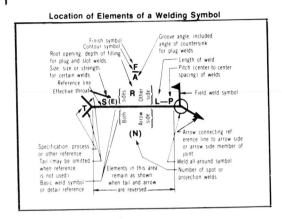

Figure 1.

The American Welding Society's standard welding symbols are used on engineering drawings to transmit information from the designer to the fabricator. The system is complete and can be used to convey all needed information. Most of the information can be told with the standard symbols; if more details are required, simple reference notes are used.

The basic component of the standard symbol is the arrow and reference line to which other symbols are added. The significance and use of these components is described in Lesson 1.35. With these parts of the symbol as a foundation, other marks are added to better describe the required welding. Figure 1 is a model symbol showing most of the information that can be included in the complete welding symbol.

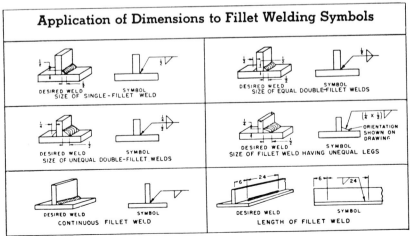

Figure 2.

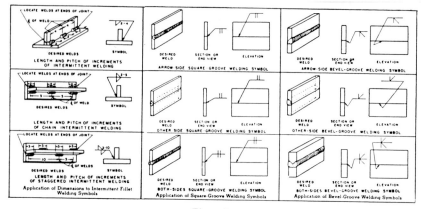

Figure 3.

The size and length of the desired weld are frequently specified on drawings. This information is placed on either side of the basic symbol. On the left side is the size of the weld, and on the right is the length and spacing. Figures 2 and 3 are illustrations of the application of this information to a symbol.

On groove welds it is frequently necessary to specify the edge preparation. The first step is to specify which plate is to be bevelled. If both plates receive similar preparation no notation is necessary, but if only one plate is bevelled it is necessary to indicate which one. This is done by breaking the arrow and pointing

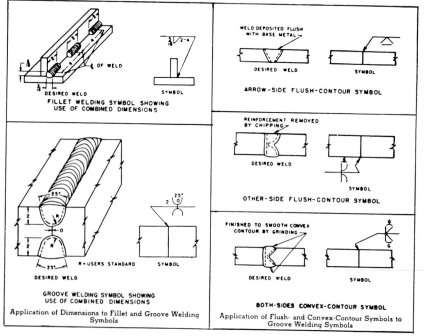

Figure 4.

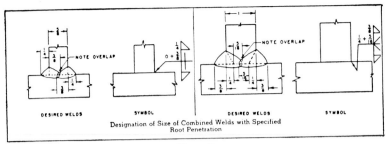

Designation of Size of Combined Welds with Specified
Root Penetration

Figure 5.

it to the plate that is to be prepared. Figures 3 and 4 are illustrations of this. The type of preparation is indicated by the basic welding symbol, but dimensions may also be added to further define the joint preparation. Figures 4 and 5 show how this is done.

It is possible to show both the preparation and another bead on top by simply placing one symbol on top of the other as shown in Figure 5.

Two supplementary symbols may be placed on the junction of the arrow and the reference line. The first is the "weld all around" symbol, which is a circle and means that a weld is to be made completely around the joint. The second is the "field weld" symbol and is a solid dot. It means that the weld is to be made in the field instead of in the shop.

A summary chart of all the welding symbols and examples of their use is included on the following page. Note that this chart has symbols for resistance welding. It is well to be familiar with these so that there is no confusion with arc welding symbols.

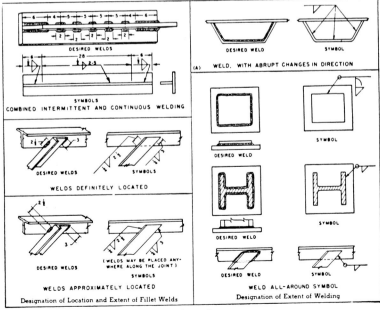

Figure 6.

STANDARD WELDING SYMBOLS

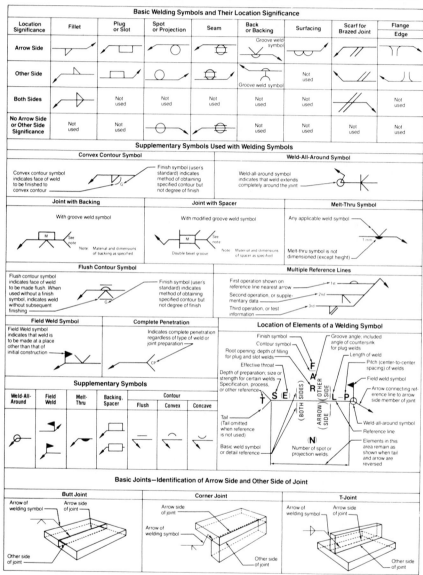

Figure 7.

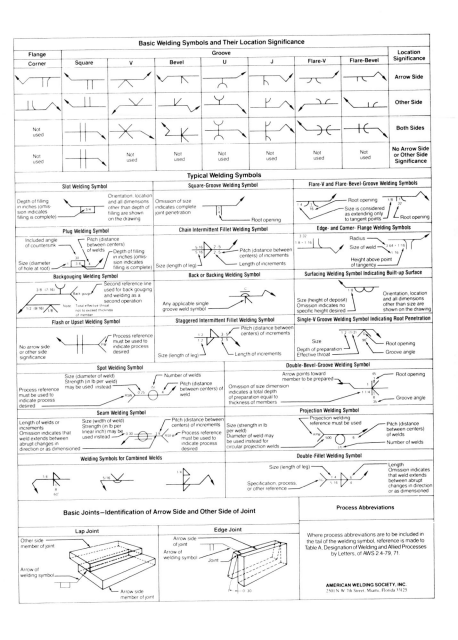

The Lincoln Welding School provides an effective foundation for a career in arc welding. This is not a "school" in the ordinary sense of the word, for the instructions are practical with little theoretical work involved. The welding courses, both Basic and Advanced, enable you to learn not only the fundamental principles of arc welding, but also the latest procedures and techniques.

For the industrious individual with welding ambitions, the Welding School offers a real opportunity. Lincoln's experienced, congenial instructors keep close watch at all times to see that each student progresses. And each student is assigned to his own welding booth and welding machine as his private "shop."

The fees for the following courses are based on the *cost of expenses only*. A deposit is required upon registration. This is applied to the total fee. Protective clothing, shields, gloves, etc., can be purchased at low cost.

Basic Course

Five weeks intensive training — 150 hours continuous practice. Subjects include: study of arc-welding machine, its performance and control; practice with bare electrodes — striking the arc, buildup of plates and shafts; practice with shielded-arc electrodes — effect of arc length, current, and speed on bead; sizes and uses of various electrodes; butt-lap-tee-fillet welds in flat, vertical, and overhead positions; sheet-metal welds; "Fleet-Welding" technique; use of iron-powder "Jetweld" electrodes; penetration cutting.

Advanced Special Courses

Pipe Welding Course. Two weeks' training in welding of pipe in all positions.
Alloys Course. Two weeks' training in welding high-tensile steels, stainless steel, chrome-moly, cast iron, copper, bronze, aluminum, and hardsurfacing.

A copy of the arc-welding "Bible," the "Procedure Handbook of Arc Welding" will be an invaluable aid for preparation and study.

An outline of the course you prefer will be sent on request. Advance notice of one week is required for registration in the course. Be sure to specify the course in which you wish to enroll. WRITE TO THE LINCOLN ELECTRIC COMPANY, CLEVELAND, OHIO 44117.

In the interests of industrial and technological advancement through the use of arc welding, the publishers of this book have other books and bulletins on the various phases of arc welding for sale. The following books are recommended for engineers, designers, production supervisors, shop men, weldors, students, and others seeking advancement through knowledge of arc welding.

"Procedure Handbook of Arc Welding"

The 12th Edition Handbook contains up-to-date facts about all aspects of the arc-welding process and its many profitable applications, compiled and edited for quick reference and easy understanding.

700 8" x 10" pages of up-to-date facts.

Contains 16 sections: (1) Introduction and Fundamentals; (2) Designing for Arc Welding; (3) Variables in Welding Fabrication; (4) Consumables and Machinery; (5) Welding Processes; (6) Welding Carbon and Low-Alloy Steel; (7) Welding Stainless Steel; (8) Welding Cast Iron and Cast Steel; (9) Welding Aluminum and Aluminum Alloys; (10) Welding Copper and Copper Alloys; (11) Quality Control; (12) Welding Costs; (13) Special Applications; (14) Installation and Maintenance; (15) Safety in Welding; (16) References and Index.

Written clearly. Profusely illustrated by over 1300 photos and drawings. Well indexed for quick, detailed reference.

Recognized throughout the world as the authentic reference guide on arc welding. More than 500,000 copies of previous editions have been sold.

Size 8-1/2" x 10-1/4" x 2" — ideal for use in office, shop or school. Printed on fine paper. Bound in black simulated leather cover board, white embossed.

"The Stabilizer"

"The Stabilizer," published by Lincoln, is virtually the official organ of the vast army of men who weld. Each issue is packed full of practical welding ideas contributed by weldors themselves, promoting good welding and the advancement of the industry. Free to employed weldors and supervisors. Give position, name, and address of company and home address.

"How To Read Shop Drawings"

A complete revision and organization of the material previously printed in "Simple Blueprint Reading." As produced, this new book for students and shop personnel provides a simplified approach to the easy mastery of reading shop drawings. Designed for use as a working manual, "How To Read Shop Drawings" enables weldors and others engaged in mechanical construction to better understand design, manufacturing, fabrication, and construction detailing.

Text contains 187 pages with more than 100 illustrations. Sizes 8-1/2" x 11" durable cloth-covered board binding.

Preheat Calculator

A slide-rule-type of calculator for determining the proper preheat and interpass temperature to be used when welding high-carbon and alloy steels that need to be preheated for the best quality welds. Temperature can be calculated for any steel whose analysis and thickness is known; eliminates guessing.

Films

A color and sound film is available to schools, firms, and organizations. It is titled, "Prevention and Control of Distortion in Arc Welding." Film size, 16mm. No charge except for transportation. Write Lincoln for further information.

Plastic Demonstration Shield WC-37

It's easy to make a welding booth for effective group demonstrations with this flexible, 20" x 50", plastic screen. Rugged, versatile, inexpensive.

THE JAMES F. LINCOLN ARC WELDING FOUNDATION

The James F. Lincoln Arc Welding Foundation was established in 1936 by the Lincoln Electric Company for the scientific and/or practical development of the arc-welding process. As a contribution to scientific progress and to promote industrial progress through education, the Foundation has produced and published the following books. Copies should be ordered from the James F. Lincoln Arc Welding Foundation, Box 17035, Cleveland, Ohio, 44117.

"Metals and How to Weld Them" — Second Edition

This nationally used reference text by T. B. Jefferson and Gorham Woods has been completely revised and rewritten. Result: the easy-reading text clearly explains elementary metallurgy, using readily understood terms and illustrations. The book describes the internal structure of metals and its relation to mechanical properties and weldability. Existing arc-welding processes are described and their applications discussed. Physical characteristics are reviewed and welding procedures outlined for the commonly used metals. An entirely new chapter discusses the "space-age-developed" exotic metals. 400 pages, 195 illustrations, gold-embossed cloth-bound cover.

"Design of Weldments"

This reference handbook describes in detail techniques used to create machine designs in arc-welded steel. Much of this material has had no previous publication. Theoretical analysis and case history studies explain how to design machine components for manufacturing economies and improvement of product performance through efficient use of steel's excellent physical properties. Text covers designing for fatigue, tension, compression, deflection, impact, vibration, and torsional load conditions. 464 pages, 923 illustrations, 24 full-size nomographs, 8-1/2 x 11 inch page size; bound in gold-embossed cloth-covered board.

"Design Ideas for Weldments" — Volume III

Weldment design ideas abstracted from 113 outstanding design entries in the Foundation-sponsored professional awards programs. Here is the third in a series of reference manuals to help designers and engineers use steel more effectively and efficiently in their designs. The abstracts present hundreds of tested answers for design problems related to cost, vibration, impact, appearance, machining, strength, and rigidity. 284 pages, many illustrations and tables, 8-1/2 x 11 inch page size.

"Modern Welded Structures" — Volume III

A series of reports reviewing current design approaches to buildings, bridges, and other structures. These 100 structural ideas were abstracted from the design entries of recognized design authorities in the Foundation-sponsored professional award program. 324 pages, 8-1/2 x 11-inch page size, many illustrations and tables.

"Design of Welded Structures"
By OMER W. BLODGETT, *Design Consultant*

This text presents methods of designing with arc welded steel for buildings, bridges, towers, containers and all types of miscellaneous structures. These methods can be applied to the whole structure or its component parts.

This 8-1/2 x 11-inch 832 page book contains 966 drawings, 28 nomographs, 163 tables, 190 charts, and 145 photographs. Seven "working" sections contain detailed analysis and practical examples that show how to create more efficient designs that can be fabricated more economically.

"Principles of Industrial Welding"

This book has been developed as a reference text for career students enrolled in welding technology as well as the professional weldor or welding supervisor. Virtually all welding processes are described with a major emphasis on manual and semiautomatic processes which are most widely used today. Specific procedures for various joint designs, plate thickness, and welding position are also included.

Note: This book draws heavily on The Procedure Handbook of Arc Welding published by The Lincoln Electric Company. Owners of that book may wish to purchase Principles of Industrial Welding for the added information on gas welding and cutting. A hardbound text with 384 pages.

"Arc-Welding Lessons for School and Farm Shop"

A book for teaching and learning the skills used with farm arc-welding equipment. Contains both informational and operational lessons. Explains how to weld, solder, braze, heat, cut, temper, and hard-surface with arc-welding equipment. Clear step-by-step outline for each lesson given, with a typical job explained for practicing the lesson. 343 pages, 550 illustrations, illustrated glossary,

26 pages of welded projects; bound in semiflexible simulated leather, gold embossed.

"Arc-Welded Projects for the School Shop" — Volume I

This handy student project manual presents full details on how to make 44 shop-tested projects. Included are pictures, drawings, bills of material, and instructions. Ideally suited to industrial arts training, the projects cover items that are useful in the home or in a workshop. A few of the projects included in the manual are: Lamps, TV Stand, Portable Grill, Bench Shears, Basketball Goal, Telephone Bench, Wood Lathe, and Table Saw.

Written by Wm. A. Sellon (see above). Manual has 77 pages, 8-1/2 x 11-inch size, paper bound and punched.

"Arc-Welded Projects" — Volume II

A collection of entries submitted to the foundations High School Award Program. Projects tend to be more complex than in Arc Welded Projects Volume I.

The book is divided into 4 sections with projects describing procedures and a bill of material for each. The sections are: Agricultural, 24 projects; Home and Recreational, 28 projects; Shop Tools, 44 projects; and Trailers, 16 projects.

Typical projects are: Hydraulic Wood Splitter, scraper grader, wood stove, pontoon boat, engine hoist, band saw, anvil, pipe bending machine, 2 horse trailers, and flatbed trailer. Written in a simple and easy to understand style. 112 projects covering 272 pages.

Lesson 1.2

1. Electrical shock can kill and damage equipment; water is a good electrical conductor.
2. 10   14 depending on process.
3. Yes.
4. Whenever in the welding shop.
5. Fumes could cause an explosion.
6. Safeguard from electrical shock and to keep the engine from turning over on portable models.
7. Avoid breathing fumes and gases which could be hazardous.

Lesson 1.3

1. As strong or stronger than base metal.
2. Continuous supply of AC or DC sufficient in voltage and amperage to hold an arc.
3. Motor-generator, rectifier, or engine generator.
4. Transformer welders.
5. National Electrical Manufacturers Association.
6. Percentage of a 10 minute period that a welder can operate at maximum rated capacity.
7. Yes, with caution.
8. High amperage, low voltage.
9. AC-DC combination welder.
10. Gasoline or diesel engine driven generator.
11. Yes.

Lesson 1.4

1. It enables the weldor to handle and control the arc.
2. A chemical coating shields the arc and the weld from the air.
3. To effect proper fusing action of the weld and to minimize welding costs.
4. No, depends upon type of electrode.
5. Floats impurities out of puddle, shields the arc and puddle, stabilizes the arc.

6. Oxygen and nitrogen.
7. Stabilizes and regulates the arc during current alternations.
8. To slow cooling, protect hot metal from the air.
9. Lower tensile strength and impact resistance.

Lesson 1.5

1. An arc is formed.
2. Scratching and tapping.
3. Scratching.
4. Scratching.
5. Snap it backward to break it loose, or release from the holder.
6. No, the electrode will "flash".
7. Yes.
8. Yes.
9. Withdraw electrode tip to form a long arc.
10. $1/16''$ to $1/8''$.
11. 65 to 70 degrees.

Lesson 1.6

1. Sound beads are the basis of sound welds.
2. Perpendicular, inclined 65 to 70 degrees.
3. Yes.
4. Yes.
5. Chip slag with chipping hammer and brush clean with wire brush.
6. 11 or 12 inches.
7. $1\frac{1}{2}''$.
8. The depth of fusion below the surface of the base metal.
9. Amperage setting, electrode angle, arc length, travel speed.

Lesson 1.7

1. Welding speed.
2. Lower rate of metal deposition, more electrode changes, more working time.
3. Electrode diameter should not exceed base metal thickness.

4. ³/₁₆".
5. Conditions under which electrode is used are too varied.
6. About the middle of the range.
7. Maximum electrode size and maximum amperage.

Lesson 1.8

1. The spot where the force of the arc has left an unfilled depression.
2. A depression or lump to spoil uniformity.
3. The bead covers up the striking marks.
4. Stress points in the weld which may result in cracks.
5. Extinguish the arc, let it cool, clean, and refill.
6. Running back over the bead, or jumping to the end and welding back to the bead.

Lesson 1.9

1. An oscillating motion, crosswise to the direction of the bead.
2. Give a wider bead, float out slag, secure better penetration.
3. Yes.
4. Three times the electrode diameter.
5. No, in all positions.

Lesson 1.10

1. Whipping is lengthwise movement, weaving is crosswise to the bead.
2. Keep metal "hot" for penetration or "cool" for build-up.
3. Forward motion.
4. To avoid depositing metal until puddle partially solidifies.
5. No, backward on "hot" whip, forward on "cool" whip.

Lesson 1.11

1. Building up by overlaying weld passes.
2. Rebuilding worn parts or correcting machining errors.
3. Yes.
4. Running alternate layers of passes 90 degrees to each other.
5. No, straight passes may be used.

6. Cutting through and etching with acid.
7. Put acid into water, one to three.
8. Yes.
9. To minimize distortion.
10. No, let them cool slowly.

Lesson 1.13

1. Negative.
2. Negative.
3. No.
4. DC negative.
5. Negative.
6. High cellulose.
7. Break up oxide films.

Lesson 1.14

1. At the start and finish of joints and in corners and deep grooves.
2. Yes.
3. No.
4. Reduce current; this lowers welding speed. Use AC welding current.
5. Yes. The strength of the flux is reduced because it collapses and builds up 120 times a second.
6. Stainless, non-ferrous, low hydrogen in small sizes, and hardsurfacing electrodes.
7. AC.
8. 250 — 300 is sufficient on most jobs.
9. Weldors reduce current when arc blow is present. Reduced current means slower welding.
10. Yes.

Lesson 1.15

1. Gets larger, expands.
2. Gets smaller, contracts.
3. Decreased.
4. Yes.
5. Depth or size of throat.
6. 30 degrees or less.
7. ¹/₃₂" to ¹/₁₆".
8. Yes.
9. Yes.
10. Yes.
11. Stretches and work hardens metal.
12. Use jigs and fixtures.

Lesson 1.18

1. Fillet weld.

2. Welding speed and quality of the weld are increased.
3. "Fleetweld 7".
4. Straight bead.
5. Greater welding speed.
6. Either a straight bead or a weave.
7. Smooth, uniform, even penetration into each plate and into the corner.

Lesson 1.19

1. Lap weld.
2. Very short to contact.
3. Heat is directed on the thicker plate.
4. Greater welding speed.
5. Depends upon the resultant bead shape.
6. Smooth bead, equal penetration in each member and into the corner.

Lesson 1.20

1. Square, vee, groove.
2. Welding from both sides.
3. For maximum strength.
4. Complete penetration must be secured on the first pass.
5. Enough to build the weld bead slightly above base metal surface.
6. Yes.
7. Higher amperages for greater speed; larger electrodes may be used without burn-through.
8. Steel, copper, or ceramic.

Lesson 1.21

1. By the force of the arc.
2. Electrode movement and arc length.
3. Whipping motion, amperage adjustment.
4. Yes.

Lesson 1.22

1. Horizontal corner weld.
2. Square, bevel one plate, bevel both plates.
3. About the same or slightly lower.
4. Shorten arc, reduce amperage.
5. Short.

Lesson 1.23

1. Welding up and down.
2. On plate $\frac{3}{16}$" and under.
3. For plate $\frac{1}{4}$" and over.
4. Down welding.
5. Fast enough to keep ahead of the molten slag.
6. Yes.

Lesson 1.24

1. Yes.
2. By weaving with one of several patterns.
3. To make different sizes or types of deposits.

Lesson 1.25

1. Vertical down welding is generally used on lighter metals.
2. To hold them in place before and during welding.
3. To provide root spacing for penetration.
4. The base metal is too thin.

Lesson 1.26

1. On tanks and containers.
2. Downhand whenever possible.
3. No, vertical down welding.
4. Any thickness may be corner welded.
5. Open, half open, closed.
6. Not usually.

Lesson 1.27

1. 12 to 16 gauge.
2. Flange welds.
3. No.
4. Carbon arc or arc torch.
5. Downhand.
6. Downward.

Lesson 1.28

1. Less than $\frac{1}{8}$".
2. Mild steel.
3. Mild steel with a zinc coating.
4. Mild steel with an oxide coating.
5. Distortion and correct amperage adjustment.
6. Lap weld.

7. 16 gauge.
8. Soft arc, spray type deposit.
9. Use back-up strip, preferably copper.
10. Tilting metal 10 to 15 degrees and welding downward.
11. Heat may be more carefully controlled.
12. Clean metal, retard oxidation, aid fusion.
13. Fumes are toxic and should not be breathed in.

Lesson 1.29

1. ¼" or thicker.
2. More passes are needed, less penetration obtained.
3. Up welding.
4. Allow the puddle to remain small and solidify.

Lesson 1.30

1. For maximum penetration and minimum number of passes.
2. To more easily control the molten puddle and produce a uniform bead.
3. To carry more metal needed in filler and cover passes.

Lesson 1.31

1. Square (welded from both sides), vee, or groove.
2. Yes, if joint design and space allow.

Lesson 1.32

1. Holding the electrode steady and keeping the molten metal in the puddle.
2. Using both hands and resting one arm against the body or an object.
3. To allow the sparks and spatter to roll off easier.
4. Perpendicular, inclined 5 to 10 degrees in the direction of travel.
5. Keep a very short arc, use a whipping motion.

Lesson 1.33

1. Yes.
2. Multiple stringer or weave passes.

3. Stringer bead.
4. Fused evenly into each plate and into the corner, no undercut or overlap on members.
5. Two.

Lesson 1.34

1. Very short.
2. Yes.
3. Copper.
4. It is often impossible to use on jobs.

Lesson 1.35

1. Four.
2. Procedures or special notes.
3. Two.
4. The "other" side.
5. No.
6. No.

Lesson 1.36

1. It becomes brittle.
2. Yes.
3. No.
4. Keeping it either "hot" or "cold".
5. High carbon dilution causes it to be brittle.
6. Leave the crater on the top of the previous bead.
7. Keeping it all "hot".
8. If uniform preheating is impossible.
9. Relieves stress.
10. A minimum of 500 to a red heat.
11. Yes.
12. Increase the strength.
13. As low as will give adequate fusion.

Lesson 1.37

1. Composed of relatively soft, ductile constituents.
2. Higher mechanical properties and better corrosion resistance.
3. Composed of relatively hard, brittle constituents.
4. Abrasion-resistant.
5. Low-hydrogen.

Lesson 1.38

1. Research men, metallurgists, chemists, engineers.

2. Report special problems to the manufacturers.
3. Hydrogen affects the molten metal.
4. The use of low hydrogen electrode.
5. No, it is a shielding agent.
6. A crack occurring in the fusion zone under the weld deposit.
7. The coating has a low hydrogen content.
8. Steels may have unpredictable sulphur content.
9. Must be kept dry.
10. Faster deposition rate, easier to apply, smooth bead, easy slag removal.

Lesson 1.39

1. Brazing, preheating, welding, hard-surfacing, etc.
2. Welding current forced across the gap between two carbons.
3. Copper-coated, soft center carbons.
4. AC.
5. Positive carbon must be one size larger.
6. No.
7. About $\frac{3}{16}$".
8. No.
9. Baked carbon.
10. It can be concentrated for thin work.
11. Yes.
12. Soldering.

Lesson 1.40

1. Most ferrous and non-ferrous metals.
2. Yes.

Lesson 1.41

1. Carbon electrode, ECuSn — A filler rod.
2. Veed, same as on steel.
3. Carbon or graphite blocks.
4. Long arc.
5. Fast travel speed.
6. Negative.
7. One.
8. Deoxidized.
9. Pure copper.
10. Porosity.

Lesson 1.43

1. Refineries, power plants, chemical plants, heating and ventilating, and structural jobs.
2. Makes a joint quickly; high quality permits use of lighter pipe.
3. Transmission line; industrial.
4. Yes.
5. Yes.
6. Yes.
7. Because of the possible damage which might result from the failure.
8. Yes.
9. No.
10. Vertical down.
11. "Hot" pass.
12. $\frac{1}{16}$ inch.
13. Stricter codes; a greater variety of alloy steels; vertical as well as horizontal axis pipe joints; cramped quarters.
14. Vertical up.
15. $\frac{1}{8}$ inch; to permit full penetration.
16. Yes.

Lesson 1.44

1. Welding in a downhand position while the pipe is turned.
2. Perpendicular or inclined slightly in the direction of travel.
3. Because of the curved pipe surface.
4. The rolling motion of the pipe.
5. Yes.
6. The farther distance the hand has to travel as compared with the electrode tip.
7. The root pass.
8. Yes.

Lesson 1.45

1. 35 degrees for a 70 degree vee.
2. $\frac{1}{16}$".
3. $\frac{1}{16}$".
4. 4 tacks, 90 degrees apart.
5. Only the root pass.
6. Yes.
7. Slightly concave and washed in well on the sides.
8. Yes.
9. No, they should be staggered.
10. 100%.

Lesson 1.46

1. Vertical up.
2. Gap is larger for vertical up: $\frac{1}{8}$ inch as compared to $\frac{1}{16}$ inch for vertical down.
3. 70 degrees.
4. No.
5. $\frac{1}{8}$ inch; $\frac{5}{32}$ inch.
6. Four; equally spaced.
7. $\frac{1}{8}$ inch.
8. Slightly larger than the electrode; $\frac{3}{16}$ inch.
9. Side-to-side weave.
10. Properly fuse both sides of the joint and the previous bead.

Lesson 1.47

1. Drag or short arc.
2. $\frac{1}{16}$".
3. 4, equally spaced.
4. Yes.

Lesson 1.48

1. Passing the 6G test qualifies for all of the other positions too.
2. The low-hydrogen electrodes produce faster deposit rates and a higher strength weld.
3. Use a drag technique with $10 - 15°$ push angle.
4. ASME.
5. Two root and two face bends.

Lesson 7.6

1. Because most of the gases used with GMAW are not inert. Only when argon or helium are used either separately or as mixtures, is the welding truly by inert gas shielding.
2. A gas that is chemically *nonreactive* with any substance. Helium and argon are inert gases used for gas shields in welding. CO_2, the most frequently used gas in GMAW is a very reactive chemical — but not with the metals being welded.
3. Steels, iron, aluminum, magnesium, nickel, copper, and nonferrous alloys.
4. A semiautomatic welding gun, through which electrode wire and shielding gas would be fed to the arc and weld puddle.
5. To shield the arc and molten weld metal from the atmosphere and to provide desirable metal-transfer properties in the arc column.
6. As long as the wire on the reel or in the container supplied by the manufacturer. It can be hundreds of feet long.
7. In outdoor welding, wind is always a factor. Wind can destroy the gas shield, causing welding defects.
8. Welding aluminum, magnesium, copper, and alloys of these reactive metals.
9. Innershield puts inside the electrode wire the materials needed to generate a gaseous shield under the heat of the arc. With gas metal-arc welding, the gaseous shield is externally supplied through a nozzle around the electrode.

Lesson 7.7

1. Submerged-arc, self-shielded flux-cored arc (Innershield), and gas metal-arc.
2. The welding operation can proceed without need to stop and change electrode. Greater efficiency is a consequence.
3. Both submerged-arc and flux-cored arc welding require slag removal from the finished weld. There is no slag with GMAW.
4. The output characteristics of a constant-voltage power source gives the relatively flat slope to the volt-ampere curve needed in gas metal-arc welding.
5. The electrode wire (with rare exceptions) is always positive (DCRP) in gas metal-arc welding, whatever the metal being welded.
6. CO_2 often eliminates the need for either water or air-cooling. This reduces the weight of the semiautomatic gun and makes for greater maneuverability.

Lesson 7.8

1. With spray transfer, a mist of molten electrode droplets are forcibly ejected against the weld joint. With globular transfer, small globules of molten metal drop — under gravity — into the joint.
2. Drops do not drop uphill-against the force of gravity.
3. In pulsed-arc transfer, there is a point in the pulsed current where spray transfer starts to take place. This current is called spray threshold current. In operation, the pulsed amperage must be set slightly above the threshold current for metal transfer to occur.
4. Because the electrode wire, including the molten globule on its tip, actually touches the work piece, creating a true electrical short.
5. No, after the globule has been transferred to the work, for a fraction of a second there is an open space between the electrode and the work.
6. The short-circuit technique.
7. Sticking is likely to result.

Lesson 7.9

1. CO_2, because it is less expensive and does a good job when welding carbon steel.
2. The gases of the atmosphere are not in proper proportions. There is too much nitrogen (78%), too much oxygen (21%), and less than 1% each of CO_2 and argon in *completely dry air*. However, the atmosphere is never completely dry. It contains water (H_2O), which would cause hydrogen embrittlement in welds. Excessive oxygen and nitrogen are also deleterious to many weld metals.
3. Helium, in the ionized arc column, has excellent heat conductivity. More heat is imparted to the weld puddle at a given amperage with helium as the shielding gas than with argon.

4. Oxygen, in argon, increases the temperature of the weld metal as it crosses the arc. This results in good flow properties and the elimination of the undercut and excessive high weld crowns that occur with argon alone.
5. It protects the wire from oxidation and also acts to smooth the flow of the wire through the wire-feeding mechanism.
6. With L-50 electrode wire, the user has on hand one wire that can be used either with gas metal-arc or submerged-arc welding with optimum performance and desired weld properties.
7. The American Welding Society's Handbook.
8. Silicon and aluminum.

Lesson 7.10

1. The forehand push technique is used for heavy material. The backhand drag technique is used for lighter material.
2. There will be increased spatter and the arc will pop and sputter from inadequate shielding. The gun may seem to try to push your hand away.
3. High voltage will produce increased spatter and a very flat bead, possibly with porosity.
4. Low WFS causes the arc to go out intermittently. This may result in the electrode burning back into the tip and a "bird nest" forming at the drive rolls.
5. Cut the wire before it reaches the drive rolls. Remove all wire from the cable and drive rolls and replace the contact tip. Restart the wire as if it were a new coil.

Lesson 7.11

1. For faster travel speeds and to prevent burnthrough.
2. It improves the molten metal flow, bead contour, and gives better gas protection.
3. $3/8'' - 1/2''$.

Lesson 7.12

1. The fillet weld.
2. 45°.
3. 20 — 25°.
4. 60° — second; 30° — third.

Lesson 7.13

1. 1/4".
2. To make it uniform.
3. 3/8" — 1/2".
4. Straight side to side motion with a pause at each side.

Lesson 7.14

1. Open joint or back-up ring.
2. Shielded-Metal-Arc and Gas-Tungsten-Arc.
3. It is difficult to obtain an x-ray quality deposit.
4. Cross-country transmission lines.
5. Pressure and power piping.

Lesson 7.15

1. 3/16".
2. Bevel to feather edge with no land.
3. It gives the operator something to weld into, making it easier.
4. To feather out the thickness of the tacks.

Lesson 7.16

1. The welding helmet and leathers are not needed for submerged arc welding because the arc is buried under a blanket of flux.
2. The six advantages are: "Fast-Fill", "Fast-Follow", Deep penetration, Greater operator comfort, Excellent slag removal, and consistent weld quality.
3. Flux can be brought to the arc from the canister called the "flux cone assembly" or fed by air from a tank with the pressurized system as shown in Figure 4.
4. If flux falls through the open butt joint, some type of backing bar will be required.

Lesson 7.17

1. Cutting the wire to a sharp point and flush with the end of the flux cone makes starting the arc much easier and more consistent.
2. The proper flux cone determines proper flux coverage — a necessity for quality welds.
3. The welding operator must hold the gun at the proper angle and drag it at the proper travel speed.

Lesson 7.18

1. Backing bars provide material to weld into for the first pass. Since submerged arc is a deep penetrating process with DC(+) polarity, backing bars are often used.
2. A copper backup bar provides a means of getting a good bead on the back side of the joint without additional weight and metal as would a steel backing bar.

Lesson 7.19

1. The travel speed of the gun is of prime importance to make good uniform welds. Gun position is important too, but few weldors find difficulty with it.
2. Deposition rates can be dramatically increased by using a larger wire such as 3/32" or using the LINC-FILL extension guide for long stick-out. Using DC(–) polarity will also increase deposition rates while reducing penetration as long as you are using Lincoln agglomerated fluxes.

NOTES

NOTES

NOTES

NOTES